INTERNATIONAL AWARD WINNING
HARRIS REFERENCE
CATALOG

POSTAGE STAMP PRICES

UNITED STATES
UNITED NATIONS
CANADA & PROVINCES

Plus: Confederate States, U.S. Possessions,
U.S. Trust Territories,
Albums and Accessories,
Comprehensive U.S. Stamp Identifier

H.E. Harris & Co. ®
Serving the Collector Since 1916

H.E. Harris & Company was founded by Henry Ellis Harris. Harris began the business in 1916 at an early age of fourteen and took advantage of free advertising in the Washington Post to begin his mail-order business. He built an enormously successful stamp company and garnered the support and confidence of the philatelic community. This annual US/BNA Catalog began publication in 1935 and was 64 pages.

Stock No. 0794826555
ISBN: 0-7948-2655-5

ABOUT OUR CATALOG PRICES

The prices quoted in this catalog are the prices for which H.E. Harris offers stamps for retail sale at the time of publication.

These prices are based on current market values as researched by our staff, but, more importantly, on our day-to-day buying and selling activities in the stamp market.

Although you may certainly use this catalog as a guide to current market prices, you must keep in mind the fact that prices can change in response to varying levels of collector demand, or dealer promotions, and/or special purchases. We are not responsible for typographical errors.

You should also remember that condition is always the key factor in determining the value and price of a given stamp or set of stamps. Unlike some other stamp catalogs, we price U.S. stamps issued up to 1935 in three different condition grades for unused and used examples. For these earlier issues, we have also shown the percentage premium that would apply to Never Hinged Mint examples.

Our illustrated definitions of condition grades are presented on pages X-XII.

We have not found it possible to keep every stamp in stock that is listed in this catalog, and we cannot guarantee that we can supply all of the stamps in all conditions that are listed.

However, we will search for any stamp in any condition that a customer may want if that stamp is not in our stock at the time the customer places an order for it.

Serving the Collector Since 1916

INDEX

In this section we will attempt to define and explain some of the terms commonly used by stamp collectors. Instead of listing the terms in an alphabetical dictionary or glossary format, we have integrated them. In this way, you can see how an individual term fits within the total picture.

PRODUCTION

The manufacture of stamps involves a number of procedures. We will discuss the major steps here, with emphasis on their implications for stamp collectors. Although we present them separately, modern printing presses may combine one or more operations so that the steps tend to blend together. There also are steps in the process that we do not cover here. While they may be important to the production process, their direct implications for most collectors are minimal.

PLATE MAKING

Before anything can be printed, a printing plate must be made. Using the intaglio printing process (which is explained under **printing**) as an example, the steps involved in plate production are as follows:

- A **master die** is made. The design is recess engraved in a reverse mirror-image. Most master dies consist of only one impression of the design.
- The next step is to prepare a **transfer roll**. The soft steel of the transfer roll is rocked back and forth under pressure against the hardened master die and a series of multiple impressions, called **reliefs**, are created in the transfer roll. Note that the impression on the transfer roll will be raised above the surface, since the roll was pressed into the recesses of the master die.
- Once the transfer roll has been made and hardened, it is used to impress designs in to the soft steel of a **printing plate** that can fit up to 400 impressions of small, definitive-sized stamps or 200 impressions of large, commemorative-sized stamps. This time, the raised design on the transfer roll impresses a recessed design into the plate.

The process is much more complex than this, but these are the basics. Once the printing plate is hardened, it is almost ready to be used to create printed sheets of stamps. Depending on the printing equipment to be used, the printing plate will be shaped to fit around a cylinder for rotary press printing or remain flat for flat-bed press printing. In either form, the plate is then hardened and is ready for use in printing.

DESIGN VARIETIES

The complexity of the platemaking process can result in major or minor flaws. The inspection process will catch most of these flaws, but those that escape detection will result in **plate varieties**.

The early United States Classic issues have been examined in minute detail over the decades. Through **plating** studies, minor differences in individual stamps have been used to identify the position on the printing plate of each design variety. Sometimes called **"flyspeck philately"** because it involves the detection of minute "flyspeck" differences, such plating work has resulted in the identification of some of our greatest rarities. Compare the prices for the one cent blue issues of 1851 and 1857 (#s 5-9 and 18-24) and you will see the tremendous dollar difference that can result from minute design variations. (The Harris Stamp Identifier in this catalog explains the design differences.)

During the plate making or subsequent printing process, plate flaws that are detected will be corrected, sometimes incompletely or incorrectly. Corrections or revisions in an individual die impression or in all plate impressions include the following:

- **Retouching**—minor corrections made in a plate to repair damage or wear.
- **Recutting** or **re-engraving**—similar to, but more extensive than, retouching. Recutting usually applies to changes made before a plate has been hardened, while re-engraving is performed on a plate that has had to be tempered (softened) after hardening.
- **Redrawing**—the intentional creation of a slightly different design. The insertion of secret marks on the National Bank Notes plates when they were turned over to the Continental Bank Note Company in 1873 can be considered redrawings.
- **Reentry**—the reapplication of a design from a transfer roll to the plate, usually to improve a worn plate. If the reentry is not done completely, or if it is not done precisely on top of the previous design, a double transfer will result. Such double transfers will show on the printed stamp as an extra line at one or more points on the stamp.

Other design varieties may result from undetected plate flaws. A **plate crack** (caused by the hardened plate cracking under wear or pressure) or a **plate scratch** (caused by an object cutting into the plate) will show as an ink line on the printed stamp.

One other group that can be covered here to avoid possible confusion includes **reissues, reprints, special printings** and **reproductions**. None of these are design varieties that result from plate flaws, corrections or revisions. In fact, reissues, reprints and special printings are made from the same, unchanged plates as the originals. They show no differences in design and usually can be identified only by variations in paper, color or gum.

Reproductions (such as U.S. #3 and #4), on the other hand, are made from entirely new plates and, therefore, can be expected to show some variation from the originals.

ERRORS, FREAKS, ODDITIES

"**EFOs**", as they are called, are printed varieties that result from abnormalities in the production process. They are design varieties, but of a special nature because the result looks different from the norm. When you see them, you know something went wrong.

Basically, freaks and oddities can be loosely defined as minor errors. They include the following:

- **Misperforations**, that is, the placement of the perforations within the design rather than at the margins.
- **Foldovers**, caused by a sheet being turned, usually at a corner, before printing and/or perforating. The result is part of a design printed on the reverse of the sheet or placement of perforations at odd angles. Such freaks and oddities may be of relatively minor value, but they do make attractive additions to a collection. Truly major errors, on the other hand, can be of tremendous value. It would not be overstating the case to argue that many collectors are initially drawn to the hobby by the publicity surrounding discoveries of valuable errors and the hope that they might someday do the same. Major errors include the following:
- **Inverts.** These are the most dramatic and most valuable of all major errors and almost always result from printing processes that require more than one pass of a sheet through the presses. If the sheet inadvertently gets "flipped" between passes, the portion printed on the second pass will emerge inverted.

Two definitions we should introduce here are "**frame**" and "**vignette**". The vignette is the central design of the stamp; the frame encloses the vignette and, at its outer edges, marks the end of the printed stamp design. Oftentimes, stamps described as inverted centers (vignettes) actually are inverted frames. The center was properly printed in the first pass and the frame was inverted in the second pass.

- **Color errors.** The most noticeable color errors usually involve one or more omitted colors. The sheet may not have made it through the second pass in a two-step printing process. In the past such errors were extremely rare because they were obvious enough to be noticed by inspectors. In modern multi-color printings, the chances of such errors escaping detection have increased. Nonetheless, they still qualify as major errors and carry a significant premium.

*Other color errors involve the use of an incorrect color. They may not seem as dramatic as missing colors, but the early issues of many countries include some very rare and valuable examples of these color errors.

Although technically not a color error, we can include here one of the most unusual of all errors, the United States 1917 5-cent stamps that are supposed to be blue, but are found in the carmine or rose color of the 2-cent stamps. The error was not caused by a sheet of the 5-centers being printed in the wrong color, as you might expect. Rather, because a few impressions on a 2-cent plate needed reentry, they were removed. But an error was made and the 5-cent design was entered. Thus it is a reentry error, but is described in most catalogs as a color error because that is the apparent result. Whatever the description, the 5-cent denomination surrounded by 2-cent stamps is a real showpiece.

- **Imperfs.** A distinction should be drawn here between imperforate errors and intentionally imperforate stamps. When the latter carry a premium value over their perforated counterparts, it is because they were printed in smaller quantities for specialized usages. They might have been intended, for example, for sale to vending machine manufacturers who would privately perforate the imperforate sheets

On the other hand, errors in which there is absolutely no trace of a perforation between two stamps that were supposed to be perforated carry a premium based on the rarity of the error. Some modern United States coil imperforate errors have been found in such large quantities that they carry little premium value. But imperforate errors found in small quantities represent tremendous rarities.

Be they intentional or errors, imperforate stamps are commonly collected in pairs or larger multiples because it can be extremely difficult—often impossible, to distinguish them from stamps that have had their perforations trimmed away in an attempt to pass them off as more valuable imperfs. Margin singles that show the stamp and a wide, imperforate selvage at one of the edges of the sheet are another collecting option.

PRINTING

There are three basic printing methods:

1. **Intaglio,** also known as **recess** printing. Line engraved below the surface of the printing plate (that is, in recess) accept the ink and apply it to damp paper that is forced into the recesses of the plate. Intaglio methods include **engraved** and **photogravure** (or **rotogravure**). Photogravure is regarded by some as separate from intaglio because the engraving is done by chemical etching and the finished product can be distinguished from hand or machine engraving.

2. **Typography.** This is similar to intaglio, in that it involves engraving, but the action is in reverse, with the design left at the surface of the plate and the portions to be unprinted cut away. Ink is then applied to the surface design, which is imprinted onto paper. **Typeset** letterpress printing is the most common form of typography.

3. **Lithography.** This method differs from the previous two in that it involves **surface printing**, rather than engraving. Based on the principle that oil and water do not mix, the design to be printed is applied with a greasy ink onto a plate that is then wet with a watery fluid. Printing ink run across the plate is accepted only at the greased (oiled) points. The ink applies the design to paper that is brought in contact with the plate. **Offset** printing, a modern lithographic

method, involves a similar approach, but uses a rubber blanket to transfer the inked design to paper.

The printing method that was used to produce a given stamp can be determined by close inspection of that stamp.

1. Because the paper is pressed into the grooves of an intaglio plate, when viewed from the surface the design appears to be slightly raised. Running a fingernail lightly across the surface also will reveal this raised effect. When viewed from the back, the design will appear to be recessed (or pressed out toward the surface). Photogravure stamps have a similar appearance and feel, but when viewed under a magnifier, they reveal a series of dots, rather than line engravings.

2. Because the raised design on a plate is pressed into the paper when the typograph process is used, when viewed from the surface, the printing on the stamp does not have the raised effect of an intaglio product. On the other hand, when viewed from the reverse, a raised impression will be evident where the design was imprinted. Overprints often are applied by typography and usually show the raised effect on the back of the stamp.

3. Unlike either of the previous two methods, lithographed stamps look and feel flat. This dull, flat effect can be noticed on any of the United States 1918-20 offset printings, #s 525-536.

Overprints and **surcharges** are inscriptions or other markings added to printed stamps to adapt them to other uses. A **surcharge** is an overprint that changes or restates the value of the stamp. The United States Offices in China (K1-18) issues carry surcharges.

Some foreign semi-postal issues are stamps with a printed denomination that is applied to the postage fee and an overprinted surcharge that is applied to a specified charity.

Overprints can be applied for reasons other than to change their value. Examples would be for commemorative purposes (#s 646-648), to hinder the use of stolen stamps (#s 658-679 the Kansas-Nebraska issues), to change or designate the usage of the stamp (modern precancels), or to indicate usage in a distinct political unit (Canal Zone, Guam and Philippines overprints on United States stamps used during the early period of U.S. administration until new stamps could be printed).

Overprints can be applied by handstamp or even typewriter, but the most efficient and commonly used technique seen on stamps is typeset press printing.

WATERMARKS

This actually is one of the first steps in the stamp production process because it is part of paper manufacturing. A **watermark** is a slight thinning of the paper pulp, usually in the form of a relevant design. It is applied by devices attached to the rolls on papermaking machines. Without getting involved in the technical aspects, the result is a watermark that can sometimes be seen when held to the light, but more often requires watermark detector fluid.

A word of caution here. Such detector fluids may contain substances that can be harmful when inhaled. This is particularly true of lighter fluids that often are used by collectors in lieu of specially made stamp watermark detector fluids.

Watermarks are used to help detect counterfeits. Although it is possible to reproduce the appearance of a watermark, it is extremely difficult. The authorities have at times been able to identify a counterfeit by the lack of a watermark that should be present or by the presence of an incorrect watermark.

On the other hand, there are occasions when the incorrect or absent watermark did not indicate a counterfeit, but a printing error. The wrong paper may have been used or the paper may have been inserted incorrectly (resulting in an inverted or sideways watermark). The United States 30 cent orange red that is listed among the 1914-17 issues on unwatermarked paper (#467A) is an example of a printing error. It was produced on watermarked paper as part of the 1914-15 series, but a few sheets were discovered without watermarks.

Unfortunately, the difficulty encountered in detecting watermarks on light shades, such as orange or yellow, makes experts very reluctant to identify single copies of #476A. Although not visible, the watermark just might be there.

Because an examination of a full sheet allows the expert to examine the unprinted selvage and all stamps on that sheet at one time, positive identification is possible and most of the stamps that come down to us today as #476A trace back to such full sheets.

GUMMING

Gumming once was almost always applied after printing and before perforating and cutting of sheets into panes. Today, pregummed paper may be used, so the placement of this step in the process cannot be assured—nor is it the sequence of much significance.

The subject of gum will be treated more fully in the **Condition** section of this catalog. At this point, we will only note that certain stamps can be identified by their gum characteristics. Examples include the identification of rotary press stamps by the presence of gum breaker ridges or lines and the detection of the presence of original gum on certain stamps that indicates they can not be a rarer issue that was issued without gum, such as #s 40-47. Others, such as #s 102-111 can be identified in part by their distinctive white, crackly original gum.

PERFORATING

We have already discussed the absence of perforations in the **Errors** section. Here we will concentrate on the perforating process itself.

All perforating machines use devices to punch holes into the printed stamp paper. The holes usually are round and are known as perforations. When two adjacent stamps are separated, the semicircular cutouts are the **perforations**; the remaining paper between the perforations forms **perf tips**, or **"teeth"**.

Most perforations are applied by perforators that contain a full row of punches that are driven through the paper as it is fed through the perforating equipment. **Line Perforators** drive the punches up and down; **rotary perforators** are mounted on cylinders that revolve. There are other techniques, but these are the most common.

To clear up one point of confusion, the **perforation size** (for example, "perf 11") is not the size of the hole or the number of perforations on the side of a given stamp. Rather, it describes the number of perforations that could be fit within two centimeters.

A perf 8 stamp will have visibly fewer perforations than a perf 12 stamp, but it is much harder to distinguish between perf 11 and perf 10-1/2. **Perforation gauges** enable collectors to make these distinctions with relative ease.

TAGGING

Modern, high-speed, mechanical processing of mail has created the need for "tagging" stamps by coating them with a luminescent substance that could be detected under ultraviolet (U.V.) light or by printing them on paper that included such substances. When passed under a machine capable of detecting these substances, an envelope can be positioned and the stamp automatically cancelled, thereby eliminating time-consuming and tedious manual operations. The tagged varieties of certain predominantly untagged stamps, such as #s 1036 and C67, do carry modest premiums. There also are technical differences between phosphorescent and fluorescent types of luminescent substances. But these details are primarily of interest to specialists and will not be discussed in this general work.

PAPER

The fact that we have not devoted more attention to paper should not be an indication of any lack of interest or significance. Books have been written on this one subject alone, and a lack of at least a rudimentary knowledge of the subject can lead to mis-identification of important varieties and resultant financial loss.

The three most common categories of paper on which stamps are printed are **wove**, **laid**, and **India**. The most frequently used is machine-made **wove paper**, similar to that used for most books. The semiliquid pulp for wove paper is fed onto a fine wire screen and is processed much the same as cloth would be woven. Almost all United States postage stamps are printed on wove paper.

Laid paper is formed in a process that uses parallel wires rather than a uniform screen. As a result, the paper will be thinner where the pulp was in contact with the wires. When held to the light, alternating light and dark lines can be seen. Laid paper varieties have been found on some early United States stamps.

India paper is very thin and tough, without any visible texture. It is, therefore, more suited to obtaining the sharp impressions that are needed for printers' pre-production proofs, rather than to the high-volume printing of stamps.

Other varieties include **bluish** paper, so described because of the tone created by certain substances added to the paper, and silk paper, which contains threads or fibers of silk that usually can be seen on the back of the stamp. Many United States revenue stamps were printed on silk paper.

COLLECTING FORMATS

Whatever the production method, stamps reach the collector in a variety of forms. The most common is in sheet, or more correctly, pane form.

Sheets are the full, uncut units as they come from a press. Before distribution to post offices, these sheets are cut into **panes**. For United States stamps, most regular issues are printed in sheets of 400 and cut into panes of 100; most commemoratives are printed in sheets of 200 and cut into panes of 50. There are numerous exceptions to this general rule, and they are indicated in the mint sheet listings in this catalog.

Sheets also are cut in **booklet panes** for only a few stamps—usually four to ten stamps per pane. These panes are assembled in complete booklets that might contain one to five panes, usually stapled together between two covers. An intact booklet is described as **unexploded**; when broken apart it is described as exploded.

Coils are another basic form in which stamps reach post offices. Such stamps are wound into continuous coil rolls, usually containing from 100 to 5,000 stamps, the size depending on the volume needs of the expected customer. Almost all coils are produced with perforations on two opposite sides and straight edges on the remaining two sides.

Some serious collectors prefer collecting coils in pairs or strips—two or more adjacent stamps—as further assurance of genuineness. It is much easier to fake a coil single that shows only portions of each perforation hole than a larger unit that shows the complete perf hole.

A variation on this theme is the **coil line pair**—adjacent stamps that show a printed vertical line between. On rotary press stamps the line appears where the two ends of a printing plate meet on a rotary press cylinder. The joint is not complete, so ink falls between the plate ends and is transferred onto the printed coil. On flat plate stamps the guideline is the same as that created for sheet stamps, as described below.

Paste-up coil pairs are not as popular as line pairs. They were a necessary by-product of flat plate printings in which the coil strips cut from separate sheets had to be pasted together for continuous winding into roll form.

The modern collecting counterpart to coil line pairs is the plate **number strip**—three or five adjacent coil stamps with the plate number displayed on the middle stamp. Transportation coil plate strips have become particularly sought after. On most early coil rolls, the plate numbers were supposed to be trimmed off. Freaks in which the number remains are interesting, but do not carry large premiums since they are regarded as examples of miscut oddities rather than printing errors.

 Miniature sheets and **souvenir sheets** are variations on one theme—small units that may contain only one or at most a much smaller quantity of stamps than would be found on the standard postal panes. Stamps may be issued in miniature sheet format for purposes of expedience, as for example the Bret Harte $5 issue (#2196), which was released in panes of 20 to accommodate the proportionately large demand by collectors for plate blocks rather than single stamps.

 As the name implies, a souvenir sheet is a miniature sheet that was released as a souvenir to be saved, rather than postally used—although such sheets or the stamps cut out from them can be used as postage. Note: **souvenir cards** are created strictly for promotional and souvenir purposes. They contain stamp reproductions that may vary in size, color or design from the originals and are not valid for postal use.

 Often, a common design may be produced in sheet, coil and booklet pane form. The common design is designated by collectors as one **type**, even though it may be assigned many different catalog numbers because of variations in color, size, perforations, printing method, denomination, etc. On the other hand, even minor changes in a basic design represent a new type.

 Sheet stamps offer the greatest opportunity for format variation and collecting specialization. Using the following illustration for reference, the varieties that can be derived include the following:

 Block (a)—this may be any unit of four stamps or more in at least 2 by 2 format. Unless designated as a different size, blocks are assumed to be blocks of four.

 Specialized forms of blocks include:

 Arrow block (b)—adjacent stamps at the margin of a sheet, showing the arrow printed in the margin for registration in the printing process, as, for example, in two-color printings. When the arrow designates the point at which a sheet is

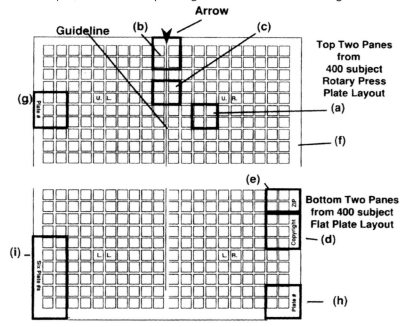

(This diagram is for placement purposes only, and is not an exact reproduction of margin markings)

 Guideline block (c)—similar to arrow block, except that it can be any block that shows the registration line between two rows of two stamps each.

 Gutter block—similar to guideline block, except that an uncolored gutter is used instead of a printed line. The best known United States gutter blocks are those cut from full-sheet "Farley printings". Pairs of stamps from adjacent panes on each side of the gutter form the gutter block.

 Imprint, or **inscription blocks (d)**—include **copyright, mail early,** and **ZIP (e)** blocks. On most modern United States sheets, the **selvage**, that is, the margin that borders the outer rows of stamps **(f)**, includes one or more inscriptions in addition to the plate numbers. It may be a copyright protection notice or an inscription that encourages mail users to post their mail early or to use the ZIP code on their mail.

 Because the inscription appears along the margin, rather than in one of the corners, it is customary to collect copyright blocks and mail early blocks in two rows of three stamps each, with the inscription centered in the margin. The ZIP inscription appears in one of the corners of each pane, so it is collected in corner margin blocks of four.

 Plate number block—this is by far the most popular form of block collecting. On each sheet of stamps, a plate number (or numbers) is printed to identify the printing plate(s) used. Should a damage be discovered, the plate can easily be identified.

 On flat plate sheets, where the plate number appeared along the margin, the format usually is in plate blocks of six, with the plate number centered in the margin **(g)**.

On rotary press and other sheets where a single plate number appears in one of the four corners of the margin, the customary collecting format is a corner margin block of four **(h)**. This also is true for plate blocks with two plate numbers in two adjacent corner stamps and for modern plates where single digits are used to designate each plate number and the complete series (containing one digit for each printing color) appears in the corner.

Before single digits were adopted for modern multi-color printings, the five-digit numbers assigned to each plate might run down a substantial portion of the sheet margin. **Plate strips** are collected in such instances. Their size is two rows times as many stamps as are attached to the margin area that shows all plate numbers **(i)**.

Because a sheet of stamps is cut into separate panes, printing plates include plate numbers that can be seen on each of the cut panes. On modern sheets the plate numbers would be located in each of the four corners of the uncut sheet. Once cut, each of the four panes would show the same plate number in one of its corners. The position of the plate number, which matches the position of the pane on the uncut sheet, is designated as upper left or right and lower left or right. Some specialists seek matched sets. A **matched set** is one of each of the four positions for a given plate number. A **complete matched set** is all positions of all plate numbers for a given issue.

Other definitions that relate in one way or another to the format in which stamps are produced include:

Se-tenant—from the French, meaning joined together. A pair, block, or larger multiple that contains different designs. The 1967 Space Twins issue is an example of a se-tenant pair in which the two different stamps are part of an integral design. The 1968 Historic Flags se-tenant strip contains ten separate designs, each of which can stand alone.

Tete-beche pair—from the French, meaning head-to-tail. Such pairs show adjacent stamps, one of which is upside down in relation to the other.

Proof—any trial impression used in the evaluation of prospective or final designs. **Final die proofs**—that is, those made from a completed die preparatory to its being used in the production of printing plates—are the standard proof collecting form.

Essay—a partial or complete illustration of a proposed design. In the strict philatelic sense, essays are printed in proof form.

Color trials—a preliminary proof of a stamp design in one or more colors. Trial color proofs are used to select the color in which the stamp will be printed.

Grill—a pattern of embossed cuts that break the stamp paper. See the information at the head of the 1861-67 Issue listings and the section of grills in the Harris Stamp Identifier.

POSTAL MARKINGS

The extensive subject of cancellations and postal markings on stamps and covers is too specialized to present in detail here. Volumes have been written on individual categories of markings—straight line markings, ship cancels, foreign mail cancels, flight covers, etc. In this section we will limit ourselves to the basic definitions related to the stamp and the manner in which it is cancelled, rather than the specialized usage of the envelope to which the stamp is affixed.

- **Manuscript**, or **pen cancels** were the earliest form of "killing" a stamp—that is, marking it to indicate it had been postally used.
- **Handstamps** were created shortly after the first stamps were issued. The early devices might only show a pattern such as a grid and often were carved from cork.
- **Fancy cancels** were an extension of the handstamp. Local postmasters carved cork cancelers that depicted bees, kicking mules, flowers, and hundreds of other figures. Stamps with clear strikes of such fancy cancels usually carry hefty premiums over those with standard cancels.
- **Machine cancels** are applied by mechanical rather than manual means.
- A stamp is **tied** to a cover (or piece) when the cancellation, whatever its form, extends beyond the margins of the stamp onto the cover. Such a tie is one indication of the authenticity of the cover.

Specialized cancellations include the following:

- **Cut cancel**—as the name implies, a cancel that actually cuts the stamp, usually in the form of a thin, straight incision. The most common usage of cut cancels on United States stamps is on Revenue issues.
- **Perfin**, or perforated initial—usually not a cancellation as such, but rather a privately administered punching into the stamp of one or more initials. Most often, the initials were those of a large firm that wished to prevent personal use of their stamps by employees.
- **Precancel**—a cancellation printed on stamps in advance of their sale. The primary purpose of precancels is for sale to large volume mailers, whose mail is delivered to post offices and processed in bulk without necessarily receiving further cancellation.
- **Non-contemporary cancel**—a cancellation applied to a stamp long after the normal period of use for that stamp. A stamp that is worth more used than unused or a damaged unused stamp that would be worth more on cover are examples of candidates for non-contemporary markings.
- **Cancel-to-order**, or **C.T.O.**—a cancel that is printed on a stamp by an issuing country to give it the appearance of having been used, or to render it invalid for postage in that country. Special fancy cancels or "favor cancels" have been applied at various times in the countries for philatelic reasons.

The number of specialized categories into which stamps can be slotted is limited only by the imagination of the individual collector. Some collectors have attempted to collect one of each and every stamp ever issued by every nation that ever existed. Other collectors have concentrated on all the possible varieties and usages of only one stamp. Between these two extremes, stamps can be divided into certain generally accepted categories, whether or not they are used as boundaries for a collection. These categories are as follows:

- **Definitives**, or **regulars**—stamps that are issued for normal, everyday postage needs. In the United States, they are put on sale for a period limited only by changing rate needs or infrequent issuance of a new definitive series. Post offices can requisition additional stocks of definitives as needed.
- **Commemoratives**—stamps issued to honor a specific event, anniversary, individual or group. They are printed in a predetermined quantity and are intended for sale during a limited period. Although they can be used indefinitely, once stocks are sold out at a local post office, commemoratives usually are not replenished unless the issue has local significance.
- **Pictorials**—stamps that depict a design other than the portrait of an individual or a static design such as a coat of arms or a flag. While some collectors think of these strictly as commemoratives (because most commemoratives are pictorials), some definitives also can be pictorials. Any number of definitives that depict the White House are examples.
- **Airmails**, or **air posts**—stamps issued specifically for airmail use. Although they do not have to bear a legend, such as "airmail", they usually do. Airmail stamps usually can be used to pay other postage fees.

When air flights were a novelty, airmail stamp collecting was an extremely popular specialty. Part of this popularity also can be ascribed to the fact that the first airmail stamps usually were given special attention by issuing postal administrations. Produced using relatively modern technology, they often were among the most attractive of a nation's issues.

- **Zeppelin stamps**—although these do not rate as a major category, they deserve special mention. Zeppelin issues were primarily released for specific use on Zeppelin flights during the 1920s and 1930s. They carried high face values and were issued during the Great Depression period, when most collectors could not afford to purchase them. As a result, most Zeppelin issues are scarce and command substantial premiums. United States "Zepps" are the Graf Zeppelins (C13-C15) and the Century of Progress issue (C18).
- **Back-of-the-book**—specialized stamps that are identified as "back-of-the-book" because of their position in catalogs following the listings of regular and commemorative postal issues. Catalogs identified them with a prefix letter.

Some collectors include airmail stamps in this category, in part because they carry a prefix letter (C) and are listed separately. Most collectors treat the airmails as part of a standard collection and begin the back-of-the-book section with semi-postals (B) or, for the United States, special deliveries (E).

Other frequently used "b-o-b" categories include postage dues (J), offices in China, or Shanghais (K), officials (O), parcel posts (Q), newspapers (PR), and revenues (R), the latter including "Duck" hunting permit stamps (RW).

Postal stationery and postal cards are the major non-stamp back-of-the-book categories. A complete envelope or card is called an **entire**; the cutout corner from such a piece, showing the embossed or otherwise printed design, is described as a **cut square**.

Some collecting categories do not relate to the intended use of the stamps. Examples include **topicals** (stamps collected by the theme of the design, such as sports, dance, paintings, space, etc.) and **first day covers**. Modern first day covers show a stamp or stamps postmarked in a designated first day city on the official first day of issue. The cancel design will relate to the issue and the cover may bear a privately-printed cachet that further describes and honors the subject of the stamp.

One of the oddities of the hobby is that **stampless covers** are an accepted form of "stamp" collecting. Such covers display a usage without a stamp, usually during the period before stamps were required for the payment of postage. They bear manuscript or handstamps markings such as "due 5," "PAID," etc. to indicate the manner in which postage was paid.

Although they do not constitute a postal marking, we can include **bisects** here for want of a better place. A bisect is a stamp cut in half and used to pay postage in the amount of one-half of the stamp's denomination. The 1847 ten cent stamp (#2) cut in half and used to pay the five cent rate is an example.

Bisects should be collected only on cover and properly tied. They also should reflect an authorized usage, for example, from a post office that was known to lack the proper denomination, and sould pay an amount called for by the usuage shown on the cover.

Not discussed in detail here is the vast subject of **covers**, or postal history. Envelopes, usually but not necessarily showing a postal use, are described by collectors as covers. Early "covers" actually were single letter sheets with a mes-

H.E. Harris Pictorial Guide to Centering

Cat #	Very Fine	Fine	Average
1 to 293 1847 to 1898	Perfs clear of design on all four sides. Margins may not be even.	Perfs well clear of design on at least three sides. But may almost touch design on one side.	Perfs cut into design on at least one side.
294 to 749 1901 to 1934	Perfs clear of design. Margins relatively even on all four sides.	Perfs clear of design. Margins not even on all four sides.	Perfs touch design on at least one side.
750 to Date 1935 to Present	Perfs clear of design. Centered with margins even on all four sides.	Perfs clear of design. Margins may be uneven.	Perfs may touch design on at least one side.

Note: Margins are the area from the edges of stamp to the design. Perfs are the serrations between stamps that aid in separating them.

CENTERING

One major factor in the determination of a stamp's fair value is its **centering**, the relative balance of the stamp design within its margins. Whether the stamp has perforations or is imperforate, its centering can be judged. Because the stamp trade does not have an established system for grading or measuring centering, "eyeballing" has become the standard practice. As a result, one collector's definition may vary from another's. This can create some confusion, but the system seems to work, so it has remained in force.

Centering can range from poor to superb, as follows:

- **Poor**—so far off center that a significant portion of the design is lost because of bad centering. On a poorly centered perforated stamp, the perforations cut in so badly that even the perf tips may penetrate the design.
- **Average**—a stamp whose frame or design is cut slightly by the lack of margins on one or two sides. On a perforated stamp, the perf holes might penetrate the stamp, but some margin white space will show on the teeth. Average stamps are accepted by the majority of collectors for 19th century stamps and early 20th century stamps, as well as for the more difficult later issues.
- **Fine**—the perforations are clear of the design, except for those issues that are known to be extremely poorly centered, but the margins on opposite sides will not be balanced, that is, equal to each other. (Note: a stamp whose top and bottom margins are perfectly balanced may still be called fine if the left and right margins differ substantially from each other.)
- **Very fine**—the opposite margins may still appear to differ somewhat, but the stamp is closer to being perfectly centered than it is to being fine centered. Very fine stamps are sought by collectors who are particularly interested in high quality and who are willing to pay the premiums such stamps command.
- **Superb**— perfect centering. They are so scarce that no comprehensive price list could attempt to include a superb category. Superb stamps, when they are available, command very high premiums.
- **"Jumbo"**—an abnormal condition, in which the stamp's margins are oversized compared to those of the average stamp in a given issue. Such jumbos can occur in the plate making process when a design is cut into the printing plate and excessive space is allowed between that design and the adjacent stamps.

Note: Some collectors also define a "fine to very fine" condition, in which the margin balance falls into a mid-range between fine and very fine. In theory it may be an attractive compromise, but in practice the range between fine and very fine is too narrow to warrant a separate intermediate category.

Quality and Condition Definitions

In determining the value of a given stamp, a number of factors have to be taken into consideration. For mint stamps, the condition of the gum, whether or not it has been hinged, and the centering are all major factors that determine their value. For used stamps, the factors to consider are cancellation and centering. The following H.E. Harris guidelines will enable you to determine the quality standards you may choose from in acquiring stamps for your collection.

Mint Stamp Gum

Unused—A stamp that is not cancelled (used), yet has had all the original gum removed. On early U.S. issues this is the condition that the majority of mint stamps exist in, as early collectors often soaked the gum off their stamps to avoid the possibility of the gum drying and splitting.

Original Gum (OG)—A stamp that still retains the adhesive applied when the stamp was made, yet has been hinged or has had some of the gum removed.

Mint stamps from #215 to date can be supplied in this condition.

Never Hinged (NH)—A stamp that is in "post office" condition with full gum that has never been hinged. For U.S. #215 to #1241 (1963), separate pricing columns or percentages are provided for "Never Hinged" quality. From #1242 (1964) to date, all stamps are priced as Never Hinged. Hinged Stamps 1964 to date are available at 20% off the NH price.

Cancellations

The cancellations on Used stamps range from light to heavy. A lightly cancelled stamp has the main design of the stamp clearly showing through the cancel, while a heavy cancel usually substantially obliterates the design elements of the stamp. In general it should be assumed that Very fine quality stamps will have lighter cancels than Average cancellation stamps.

Heavy Cancel   **Light Cancel**

GUM

The impact of the condition of the back of an unused stamp (i.e. the gum) upon that stamp's value in today's market needs careful consideration. The prices for 19th century stamps vary widely based on this element of condition.

Some traditional collectors feel that modern collectors pay too much attention to gum condition. Around the turn of the century, some collectors washed the gum off the stamps to prevent it from cracking and damaging the stamp themselves. But that generation has passed and the practice not only is no longer popular, it is almost unheard of.

To some extent the washing of gum is no longer necessary, since modern gums are not as susceptible to cracking. A more important development, however, has been the advent of various mounts that allow the collector to place a stamp in an album without the use of a hinge. With that development, "never hinged" became a premium condition that could be obtained on stamps issued from the 1930s to date. As a result, gum took on added significance, and its absence on 20th century stamps became unacceptable.

The standard definitions that pertain to gum condition are as follows:

- **Original gum**, or **o.g.**—the gum that was applied when the stamp was produced. There are gradations, from "full" original gum through "partial" original gum, down to "traces". For all intents and purposes, however, a stamp must have most of its original gum to be described as "o.g."
- **Regummed**— the stamp has gum, but it is not that which would have been applied when the stamp was produced. Many collectors will avoid regummed stamps because the gum may hide some repair work. At best, regumming may give the stamp an appearance of completeness, but a premium should not be paid for a stamp that lacks its original gum.
- **Unused**—while many collectors think of this as any stamp that is not used, the narrow philatelic definition indicates a stamp that has no gum or is regummed.
- **Unhinged**—as with "unused", the term has a specific meaning to collectors: a regumming that shows no traces of a hinge mark. Unfortunately, in their confusion some collectors purchase stamps described as "unused" and "unhinged" as if they bore original gum.
- **No gum**—the stamp lacks its gum, either because it was intentionally produced without gum (also described as **ungummed**) or had the gum removed at a later date. It is customary to find 19th century stamps without gum, and the condition is acceptable to all but the most fastidious collectors. On 20th century stamps, original gum is to be expected.

- **Hinged**—the gum shows traces of having been mounted with a hinge. This can range from **lightly hinged** (the gum shows traces, but none of the hinge remains) to **heavily hinged** (a substantial portion of one or more hinge remnants is stuck to the stamp, or a significant portion of the gum has been lost in the removal of a hinge).
- **Thinned**— not only has the gum been removed, but a portion of the stamp paper has been pulled away. A thin usually will show when the stamp is held to a light. One of the faults that may be covered over on regummed stamps is a thin that has been filled in.
- **Never hinged**—as the name implies, the stamp has its original gum in post office condition and has never been hinged. Although some collectors think of **"mint"** stamps as any form of unused, o.g. stamps, the more accepted "mint" definition is never hinged.

USED STAMPS

For used stamps, the presence of gum would be the exception, since it would have been removed when the stamp was washed from the envelope, so gum is not a factor on used stamps.

The centering definitions, on the other hand, would be the same as for unused issues. In addition, the cancellation would be a factor.

We should point out here that we are not referring to the type of cancellation, such as a fancy cancel that might add considerably to the value of a stamp, or a manuscript cancel that reduces its value. Rather, we are referring to the degree to which the cancellation covers the stamp.

A **lightly cancelled** used stamp, with all of the main design elements showing and the usage evidenced by an unobtrusive cancel, is the premier condition sought by collectors of used stamps. On the other hand, a stamp whose design has been substantially obliterated by a **heavy cancel** is at best a space filler that should be replaced by a moderate to lightly cancelled example.

PERFORATIONS

The condition of a stamp's perforations can be determined easily by visual examination. While not necessarily perfect, all perforations should have full teeth and clean perforation holes. A **blunt perf** is one that is shorter than it should be, while a **pulled perf** actually shows a portion of the margin or design having been pulled away. **Blind perfs** are the opposite: paper remains where the perforation hole should have been punched out.

One irony of the demand for perforation is that **straight edges**, that is, the normal sheet margin straight edge that was produced when flat-plate sheets were cut into panes, are not acceptable to many collectors. In fact, many collectors will prefer a reperforated stamp to a straight edge. (Technically, **"re"perforated** can only apply to a stamp that is being perforated again, as when a damaged or excessive margin has been cut away and new perforations are applied, but we will follow the common practice of including the perforation of normal straight edges in this category).

As a result of this preference, many straight edges no longer exist as such. When one considers that they were in the minority to start with (a pane of 100 flat plate stamps would include 19 straight edges) and that even fewer come down to us today, an argument could be made that they may someday be rarities...although it is hard to conceive of anyone paying a premium for straight edges.

FAKES, FAULTS, AND EXPERTIZING

Below the first quality level—stamps free of defects—a range of stamps can be found from attractive **"seconds"** that have barely noticeable flaws to **space fillers** that may have a piece missing and which ought to be replaced by a better copy— unless we are talking about great rarities which would otherwise be beyond the budget of most collectors.

The more common flaws include **thins, tears, creases, stains, pulled perfs, pinholes** (some dealers and collectors used to display their stamps pinned to boards), **face scuffs** or erasures, and **fading**.

Stamps with faults sometimes are **repaired**, either to protect them from further damage or to deceive collectors.

While the terms that are applied to stamps that are not genuine often are used interchangeably, they do have specific meaning, as follows:

- **fakes** (in French, faux; in German, falsch)—stamps that appear to be valuable varieties, but which were made from cheaper genuine stamps. Trimming away the perforations to create an imperforate is a common example of a fake.

- **bogus** stamps, **phantoms, labels**—outright fantasies, usually the product of someone's imagination, produced for amusement rather than deception.

While most stamps are genuine, and the average collector need not be concerned about the possibility of repairs, **expertizing** services do exist for collectors who are willing to pay a fee to obtain an independent opinion on their more

Shows you how to distinguish between the rare and common U.S. stamps that look alike.

Types of 1¢ Franklin Design of 1851-60

TYPE I   has the most complete design of the various types of stamps. At top and bottom there is an unbroken curved line running outside the bands reading "U.S. POSTAGE" and "ONE CENT". The scrolls at bottom are turned under, forming curls. The scrolls and outer line at top are complete.

TYPE Ia   is like Type I at bottom but ornaments and curved line at top are partly cut away.

TYPE Ib   (not illustrated) is like Type I at top but little curls at bottom are not quite so complete nor clear and scroll work is partly cut away.

TYPE II   has the outside bottom line complete, but the little curls of the bottom scrolls and the lower part of the plume ornament are missing. Side ornaments are complete.

  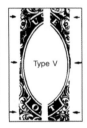

TYPE III   has the outside lines at both top and bottom partly cut away in the middle. The side ornaments are complete.

TYPE IIIa   (not illustrated) is similar to Type III with the outer line cut away at top or bottom, but not both.

TYPE IV   is similar to Type II but the curved lines at top or bottom (or both) have been recut in several different ways, and usually appear thicker than Type IIs.

TYPE V   is similar to Type III but has the side ormanents parlty cut away. Type V occurs only on perforated stamps.

Types of 3¢ Washington & 5¢ Jefferson Designs of 1851-60

3¢ WASHINGTON
TYPE I   has a frame line around the top, bottom and sides.

TYPE II   has the frame line removed at top and bottom, while the side frame lines are continuous from the top to bottom of the plate.

TYPE IIa   is similar to Type II, but the side frame lines were recut individually, and therefore are broken between stamps.

5¢ JEFFERSON
TYPE I   is a complete design with projections (arrow) at the top and bottom as well as at the sides.

TYPE II   has the projections at the top or bottom partly or completely cut away.

Types of the 10¢ Washington Design of 1851-60

TYPE I   has the "shells" at the lower corners practically complete, while the outer line below "TEN CENTS" is very nearly complete. At the top, the outer lines above "U.S. POSTAGE" above the "X" in each corner are broken.

TYPE II   has the design complete at the top, but the outer line at the bottom is broken in the middle and the "shells" are partially cut away.

TYPE III   has both top and bottom outer lines cut away; similar to Type I at the top and Type II at the bottom.

TYPE IV   has the outer lines at the top or bottom of the stamp, or at both place, recut to show more strongly and heavily.

Types I, II, III and IV have complete ornaments at the sides and three small circles or pearls (arrow) at the outer edges of the bottom panel.

TYPE V   has the side ornaments, including one or two of the small "pearls" partly cut away. Also, the outside line, over the "X" at the right top, has been partly cut away.

Types of the 12¢ Washington issues of 1851-60

PLATE 1 has stronger, more complete outer frame lines than does Plate 3. Comes imperforate (#17 or perf #36).

PLATE 3 has uneven or broken outer frame lines that are particularly noticeable in the corners. The stamps are perf 15. (#36b)

The REPRINT plate is similar to plate 1, but the Reprint stamps are greenish black and slightly taller than plate 1 stamps (25mm from top to bottom frame lines versus 24.5 mm) The paper is whiter and the perforations are 12 gauge.

UNITED STATES STAMP IDENTIFIER

Types of the 1861 Issue, Grills & Re-Issues

Shortly after the outbreak of the Civil War in 1861, the Post Office demonitized all stamps issued up to that time in order to prevent their use by the Confederacy. Two new sets of designs, consisting of six stamps shown below plus 24¢ and 30¢ demonitized, were prepared by the American Bank Note Company. The first designs, except for the 10¢ and 24¢ values, were not regularly issued and are extremely rare and valuable. The second designs became the regular issue of 1861. The illustrations in the left column show the first (or unissued) designs, which were all printed on thin, semi- transparent paper. The second (or regular) designs are shown at right.

Types of the 1861 Issues

1st

SECOND DESIGN shows a small dash (arrow) under the tip of the ornaments at the right of the figure "1" in the upper left-hand corner of the stamp.

2nd

1st   2nd

FIRST DESIGN has rounded corners. **SECOND DESIGN** has a oval and a scroll (arrow) in each corner of the design

1st

SECOND DESIGN, 3¢ value, shows a small ball (arrow) at each corner of the design. Also, the ornaments at the corners are larger than in the first design.

2nd

Types of the 15¢ "Landing of Columbus" Design of 1869

Type I

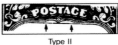

Type II

1st

SECOND DESIGN, 5¢ value has a leaflet (arrow) projecting from the scrolled ornaments at each corner of the stamp.

2nd

TYPE I has the central picture without the frame line shown in Type II.
TYPE II has a frame line (arrows) around the central picture; also a diamond shaped ornament appears below the "T" of "Postage".
TYPE III (not illustrated) is like Type I except that the fringe of brown shading lines which appears around the sides and bottom of the picture on Types I and II has been removed.

1st

FIRST DESIGN has no curved line below the row of stars and there is only one outer line of the ornaments above them.
SECOND DESIGN has a heavy curved line below the row of stars (arrow); ornaments above the stars have double outer line.

2nd

IDENTIFIER CHART
1861-1867 Bank Notes

Description and Identifying Features	1¢	2¢	3¢	5¢	10¢	12¢	15¢	24¢	30¢	90¢
1861. National. First designs. Thin, semi-transparent paper. No grill.	55		56	57	58[1], 62B	59		60	61	62
1861-62. National. Modified designs[3]. Thicker, opaque paper. No grill.	63	64[2], 65[2], 66[2]		67	68	69		70[2]	71	72
1861-66. National. Thicker, opaque paper. No grill. a. New designs.		73					77			
b. Same designs, new shades.			74[2]		75[2], 76[2]			78[2]		

1867. National. Grills. All on thick, opaque paper.													
Grills	Pts. as seen from stamp face	Area of covered Horiz. x Vert.	# of rows of Pts.										
A	Up	All over	—			79	80					81	
B	Up	18 x 15 mm	22 x 18			82							
C	Up	c. 13 x 16 mm	16-17 x 18-21			83							
D	Down	c. 12 x 14 mm	15 x 17-18		84	85							
Z	Down	c. 11 x 14 mm	13-14 x 17-18	85A	85B	85C		85D	85E	85F			
E	Down	c. 11 x 13 mm	14 x 15-17	86	87	88		89	90	91			
F	Down	c. 9 x 13 mm	11-12 x 15-17	92	93	94	95	96	97	98	99	100	101
1875. National. Re-issues. Hard, white paper. White crackly gum. No grill.	102	103	104	105	106	107	108	109	110	111

FOOTNOTES:
1. #58 does not exist used. Unused, it cannot be distinguished from #62B.
2. Different from corresponding 1861-66 issues only in color.
3. See diagrams for design modification.

UNITED STATES STAMP IDENTIFIER

Shows you how to distinguish between the rare and common U.S. stamps that look alike.

Types of the 1870-71 Through 1887 Bank Notes

The stamps of the 1870-71 issue were printed by the National Bank Note Company. The similar issue of 1873 was printed by the Continental Bank Note Company. When Continental took over the plates previously used by National, they applied the so-called "secret marks" to the designs of the 1¢ through 15¢ denominations by which the two issues can be distinguished as shown below. The illustrations at the left show the original designs of 1870-71; those at the right show secret marks applied to the issue of 1873.

 1¢ Secret mark is a small curved mark in the pearl at the left of the figure "1".

 7¢ Secret mark is two tiny semicircles drawn around the end of the lines which outline the ball in the lower right-hand corner.

 2¢ 1870-71 are red brown. The 1873 issue is brown and in some copies has a small diagonal line under the scroll at the left of the "U.S." (arrow).

 10¢ Secret mark is a small semicircle in the scroll at the right-hand side of the central design.

 **3¢** Secret mark is the heavily shaded ribbon under the letters "RE".

 12¢ Secret mark shows the "balls" at the top and bottom on the figure "2" crescent-shaped (right) instead of nearly round as at the left.

 6¢ Secret mark shows the first four vertical lines of shading in the lower part of the left ribbon greatly strengthened.

 15¢ Secret mark shows as strengthened lines (arrow) in the triangle in the upper left-hand corner, forming a "V".

IDENTIFIER CHART
1870-1887 Bank Notes

Description and Identifying Features	1¢	2¢	3¢	5¢	6¢	7¢	10¢	12¢	15¢	21¢	30¢	90¢
1870-71. National. No secret marks. White wove paper, thin to medium thick. With grills.	134	135	136		137	138	139	140	141	142	143	144
1870-71. National. As above, except without grills.	145	146	147		148	149	150	151	152	153	154[2]	155[2]
1873. Continental. White wove paper, thin to thick. No grills.												
a. With secret marks.	156	157	158		159	160	161	162	163			
b. No secret marks.											165[2]	166[2]
1875. Continental. Special Printing. Same designs as 1873 Continental. Hard, white wove paper. No gum.	167	168	169		170	171	172	173	174	175	176	177
1875. Continenal. New color or denomination. Hard yellowish, wove paper.		178		179								
1875. Continental. Special printing. Same designs as 1875 Continental. Hard, white wove paper. No gum.		180		181								
1879. American. Same designs as 1873-75. Continental. Soft, porous paper.	182	183[3]	184[3]	185	186[3]		188		189[3]		190[3]	191[3]
a. Without secret mark.							187[3]					
1880. American. Special printing. Same as 1879 issue. Soft, porous paper. No gum.	192	193, 203[3]	194[3]	204	195[3]	196	197[3]	198	199[3]	200	201[3]	202[3]
1881-82. American. Designs of 1873. Re-engraved[4]. Soft, porous paper.	206		207[5]		208		209					
1887. American. Same designs as 1881-82. New colors.		214[5]									217	218

FOOTNOTES:
1. See diagrams for secret marks.
2. Corresponding denominations differ from each other only in color.
3. Corresponding denominations differ from each other only in color and gum. The special printings are slightly deeper and richer. The lack of gum is not positive identifier because it can be washed from the 1879 issues.
4. See diagrams for re-engravings.
5. Corresponding denominations differ from each other in color.

Shows you how to distinguish between the rare and common U.S. stamps that look alike.

Re-Engraved Designs 1881-82

1¢ has strengthened vertical shading lines in the upper part of the stamp, making the background appear almost solid. Lines of shading have also been added to the curving ornaments in the upper corners.

3¢ has a solid shading line at the sides of the central oval (arrow) that is only about half the previous width. Also a short horizontal line has been cut below the "TS" of "CENTS".

6¢ has only three vertical lines between the edge of the panel and the outside left margin of the stamp. (In the preceding issues, there were four such lines.)

10¢ has only four vertical lines between the left side of the oval and the edge of the shield. (In the preceding issues there were five such lines.) Also, the lines in the background have been made much heavier so that these stamps appear more heavily linked than previous issues.

2¢ Washington Design of 1894-98

TYPE I has horizontal lines of the same thickness within and without the triangle.

TYPE II has horizontal lines which cross the triangle but are thinner within it than without.

TYPE III has thin lines inside the triangle and these do not cross the double frame line of the triangle.

2¢ Columbian "Broken Hat" Variety of 1893

231

As a result of a plate defect, some stamps of the 2¢ Columbian design show a noticeable white notch or gash in the hat worn by the third figure to the left of Columbus. This "broken hat" variety is somewhat less common than the regular 2¢ design.

Broken Hat variety, 231c

4¢ Columbian Blue Error

Collectors often mistake the many shades of the normal 4¢ ultramarine for the rare and valuable blue error. Actually, the "error" is not ultramarine at all, but a deep blue, similar to the deeper blue shades of the 1¢ Columbian.

$1 Perry Design of 1894-95

TYPE I shows circles around the "$1" are broken at point where they meet the curved line below "ONE DOLLAR" (arrows).

TYPE II shows these circles complete.

10¢ Webster design of 1898

TYPE I has an unbroken white curved line below the words "TEN CENTS".

TYPE II shows white line is broken by ornaments at a point just below the "E" in "TEN" and the "T" in "CENTS" (arrows).

2¢ Washington Issue of 1903

Die I
319, 319g, 320

The rounded inner frame line below and to the left "T" in "TWO" has a dark patch of color that narrows, but remains strong across the bottom.

Die II
319f, 320a

2¢ "cap of 2" Variety of 1890

Cap on left "2"

Plate defects in the printing of the 2¢ "Washington" stamp of 1890 accounts for the "Cap of left 2" and "Cap on both 2s" varieties illustrated.

Cap on right "2"

UNITED STATES STAMP IDENTIFIER

Shows you how to distinguish between the rare and common U.S. stamps that look alike.

FRANKLIN AND WASHINGTON ISSUES OF 1908-22

Perforation	Watermark	Other Identifying Features		1¢	2¢	1¢	2¢	3¢ thru $1 denominations	8¢ thru $1 denominations
PERF. 12	USPS	White paper		331	332			333-42	422-23
		Bluish gray paper		357	358			359-66	
	USPS	White paper		374	375	405	406	376-82, 407	414-21
COIL 12	USPS	Perf. Horizontal		348	349			350-51	
		Perf. Vertical		352	353			354-56	
	USPS	Perf. Horizontal		385	386				
		Perf. Vertical		387	388			389	
IMPERF.	USPS			343	344			345-47	
	USPS	Flat Plate		383	384	408	409		
		Rotary Press					459		
	Unwmkd.	Flat Plate				481	482-82A	483-85	
		Offset				531	532-34B	535	
COIL 8-1/2	USPS	Perf. Horizontal		390	391	410	411		
		Perf. Vertical		392	393	412	413	394-96	
PERF. 10	USPS								460
	USPS					424	425	426-30	431-40
	Unwmkd.	Flat Plate				462	463	464-69	470-78
		Rotary Press				543			
COIL 10	USPS	Perf. Horizontal	Flat			441	442		
			Rotary			448	449-50		
		Perf. Vertical	Flat			443	444	445-47	
			Rotary			452	453-55	456-58	
	Unwmkd.	Perf. Horizontal				486	487-88	489	
		Perf. Vertical				490	491-92	493-96	497
PERF. 11	USPS				519				
	USPS						461		
	Unwmkd.	Flat Plate				498	499-500	501-07	508-18
		Rotary Press				*544-45	546		
		Offset				525	526-28B	529-30	
Perf. 12-1/2	Unwkmd.	Offset				536			
11 x 10	Unwkmd.	Rotary				538	539-40	541	
10 x 11	Unwkmd.	Rotary				542			

* Design of #544 is 19 mm wide x 22-1/2 mm high. #545 is 19-1/2 to 20 mm wide x 22 mm high.

Size of Flat Plate Design — 22mm — 18-1/2 to 19mm

Stamps printed by rotary press are always slightly wider or taller on issues prior to 1954. Measurements do not apply to booklet singles.

HOW TO USE THIS IDENTIFICATION CHART

Numbers referred to herein are from Scott's Standard Postage Stamp Catalog. To identify any stamp in this series, first check the type by comparing it with the illustrations at the top of the chart. Then check the perforations, and whether the stamp is single or double line watermarked or unwatermarked. With this information you can quickly find out the Standard Catalog number by checking down and across the chart. For example, a 1¢ Franklin, perf. 12, single line watermark, must be Scott's #374.

Types of The 2¢ Washington Design of 1912-20

Type I

Type I where the ribbon at left above the figure "2" has one shading line in the first curve, while the ribbon at the right has one shading line in the second curve. Bottom of toga has a faint outline. Top line of toga, from bottom to front of throat, is very faint. Shading lines of the face, terminating in front of the ear, are not joined. Type I occurs on both flat and rotary press printings.

Type Ia is similar to Type I except that all of the lines are stronger. Lines of the Toga button are heavy. Occurs only on flat press printings.

Type Ia

Type II

Type II has ribbons shaded as in Type I. Toga button and shading lines to left of it are heavy. Shading lines in front of ear are joined and end in a strong vertically curved line (arrow). Occurs only on rotary press printings.

Type III where ribbons are shaded with two lines instead of one; otherwise similar to Type II. Occurs on rotary press printings only.

Type III

Type IV

Type IV where top line of toga is broken. Shading lines inside the toga bottom read "Did". The Line of color in the left "2" is very thin and usually broken. Occurs on offset printings only.

Type V in which top line of toga is complete. Toga button has five vertical shaded lines. Line of color in the left "2" is very thin and usually broken. Nose shaded as shown in illustration. Occurs on offset printings only.

Type V

Type Va

Type Va is same as Type V except in shading dots of nose. Third row of dots from bottom has four dots instead of six. Also, the Overall height of Type Va is 1/3 millimeter less than Type V. Occurs on offset printings only.

Type VI is same as Type V except that the line of color in left "2" is very heavy (arrow). Occurs in offset printings only.

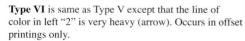

Type VI

Type VII

Type VII in which line of color in left "2" is clear and continuous and heavier than Types V or Va, but not as heavy as in Type VI. There are three rows of vertical dots (instead of two) in the shading of the upper lip, and additional dots have been added to hair at top of the head. Occurs on offset printings only.

Types of The 3¢ Washington Design of 1908-20

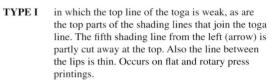

Type I

TYPE I in which the top line of the toga is weak, as are the top parts of the shading lines that join the toga line. The fifth shading line from the left (arrow) is partly cut away at the top. Also the line between the lips is thin. Occurs on flat and rotary press printings.

Type II

TYPE II where top line of toga is strong and the shading lines that join it are heavy and complete. The line between the lips is heavy. Occurs on flat and rotary press printings.

Type III

TYPE III in which top line of toga is strong, but the fifth shading line from the left (arrow) is missing. The center line of the toga button consists of two short vertical lines with a dot between them. The "P" and "O" of "POSTAGE" are separated by a small line of color. Occurs on offset printings only.

Type IV

TYPE IV in which the shading lines of the toga are complete. The center line of the toga button consists of a single unbroken vertical line running through the dot in the center. The "P" and the "O" of "POSTAGE" are joined. Type IV occurs only in offset printings.

The following handy identifier is a list of commemoratives organized alphabetically by key words on the stamp, which are the most prominent after "U.S. Postage," and matches the stamp with its corresponding Scott number.

UNITED STATES COMMEMORATIVE IDENTIFIER

McLoughlin, John ... 964
McMahon, Sen. Brien ... 1200
McMein, Neysa ... 3502m
McPhatter, Clyde ... 2726, 2733
McQueen's Jupiter ... 2844
Mead, Margaret, anthropologist ... 3184g
Meadow Beauty ... 2649
Meany, George ... 2848
Medal of Honor ... 2013, 2045, 2103
Medical Imaging ... 3189o
Medics treat wounded ... 2765b
Medussa ... 3443
Mellon, Andrew W. ... 1072
Melville, Herman ... 2094
Memorial ... 1318
Poppy ... 977
Mendez Vs. Westminster ... 4201
Mentoring A Child ... 3556
Mercer, Johnny ... 3101
Merchant Marine ... 939
Mercury ... 1557, 2568, 2634
Helmet and Olive Branch ... E7
Project ... 1193
Merengue ... 3939
Merganthaler, Ottmar ... 3062
Mermaid ... 1112
Merman, Ethel ... 2853
Mesa Verde National Park ... 743, 759
Messenger
on Bicycle ... E6, E8-E11
Running ... E1-E4, E5
Metropolitan Opera ... 2054
Mexican
Hat ... 2688
Independence ... 1157
Michael, Moina ... 977
Michener, James ... 3427A
Michigan ... 1658, 1974, 3582, 3717
Landing of Cadillac ... 1000
State College ... 1065
Statehood ... 775, 2246
Mickey Mouse ... 3912, 4025, 4192
Micronesia, Federated States of ... 2506-2507
Microphone ... 1502
Microscope ... 1080, 1263, 1754, 1925
Midway, battle of ... 2697g
Mighty Casey ... 3083
Migratory
Bird Hunting & Conservation Stamp Act ... 2092
Bird Treaty ... 1306
Miquel Locks, Pedro ... 398
Military
Academy ... 3560
Uniforms ... 1565-1568
Militia, American ... 1568
Milk Wagon ... 2253
Millay, Edna St. Vincent ... 1926
Millikan, Robert ... 1866
Mineral Heritage ... 1538-1541
Minerals ... 2700-2703
Mingus, Charles ... 2989
Mining Prospector ... 291
Minnesota ... 1664, 1975, 3583, 3718
(Hubert Humphrey) ... 2190
Statehood ... 1106, 4266
Territory ... 981
Minnie Mouse ... 4025
Minute Man, The ... 619
Mirror Lake ... 742, 750, 758, 770
Miss Piggie ... 3944d
Missiing in Action ... 2966
Mission Belfry, CA ... 1373
Missions ... 1373, 1443, C116
Mississippi ... 1652, 1976, 3584, 3719
(Great River Road) ... 1319
-Missouri River System ... 4065
River ... 285, 1356
River Bridge ... 293
River Delta ... 4058
Statehood ... 1337
Territory ... 955
Mississippian Effigy ... 3873f
Missouri ... 1656, 1977, 3585, 3720
Kansas City ... 994
River ... 1063
Statehood ... 1426
Mistletoe ... 1255
Mitchell
Billy ... 3330
Margaret ... 2168
Pass, NE ... 1060
Mobile, Battle of ... 1826
Mockingbird ... 2330
Model B Airplane ... 3142b
Model T Ford ... 3182a
Modern Dance ... 1752
Mold-Blown Glass ... 3326
Molded Plastic Sculpture ... 4333m
Moloka'I ... 4034
Monarch Butterfly ... 2287, 3351k
Monarch caterpillar ... 3351j
Monday Night Football ... 3189l
Monitor and Virginia ... 2975a
Monk, Thelonius ... 2990
Monmouth, Battle of (Molly Pitcher) ... 646
Monongahela River ... 681
Monorail ... 1196
Monroe
James . 325, 562, 591, 603, 642, 668, 679, 810, 845, 1020, 1038, 1105, 2201, 2216e
Marilyn ... 2967
Monopoly Game, The ... 3185o
Montana ... 1673, 1978, 3586, 3721
(Glacier National Park) ... 748, 764
Statehood ... 858, 2401
Montgomery, Alabama Bus Boycott ... 3937e
Monticello ... 1047
Monument, George Washington ... 2149
Moon . . . 126, 1021, 1192, 1345, 1371, 1434-1435, 1548, 1909, 2122, 2246, 2394, 2404, 2419, 2571, 2631, 2634, C124
First Landing ... 2841
Landing ... 2419, 2842, 3188c, 3413, C76
Rover ... 1435, C124, C126
Moore
John Bassett ... 1295
Marianne ... 2449
Moorish Idol ... 1829
Moose ... 1757e, 1887, 2298
Moran, Thomas ... 3236l
Morgan
Charles W. ... 1441, 2340
Horse ... 2156
Silver Dollar ... 1557
Morning Light, S.S. ... 1239
Morocco, Friendship with ... 2349
Morill, Justin ... 2941
Morris, Robert ... 1004
Morris Island, South Carolina ... 3789
Morris Township School ... 1606
Morrison's Bumblebee ... 4153, 4153a
Morro Castle, San Juan, Puerto Rico ... 1437
Morse, Samuel F.B. ... 890, 924
Morton
Jelly Roll ... 2986
Julius Sterling, (Arbor Day) ... 717
Moses
Grandma ... 1370
Horace A. ... 2095
Moss Campion ... 2686
Mothers
Gold Star ... 969
of America ... 737-738, 754
Motion
Pictures ... 926, 1555, 1727
-Picture Camera ... 1555
Motorcycle ... 1899, 4085-4088
Mott, Lucretia ... 959
Moultrie Flag, Fort ... 1345
Mount
Davidson ... 1130
Hood ... 1124
McKinley National Park ... 800, 1454, C137
Ranier ... 2404
Ranier National Park ... 742, 750, 758, 770
Rockwell (Mt. Sinopah) ... 748, 764
Rushmore ... 2523-2523A, C88
Rushmore Memorial ... 1011
Surabachi ... 929
Vernon ... 785, 1032
Wai'ale'ale ... 4066
Washington ... 4053
Mountain
Bluebird ... 2439
Goat ... 2323
Habitats ... 1923
Lion ... 2292
Nonprofit ... 2903-2904A
Movies go 3-D ... 3187o
Mrs Elizabeth Freake and Baby Mary by the Freake Limner ... 3236b
Muddler Minnow ... 2549
Muir, John ... 1245, 3182j
Mule Deer ... 2294
Mummy, The ... 3171
Munor Marin, Luis ... 2173
Muppets ... 3944a-3944j
Murphy,
Audie L. ... 3396
Robert D. ... 4076a
Murrow, Edward R. ... 2812
Muscogee Seal ... 972
Museum
National Postal ... 2779
Smithsonian Institution ... 3059
Music ... 3772d
American ... 1252
and Literature by William Harnett ... 3236i
Big Band ... 3096-3099
Films ... 3772d
Musicals ... 2767-2770
Musicians Rock & Roll/Rhythm & Blues ... 2721, 2724-2737
Muskellunge ... 2205
Mustang Airplane ... 3142a
Muybridge, Eadweard ... 3061
My
Fair Lady ... 2770
Old Kentucky Home State Park ... 2636
Myron's Discobolus ... 719
Nagurski, Bronko ... 3808
Naismith—Basketball ... 1189
Nancy ... 3000o
Narrows Bridge, Verrazano- ... 1258
Nash
Healey ... 3934
,Ogden ... 3659
Nassau Hall (Princeton University) ... 1083, 1704
Nation of Readers, A ... 2106
National
Academy of Science ... 1237
Apprenticeship Program ... 1201
Archives ... 227, 2081
Capitol ... 990-992
Defense ... 899-901
Education Association ... 1093
Farmer's Bank ... 1931
Gallery of Art ... 3910g
Grange ... 1323
Guard ... 1017
Letter Writing Week ... 1805-1810
Park Service ... 1314
Parks ... 740-751, 756-765, 769-770, 952, 1448-1454, 2018, C84, C135, C138, C139, C140, C141
Postal Museum ... 2779-2782
Recovery Act ... 732
Stamp Exhibition ... 735, 768
Native American Culture ... 2869e, 2870e
Nativity, by John Singleton Copley ... 1701
NATO ... 1008, 1127, 3354
Natural History ... 1387-1390
Nautical Figure ... 2242
Nautilus ... 1128
Navajo
Blanket ... 2235-2238
Necklace ... 3749-3749B
Weaving ... 3873h
Naval
Academy, US ... 794
Aviation ... 1185
Review, International ... 1091
Navigation, Lake ... 294
Navigation, Ocean ... 299
Navy ... 790-794
Continental ... 1566
Department ... O35-O45
US ... 935, 1013, 1067
Nebraska ... 1669, 1979, 3587, 3722
Statehood ... 1328
Territory ... 1060
Nelson, Thomas, Jr. ... 1686d, 1687c
Neptune ... 1112, 2576
New England ... 2119
Netherlands ... 913, 2003
Neumann, John von ... 3908
Neuter/Spay ... 3670-71
Nevada ... 1668, 1980, 3588, 3723
Settlement ... 999
Statehood ... 1248
Nevelson, Louise ... 3379-83
Nevers, Ernie ... 3809
Nevin, Ethelbert ... 883
New
Amsterdam Harbor, NY ... 1027
Baseball Records ... 3191a
England Neptune ... 2119
Hampshire ... 1068, 1641, 1981, 3589, 3724
Hampshire Statehood ... 2344
Jersey ... 1635, 1982, 3590, 3725
Jersey, Settlement ... 1247
Jersey, Statehood ... 2338
Mexico ... 1679, 1983, 3591, 3726
Mexico (Chavez, Dennis) ... 2185
Mexico, Statehood ... 1191
Orleans ... 2407
Sweden ... C117
Year, Chinese ... 2817
Year, Happy ... 2720, 3370, 3500
York ... 1643, 1984, C38, 3592, 3727
York City ... 1027
York City Coliseum ... 1076
York, Newburgh ... 727, 731, 767
York, Skyline ... C35
York Statehood ... 2346
York Stock Exchange ... 2630
York World's Fair '39 ... 853

Protect your stamps with the best…

Manufactured in Germany, Prinz mounts consist of two sheets of polystyrol foil welded together along top and bottom, with the mount split across the backing foil for insertion of your stamp. The black onyx backing (also available in clear backing) is completely opaque for brilliant and sharper framing. The face of the mount is specially diffused to prevent harsh reflections. Two layers of gum assure 100% contact with the album page. Many of the mounts come in convenient resealable packaging, providing re-usable storage trays.

…and at low, low discount prices!

Fast Service: 99%+ orders shipped within one business day!

Free Shipping: On all orders of $25 or more!

Low Prices: Compare and see!

Huge Stock: We carry a gigantic stock. Unlike other suppliers, out of stocks are a rarity.

More Sizes: We have more sizes of Prinz mounts than any other U.S. source. Check our website for new sizes.

Available in your choice of
BLACK or **CLEAR**
backgrounds.

Write or call for a free mount list and size guide or visit our website
www.globalstamps.com
for a complete pricelist of mounts

MOUNT ORDER LINE **1-800-387-5040**

**Dept. H
PO Box 7429
Olympia, WA 98507**

(No orders are accepted for shipment outside of the U.S. or its territories)

Global Stamps: serving stamp collectors since 1963

GENERAL ISSUES

1847 – THE FIRST ISSUE
Imperforate

"For every single letter in manuscript or paper of any kind by or upon which information shall be asked or communicated in writing or by marks or signs conveyed in the mail, for any distance under three hundred miles, five cents; and for any distance over three hundred miles, ten cents . . . and every letter or parcel not exceeding half an ounce in weight shall be deemed a single letter, and every additional weight of half ounce, shall be charged with an additional single postage."

With these words, the Act of March 3, 1845, authorized, but not required, the prepayment of postage effective July 1, 1847, and created a need for the first United States postage stamps. Benjamin Franklin, as the first Postmaster General of the United States and the man generally regarded as the "father" of the postal system, was selected for the 5 cent stamp. As the first President of the United States, George Washington was designated for the 10 cent issue.

The 1847 stamps were released July 1, 1847, but were available only in the New York City post office on that date. The earliest known usages are July 7 for the 5 cent and July 2 for the 10 cent.

The best estimates are that 4,400,000 of the 5 cent and 1,050,000 of the 10 cent stamps reached the public. The remaining stocks were destroyed when the stamps were demonetized and could no longer be used for postage as of July 1, 1851.

Like most 19th century United States stamps, the first Issue is much more difficult to find unused than used. Stamps canceled by "handstamp" marking devices—usually carved from cork—are scarcer than those with manuscript, or "pen", cancels.

Issued without gum, the Reproductions of the 1847 issue were printed from entirely new dies for display at the 1876 Centennial Exposition and were not valid for postal use. The issue also was reproduced on a souvenir sheet issued in 1947 to celebrate the centenary of the First Issue. Differences between the 1847 issue, 1875 Reproductions and 1948 stamps are described in the Stamp Identifier at the front of this catalog.

1, 3, 948a
Franklin

2, 4, 948b
Washington

SCOTT NO.	DESCRIPTION	UNUSED VF	F	AVG	USED VF	F	AVG
			1847 Imperforate (OG + 100%)				
1	5¢ red brown	4250.00	3000.00	1900.00	975.00	700.00	450.00
1	— Pen cancel	....	....	....	525.00	350.00	275.00
2	10¢ black . . .	23650.00	16250.00	10000.00	2800.00	2000.00	1300.00
2	— Pen cancel	....	....	....	1200.00	925.00	725.00
			1875 Reprints of 1847 Issues, without gum				
3	5¢ red brown	1395.00	1050.00	850.00	....	....	....
4	10¢ black	1800.00	1200.00	1050.00	....	....	....

1851-61 – THE CLASSIC ISSUES

An act of Congress approved March 3, 1851, enacted new, reduced postage rates, introduced additional rates and made the prepayment of additional postage compulsory. Although the use of postage stamps was not required, the 1851 Act stimulated their use and paved the way for their required usage from July 1, 1855 on.

Under the Act of 1851, the basic prepaid single letter rate (defined as one-half ounce or less) was set at 3 cents. As this would be the most commonly used value, it was decided that a likeness of George Washington should grace the 3 cent stamp. Benjamin Franklin was assigned to the 1 cent stamp, which, among other usages, met the newspaper and circular rate.

Washington also appears on the 10, 12, 24 and 90 cent stamps and Franklin on the 30 cent value. Thomas Jefferson was selected for the new 5 cent stamp that was issued in 1856.

By 1857, improved production techniques and the increasing usage of stamps led to the introduction of perforated stamps that could be more easily separated. The result was the 1857-61 series whose designs are virtually identical to the 1851 set. The 1857-61 perforated stamps were set in the printing plates with very little space between each stamp. As a result, insufficient space was allowed to accommodate the perforations, which often cut into the design on these stamps. In fact, stamps with complete designs and wide margins on all four sides are the exception and command very substantial premiums.

The most fascinating—and most challenging—feature of the 1851-61 stamps is the identification of many major and minor types. An extremely slight design variation can mean a difference of thousands of dollars and collectors even today can apply their knowledge to discover rare, mis-identified types.

The various "Types", identified below by Roman numerals in parentheses, resulted from minor changes in the printing plates caused by wear or plate retouching. The 1851-57 one-cent blue stamp may be the most studied of all the United States issues and is found in seven major catalog-listed Types (14, if we count imperforate and perforated stamps separately), plus countless minor listed and unlisted varieties. A thorough explanation of the differences in the major types for all denominations of the 1857-61 series is contained in the Harris Stamp Identifier in this catalog.

Shortly after the outbreak of the Civil War, the 1851-61 stamps were demonetized to prevent Southern post offices from selling the stamps in the North to raise cash for the Confederate States. After the war, large supplies of unused 1857-61 stamps were located in Southern post offices and purchased by stamp dealers and collectors. This explains the relatively large supply of unused 1857-61 issues that still exist today. The short life and limited use of 90 cent high value, which was issued in 1860, and the 5 cent orange brown, released May 8, 1861, explains why those stamps sell for more used than unused.

5-9, 18-24, 40
Franklin

10, 11, 25, 26, 41
Washington

12, 27-30A, 42
Jefferson

13-16, 31-35, 43
Washington

17, 36, 44
Washington

SCOTT NO.	DESCRIPTION	UNUSED VF	F	AVG	USED VF	F	AVG
			1851-57 Imperforate (OG + 100%)				
5	1¢ blue (I)	....	....	....	75000.00	....	....
5A	1¢ blue (Ib)	8400.00	7000.00	5750.00	8500.00	5750.00	4000.00
6	1¢ dark blue (Ia)	24675.00	18750.00	13750.00	12000.00	8750.00	5750.00
7	1¢ blue (II)	900.00	625.00	475.00	250.00	195.00	150.00
8	1¢ blue (III)	7770.00	5000.00	3400.00	3500.00	2800.00	1700.00
8A	1¢ blue (IIIa)	5000.00	3400.00	2100.00	1500.00	1075.00	825.00
9	1¢ blue (IV)	580.00	450.00	325.00	195.00	140.00	90.00
10	3¢ orange brown (I) . .	2500.00	2000.00	1600.00	200.00	125.00	75.00
11	3¢ deep claret (I)	250.00	175.00	125.00	19.00	11.00	9.50
12	5¢ red brown (I)	13650.00	10250.00	6750.00	1750.00	1300.00	1000.00
13	10¢ green (I)	11050.00	8500.00	6000.00	1850.00	1350.00	1075.00
14	10¢ green (II)	2300.00	1750.00	1350.00	425.00	300.00	240.00
15	10¢ green (III)	2500.00	1800.00	1300.00	390.00	300.00	220.00
16	10¢ green (IV)	18900.00	12500.00	10000.00	2000.00	1500.00	1150.00
17	12¢ black	3250.00	2500.00	1750.00	500.00	400.00	295.00

NOTE: For further details on the various types of similar appearing stamps please refer to our U.S. Stamp Identifier.

37, 45	38, 46	39, 47
Washington	*Franklin*	*Washington*

73, 84, 85B, 87, 93, 103	77, 85F, 91, 98, 108
Jackson	*Lincoln*

SCOTT NO.	DESCRIPTION	UNUSED VF	F	AVG	USED VF	F	AVG
	1857-61 Same design as preceding Issue, Perf. 15-1/2 (†) (OG + 75%)						
18	1¢ blue (I)	1500.00	950.00	700.00	900.00	650.00	425.00
19	1¢ blue (Ia)	17500.00	10000.00	7250.00	9500.00	6250.00	4000.00
20	1¢ blue (II)	750.00	525.00	400.00	365.00	275.00	200.00
21	1¢ blue (III)	8150.00	5500.00	4200.00	3350.00	2200.00	1400.00
22	1¢ blue (IIIa)	1350.00	950.00	650.00	800.00	525.00	345.00
23	1¢ blue (IV)	4900.00	3400.00	2400.00	1000.00	700.00	425.00
24	1¢ blue (V)	175.00	120.00	90.00	90.00	55.00	43.50
25	3¢ rose (I)	1750.00	1300.00	1000.00	175.00	115.00	75.00
26	3¢ dull red (II)	110.00	77.50	60.00	15.00	8.75	6.50
26a	3¢ dull red (IIa)	350.00	265.00	185.00	110.00	77.50	54.50
27	5¢ brick red (I)	14700.00	10500.00	7250.00	2000.00	1500.00	800.00
28	5¢ red brown (I)	2750.00	2200.00	1500.00	1500.00	1000.00	600.00
28A	5¢ Indian red (I)	25000.00	18000.00	12750.00	3600.00	2800.00	2000.00
29	5¢ brown (I)	1400.00	975.00	725.00	550.00	425.00	275.00
30	5¢ orange brown (II) . .	925.00	650.00	500.00	1900.00	1250.00	700.00
30A	5¢ brown (II)	1250.00	975.00	650.00	400.00	325.00	220.00
31	10¢ green (I)	10500.00	7500.00	5500.00	1500.00	1100.00	650.00
32	10¢ green (II)	3200.00	2200.00	1650.00	400.00	325.00	205.00
33	10¢ green (III)	3200.00	2200.00	1650.00	350.00	275.00	180.00
34	10¢ green (IV)	22500.00	15750.00	12500.00	2600.00	2100.00	1650.00
35	10¢ green (V)	275.00	195.00	150.00	180.00	100.00	65.00
36	12¢ black, Plate I . . .	925.00	675.00	500.00	500.00	350.00	220.00
36b	12¢ black, Plate III . . .	550.00	375.00	250.00	200.00	175.00	125.00
37	24¢ gray lilac	950.00	700.00	475.00	500.00	450.00	290.00
38	30¢ orange	1250.00	850.00	600.00	800.00	400.00	285.00
39	90¢ blue	2150.00	1550.00	1200.00	8000.00	6150.00	4700.00
	1875 Reprints of 1857-61 Issue. Perf. 12 Without Gum						
40	1¢ bright blue	900.00	625.00	425.00	. . . . . .	. . . . . .	. . . . . .
41	3¢ scarlet	3900.00	2600.00	1750.00	. . . . . .	. . . . . .	. . . . . .
42	5¢ orange brown	1650.00	1100.00	700.00	. . . . . .	. . . . . .	. . . . . .
43	10¢ blue green	3750.00	2500.00	1600.00	. . . . . .	. . . . . .	. . . . . .
44	12¢ greenish black . . .	4500.00	3000.00	2000.00	. . . . . .	. . . . . .	. . . . . .
45	24¢ blackish violet . . .	4875.00	3300.00	2200.00	. . . . . .	. . . . . .	. . . . . .
46	30¢ yellow orange . . .	4725.00	3200.00	2100.00	. . . . . .	. . . . . .	. . . . . .
47	90¢ deep blue	7455.00	5000.00	3400.00	. . . . . .	. . . . . .	. . . . . .

THE 1861-67 ISSUE

The 1861-66 Issue and its 1867 Grilled varieties are among the most interesting and controversial of all stamps. Born out of the need to demonetize previously-issued stamps in the possession of Southern post offices, they were rushed into service shortly after the outbreak of the Civil War.

The controversy begins with the "August Issues", catalog #s 55-62B. It is now generally accepted that all but the 10 and 24 cent values never were issued for use as postage. The set is more aptly described as "First Designs", because they were printed by the National Bank Note Company and submitted to the Post Office Department as fully gummed and perforated sample designs.

63, 85A, 86, 92, 102	64-65, 79, 82, 83, 85, 85C, 88, 94, 104	67, 75, 76, 80, 95, 105	62B, 68, 85D, 89, 96, 106
Franklin	*Washington*	*Jefferson*	*Washington*

69, 85E, 90, 97, 107	70, 78, 99, 109	71, 81, 100, 110	72, 101, 111
Washington	*Washington*	*Franklin*	*Washington*

(†) means Issue is actually very poorly centered. Perforations may touch the design on "Fine" quality.

SCOTT NO.	DESCRIPTION	UNUSED VF	F	AVG	USED VF	F	AVG
	1861 First Design (†) Perf. 12 (OG + 75%)						
62B	10¢ dark green	5250.00	3400.00	2200.00	1750.00	1150.00	700.00
	1861-62 Second Design (†) Perf. 12 (OG + 75%)						
63	1¢ blue	225.00	150.00	110.00	65.00	41.50	28.25
64	3¢ pink	5460.00	3900.00	3100.00	800.00	600.00	425.00
64b	3¢ rose pink	325.00	250.00	190.00	165.00	115.00	90.00
65	3¢ rose	130.00	77.50	52.50	5.00	3.00	2.25
66	3¢ lake	2850.00	2100.00	1500.00	. . . . . .	. . . . . .	. . . . . .
67	5¢ buff	11550.00	7250.00	5500.00	1200.00	875.00	600.00
68	10¢ yellow green	600.00	425.00	275.00	88.00	50.00	35.00
69	12¢ black	950.00	700.00	450.00	210.00	125.00	85.00
70	24¢ red lilac	1200.00	825.00	600.00	300.00	250.00	165.00
71	30¢ orange	1250.00	875.00	600.00	250.00	190.00	140.00
72	90¢ blue	2100.00	1500.00	1100.00	600.00	450.00	285.00
	1861-66 (†) (OG + 75%)						
73	2¢ black	275.00	200.00	125.00	115.00	75.00	45.00
74	3¢ scarlet	8190.00	5500.00	3700.00	. . . . . .	. . . . . .	. . . . . .
75	5¢ red brown	2800.00	2200.00	1450.00	650.00	500.00	345.00
76	5¢ brown	775.00	550.00	425.00	180.00	125.00	95.00
77	15¢ black	1400.00	1000.00	650.00	250.00	190.00	120.00
78	24¢ lilac	900.00	675.00	400.00	300.00	180.00	120.00

From 1867 to 1870, grills were embossed into the stamp paper to break the fiber and prevent the eradication of cancellations. The first "A" grilled issues were grilled all over. When postal clerks found that the stamps were as likely to separate along the grill as on the perforations, the Post Office abandoned the "A" grill and tried other configurations, none of which proved to be effective. The Grilled Issues include some of our greatest rarities. The most notable is the 1 cent "Z", only two of which are known to exist. One realized $935,000 in a 1998 auction, making it the most valuable United States stamp. The grills are fully explained and identified in the Harris Stamp Identifier.

SCOTT NO.	DESCRIPTION	UNUSED VF	F	AVG	USED VF	F	AVG
	1867 Grill with Points Up A. Grill Covering Entire Stamp (†) (OG + 75%)						
79	3¢ rose	. . . . . .	3600.00	3000.00	. . . . . .	1400.00	975.00
80	5¢ brown	. . . . . .	. . . . . .	. . . . . .	. . . . . .	130000.00	. . . . . .
81	30¢ orange	. . . . . .	. . . . . .	. . . . . .	. . . . . .	. . . . . .	75000.00
	B. Grill about 18 x 15 mm. (OG + 75%)						
82	3¢ rose	. . . . . .	. . . . . .	. . . . . .	. . . . . .	190000.00	. . . . . .
	C. Grill About 13 x 16 mm. (†) (OG + 75%)						
83	3¢ rose	3700.00	2700.00	1950.00	1000.00	775.00	575.00
	1867 Grill with Points Down D. Grill About 12 x 14 mm. (†) (OG + 75%)						
84	2¢ black	11550.00	9000.00	6500.00	4000.00	2800.00	1900.00
85	3¢ rose	3800.00	2600.00	1950.00	1200.00	850.00	650.00
	Z. Grill About 11 x 14 mm. (†) (OG + 75%)						
85A	1¢ blue	. . . . . .	. . . . . .	. . . . . .	. . . . . .	. . . . . .	. . . . . .
85B	2¢ black	6350.00	4600.00	2700.00	1350.00	1050.00	700.00
85C	3¢ rose	9500.00	6750.00	4700.00	3200.00	2800.00	1900.00
85D	10¢ green	. . . . . .	. . . . . .	. . . . . .	225000.00	165000.00	. . . . . .
85E	12¢ black	8400.00	6250.00	4700.00	2500.00	1875.00	1475.00
85F	15¢ black	. . . . . .	. . . . . .	. . . . . .	750000.00	. . . . . .	. . . . . .
	E. Grill About 11 x 13 mm. (†) (OG + 75%)						
86	1¢ blue	1900.00	1350.00	950.00	700.00	500.00	375.00
87	2¢ black	750.00	575.00	425.00	275.00	160.00	110.00
88	3¢ rose	495.00	375.00	250.00	33.00	22.50	15.00
89	10¢ green	2900.00	2200.00	1450.00	475.00	300.00	215.00
90	12¢ black	3000.00	2100.00	1200.00	550.00	325.00	235.00
91	15¢ black	5900.00	4200.00	3100.00	975.00	650.00	475.00

SCOTT NO.	DESCRIPTION	UNUSED			USED		
		VF	F	AVG	VF	F	AVG
	F. Grill About 9 x 13 mm. (†)						
	(OG + 75%)						
92	1¢ blue	975.00	725.00	500.00	650.00	400.00	255.00
93	2¢ black	400.00	285.00	205.00	95.00	60.00	45.00
94	3¢ red	225.00	165.00	115.00	13.00	7.50	5.00
95	5¢ brown	1800.00	1400.00	950.00	1125.00	775.00	475.00
96	10¢ yellow green .	1550.00	1150.00	875.00	350.00	250.00	135.00
97	12¢ black	1800.00	1400.00	975.00	475.00	350.00	195.00
98	15¢ black	2100.00	1500.00	1100.00	475.00	325.00	225.00
99	24¢ gray lilac	3500.00	2500.00	2100.00	1750.00	1050.00	665.00
100	30¢ orange	3750.00	2700.00	1950.00	1200.00	750.00	600.00
101	90¢ blue	7600.00	5000.00	3700.00	2900.00	2000.00	1400.00

The Re-Issues of the 1861-66 Issue were issued with gum and, while scarce, are found used. They can be distinguished by their bright colors, sharp printing impressions, hard paper and white, crackly original gum.

		UNUSED			USED		
	1875. Re-Issue of 1861-66 Issue. Hard White Paper						
	(OG + 75%)						
102	1¢ blue	650.00	550.00	450.00	1200.00	950.00	750.00
103	2¢ black	2100.00	1700.00	1400.00	6500.00	5300.00	4100.00
104	3¢ brown red	2600.00	2000.00	1650.00	11500.00	10000.00	7000.00
105	5¢ brown	1900.00	1600.00	1250.00	5000.00	4100.00	3350.00
106	10¢ green.	2000.00	1700.00	1400.00	20000.00	15275.00	12500.00
107	12¢ black	2700.00	2100.00	1700.00	8500.00	6800.00	5200.00
108	15¢ black	2700.00	2200.00	1850.00	15000.00	12000.00	9250.00
109	24¢ deep violet. . .	3200.00	2700.00	2300.00	17500.00	14000.00	11500.00
110	30¢ brownish orange	3400.00	2800.00	2300.00	17500.00	14000.00	11500.00
111	90¢ blue	4500.00	3600.00	3000.00	110000.00	. . . .	. . . .

THE 1869 PICTORIALS

As the first United States series to include pictorial designs, the 1869 issue is one of the most popular today. They were so unpopular that they were removed from sale less than a year after issue. Most protests were directed toward their odd size and the tradition-breaking pictorial designs.

The 1869 issue broke important new ground in the use of two color designs. Not only does this add to their attractiveness; it also is the source for the first United States "Inverted Centers". These inverted errors appear on the bi-colored 15, 24 and 30 cent values. The printing technology of the time required a separate printing pass for each color. On the first pass, the central designs, or vignettes, were printed. The second pass applied the frames.

In a very few instances, the sheets with their central designs already printed were passed upside down through the printing press. As a result, the frames were printed upside down. So the description "inverted center" for the 15 and 24 cent errors is technically incorrect, but the form in which these errors are photographed and displayed is with the center, rather than the frame, inverted.

Used copies of the 1869 Pictorials are not as scarce as might be expected. Any of the stamps above the 3 cent denomination were used on mail to Europe and were saved by collectors overseas. When stamp collecting became popular in the United States and Americans were able to purchase stamps abroad at relatively low prices, many of these used 1869 Pictorials found their way back to this country. On the other hand, because of the short life of the issue in post offices and their sudden withdrawal, unused stamps—particularly the high values—are quite rare.

All values of the 1869 Pictorials are found with the "G" grill. Ungrilled varieties are known on all values except the 6, 10, 12 and type II 15 cent stamps. (The Harris Stamp Identifier describes the difference in the three 15 cent types.)

The 1869 Pictorials were re-issued in 1875 in anticipation of the 1876 Centennial Exposition. Most collectors who had missed the original 1869 issue were delighted to have a second chance to purchase the stamps, which explains why the high value re-issues carry lower prices today than do the original 1869 pictorials. At the time, most collectors did not realize they were buying entirely different stamps. The same designs were used, but the re-issues were issued on a distinctive hard, white paper without grills.

The 1 cent stamp was re-issued a second time, in 1880. This re-issue can be distinguished by the lack of a grill and by the soft, porous paper used by the American Bank Note Company.

112, 123, 133,133a
Franklin

113, 124
Pony Express Rider

114, 125
Locomotive

115, 126
Washington

116, 127
Shield & Eagle

117, 128
S.S. Adriatic

118, 119, 129
Landing of Columbus

120, 130
Signing of Declaration

121, 131
Shield, Eagle & Flags

122, 132
Lincoln

SCOTT NO.	DESCRIPTION	UNUSED			USED		
		VF	F	AVG	VF	F	AVG
	1869 G. Grill measuring 9-1/2 x 9-1/2 mm. (†)						
	(OG + 75%)						
112	1¢ buff	425.00	300.00	240.00	250.00	165.00	135.00
113	2¢ brown	425.00	300.00	240.00	140.00	75.00	50.00
114	3¢ ultramarine . . .	235.00	185.00	145.00	27.00	20.00	15.00
115	6¢ ultramarine . . .	1600.00	1200.00	850.00	350.00	225.00	175.00
116	10¢ yellow	1750.00	1350.00	1050.00	225.00	145.00	105.00
117	12¢ green.	1500.00	1150.00	875.00	225.00	145.00	110.00
118	15¢ brown & blue (I)	4500.00	3500.00	2800.00	1000.00	575.00	450.00
119	15¢ brown & blue (II)	2100.00	1350.00	1000.00	375.00	250.00	190.00
120	24¢ green & violet	4400.00	3000.00	2100.00	1000.00	675.00	500.00
121	30¢ blue & carmine	4400.00	3000.00	2100.00	825.00	500.00	355.00
122	90¢ carmine & black.	6300.00	4700.00	3700.00	3200.00	2225.00	1700.00
	1875 Re-Issue of 1869 Issue. Hard White Paper. Without Grill						
	(OG + 75%)						
123	1¢ buff	500.00	350.00	250.00	450.00	325.00	230.00
124	2¢ brown	600.00	450.00	300.00	900.00	625.00	450.00
125	3¢ blue	4500.00	3000.00	2100.00	. . . .	25000.00	. . . .
126	6¢ blue	1200.00	800.00	550.00	2500.00	1550.00	950.00
127	10¢ yellow	1900.00	1300.00	950.00	2000.00	1400.00	975.00
128	12¢ green.	2000.00	1500.00	1000.00	3200.00	2050.00	1175.00
129	15¢ brown & blue (III)	1800.00	1250.00	800.00	1250.00	800.00	500.00
130	24¢ green & violet	1800.00	1200.00	750.00	1750.00	1050.00	665.00
131	30¢ blue & carmine	2500.00	1600.00	1100.00	3000.00	2000.00	1225.00
132	90¢ carmine & black	4500.00	3500.00	2800.00	6500.00	4775.00	3575.00
	1880 Re-Issue. Soft Porous Paper, Issued Without Grill (†)						
	(#133 OG +50%)						
133	1¢ buff	295.00	225.00	180.00	350.00	250.00	200.00
133a	1¢ brown orange .	325.00	195.00	150.00	300.00	225.00	175.00
	(issued w/o gum)						

THE 1870-88 BANK NOTE ISSUES

The "Bank Notes" are stamps that were issued between 1870 and 1888 by the National, Continental and American Bank Note Companies.

The myriad of varieties, secret marks, papers, grills, re-engravings and special printings produced by the three companies resulted in no less than 87 major catalog listings for what basically amounts to 16 different designs. For collectors, what seems to be the very difficult task of properly identifying all these varieties can be eased by following these guidelines:

1. The chronological order in which the three Bank Note companies produced stamps is their reverse alphabetical order: National, Continental, American.

2. "3, 6, 9" identifies the number of years each of the companies printed stamps within the 18-year Bank Note period. Starting in 1870, National continued its work for 3 more years, until 1873, when the Continental Company began printing stamps. That company served for the next 6 years, until 1879, when American took over the Continental company. Although American printed some later issues, the "Bank Note" period ended 9 years later, in 1888.

3. The first Bank Note issue, the Nationals of 1870-71, continued the practice of grilling stamps. Although some specialists contend there are grilled Continental stamps, for all intents and purposes, if a Bank Note stamp bears a genuine grill, it must be from the 1870-71 National issue.

4. The secret marks on values through the 12 cent, and possibly the 15 cent value, were added when the Continental Company took over. They enabled the government to distinguish between National's work and that of its successor. If a Bank Note stamp did not show a secret mark, the Post Office could identify it as the work of the National Bank Note Company. You can do the same.

5. The paper used by the National and Continental companies is similar, but that of the American Bank Note company is noticably different from the first two. When held to the light, the thick, soft American paper shows its coarse, uneven texture, while that of its two predecessors is more even and translucent. The American Bank Note paper also reveals a yellowish hue when held to the light, whereas the National and Continental papers are whiter.

6. Experienced collectors also apply a "snap test" to identify American Bank Note paper by gently flexing a Bank Note stamp at one of its corners. The American Bank Note paper will not "snap" back into place. The National and Continental stamps, on the other hand, often give off a noticeable sound when the flex is released.

7. By purchasing one Bank Note design put into use after 1882 (which can only be an American) and one early Bank Note stamp without the secret mark, (which can only be a National), the collector has a reference point against which to compare any other Bank Note stamp. If it is a soft paper, it is an American Bank Note issue; if a harder paper, it is either a National or a Continental—and these two can be classified by the absence (National) or presence (Continental) of the secret marks or other distinguishing features or colors. The Harris Stamp Identifier in this catalog provides illustrations of the secret marks and further information on the distinguishing features of the various Bank Notes. With two reference stamps, some practice and the use of the information in this catalog, collectors can turn the "job" of understanding the Bank Notes into a pleasant adventure.

134, 145, 156, 167,
182, 192, 206
Franklin

135, 146, 157, 168,
178, 180, 183, 193,
203
Jackson

136, 147, 158, 169,
184, 194, 207, 214
Washington

NOTE: For further details on the various types of similar appearing stamps please refer to our U.S. Stamp Identifier.

137, 148, 159, 170,
186, 195, 208
Lincoln

138, 149, 160, 171,
196
Stanton

139, 150, 161, 172,
187, 188, 197, 209
Jefferson

140, 151, 162, 173,
198
Clay

141, 152, 163, 174,
189, 199
Webster

142, 153, 164,
175, 200
Scott

143, 154, 165, 176,
190, 201, 217
Hamilton

144, 155, 166, 177,
191, 202, 218
Perry

SCOTT NO.	DESCRIPTION	UNUSED VF	F	AVG	USED VF	F	AVG

1870 National Bank Note Co., without Secret Marks.
With H Grill about (10 x 12 mm. or 8-1/2 x 10 mm.) Perf 12. (†)
(OG +75%)

SCOTT NO.	DESCRIPTION	VF	F	AVG	VF	F	AVG
134	1¢ ultramarine . . .	1350.00	850.00	550.00	300.00	200.00	144.00
135	2¢ red brown	850.00	575.00	400.00	110.00	77.50	49.00
136	3¢ green	650.00	400.00	300.00	30.00	21.00	14.00
137	6¢ carmine	3500.00	1950.00	1200.00	775.00	525.00	325.00
138	7¢ vermillion	2500.00	1750.00	1050.00	700.00	425.00	280.00
139	10¢ brown	4000.00	2600.00	1750.00	1200.00	750.00	485.00
140	12¢ dull violet	16800.00	11500.00	8250.00	3800.00	2400.00	1650.00
141	15¢ orange	4750.00	2700.00	1850.00	1450.00	925.00	575.00
142	24¢ purple	. . . . . .	. . . . . .	. . . . . .	7500.00	6000.00	4300.00
143	30¢ black	10000.00	6750.00	4800.00	3500.00	2300.00	1500.00
144	90¢ carmine	12100.00	7250.00	4500.00	2000.00	1500.00	950.00

1870-71. National Bank Note Co., without Secret Marks.
Without Grill. Perf 12. (†)
(OG +75%)

SCOTT NO.	DESCRIPTION	VF	F	AVG	VF	F	AVG
145	1¢ ultramarine . . .	400.00	275.00	150.00	27.50	17.00	11.00
146	2¢ red brown	235.00	145.00	95.00	17.00	11.00	7.00
147	3¢ green	235.00	145.00	95.00	2.50	1.75	1.00
148	6¢ carmine	675.00	400.00	225.00	40.00	25.00	15.00
149	7¢ vermillion	700.00	450.00	250.00	130.00	72.50	45.00
150	10¢ brown	850.00	600.00	400.00	40.00	27.50	17.25
151	12¢ dull violet	1500.00	1000.00	600.00	250.00	165.00	105.00
152	15¢ bright orange .	1500.00	1000.00	600.00	275.00	185.00	115.00
153	24¢ purple	1250.00	800.00	550.00	250.00	150.00	100.00
154	30¢ black	4000.00	2800.00	1600.00	350.00	250.00	140.00
155	90¢ carmine	3000.00	2000.00	1150.00	550.00	350.00	215.00

1873. Continental Bank Note Co.
Same designs as 1870-71, with Secret Marks, on thin hard grayish white paper. Perf 12 (†)
(OG + 75%)

SCOTT NO.	DESCRIPTION	VF	F	AVG	VF	F	AVG
156	1¢ ultramarine . . .	240.00	135.00	100.00	5.00	3.75	2.25
157	2¢ brown	340.00	195.00	110.00	25.00	17.50	10.00
158	3¢ green	110.00	60.00	35.00	1.25	.75	.50
159	6¢ dull pink	375.00	225.00	125.00	28.00	16.00	11.00
160	7¢ orange vermillion	900.00	600.00	375.00	135.00	95.00	62.50
161	10¢ brown	700.00	450.00	295.00	35.00	24.50	14.50
162	12¢ black violet . .	1600.00	1100.00	600.00	155.00	100.00	67.50
163	15¢ yellow orange .	1600.00	1100.00	600.00	175.00	115.00	70.00
165	30¢ gray black . . .	1950.00	1250.00	700.00	160.00	105.00	65.00
166	90¢ rose carmine .	2200.00	1350.00	850.00	400.00	250.00	150.00

1875 Special Printing–On Hard White Wove Paper–Without Gum
Perf. 12

SCOTT NO.	DESCRIPTION	VF	F	AVG	VF	F	AVG
167	1¢ ultramarine . . .	17775.00	12000.00	6750.00	. . . . . .	. . . . . .	. . . . . .
168	2¢ dark brown . . .	8000.00	5250.00	3500.00	. . . . . .	. . . . . .	. . . . . .
169	3¢ blue green	20000.00	13500.00	9000.00	. . . . . .	. . . . . .	. . . . . .
170	6¢ dull rose	20000.00	13500.00	9000.00	. . . . . .	. . . . . .	. . . . . .
171	7¢ reddish vermillion	5000.00	3300.00	2300.00	. . . . . .	. . . . . .	. . . . . .
172	10¢ pale brown . . .	20000.00	13500.00	9000.00	. . . . . .	. . . . . .	. . . . . .
173	12¢ dark violet	7000.00	4500.00	3300.00	. . . . . .	. . . . . .	. . . . . .
174	15¢ bright orange . .	20000.00	13500.00	9000.00	. . . . . .	. . . . . .	. . . . . .
175	24¢ dull purple . . .	4900.00	3200.00	2200.00	. . . . . .	. . . . . .	. . . . . .
176	30¢ greenish black	16000.00	17250.00	7250.00	. . . . . .	. . . . . .	. . . . . .
177	90¢ violet carmine	20000.00	13250.00	9250.00	. . . . . .	. . . . . .	. . . . . .

179, 181, 185, 204
Taylor

205, 205C, 216
Garfield

SCOTT NO.	DESCRIPTION	UNUSED VF	F	AVG	USED VF	F	AVG
		1875 Continental Bank Note Co. Hard yellowish paper, Perf 12. (†) (OG + 50%)					
178	2¢ vermillion	350.00	225.00	135.00	15.00	10.00	7.00
179	5¢ blue	450.00	325.00	200.00	35.00	27.00	15.00
		1875 Continental Bank Note Co., Special Printings. Same as 1875, on hard white paper, without gum. Perf 12.					
180	2¢ carmine vermillion	80000.00	60000.00	36500.00	....	....	....
181	5¢ bright blue	450000.00	337000.00	214000.00	....	....	....
		1879 American Bank Note Co. Same designs as 1870-71 Issue (with Secret Marks) and 1875 Issue on soft, porous, coarse, yellowish paper. Perf 12. (†) (OG + 60%)					
182	1¢ dark ultramarine	200.00	135.00	75.00	4.75	3.00	2.00
183	2¢ vermillion	125.00	80.00	47.00	4.25	2.75	1.75
184	3¢ green	85.00	55.00	35.00	1.00	.70	.50
185	5¢ blue	395.00	230.00	125.00	26.00	17.50	12.00
186	6¢ pink	650.00	425.00	280.00	35.00	26.00	15.25
187	10¢ brown (no secret mark) . .	1650.00	1100.00	600.00	48.00	35.00	21.00
188	10¢ brown (secret mark)	1075.00	700.00	450.00	41.00	30.00	18.00
189	15¢ red orange . . .	300.00	165.00	100.00	30.00	22.50	13.00
190	30¢ full black	800.00	475.00	275.00	125.00	82.5.00	55.00
191	90¢ carmine	1800.00	1150.00	725.00	500.00	325.00	230.00
		1880 American Bank Note Co., Special Printings. Same as 1879 Issue, on soft, porous paper, without gum. Perf 12.					
192	1¢ dark ultramarine	45000.00	28000.00	16750.00	....	....	....
193	2¢ black brown . . .	22500.00	1600.00	10250.00	....	....	....
194	3¢ blue green	70000.00	45000.00	28000.00	....	....	....
195	6¢ dull rose.	60000.00	37000.00	22750.00	....	....	....
196	7¢ scarlet vermillion	7000.00	4800.00	3300.00	....	....	....
197	10¢ deep brown . . .	40000.00	25000.00	15250.00	....	....	....
198	12¢ black purple . .	12000.00	8500.00	5750.00	....	....	....
199	15¢ orange	37500.00	23750.00	14250.00	....	....	....
200	24¢ dark violet . . .	11000.00	7750.00	5250.00	....	....	....
201	30¢ greenish black .	22500.00	14250.00	8500.00	....	....	....
202	90¢ dull carmine . .	37500.00	24000.00	14000.00	....	....	....
203	2¢ scarlet vermillion	120000.00	73000.00	46500.00	....	....	....
204	5¢ deep blue	320000.00	196000.00	120000.00	....	....	....
		1882 American Bank Note Company Perf 12. (OG + 60%)					
205	5¢ yellow brown . .	180.00	120.00	85.00	11.00	8.00	5.00
		1882 American Bank Note Co., Special Printing. Same as in 1882 Issue, on soft, porous Paper. Perf 12.					
205C	5¢ gray brown . . .	....	65000.00	....	....	....	....

210, 211B, 213
Washington

211, 211D, 215
Jackson

212
Franklin

SCOTT NO.	DESCRIPTION	UNUSED VF	F	AVG	USED VF	F	AVG
		1881-82 American Bank Note Co. Same designs as 1873, Re-Engraved. On soft, porous paper. Perf 12. (†) (OG + 100%)					
206	1¢ gray blue	52.50	33.00	20.00	2.00	125	.90
207	3¢ blue green	52.50	33.00	20.00	1.25	.75	.55
208	6¢ rose	375.00	240.00	135.00	135.00	100.00	70.00
208a	6¢ brown red	300.00	195.00	110.00	160.00	120.00	80.00
209	10¢ brown	150.00	105.00	70.00	6.50	5.00	3.00
209b	10¢ black brown . .	800.00	500.00	325.00	325.00	200.00	130.00
210	2¢ red brown	45.00	29.00	19.00	.75	.45	.35
211	4¢ blue green	170.00	110.00	75.00	25.00	17.50	13.00

SCOTT NO.	DESCRIPTION	UNUSED VF	F	AVG	USED VF	F	AVG
		1883 American Bank Note Co. Special Printing. Same design as 1883 Issue, on soft porous paper. Perf 12.					
211B	2¢ pale red brown	500.00	400.00	275.00	....	....	....
211D	4¢ deep blue green	47500.00	....	....	....	....	....
		1887 American Bank Note Co. New designs or colors. Perf 12. (OG + 60%)					
212	1¢ ultramarine . . .	100.00	65.00	40.00	2.10	1.50	.95
213	2¢ green	37.50	23.00	15.00	.60	.40	.30
214	3¢ vermillion	70.00	42.00	25.00	52.50	33.75	21.00

SCOTT NO.	DESCRIPTION	UNUSED O.G. VF	F	AVG	USED VF	F	AVG
		1888 American Bank Note Company. New Colors Perf 12. (NH + 100%)					
215	4¢ carmine	300.00	195.00	130.00	30.00	21.00	12.50
216	5¢ indigo	300.00	195.00	130.00	15.00	10.50	2.50
217	30¢ orange brown . .	575.00	375.00	225.00	160.00	110.00	65.00
218	90¢ purple	1450.00	950.00	525.00	355.00	250.00	150.00

THE 1890-93 SMALL BANK NOTE ISSUES

Unlike the complex Large Bank Notes, the 1890-93 series is the simplest of the 19th century definitive issues. They were printed by the American Bank Note Company and what few printing varieties there are can easily be determined by using the Harris Stamp Identifier.

The two major printing varieties are the 2 cent carmine with a "cap" on the left 2 (#219a) or both 2s (#219c).

The "cap" appears to be just that—a small flat hat just to the right of center on top of the denomination numeral 2. It was caused by a breakdown in the metal of the transfer roll that went undetected while it was being used to enter the designs into a few printing plates.

219 Franklin	**219D, 220** Washington	**221** Jackson	**222** Lincoln
223 Grant	**224** Garfield	**225** Sherman	**226** Webster
227 Clay	**228** Jefferson	**229** Perry	

SCOTT NO.	DESCRIPTION	UNUSED O.G. VF	F	AVG	USED VF	F	AVG
		(NH +100%)					
219	1¢ dull blue	37.50	21.00	17.00	.60	.45	.25
219D	2¢ lake	300.00	175.00	125.00	2.00	1.40	.75
220	2¢ carmine	30.00	19.00	14.00	.55	.40	.30
220a	Cap on left "2" . . .	195.00	110.00	70.00	10.00	6.50	4.50
220c	Cap on both "2"s . .	750.00	400.00	275.00	28.00	17.50	13.00
221	3¢ purple	95.00	60.00	45.00	11.00	6.50	5.00
222	4¢ dark brown . . .	135.00	80.00	60.00	4.25	3.25	2.25
223	5¢ chocolate	100.00	65.00	45.00	4.00	3.00	2.00
224	6¢ brown red	95.00	60.00	45.00	34.00	22.50	16.00
225	8¢ lilac	80.00	55.00	40.00	16.00	10.00	7.00
226	10¢ green	225.00	145.00	100.00	5.00	3.25	2.00
227	15¢ indigo	350.00	210.00	150.00	42.00	30.00	19.00
228	30¢ black	475.00	300.00	210.00	58.00	37.50	23.00
229	90¢ orange	795.00	475.00	325.00	230.00	140.00	80.00

230	231	232	233
In Sight of Land	Landing of Columbus	Flagship	Fleet of Columbus
234	235	236	237
Soliciting Aid	At Barcelona	Restored To Favor	Presenting Natives
238	239	240	241
Discovery	At La Rábida	Recall of Columbus	Pledging Jewels
242	243	244	245
Columbus in Chains	Describing Third Voyage	Isabella & Columbus	Portrait of Columbus

THE COLUMBIANS

Perhaps the most glamorous of all United States issues is the 1893 Columbians set. Consisting of 16 denominations, the set was issued to celebrate the 1893 World's Columbian Exposition.

Even then, the Post Office Department was aware that stamps could be useful for more than just the prepayment of postage. We quote from an internal Post Office Department report of November 20, 1892:

"During the past summer the determination was reached by the Department to issue, during the progress of the Columbian Exposition at Chicago, a special series of adhesive postage stamps of such a character as would help to signalize the four hundredth anniversary of the discovery of America by Columbus. This course was in accordance with the practice of other great postal administrations on occasions of national rejoicing.

The collecting of stamps is deserving of encouragement, for it tends to the cultivation of artistic tastes and the study of history and geography, especially on the part of the young. The new stamps will be purchased in large quantities simply for the use of collections, without ever being presented in payment of postage; and the stamps sold in this way will, of course, prove a clear gain to the department."

As it turned out, the Columbians issue did sell well, being purchased in large quantities not only by collectors, but by speculators hoping to capitalize on the expected demand for the stamps and the fact that they were supposed to be on sale for only one year, from January 2 to December 31, 1893. (The 8 cent stamp was issued March 3, 1893 to meet the new, reduced Registration fee.)

Although sales of the stamps were brisk at the Exposition site in Chicago, speculation proved less than rewarding. The hordes that showed up on the first day of sale in Chicago (January 3rd) and purchased large quantities of the issue ended up taking losses on most of the stamps.

The set was the most expensive postal issue produced to date by the Post Office. The lower denominations matched those of the previous, "Small" Bank Note issue and the 50 cent Columbian replaced the 90 cent Bank Note denomination. But the $1 through $5 denominations were unheard of at that time. The reason for their release was explained in the November 20, 1892 report: "...such high denominations having heretofore been called for by some of the principal post offices".

The Columbians were an instant success. Businesses did not like the wide size, but they usually could obtain the smaller Bank Note issue. Collectors enjoyed the new stamps, although at least one complained that some of the high values purchased by him had straight edges—and was quickly authorized to exchange "the imperfect stamps" for perfect ones.

The one major variety in this set is the 4 cent blue error of color. It is similar to, but richer in color than, the 1 cent Columbian and commands a larger premium over the normal 4 cent ultramarine color.

The imperforates that are known to exist for all values are proofs which were distributed as gifts and are not listed as postage stamps. The only exception, the 2 cent imperforate, is believed to be printers' waste that was saved from destruction.

SCOTT NO.	DESCRIPTION	UNUSED O.G.			USED		
		VF	F	AVG	VF	F	AVG
	1893 COLUMBIAN ISSUE **(NH + 100%)**						
230	1¢ deep blue	33.00	21.00	14.00	.75	.50	.40
231	2¢ brown violet...	30.00	19.00	13.00	.30	.25	.20
231C	2¢ "broken hat"...	95.00	60.00	45.00	1.50	1.00	.60
232	3¢ green.........	85.00	50.00	40.00	39.00	28.50	20.00
233	4¢ ultramarine ...	110.00	70.00	45.00	11.00	7.25	4.50
234	5¢ chocolate.....	125.00	75.00	50.00	11.00	7.50	4.75
235	6¢ purple	110.00	70.00	45.00	53.00	35.00	25.00
236	8¢ magenta	100.00	65.00	38.00	19.00	12.50	7.50
237	10¢ black brown..	175.00	115.00	85.00	13.00	8.25	5.50
238	15¢ dark green...	375.00	240.00	150.00	145.00	85.00	55.00
239	30¢ orange brown	425.00	300.00	195.00	175.00	120.00	85.00
240	50¢ slate blue...	825.00	575.00	400.00	290.00	185.00	130.00
241	$1 salmon.......	1900.00	1250.00	975.00	1150.00	775.00	475.00
242	$2 brown red	2000.00	1300.00	1000.00	1150.00	750.00	475.00
243	$3 yellow green ..	3350.00	2300.00	1550.00	2200.00	1450.00	975.00
244	$4 crimson lake ..	4650.00	3300.00	2300.00	2500.00	1700.00	1100.00
245	$5 black	5650.00	3200.00	2300.00	3400.00	2100.00	1350.00

**246, 247, 264,
279**
Franklin

**248-252,
265-267, 279B**
Washington

253, 268
Jackson

254, 269, 280
Lincoln

255, 270, 281
Grant

256, 271, 282
Garfield

257, 272
Sherman

**258, 273, 282C,
283**
Webster

259, 274, 284
Clay

260, 275
Jefferson

**261, 261A, 276,
276A**
Perry

262, 277
Madison

263, 278
Marshall

1894-98 THE FIRST BUREAU ISSUES

In 1894, the United States Bureau of Engraving and Printing replaced the American Bank Note Company as the contractor for all United States postage stamps. The "First" Bureau issues, as they are commonly known, actually consist of three series, as follows:

The 1894 Series. In order to expedite the transfer of production to the Bureau, the plates then being used by the American Bank Note Company for the 1890-93 Small Bank Notes were modified, small triangles being added in the upper corners. The 1 cent through 15 cent stamps are otherwise essentially the same as the 1890-93 issue although minor variations have been noted on some values. The 30 cent and 90 cent 1890-93 denominations were changed to 50 cents and $1, respectively, and new $2 and $5 denominations were added.

The 1895 Series. To protect against counterfeiting of United Sates stamps, the Bureau adopted the use of watermarked paper. (A scheme for counterfeiting 2 cent stamps had been uncovered around the same time the watermarked paper was being adopted. Some of these counterfeits are known postally used.) This series is almost exactly the same as the 1984 series except for the presence of watermarks. The watermarks can be difficult t detect on this series, particularly on the light-colored stamps, such as the 50 cent, and on used stamps. Since the 1894 unwatermarked stamps (with the exception of the 2 cent carmine type I) are worth more than the 1895 watermarked stamps, collectors will want to examine their 1894 stamps carefully. (Some collectors feel they can recognize the 1894 stamps by their ragged perforations, caused by difficulties the Bureau encountered when it first took over the produciton of postage stamps. This is not a reliable method.)

The 1898 "Color Changes." With the adoption of a Universal Postal Union code that recommended standard colors for international mail, the United States changed the colors for the lower values in the 1895 Series. The stamps were printed on the same watermarked paper as that used for the 1895 Series. Except for the 2 cent, which was changed from carmine to red, the colors of the 1898 Series are easily differentiated from the 1895 set. The 2 cent value is the most complicated of the First Bureau Issues. In addition to the color changes that took place, three different triangle types are known. The differences are attributed to the possibility that the work of engraving the triangles into the American Bank Note plates was performed by several Bureau engravers.

The 10 cent and $1 types I and II can be distinguished by the circles surrounding the numeral denominations. The Type IIs are identical to the circles of the 1890-93 Small Bank Notes.

All stamps in these series are perf. 12. The Harris Stamp Identifier at the front of this catalog provides additional information on the major types and watermarks of all three series.

SCOTT NO.	DESCRIPTION	UNUSED O.G. VF	F	AVG	USED VF	F	AVG
		1894 Unwatermarked (†)					
		(NH + 100%)					
246	1¢ ultramarine . . .	38.00	25.00	18.00	8.50	5.50	3.50
247	1¢ blue	85.00	50.00	35.00	4.00	2.50	1.75
248	2¢ pink (I)	35.00	22.00	16.00	8.50	5.50	3.50
249	2¢ carmine lake (I)	225.00	130.00	90.00	6.00	4.00	2.50
250	2¢ carmine (I)	35.00	23.00	16.00	1.50	.85	.55
251	2¢ carmine (II) . . .	400.00	250.00	150.00	11.00	8.00	5.00
252	2¢ carmine (III) . . .	150.00	90.00	60.00	11.00	8.00	5.00
253	3¢ purple	145.00	85.00	60.00	16.00	9.00	6.00
254	4¢ dark brown . . .	195.00	110.00	80.00	9.00	5.50	3.50
255	5¢ chocolate.	160.00	90.00	70.00	9.00	5.50	3.50
256	6¢ dull brown	210.00	125.00	85.00	39.00	27.50	19.00
257	8¢ violet brown . . .	170.00	110.00	80.00	33.00	20.00	16.00
258	10¢ dark green . . .	325.00	210.00	140.00	20.00	10.00	7.00
259	15¢ dark blue	375.00	240.00	180.00	96.00	57.50	38.00
260	50¢ orange	695.00	400.00	300.00	185.00	115.00	70.00
261	$1 black (I)	1300.00	800.00	550.00	625.00	375.00	260.00
261A	$1 black (II)	2700.00	1750.00	1200.00	875.00	575.00	400.00
262	$2 bright blue	4000.00	2300.00	1850.00	1350.00	975.00	650.00
263	$5 dark green. . . .	6050.00	3700.00	2900.00	2800.00	2000.00	1400.00
		1895 Double Line Watermark					
		"USPS" (†) (NH + 75%)					
264	1¢ blue	8.50	5.50	3.75	.50	.35	.25
265	2¢ carmine (I)	38.00	24.00	17.00	3.00	2.00	1.25
266	2¢ carmine (II) . . .	42.00	27.00	19.00	5.00	3.50	2.25
267	2¢ carmine (III) . . .	6.50	4.00	3.00	.35	.30	.25
268	3¢ purple	45.00	28.00	20.00	2.75	1.75	1.25
269	4¢ dark brown . . .	50.00	32.00	22.00	3.00	2.00	1.00
270	5¢ chocolate	52.50	36.00	22.00	3.25	2.10	1.25
271	6¢ dull brown	150.00	90.00	65.00	8.00	5.50	4.00
272	8¢ violet brown . . .	85.00	50.00	35.00	3.50	2.00	1.25
273	10¢ dark green . . .	110.00	70.00	50.00	2.75	1.75	1.00
274	15¢ dark blue	300.00	170.00	110.00	19.00	12.50	8.50
275	50¢ orange	350.00	210.00	150.00	49.00	35.00	21.00
276	$1 black (I)	750.00	425.00	300.00	155.00	100.00	65.00
276A	$1 black (II)	1700.00	1000.00	700.00	225.00	160.00	110.00
277	$2 bright blue	1350.00	800.00	600.00	600.00	450.00	290.00
278	$5 dark green. . . .	3000.00	1800.00	1050.00	850.00	550.00	375.00
		1898 New Colors					
		(NH + 75%)					
279	1¢ deep green . . .	15.00	9.00	6.50	.50	.35	.25
279B	2¢ red (IV)	13.00	7.50	5.00	.50	.30	.25
279Bc	2¢ rose carmine (IV)	325.00	195.00	120.00	150.00	95.00	70.00
279Bd	2¢ orange red (IV)	17.50	10.00	7.00	.50	.35	.25
280	4¢ rose brown . . .	40.00	27.00	18.00	3.00	2.00	1.25
281	5¢ dark blue	48.00	29.00	18.00	2.25	1.50	.85
282	6¢ lake	60.00	40.00	30.00	6.00	4.00	2.50
282C	10¢ brown (I)	250.00	170.00	120.00	6.00	4.00	2.50
283	10¢ orange brown (II)	175.00	110.00	70.00	5.00	3.25	2.00
284	15¢ olive green. . .	180.00	110.00	75.00	15.00	9.50	6.50

1898 THE TRANS-MISSISSIPPI ISSUE

Issued for the Trans-Mississippi Exposition in Omaha, Nebraska, the "Omahas", as they also are known, did not receive the same welcome from collectors as that accorded the first commemorative set, the 1893 Columbians. Although the uproar was ascribed to the fact that collectors felt put upon by another set with $1 and $2 values, had the $1 to $5 values in the Columbian series appreciated in value, no doubt the protests would have been muted.

On the other hand, the public at large enjoyed the new issue. The Trans-Mississippi issues depict various works of art and are among the most beautiful stamps ever issued by the United States. The 8 and 10 cent values reproduce works by Frederic Remington and the $1 "Western Cattle in Storm", based on a work by J.A. MacWhirter, is regarded as one of our finest examples of the engraver's art.

As appealing as these stamps are in single colors, the set might have been even more beautiful. The original intent was to print each stamp with the vignette, or central design, in black and the frame in a distinctive second color that would be different for each denomination. That plan had to be dropped when the Bureau was called upon to produce large quantities of revenue stamps at the outbreak of the Spanish-American War.

285
Marquette on the Mississippi

286
Farming in the West

287
Indian Hunting Buffalo

288
Fremont on the Rocky Mountains

289
Troops Guarding Train

290
Hardships of Emigration

291
Western Mining Prospector

292
Western Cattle in Storm

293
Eads Bridge over Mississippi River

SCOTT NO.	DESCRIPTION	UNUSED O.G. VF	F	AVG	USED VF	F	AVG
	1898 Trans-Mississippi Exposition Issue (†) (NH + 100%)						
285	1¢ dark yellow green	45.00	30.00	21.00	10.00	6.50	4.00
286	2¢ copper red...........	35.00	23.00	18.00	3.00	2.00	1.25
287	4¢ orange..................	225.00	135.00	95.00	59.00	35.00	22.00
288	5¢ dull blue...............	195.00	115.00	80.00	32.00	20.00	11.00
289	8¢ violet brown..........	250.00	160.00	100.00	85.00	55.00	32.00
290	10¢ gray violet...........	250.00	160.00	100.00	56.00	32.50	19.00
291	50¢ sage green.........	900.00	550.00	450.00	385.00	225.00	150.00
292	$1 black....................	2000.00	1150.00	850.00	1400.00	875.00	625.00
293	$2 orange brown.......	3000.00	1850.00	1300.00	1900.00	1300.00	825.00

1901 THE PAN-AMERICAN ISSUE

Issued to commemorate the Pan-American Exposition in Buffalo, N.Y., this set depicts important engineering and manufacturing achievements. The beautiful engraving is showcased by the bicolored printing.

294, 294a
Fast Lake Navigation

295, 295a
Fast Express

296, 296a
Automobile

297
Bridge at Niagara Falls

298
Canal at Sault Ste. Marie

299
Fast Ocean Navigation

SCOTT NO.	DESCRIPTION	UNUSED O.G. VF	F	AVG	USED VF	F	AVG
	1901 Pan-American Issue (NH + 75%)						
294-99	1¢-10¢ (6 varieties, complete)	670.00	385.00	255.00	165.00	95.00	70.00
294	1¢ green & black.........	45.00	24.00	14.00	7.50	5.00	3.00
294a	same, center inverted	...	12500.00	...	...	7995.00	...
295	2¢ carmine & black.....	35.00	19.00	11.00	3.00	2.00	1.10
295a	same, center inverted	...	45000.00	...	...	50000.00	...
296	4¢ deep red brown & black...	190.00	115.00	80.00	47.00	26.50	18.00
296a	same, center inverted	...	35000.00	...	...	...	...
296aS	same, center inverted (Specimen).	...	5500.00	...	...	...	...
297	5¢ ultramarine & black	135.00	80.00	48.00	40.00	22.50	16.00
298	8¢ brown violet & black.	165.00	105.00	70.00	130.00	75.00	54.00
299	10¢ yellow brown & black.	240.00	125.00	90.00	60.00	35.00	24.00

	UNUSED PLATE BLOCKS OF 6 NH		OG		UNUSED ARROW BLOCKS NH		OG	
	F	AVG	F	AVG	F	AVG	F	AVG
294	400.00	285.00	240.00	180.00	160.00	100.00	65.00	50.00
295	400.00	285.00	235.00	180.00	160.00	100.00	65.00	50.00
296	3750.00	2750.00	2100.00	1650.00	800.00	550.00	350.00	290.00
297	4200.00	3250.00	2600.00	2000.00	825.00	550.00	400.00	325.00
298	7500.00	5500.00	4000.00	3200.00	1050.00	700.00	500.00	375.00
299	10500.00	8000.00	6000.00	4800.00	1500.00	900.00	695.00	500.00

THE 1902-03 SERIES

The Series of 1902-03 was the first regular issue designed and produced by the United States Bureau of Engraving and Printing, most of the work on the 1894-98 series having been performed by the American Bank Note Company. (When the Bureau was awarded the contract to produce the 1894 series, they added triangles in the upper corners of the American Bank Note designs.)

The new series filled a number of gaps and was the first United States issue to feature a woman—in this case Martha Washington, on the 8 cent value.

Modern collectors consider the 1902-03 issue one of the finest regular series ever produced by the Bureau.

The intricate frame designs take us back to a period when such work still was affordable. In its time, however, the 1902-03 set was looked upon with disdain. The 2 cent Washington, with its ornate frame design and unflattering likeness of George Washington, came in for particular scorn. Yielding to the clamor, in 1903, less than one year after its release, the Post Office recalled the much criticized 2 cent stamp and replaced it with an attractive, less ornate design that cleaned up Washington's appearance, particularly in the area of the nose, and used a shield design that was less ornate.

The issue marked the first time United States stamps were issued in booklet form, the 1 and 2 cent values being printed in panes of six stamps each. Also for the first time since perforating was adopted in 1857, United States stamps were once again deliberately issued in imperforate form for postal use. The intent was to have such stamps available in sheet and coil form for use in vending machines. The manufacturers of such machines could purchase the imperforate stamps and perforate them to fit their equipment. One of these imperforate issues, the 4 cent brown of 1908 (#314A), ranks as one of the great rarities of 20th century philately. It is found only with the private perforations of the Schermack Mailing Machine Company.

Coil stamps intended for use in stamp affixing and vending machines also made their inaugural appearance with this issue. Their availability was not widely publicized and few collectors obtained copies of these coils. All genuine coils from this series are very rare and extremely valuable. We emphasize the word "genuine" because most coils that are seen actually have been faked by trimming the perforated stamps or fraudulently perforating the imperfs.

The only major design types are found on the 1903 2 cent, catalog #s 319 and 320. Identified as Die I and Die II, the differences are described in the Harris Stamp Identifier.

300, 314, 316, 318
Franklin

301
Washington

302
Jackson

303, 314A
Grant

304, 315, 317
Lincoln

305
Garfield

306
Martha Washington

307
Webster

308
Harrison

309
Clay

310
Jefferson

311
Farragut

312, 479
Madison

313, 480
Marshall

319-22
Washington

SCOTT NO.	DESCRIPTION	UNUSED O.G. VF	F	AVG	USED VF	F	AVG
		1902-03 Perf. 12 (†)					
		(NH + 75%)					
300	1¢ blue green	16.00	9.00	6.00	.35	.25	.20
300b	1¢ booklet pane of 6	....	550.00	375.00	....	....	....
301	2¢ carmine	19.50	13.00	8.00	.35	.25	.20
301c	2¢ booklet pane of 6	....	475.00	335.00	....	....	....
302	3¢ brown violet . . .	75.00	43.00	30.00	6.00	3.95	2.25
303	4¢ brown	75.00	43.00	30.00	2.50	1.50	1.00
304	5¢ blue	82.50	50.00	35.00	3.50	1.75	.90
305	6¢ claret	90.00	50.00	35.00	7.00	3.95	2.25
306	8¢ violet black . . .	60.00	32.00	25.00	5.00	2.75	1.75
307	10¢ pale red brown	85.00	50.00	36.00	4.00	2.25	1.50
308	13¢ purple black . .	60.00	35.00	25.00	17.00	11.00	6.50
309	15¢ olive green. . .	200.00	125.00	87.50	13.00	8.25	5.50
310	50¢ orange	625.00	375.00	260.00	52.00	32.50	23.00
311	$1 black	950.00	500.00	350.00	120.00	72.50	46.00
312	$2 dark blue	1550.00	925.00	625.00	425.00	250.00	180.00
313	$5 dark green	3500.00	2200.00	1600.00	1250.00	750.00	525.00
		1906 Imperforate					
		(NH + 75%)					

This and all subsequent imperforate issues can usually be priced as unused pairs at double the single price.

SCOTT NO.	DESCRIPTION	VF	F	AVG	VF	F	AVG
314	1¢ blue green	52.50	37.00	27.00	50.00	37.50	25.00
314A	4¢ brown	....	72500.00	....	....	35000.00	....
315	5¢ blue	695.00	500.00	325.00	875.00	650.00	500.00
		1908 Coil Stamps. Perf 12 Horizontally					
316	1¢ blue green, pair	....	....	....	....	....	....
317	5¢ blue, pair	....	5500.00	....	....	....	....
		1908 Coil Stamps. Perf 12 Vertically					
318	1¢ blue green, pair	....	5500.00	....			
		1903. Perf. 12 (†)					
		(NH + 60%)					
319	2¢ carmine, Die I .	10.00	6.00	4.75	.50	.30	.20
319f	2¢ lake, Die II	17.50	11.00	7.50	1.00	.70	.50
319g	2¢ carmine, Die I, booklet pane of 6 .	....	160.00	110.00			
		1906 Imperforate					
		(NH + 75%)					
320	2¢ carmine, Die I .	55.00	40.00	27.50	79.00	45.00	31.00
320a	2¢ lake, Die I	80.00	65.00	45.00	58.00	40.00	28.00
		1908 Coil Stamps. Perf 12 Horizontally					
321	2¢ carmine, pair . .	....	....	....			
		1908 Coil Stamps. Perf 12 Vertically					
322	2¢ carmine, pair . .	....	5500.00	....			

SCOTT NO.	UNUSED NH F	AVG	UNUSED OG F	AVG	SCOTT NO.	UNUSED NH F	AVG	UNUSED OG F	AVG
	PLATE BLOCKS OF 6					**CENTER LINE BLOCKS**			
300	280.00	160.00	175.00	110.00	314	300.00	200.00	180.00	145.00
301	325.00	170.00	180.00	120.00	320	335.00	235.00	200.00	175.00
314	375.00	250.00	230.00	170.00		**ARROW BLOCKS**			
319	250.00	170.00	135.00	100.00	314	235.00	185.00	140.00	110.00
320	415.00	290.00	225.00	175.00	320	250.00	200.00	135.00	100.00

PSE is the Nation's Leading Philatelic Expertizing and Grading Service

If you're wondering why, consider these reasons...

COST

PSE has expanded our services to include options for all levels of collectors. Our service levels include Modern (Scott numbers above 704) – $12; Economy (most Scott numbers above #551) – $20; and Regular – $30 and up.

EXPERTISE

PSE conceived of and implemented the modern grading system for U.S. stamps over six years ago. Since 2001, we have graded over 150,000 stamps and remain at the forefront of independent third-party grading with comprehensive, consistent and trusted opinions.

TURNAROUND

Our regular service turnaround times typically run between 30 and 45 days. In a hurry? Try our Priority Handling option, and get your stamps back in 15 to 20 days. Why wait months for your stamps? PSE believes you have better things to do than babysit your mailbox.

RESULTS

PSE-graded stamps get results! At R.A. Siegel's recent Tahoe Sale, PSE stamps graded XF-Sup 95 and Superb 98 realized more than two and a half times the values listed in the Stamp Market Quarterly.

GUARANTEE

PSE is so confident in its opinion, we guarantee the Scott Number assigned to your stamp is correct, or we'll pay you its fair market value (as we certified it) up to $10,000.

Faster, Less Expensive, Better Results. Guaranteed.

Professional Stamp Experts

The Grading Authority

P.O. Box 6170, Newport Beach, CA 92658

For more information, call 877-STAMP88 (877-782-6788), fax 949-567-1173, or log onto our website at **www.psestamp.com.**

© 2008 Collectors Universe, Inc. 823303

1904 THE LOUISIANA PURCHASE ISSUE

Issued to commemorate the Louisiana Purchase Exposition held in St. Louis in 1904, these stamps were not well received. Collectors at the time did not purchase large quantities of the stamps, and the series was on sale for only seven months. As a result, well centered unused stamps are extremely difficult to locate.

323
Robert R. Livingston

324
Jefferson

325
Monroe

326
McKinley

327
Map of Louisiana Purchase

SCOTT NO.	DESCRIPTION	UNUSED O.G. VF	F	AVG	USED VF	F	AVG
		1904 Louisiana Purchase Issue (NH + 75%)					
323-27	1¢-10¢ (5 varieties, complete)	595.00	365.00	245.00	145.00	83.50	53.50
323	1¢ green	57.50	30.00	21.00	10.50	6.25	3.75
324	2¢ carmine	44.50	25.00	18.00	2.75	2.25	1.25
325	3¢ violet	120.00	75.00	50.00	91.00	57.50	35.00
326	5¢ dark blue	150.00	85.00	55.00	76.00	40.00	29.00
327	10¢ red brown . . .	260.00	170.00	115.00	96.00	55.00	34.00

1907 THE JAMESTOWN EXPOSITION ISSUE

This set may be the most difficult United States 20th century issue to find well centered. Issued in April, 1907 for the Jamestown Exposition at Hampton Roads, Virginia, the set was removed from sale when the Exposition closed on November 30th of that year. Very fine copies carry hefty premiums.

328
Capt. John Smith

329
Founding of Jamestown

330
Pocahontas

1907 Jamestown Exposition Issue
(NH + 60%)

SCOTT NO.	DESCRIPTION	UNUSED O.G. VF	F	AVG	USED VF	F	AVG
328-30	1¢-5¢ (3 varieties, complete)	295.00	225.50	153.00	76.00	33.00	17.50
328	1¢ green	42.50	23.50	14.75	8.50	4.25	2.75
329	2¢ carmine	50.00	25.00	15.00	7.50	4.25	2.00
330	5¢ blue	210.00	100.00	60.00	83.00	35.00	18.00

	UNUSED PLATE BLOCKS OF 6				UNUSED ARROW BLOCKS			
SCOTT NO.	NH F	AVG	OG F	AVG	NH F	AVG	OG F	AVG
323	395.00	300.00	200.00	160.00	200.00	120.00	130.00	85.00
324	400.00	300.00	210.00	160.00	160.00	100.00	95.00	65.00
325	1250.00	950.00	800.00	600.00	550.00	355.00	400.00	265.00
326	1450.00	950.00	800.00	700.00	675.00	380.00	375.00	250.00
327	3000.00	1950.00	1500.00	1150.00	1100.00	715.00	650.00	530.00
328	475.00	335.00	270.00	200.00	125.00	70.00	75.00	50.00
329	590.00	395.00	350.00	240.00	170.00	95.00	90.00	65.00
330	3600.00	2200.00	2000.00	1450.00	765.00	425.00	350.00	250.00

THE WASHINGTON-FRANKLIN HEADS

The Washington-Franklin Heads—so called because all stamps in the regular series featured the busts of George Washington and Benjamin Franklin—dominated the postal scene for almost two decades. Using a variety of papers, denominations, perforation sizes and formats, watermarks, design modifications and printing processes, almost 200 different major catalog listings were created from two basic designs.

The series started modestly, with the issuance of 12 stamps (#331-342) between November 1908 and January 1909. The modest designs on the new set replaced the ornate 1902-03 series. Their relative simplicity might have relegated the set to a secondary position in 20th century United States philately had it not been for the complexity of the varieties and the years of study the Washington-Franklin Heads now present to collectors.

The first varieties came almost immediately, in the form of imperforate stamps (#343-347) and coils, the latter being offered with horizontal (#348-351) or vertical (#352-356) perforations. The imperfs were intended for the fading vending machine technology that required private perforations while the coils were useful in standardized dispensers that were just coming into their own.

Then, in 1909, the Post Office began its experimentation. In this instance, it was the paper. As noted in our introduction to the 1909 Bluish Papers which follows, the Post Office Department and the Bureau of Engraving and Printing hoped that the new paper would reduce losses due to uneven shrinkage of the white wove paper used at the time. The experimental Washington-Franklin Bluish Papers (#357-66) are now among the most valuable in the series and the 8 cent Bluish Paper (#363) is the highest priced of the major listed items.

Attention was next directed to the double line watermark as the cause of the uneven shrinkage, as well as for weakness and thinning in the paper. As a result, a narrower, single line watermark was adopted for sheet stamps (#374-82), imperforates (#383-84), and coils with horizontal perfs (#385-86) and vertical perfs (#387-89).

Even as these experiments were being conducted, the perforation size was being examined to determine if a change was in order. Up until now, the perf 12 gauge had been used on all Washington-Franklin Heads.

The first perforation change was necessitated by the development of new coil manufacturing equipment. Under the increased pressure of the new equipment, the coil strips with the closely-spaced perf 12 gauge were splitting while being rolled into coils. To add paper between the holes, a perf 8-1/2 gauge was adopted for coil stamps and two new major varieties were created: with horizontal perfs (#390-91) and vertical perfs (#392-396).

Necessity was the driving force behind still more changes in 1912, when stamps with numeral denominations were issued to replace the "ONE CENT" and "TWO CENTS" stamps. This responded to the need for numeral denominations on foreign mail and created new sheets (#410-11) and vertically perforated (#412-13) coils. At the same time, a 7 cent value (#407) was issued to meet changing rate requirements.

In conjunction with the introduction of numerals on the 1 and 2 cent stamps, the design of the 1 cent was changed, with the bust of Washington replacing that of Franklin. Meanwhile, the bust of Franklin, which had been used only on the 1 cent stamp, was placed on all values from 8 cents to the $1 (#414-21) and a ribbon was added across their top to make the high value stamp even more noticeable to postal clerks.

As if to add just a little more variety while all the other changes were being made—but in actuality to use up a supply of old double-line watermark paper—50 cent and $1 issues with double-line watermarks (#422-23) were introduced.

The work with perforation changes on coil stamps carried over to sheet stamps in 1914 with the release of a perf 10 series (#424-40). The perf 10 size was then adapted to coils perforated horizontally (#441-42) and vertically (#443-47).

The transition to Rotary Press printing created new coils perforated 10 horizontally (#448-50) and vertically (#452-58). An imperforate Rotary coil (#459) for vending machine manufacturers also was produced.

A perf 10 double-line watermark $1 (#460) and a perf 11 two-cent sheet stamp (#461) added only slightly to the variety, but were followed by completely new runs on unwatermarked paper: perf 10 sheet stamps (#462-478) and imperforates (#481-84) were produced on the flat plate presses, while the Rotary press was used for coils perforated horizontally (#486-489) and vertically (#490-97).

While all this was taking place, the amazing 5 cent carmine error of color (#485) appeared on certain imperf 2 cent sheets. That same error (in rose, #505) was found when perf 11 sheet stamps (#498-518) were issued. The stamps turned out to be too hard to separate. Another strange issue, a 2 cent stamp on double-line watermark paper but perforated 11 (#519), came about when a small supply of old imperfs (#344) were discovered and put into the postal stream.

New $2 and $5 Franklins (#523-24), the former using an erroneous color, were released. To compensate for plate damage being caused by poor quality offset printings, perf 11 (#525-530) and imperforate (#531-535) were tried—and quickly resulted in a whole new series of "types" that had collectors spending more time with their magnifying glasses than with their families.

Odd perf sizes and printings (#538/546) came about as the Bureau cleaned out old paper stock. Then, in one final change, the Bureau corrected the color of the $2 from orange red and black to carmine and black. Almost 200 different stamps, all from two basic designs!

1909 THE BLUISH PAPERS

The Bluish Paper varieties are found on the 1 through 15 cent Washington-Franklin series of 1908-09 and on the 1909 Commemoratives. According to Post Office notices of the period, the experimental paper was a 30% rag stock that was intended to reduce paper waste. After being wet, a preliminary operation in the printing process, the standard white wove paper often would shrink so much that the perforators would cut into the designs. The rag paper did not solve the problem, the experiment was quickly abandoned and the 1909 Bluish Papers became major rarities.

The Harris Stamp Identifier provides further information on identifying the Washington-Franklin Heads.

331, 343, 348, 352, 357, 374, 383, 385, 387, 390, 392
Franklin

332, 344, 349, 353, 358, 375, 384, 386, 388, 391, 393
Washington

333, 345, 359, 376, 389, 394
Washington

334, 346, 350, 354, 360, 377, 395
Washington

335, 347, 351, 355, 361, 378, 396
Washington

336, 362, 379
Washington

337, 363, 380
Washington

338, 356, 364, 381
Washington

339, 365
Washington

340, 366, 382
Washington

341
Washington

342
Washington

NOTE: For further details on the various types of similar appearing stamps please refer to our U.S. Stamp Identifier.

SCOTT NO.	DESCRIPTION	UNUSED O.G. VF	F	AVG	USED VF	F	AVG
	1908-09 Double Line Watermark "USPS" Perf. 12 (NH + 75%)						
331-42	1¢-$1 (12 varieties, complete)	1580.00	940.00	605.00	205.00	140.00	82.50
331	1¢ green	11.25	6.65	4.00	.35	.25	.20
331a	1¢ booklet pane of 6	200.00	145.00	95.00	......	......	......
332	2¢ carmine	11.25	7.00	4.25	.35	.25	.20
332a	2¢ booklet pane of 6	185.00	120.00	85.00	......	......	......
333	3¢ deep violet (I)	52.50	29.50	17.75	6.50	4.25	2.50
334	4¢ orange brown	55.00	34.00	22.00	2.00	1.25	.80
335	5¢ blue	72.00	40.00	24.00	3.75	2.60	1.75
336	6¢ red orange	80.00	50.00	30.00	8.50	5.00	3.25
337	8¢ olive green	60.00	38.00	24.00	5.50	3.25	2.25
338	10¢ yellow	80.00	55.00	40.00	4.75	2.50	1.50
339	13¢ blue green	60.00	34.00	23.00	80.00	50.00	29.00
340	15¢ pale ultramarine	82.00	50.00	35.00	12.00	8.00	5.00
341	50¢ violet	440.00	260.00	160.00	45.00	30.00	18.00
342	$1 violet brown	675.00	400.00	260.00	145.00	100.00	62.50
	1908-09 Imperforate (NH + 75%)						
343-47	1¢-5¢ (5 varieties, complete)	138.00	103.50	70.00	110.00	76.00	53.00
343	1¢ green	18.50	13.00	9.50	9.50	7.00	4.75
344	2¢ carmine	27.50	22.00	14.00	8.00	5.50	3.75
345	3¢ deep violet (I)	67.50	52.00	39.00	82.00	57.50	38.00
346	4¢ orange brown	87.50	67.00	44.00	88.00	67.50	50.00
347	5¢ blue	110.00	80.00	53.00	140.00	90.00	62.50
	1908-10 Coil Stamps Perf. 12 Horizontally (NH + 75%)						
348	1¢ green	72.50	50.00	31.00	70.00	50.00	31.00
349	2¢ carmine	100.00	72.00	44.00	80.00	55.00	37.00
350	4¢ orange brown	285.00	185.00	135.00	300.00	200.00	140.00
351	5¢ blue	285.00	195.00	130.00	290.00	200.00	130.00

NOTE: Counterfeits are common on #348-56 and #385-89

SCOTT NO.	DESCRIPTION	UNUSED O.G. VF	F	AVG	USED VF	F	AVG
	1909 Coil Stamps Perf. 12 Vertically (NH + 75%)						
352	1¢ green	160.00	115.00	76.00	160.00	115.00	70.00
353	2¢ carmine	155.00	110.00	74.00	115.00	85.00	57.50
354	4¢ orange brown	375.00	285.00	195.00	195.00	145.00	95.00
355	5¢ blue	375.00	290.00	210.00	210.00	155.00	105.00
356	10¢ yellow	4750.00	3400.00	2100.00	4500.00	3500.00	2300.00

SCOTT NO.	UNUSED NH F	AVG	UNUSED OG F	AVG	SCOTT NO.	UNUSED NH F	AVG	UNUSED OG F	AVG
	PLATE BLOCKS OF 6					**CENTER LINE BLOCKS**			
331	90.00	60.00	65.00	48.00	343	72.00	53.50	53.50	40.00
332	90.00	70.00	65.00	47.50	344	105.00	90.00	87.50	55.00
333	450.00	325.00	290.00	210.00	345	250.00	185.00	190.00	155.00
334	500.00	340.00	360.00	255.00	346	300.00	265.00	255.00	180.00
335	850.00	635.00	575.00	465.00	347	450.00	315.00	325.00	230.00
336	1250.00	900.00	700.00	495.00					
337	700.00	495.00	375.00	275.00					
338	950.00	700.00	700.00	450.00		**ARROW BLOCKS**			
339	700.00	575.00	400.00	300.00					
343	125.00	115.00	80.00	60.00	343	57.50	52.00	52.00	37.50
344	175.00	140.00	150.00	110.00	344	100.00	87.50	85.00	55.00
345	330.00	250.00	320.00	240.00	345	240.00	180.00	185.00	150.00
346	500.00	375.00	385.00	325.00	346	295.00	260.00	250.00	175.00
347	600.00	485.00	515.00	370.00	347	390.00	300.00	320.00	210.00

		(NH + 75%)					
		COIL LINE PAIRS UNUSED OG			**COIL PAIRS UNUSED OG**		
	VF	F	AVG	VF	F	AVG	
348	350.00	225.00	155.00	150.00	100.00	65.00	
349	600.00	400.00	275.00	215.00	130.00	95.00	
350	1200.00	900.00	650.00	600.00	420.00	265.00	
351	1200.00	900.00	650.00	600.00	370.00	230.00	
352	750.00	525.00	375.00	350.00	250.00	175.00	
353	700.00	500.00	350.00	330.00	230.00	165.00	
354	1650.00	1100.00	775.00	800.00	535.00	395.00	
355	1650.00	1100.00	775.00	800.00	625.00	445.00	
356	15000.00	10000.00	7500.00	10000.00	6000.00	4500.00	

SCOTT NO.	DESCRIPTION	UNUSED O.G. VF	F	AVG	USED VF	F	AVG
	1909 Bluish Gray paper Perf. 12 (NH + 75%)						
357	1¢ green	165.00	100.00	74.00	165.00	100.00	75.00
358	2¢ carmine	215.00	135.00	96.00	230.00	145.00	92.50
359	3¢ deep violet (I)	2750.00	1800.00	1300.00	5750.00	4000.00	2900.00
360	4¢ orange brown	......	16000.00	11000.00	......	......	......
361	5¢ blue	6050.00	3400.00	2400.00	15000.00	11500.00	8500.00
362	6¢ red orange	2000.00	1200.00	800.00	7000.00	4875.00	3550.00
363	8¢ olive green	......	19500.00	14000.00	......	......	......
364	10¢ yellow	2250.00	1350.00	972.00	8000.00	5500.00	3975.00
365	13¢ blue green	3500.00	2200.00	1500.00	2800.00	1900.00	1300.00
366	15¢ pale ultramarine	2150.00	1175.00	925.00	11000.00	7425.00	4750.00

THE 1909 COMMEMORATIVES

After the 16-value Columbian commemorative set, the Post Office Department began gradually reducing the number of stamps in subsequent series. The 1909 commemoratives were the first to use the single-stamp commemorative approach that is now the common practice.

The Lincoln Memorial issue was released on the 100th anniversary of the birth of America's 16th President. The Alaska-Yukon was issued for the Alaska-Yukon Exposition held in Seattle to publicize the development of the Alaska territory. The Hudson-Fulton stamp commemorated Henry Hudson's 1609 discovery of the river that bears his name, the 1809 voyage of Robert Fulton's "Clermont" steamboat and the 1909 celebration of those two events.

As noted earlier, the 1909 Commemoratives were issued on experimental "bluish" paper in addition to the white wove standard. The stamps on white wove paper also were issued in imperforate form for private perforation by vending and stamp-affixing machine manufacturers.

367-369	370, 371	372, 373
Lincoln	William H. Seward	S.S. Clermont

SCOTT NO.	DESCRIPTION	UNUSED O.G. VF	F	AVG	USED VF	F	AVG
	1909 LINCOLN MEMORIAL ISSUE **(NH + 50%)**						
367	2¢ carmine, perf. .	14.95	11.00	7.50	5.50	3.25	2.25
368	2¢ carmine, imperf.	50.00	39.00	28.00	96.00	57.50	3800
369	2¢ carmine (bluish paper)	300.00	180.00	130.00	345.00	250.00	135.00
	1909 ALASKA-YUKON ISSUE						
370	2¢ carmine, perf. .	20.00	12.00	8.00	5.00	2.95	1.75
371	2¢ carmine, imperf.	60.00	44.00	35.00	62.00	42.50	27.00
	1909 HUDSON-FULTON ISSUE						
372	2¢ carmine, perf. .	18.00	12.00	9.50	9.50	5.75	3.75
373	2¢ carmine, imperf	67.50	48.00	40.00	80.00	55.00	43.00
	1910-11 Single Line Watermark "USPS" Perf. 12 **(NH + 50%)**						
374-82	1¢-15¢ (9 varieties, complete)	760.00	475.00	290.00	52.00	33.00	19.75
374	1¢ green	13.50	8.50	5.50	.30	.25	.20
374a	1¢ booklet pane of 6	200.00	130.00	90.00	. . . . . .	. . . . . .	. . . . . .
375	2¢ carmine	14.50	9.00	6.00	.30	.30	.20
375a	2¢ booklet pane of 6	150.00	105.00	66.00	. . . . . .	. . . . . .	. . . . . .
376	3¢ deep violet (I) .	32.50	18.50	12.00	4.25	2.50	1.50
377	4¢ brown	40.00	24.00	18.00	1.25	.85	.55
378	5¢ blue	40.00	24.00	18.00	1.50	1.10	.75
379	6¢ red orange	50.00	30.00	19.00	2.25	1.25	.85
380	8¢ olive green	145.00	85.00	52.50	41.00	27.50	18.00
381	10¢ yellow	150.00	95.00	55.00	8.50	5.50	3.75
382	15¢ pale ultramarine	340.00	220.00	130.00	48.00	30.00	17.00
	1911 Imperforate						
383	1¢ green	11.00	8.50	5.00	5.50	3.75	2.25
384	2¢ carmine	20.00	17.00	9.50	3.75	2.50	1.25

SCOTT NO.	UNUSED NH F	AVG	UNUSED OG F	AVG	SCOTT NO.	UNUSED NH F	AVG	UNUSED OG F	AVG
	PLATE BLOCKS OF 6					**CENTER LINE BLOCKS**			
367	200.00	135.00	140.00	97.50	368	200.00	140.00	150.00	115.00
368	325.00	225.00	260.00	190.00	371	285.00	195.00	200.00	140.00
370	320.00	220.00	220.00	150.00	373	340.00	215.00	240.00	165.00
371	390.00	275.00	280.00	190.00	383	42.00	30.00	30.00	25.00
372	380.00	240.00	280.00	190.00	384	90.00	55.00	65.00	40.00
373	430.00	300.00	300.00	200.00					
374	100.00	65.00	70.00	50.00		**ARROW BLOCKS**			
375	105.00	65.00	75.00	50.00					
376	275.00	185.00	195.00	130.00	368	180.00	130.00	120.00	110.00
377	300.00	200.00	220.00	145.00	371	235.00	190.00	180.00	135.00
378	325.00	245.00	245.00	150.00	373	265.00	200.00	200.00	160.00
383	80.00	55.00	50.00	36.00	383	42.00	30.00	30.00	20.00
384	210.00	150.00	140.00	95.00	384	50.00	45.00	45.00	36.00

Very Fine Plate Blocks from this period command premiums.

SCOTT NO.	DESCRIPTION	UNUSED O.G. VF	F	AVG	USED VF	F	AVG
	COIL STAMPS **1910 Perf. 12 Horizontally** **(NH + 75%)**						
385	1¢ green	95.00	63.00	37.00	56.00	37.50	28.00
386	2¢ carmine	150.00	90.00	60.00	79.00	52.50	37.00
	1910-11 Perf. 12 Vertically (†)						
387	1¢ green	250.00	165.00	110.00	150.00	100.00	70.00
388	2¢ carmine	1500.00	950.00	725.00	1600.00	1350.00	975.00
389	3¢ deep violet (I) .	. . . . . .	58000.00	. . . . . .	. . . . . .	12400.00	. . . . . .
	1910 Perf. 8-1/2 Horizontally						
390	1¢ green	11.50	6.50	4.75	14.00	10.50	7.50
391	2¢ carmine	67.50	45.00	27.00	38.00	25.00	17.00
	1910-13 Perf. 8-1/2 Vertically						
392	1¢ green	51.50	35.00	21.00	64.00	42.50	32.00
393	2¢ carmine	75.00	45.00	30.00	35.00	22.50	15.00
394	3¢ deep violet (I) .	100.00	64.00	43.00	105.00	72.50	48.00
395	4¢ brown	105.00	68.00	45.00	98.00	67.50	45.00
396	5¢ blue	97.50	63.00	42.00	98.00	67.50	45.00

SCOTT NO.	COIL LINE PAIRS UNUSED OG VF	F	AVG	COIL PAIRS UNUSED OG VF	F	AVG
	(NH + 75%)					
385	450.00	300.00	195.00	200.00	125.00	87.50
386	1300.00	800.00	550.00	315.00	225.00	125.00
387	1000.00	700.00	500.00	575.00	365.00	265.00
390	50.00	35.00	22.50	25.00	16.50	9.00
391	330.00	235.00	140.00	140.00	85.00	55.00
392	225.00	140.00	95.00	110.00	72.50	43.50
393	325.00	210.00	150.00	155.00	100.00	60.00
394	450.00	295.00	200.00	200.00	135.00	85.00
395	450.00	295.00	200.00	220.00	150.00	95.00
396	450.00	295.00	200.00	200.00	135.00	85.00

THE PANAMA-PACIFIC ISSUE

The Panama-Pacific stamps were issued to commemorate the discovery of the Pacific Ocean in 1513 and the opening of the 1915 Panama-Pacific Exposition that celebrated the completion of the Panama Canal. Released in perf 12 form in 1913, the set of four denominations was changed to perf 10 in 1914. Before the perf change, the 10 cent orange yellow shade was determined to be too light. It was changed to the deeper orange color that is found both perf 12 and perf 10.

Because many collectors ignored the perf 10 stamps when they were issued, these stamps are scarcer than their perf 12 predecessors. In fact, #404 is the rarest 20th century commemorative issue.

397, 401	398, 402
Balboa	Panama Canal

399, 403	400, 400A, 404
Golden Gate	Discovery of San Francisco Bay

SCOTT NO.	DESCRIPTION	UNUSED O.G. VF	F	AVG	USED VF	F	AVG
	1913 Perf. 12 (NH + 75%)						
397-400A	1¢-10¢ (5 varieties, complete)	660.00	350.00	230.00	76.00	42.00	26.00
397	1¢ green	37.50	23.00	17.00	3.75	2.25	1.50
398	2¢ carmine	36.50	20.00	13.00	2.00	1.25	.95
399	5¢ blue	120.00	72.50	48.00	23.00	12.50	8.00
400	10¢ orange yellow	180.00	100.00	65.00	70.00	40.00	28.00
400A	10¢ orange	325.00	185.00	120.00	30.00	16.00	10.00
	1914-15 Perf. 10 (NH + 75%)						
401-04	1¢-10¢ (4 varieties, complete)	1600.00	1175.00	775.00	142.00	82.00	54.00
401	1¢ green	46.00	26.00	18.00	11.00	8.00	5.00
402	2¢ carmine	130.00	74.00	56.00	4.50	2.75	1.75
403	5¢ blue	260.00	135.00	95.00	37.00	23.50	16.00
404	10¢ orange	1250.00	1000.00	650.00	185.00	100.00	67.50

405/545 *Washington*   406/546 *Washington*   426/541 *Washington*   427, 446, 457, 465, 495, 503 *Washington*

428, 447, 458, 466, 467, 496, 504, 505 *Washington*   429, 468, 506 *Washington*   407, 430, 469, 507 *Washington*   414, 431, 470, 508 *Franklin*

415, 432, 471, 509 *Franklin*   416, 433, 472, 497, 510 *Franklin*   434, 473, 511 *Franklin*   417, 435, 474, 512 *Franklin*

513 *Franklin*   418, 437, 475, 514 *Franklin*   419, 438, 476, 515 *Franklin*   420, 439, 476A, 516 *Franklin*

421, 422, 440, 477, 517 *Franklin*   423, 478, 518 *Franklin*

SCOTT NO.	DESCRIPTION	UNUSED O.G. VF	F	AVG	USED VF	F	AVG
		1912-14 Single Line Watermark Perf. 12					
		(NH + 60%)					
405	1¢ green......	16.50	9.50	5.50	.30	.25	.20
405b	1¢ booklet pane of 6	95.00	65.00	45.00	......	......	......
406	2¢ carmine (I)..	11.00	6.75	4.25	.30	.25	.20
406a	2¢ booklet pane of 6	95.00	65.00	45.00	......	......	......
407	7¢ black	110.00	65.00	45.00	20.00	13.00	8.50
		1912 Imperforate					
408	1¢ green......	2.75	2.00	1.50	1.50	.95	.65
409	2¢ carmine (I)..	3.95	3.00	2.00	1.25	.95	.70

SCOTT NO.	UNUSED NH F	AVG	UNUSED OG F	AVG	SCOTT NO.	UNUSED NH F	AVG	UNUSED OG F	AVG
PLATE BLOCKS OF 6					**CENTER LINE BLOCKS**				
397	300.00	210.00	225.00	145.00	408	15.50	11.00	11.00	8.50
398	400.00	320.00	265.00	185.00	409	17.00	11.95	14.50	9.50
401	425.00	250.00	275.00	195.00					
405	140.00	70.00	90.00	60.00	**ARROW BLOCKS**				
406	160.00	120.00	100.00	70.00					
408	32.00	24.00	19.00	14.00	408	10.00	9.00	7.50	6.00
409	56.00	40.00	36.00	25.00	409	12.00	10.00	10.00	8.00

SCOTT NO.	DESCRIPTION	UNUSED O.G. VF	F	AVG	USED VF	F	AVG
		COIL STAMPS					
		1912 Perf. 8-1/2 Horizontally					
		(NH + 60%)					
410	1¢ green.....	8.95	5.25	3.75	15.00	8.75	5.00
411	2¢ carmine (I)..	14.00	8.50	5.50	14.00	9.00	5.50
		1912 Perf. 8-1/2 Vertically					
412	1¢ green.....	32.00	22.00	15.00	11.00	7.00	5.00
413	2¢ carmine (I)..	65.00	42.50	28.25	2.50	1.75	1.10

				(NH + 60%)			
SCOTT NO.	**COIL LINE PAIRS UNUSED OG**			**COIL PAIRS UNUSED OG**			
	VF	F	AVG	VF	F	AVG	
410	48.00	29.00	18.00	19.00	12.50	8.00	
411	70.00	45.00	30.00	30.00	20.00	12.50	
412	150.00	100.00	65.00	80.00	60.00	40.00	
413	295.00	200.00	135.00	135.00	95.00	65.00	

1912-14 Perf. 12 Single Line Watermark (NH + 60%)

SCOTT NO.	DESCRIPTION	VF	F	AVG	VF	F	AVG
414	8¢ pale olive green	67.50	44.00	28.00	3.50	2.00	1.50
415	9¢ salmon red .	80.00	51.00	30.00	40.00	25.00	16.00
416	10¢ orange yellow	60.00	38.00	24.00	.75	.50	.35
417	12¢ claret brown	65.00	43.00	28.00	7.50	5.00	3.25
418	15¢ gray.....	125.00	77.00	50.00	7.00	4.25	3.00
419	20¢ ultramarine	275.00	185.00	115.00	39.00	22.50	16.00
420	30¢ orange red.	160.00	105.00	65.00	40.00	23.50	17.00
421	50¢ violet	575.00	340.00	225.00	51.00	32.50	22.00

1912 Double Line Watermark "USPS" Perf 12

422	50¢ violet	350.00	225.00	150.00	58.00	37.50	25.00
423	$1 violet black .	675.00	425.00	250.00	185.00	110.00	70.00

1914-15 Single Line Watermark, "USPS" Perf 10 (NH + 60%)

SCOTT NO.	DESCRIPTION	VF	F	AVG	VF	F	AVG
424-40	1¢-50¢ (16 varieties, complete)	2120.00	1275.00	900.00	120.00	79.00	51.00
424	1¢ green......	6.50	4.00	2.50	.25	.20	.15
424d	1¢ booklet pane of 6	8.00	4.00	3.00	....	....	....
425	2¢ rose red....	5.00	2.50	1.75	.25	.20	.15
425e	2¢ booklet pane of 6	30.00	23.00	16.00	....	....	....
426	3¢ deep violet (I)	32.50	20.00	13.00	5.50	3.00	2.00
427	4¢ brown	47.50	29.50	21.00	1.25	.75	.50
428	5¢ blue.......	45.00	31.50	22.50	1.25	.75	.50
429	6¢ red orange..	70.00	45.00	30.00	4.25	2.75	1.50
430	7¢ black	135.00	79.00	59.00	12.00	7.25	4.25
431	8¢ pale olive green	60.00	39.00	24.00	4.50	3.25	2.25
432	9¢ salmon red .	77.50	42.00	27.00	22.00	15.00	9.00
433	10¢ orange yellow	72.50	43.00	29.00	2.75	2.00	1.25
434	11¢ dark green .	42.50	28.00	20.00	26.00	16.00	11.00
435	12¢ claret brown	40.00	26.00	18.00	10.00	7.00	4.00
437	15¢ gray......	170.00	105.00	80.00	15.00	9.00	6.00
438	20¢ ultramarine	280.00	170.00	120.00	8.00	5.50	3.50
439	30¢ orange red.	385.00	210.00	165.00	35.00	22.50	15.00
440	50¢ violet	800.00	500.00	325.00	58.00	37.50	25.00

UNUSED PLATE BLOCKS OF 6									
SCOTT NO.	**NH** F	AVG	**OG** F	AVG	SCOTT NO.	**NH** F	AVG	**OG** F	AVG
414	525.00	350.00	400.00	250.00	429	500.00	300.00	325.00	190.00
415	750.00	525.00	525.00	375.00	430	1200.00	850.00	800.00	550.00
416	650.00	425.00	400.00	280.00	431	500.00	395.00	400.00	280.00
417	700.00	475.00	450.00	300.00	432	825.00	590.00	620.00	440.00
418	900.00	650.00	600.00	450.00	433	800.00	575.00	600.00	425.00
424 (6)	55.00	40.00	30.00	20.00	434	325.00	210.00	235.00	135.00
424 (10)	190.00	120.00	130.00	80.00	435	355.00	200.00	240.00	150.00
425 (6)	30.00	20.00	20.00	15.00	437	1200.00	850.00	850.00	625.00
425 (10)	180.00	120.00	130.00	90.00	438	3850.00	2950.00	2500.00	1950.00
426	250.00	175.00	190.00	125.00	439	5250.00	3750.00	3250.00	2500.00
427	575.00	400.00	425.00	300.00	440	17000.00	11500.00	12500.00	9000.00
428	475.00	300.00	350.00	200.00					

COIL STAMPS
1914 Perf. 10 Horizontally

(NH + 60%)

441	1¢ green......	2.75	1.50	1.00	2.00	1.50	1.00
442	2¢ carmine (I)..	17.50	11.00	7.00	28.00	18.50	10.50

1914 Perf.10 Vertically
(NH + 60%)

443	1¢ green......	42.50	28.00	18.00	10.00	6.00	3.50
444	2¢ carmine (I)..	50.00	29.50	18.00	2.75	1.25	1.25
445	3¢ violet (I)....	350.00	225.00	160.00	300.00	195.00	120.00
446	4¢ brown	210.00	140.00	105.00	140.00	85.00	62.50
447	5¢ blue.......	72.50	47.00	33.00	79.00	52.50	33.00

SCOTT NO.	DESCRIPTION	UNUSED O.G. VF	F	AVG	USED VF	F	AVG
	ROTARY PRESS COIL STAMPS 1915-16 Perf. 10 Horizontally (NH + 60%)						
448	1¢ green.....	9.50	7.00	4.00	14.00	9.50	6.00
449	2¢ red (I)	3500.00	2100.00	1450.00	625.00	475.00	290.00
450	2¢ carmine (III).	27.50	20.00	14.00	10.50	7.00	3.50
	1914-16 Perf. 10 Vertically (NH + 60%)						
452	1¢ green......	22.50	16.00	12.00	3.50	2.50	1.75
453	2¢ carmine rose (I)	175.00	120.00	82.50	7.00	4.50	3.50
454	2¢ red (II)	145.00	100.00	65.00	21.00	12.00	8.00
455	2¢ carmine (III).	14.00	10.00	6.50	2.00	1.50	.75
456	3¢ violet (I)....	425.00	285.00	180.00	355.00	200.00	135.00
457	4¢ brown	55.00	28.00	20.00	56.00	35.00	21.00
458	5¢ blue.	45.00	30.00	20.00	40.00	25.00	15.00
	1914 Imperforate Coil (NH + 60%)						
459	2¢ carmine (I). .	675.00	550.00	450.00	1100.00	800.00	....
	1915 Flat Plate Printing Double Line Watermark Perf. 10 (NH + 60%)						
460	$1 violet black .	1250.00	750.00	525.00	235.00	140.00	95.00
	1915 Single Line Watermark "USPS" Perf. 11 (NH + 60%)						
461	2¢ pale carmine red (I)	200.00	115.00	65.00	525.00	275.00	165.00
	1916-17 Unwatermarked Perf. 10 (NH + 60%)						
462	1¢ green......	13.50	9.50	6.00	1.25	.60	.40
462a	1¢ booklet pane of 6	25.00	15.75	9.25	....	....	....
463	2¢ carmine (I)..	7.95	5.50	3.50	.50	.30	.20
463a	2¢ booklet pane of 6	110.00	80.00	55.00	....	....	....
464	3¢ violet (I)....	120.00	65.00	48.00	25.00	16.25	10.50
465	4¢ orange brown	66.50	42.00	25.00	3.25	2.25	1.25
466	5¢ blue......	120.00	65.00	40.00	5.00	3.50	2.00
467	5¢ carmine (error)	950.00	575.00	350.00	1000.00	650.00	450.00
468	6¢ red orange..	140.00	75.00	45.00	33.00	18.50	10.50
469	7¢ black	180.00	100.00	68.00	52.00	31.50	18.00
470	8¢ olive green	110.00	62.00	41.00	18.00	10.50	7.00
471	9¢ salmon red .	122.50	68.00	44.00	53.00	35.00	21.00
472	10¢ orange yellow	170.00	92.50	70.00	11.00	8.50	5.00
473	11¢ dark green.	67.50	43.00	25.00	66.00	37.50	25.00
474	12¢ claret brown	90.00	58.00	42.00	21.00	12.75	8.50
475	15¢ gray......	260.00	180.00	105.00	41.00	22.50	16.00
476	20¢ light ultramarine	400.00	220.00	160.00	42.00	24.50	16.00
476A	30¢ orange red.	....	4800.00	....	....	....	....
477	50¢ light violet .	1600.00	950.00	625.00	165.00	105.00	67.50
478	$1 violet black..	1175.00	675.00	500.00	48.00	32.50	19.00
	Design of 1902-03						
479	$2 dark blue ...	485.00	325.00	240.00	120.00	67.50	54.00
480	$5 light green ..	395.00	250.00	150.00	145.00	82.50	60.00
	1916-17 Imperforate (NH + 60%)						
481	1¢ green......	2.50	1.75	.75	1.50	1.00	.50
482	2¢ carmine (I)...	2.50	2.00	1.00	2.25	1.35	.90
483	3¢ violet (I)...	35.00	25.00	17.00	28.00	22.50	17.00
484	3¢ violet (II) ...	22.50	19.00	13.00	20.00	15.50	11.75

(NH + 60%)

SCOTT NO.	COIL LINE PAIRS UNUSED OG VF	F	AVG	COIL PAIRS UNUSED OG VF	F	AVG
441	10.00	7.00	4.00	5.75	3.75	2.50
442	90.00	48.00	30.00	35.00	20.00	14.00
443	180.00	120.00	75.00	90.00	55.00	37.00
444	325.00	250.00	175.00	100.00	60.00	42.00
445	1600.00	900.00	600.00	740.00	495.00	350.00
446	900.00	500.00	350.00	445.00	275.00	155.00
447	325.00	185.00	127.00	175.00	110.00	75.00
448	62.00	39.00	25.00	32.00	18.00	12.00
450	90.00	65.00	40.00	58.00	40.00	25.00
452	115.00	65.00	40.00	47.50	35.00	20.00
453	850.00	500.00	350.00	400.00	250.00	160.00
454	750.00	425.00	325.00	350.00	200.00	140.00
455	90.00	50.00	35.00	32.00	18.00	12.00
456	1350.00	900.00	550.00	900.00	625.00	365.00
457	240.00	130.00	90.00	115.00	80.00	52.00
458	250.00	145.00	95.00	115.00	85.00	50.00
459	1800.00	1250.00	900.00	1050.00	850.00	500.00

UNUSED PLATE BLOCKS OF 6

SCOTT NO.	NH F	AVG	OG F	AVG	SCOTT NO.	NH F	AVG	OG F	AVG
462	195.00	125.00	125.00	80.00	472	1600.00	1200.00	1200.00	800.00
463	155.00	100.00	100.00	60.00	473	450.00	325.00	300.00	200.00
464	1500.00	1100.00	1150.00	825.00	474	775.00	500.00	500.00	325.00
465	800.00	500.00	600.00	425.00	481	25.00	17.65	17.65	11.75
466	1100.00	850.00	950.00	565.00	482	35.00	22.00	22.50	17.00
470	675.00	500.00	545.00	320.00	483	200.00	160.00	160.00	110.00
471	850.00	675.00	595.00	400.00	484	140.00	90.00	115.00	80.00

CENTER LINE BLOCKS				ARROW BLOCKS			
481	8.00	5.00	4.00	3.00	481	8.00	5.00	4.00	3.00
482	11.00	7.00	7.75	4.75	482	11.00	7.00	7.75	4.75
483	130.00	95.00	97.50	72.50	483	125.00	90.00	95.00	70.00
484	80.00	55.00	70.00	55.00	484	75.00	50.00	65.00	50.00

SCOTT NO.	DESCRIPTION	UNUSED O.G. VF	F	AVG	USED VF	F	AVG
	ROTARY PRESS COIL STAMPS 1916-19 Perf. 10 Horizontally (NH + 60%)						
486	1¢ green.....	1.75	1.00	.50	1.00	.75	.50
487	2¢ carmine (II) .	32.50	19.00	12.00	25.00	17.50	10.50
488	2¢ carmine (III).	5.95	3.75	2.50	2.50	1.75	1.00
489	3¢ violet (I)	7.00	4.50	3.00	2.75	1.95	1.00
	1916-22 Perf. 10 Vertically (NH + 60%)						
490	1¢ green.....	1.00	.50	.50	.35	.25	.15
491	2¢ carmine (II) .	2750.00	1750.00	1100.00	800.00	550.00	375.00
492	2¢ carmine (III).	16.00	9.00	6.00	.50	.25	.20
493	3¢ violet (I)....	37.50	21.00	16.00	5.00	3.00	2.00
494	3¢ violet (II) ...	22.50	13.00	8.50	1.50	1.00	.80
495	4¢ orange brown	22.50	13.00	9.00	10.50	6.00	4.00
496	5¢ blue......	7.00	4.00	3.00	1.60	1.00	.75
497	10¢ orange yellow	35.00	20.00	15.00	15.00	10.00	5.50

(NH + 60%)

SCOTT NO.	COIL LINE PAIRS UNUSED OG VF	F	AVG	COIL PAIRS UNUSED OG VF	F	AVG
486	6.50	4.50	3.50	3.25	2.00	1.25
487	160.00	105.00	75.00	67.50	42.00	25.00
488	28.00	18.00	12.00	12.50	9.00	5.75
489	40.00	30.00	24.00	16.00	10.00	7.00
490	6.00	3.75	1.90	2.50	1.50	.90
491	....	10000.00	6000.00	6450.00	4500.00	3000.00
492	70.00	50.00	35.00	36.00	20.00	14.00
493	160.00	100.00	70.00	78.75	60.00	35.00
494	90.00	60.00	48.00	47.00	35.00	19.50
495	100.00	75.00	55.00	47.00	35.00	19.25
496	40.00	28.00	19.50	15.00	9.00	7.00
497	160.00	115.00	75.00	75.00	45.00	35.00

1917-19 Flat Plate Printing Perf. 11 (NH + 60%)

SCOTT NO.	DESCRIPTION	VF	F	AVG	VF	F	AVG
498/518	(498-99, 501-04, 506-18) 19 varieties	640.00	395.00	265.00	35.00	22.25	16.95
498	1¢ green......	.90	.55	.50	.35	.25	.20
498e	1¢ booklet pane of 6	7.50	4.50	3.25	....	....	....
498f	1¢ booklet pane of 30........	1300.00	800.00	550.00	....	....	....
499	2¢ rose (I)....	.90	.55	.28	.35	.25	.20
499e	2¢ booklet pane of 6	7.00	4.50	3.50	....	....	....
500	2¢ deep rose (Ia)	400.00	225.00	165.00	250.00	175.00	100.00
501	3c light violet (I)	21.50	13.00	8.50	.35	.25	.20
501b	3c booklet pane of 6	95.00	65.00	45.00	....	....	....
502	3c dark violet (II)	26.00	15.00	10.00	2.25	1.50	.95
502b	3c booklet pane of 6	100.00	55.00	37.50	....	....	....
503	4c brown	18.00	10.00	6.00	.50	.35	.20
504	5c blue......	15.00	8.50	5.25	.55	.40	.25
505	5c rose (error) .	680.00	400.00	275.00	700.00	475.00	300.00
506	6c red orange..	22.00	13.00	8.00	.75	.50	.35
507	7c black	42.00	25.00	17.00	2.75	2.00	1.10
508	8c olive bistre..	21.25	12.50	7.50	1.50	1.20	.80
509	9c salmon red .	24.00	14.00	9.00	4.75	2.95	2.00
510	10c orange yellow	30.00	17.25	10.50	.30	.25	.20
511	11c light green .	16.00	9.00	3.50	7.50	4.75	3.25
512	12c claret brown	20.00	11.50	4.25	1.25	.75	.60
513	13c apple green	22.50	13.00	8.25	17.00	10.00	9.00
514	15c gray......	64.00	38.00	26.00	2.50	1.50	1.25
515	20c light ultramarine	85.00	46.00	34.00	.75	.50	.35
516	30c orange red.	70.00	40.00	30.00	2.50	1.50	1.25
517	50c red violet ..	100.00	75.00	50.00	1.50	.80	.75
518	$1 violet black .	95.00	65.00	45.00	4.25	2.75	1.75

1917 Design of 1908-09 Double Line Watermark Perf. 11

519	2¢ carmine	700.00	375.00	250.00	1800.00	1400.00	800.00

NOTE: For further details on the various types of similar appearing stamps please refer to our U.S. Stamp Identifier.

UNUSED PLATE BLOCKS OF 6

SCOTT NO.	NH F	AVG	OG F	AVG	SCOTT NO.	NH F	AVG	OG F	AVG
498	19.50	14.75	14.00	12.00	511	200.00	110.00	150.00	90.00
499	19.50	14.75	14.00	12.00	512	185.00	110.00	130.00	85.00
501	170.00	128.00	140.00	100.00	513	185.00	105.50	145.00	85.00
502	190.00	175.00	165.00	128.00	514	835.00	465.00	595.00	385.00
503	190.00	150.00	135.00	115.00	515	975.00	565.00	675.00	425.00
504	165.00	100.00	135.00	80.00	516	750.00	440.00	600.00	350.00
506	230.00	155.00	180.00	125.00	517	2000.00	1350.00	1300.00	900.00
507	350.00	265.00	250.00	210.00	518	1500.00	925.00	1050.00	685.00
508	235.00	160.00	185.00	127.50	519	3500.00	1950.00	2500.00	1500.00
509	220.00	150.00	175.00	120.00			ARROW	BLOCK	
510	260.00	215.00	165.00	125.00	518	450.00	280.00	300.00	225.00

523, 547
Franklin

524
Franklin

SCOTT NO.	DESCRIPTION	UNUSED O.G. VF	F	AVG	USED VF	F	AVG

1918 Unwatermarked (NH + 60%)

| 523 | $2 orange red & black . . . . . . | 1250.00 | 850.00 | 600.00 | 450.00 | 300.00 | 190.00 |
| 524 | $5 deep green & black . . . . . . | 425.00 | 305.00 | 215.00 | 75.00 | 52.50 | 30.00 |

1918-20 Offset Printing Perf. 11 (NH + 60%)

525	1¢ gray green . .	6.00	4.00	2.50	1.25	.85	.50
526	2¢ carmine (IV)	42.50	30.00	16.00	7.00	5.00	3.25
527	2¢ carmine (V) .	35.00	23.00	14.00	2.25	1.50	.85
528	2¢ carmine (Va) .	17.00	11.00	8.00	1.00	.75	.55
528A	2¢ carmine (VI)	72.50	55.00	36.25	2.00	1.50	1.00
528B	2¢ carmine (VII)	38.50	25.00	18.00	.60	.50	.35
529	3¢ violet (III) . . .	7.50	5.50	4.50	.50	.35	.25
530	3¢ purple (IV) . .	2.50	1.75	1.25	.50	.30	.20

1918-20 Offset Printing Imperforate

531	1¢ gray green . .	22.50	14.00	10.50	21.50	13.00	10.00
532	2¢ carmine rose (IV)	85.00	60.00	46.00	80.00	55.00	37.00
533	2¢ carmine (V) .	345.00	260.00	190.00	210.00	150.00	110.00
534	2¢ carmine (Va) .	37.50	33.00	19.00	35.00	25.00	17.00
534A	2¢ carmine (VI)	75.00	55.00	39.50	44.00	29.00	22.00
534B	2¢ carmine (VII)	2500.00	1800.00	1350.00	1200.00	1050.00	675.00
535	3¢ violet (IV) . . .	18.50	13.00	9.00	15.00	9.50	5.75

1919 Offset Printing Perf. 12-1/2

| 536 | 1¢ gray green . . | 40.00 | 28.00 | 18.00 | 65.00 | 40.00 | 26.00 |

537
"Victory" and Flags

1919 VICTORY ISSUE (NH + 50%)

| 537 | 3¢ violet . . . . . . | 18.50 | 10.50 | 6.50 | 7.50 | 4.50 | 2.75 |

1919-21 Rotary Press Printings—Perf. 11 x 10 (†) (NH + 50%)

538	1¢ green	18.50	10.50	7.00	15.00	10.00	7.50
538a	Same, imperf. horizontally	80.00	50.00	36.00	. . . .	. . . .	. . . .
539	2¢ carmine rose (II)	3300.00	2700.00	1800.00	. . . .	4000.00	. . . .
540	2¢ carmine rose (III)	17.50	10.00	6.00	15.00	9.00	6.25
540a	Same, imperf. horizontally	80.00	47.50	38.50	. . . .	. . . .	. . . .
541	3¢ violet (II) . . .	60.00	36.00	28.00	50.00	28.95	21.50

Perf. 10 x 11

| 542 | 1¢ green . . . . . . | 17.00 | 11.00 | 7.00 | 2.25 | 1.35 | 1.00 |

Perf. 10

| 543 | 1¢ green . . . . . . | 1.35 | .75 | .50 | .75 | .40 | .20 |

SCOTT NO.	DESCRIPTION	UNUSED O.G. VF	F	AVG	USED VF	F	AVG

Perf. 11

544	1¢ green (19 x 22-1/2mm)	. . . .	18000.00	14200.00	. . . .	3300.00	. . . .
545	1¢ green (19-1/2 x 22mm)	250.00	165.00	105.00	275.00	170.00	115.00
546	2¢ carmine rose (III)	145.00	95.00	60.00	300.00	185.00	125.00

1920 Flat Plate Printing Perf. 11

| 547 | $2 carmine & black | 435.00 | 310.00 | 205.00 | 79.00 | 50.00 | 38.00 |

SCOTT NO.	NH F	AVG	OG F	AVG	SCOTT NO.	NH F	AVG	OG F	AVG
UNUSED PLATE BLOCKS OF 6					**UNUSED PLATE BLOCKS OF (—)**				
525 (6)	29.00	22.50	20.00	14.00	535 (6)	105.00	85.00	85.00	65.00
526 (6)	290.00	225.00	200.00	150.00	536 (6)	215.00	155.00	155.00	115.00
527 (6)	225.00	150.00	140.00	100.00	537 (6)	250.00	175.00	165.00	125.00
528 (6)	125.00	85.00	80.00	50.00	538 (4)	110.00	80.00	75.00	50.00
528A (6)	500.00	325.00	350.00	225.00	540 (4)	130.00	80.00	80.00	50.00
528B (6)	250.00	165.00	170.00	120.00	541 (4)	465.00	325.00	310.00	210.00
529 (6)	75.00	50.00	50.00	35.00	542 (6)	195.00	135.00	135.00	90.00
530 (6)	30.00	20.00	20.00	13.00	543 (6)	23.00	16.00	15.00	10.00
531 (6)	135.00	100.00	105.00	75.00	543 (6)	45.00	32.00	30.00	20.00
532 (6)	500.00	395.00	375.00	290.00	545 (6)	1200.00	800.00	950.00	675.00
533 (6)	2100.00	1800.00	1575.00	1175.00	546 (4)	1000.00	700.00	700.00	475.00
534 (6)	135.00	100.00	215.00	75.00	547 (8)	5250.00	4000.00	3800.00	2750.00
534A (6)	425.00	295.00	280.00	220.00	548 (6)	75.00	55.00	55.00	40.00
					549 (6)	95.00	65.00	70.00	50.00
					550 (6)	725.00	525.00	475.00	330.00
CENTER LINE					**ARROW BLOCKS**				
531	80.00	50.00	55.00	35.00	531	60.00	45.00	50.00	40.00
532	325.00	200.00	225.00	145.00	532	275.00	170.00	195.00	120.00
533	2000.00	1250.00	1000.00	650.00	533	1000.00	700.00	700.00	500.00
534	95.00	55.00	70.00	50.00	534	90.00	55.00	60.00	45.00
534A	275.00	200.00	185.00	125.00	534A	220.00	160.00	160.00	120.00
535	90.00	65.00	55.00	40.00	535	85.00	60.00	52.50	37.50
547	1400.00	975.00	1175.00	835.00	547	1275.00	900.00	1100.00	825.00

548
The "Mayflower"

549
Landing of the Pilgrims

550
Signing of the Compact

SCOTT NO.	DESCRIPTION	UNUSED O.G. VF	F	AVG	USED VF	F	AVG

1920 PILGRIM TERCENTENARY ISSUE (NH + 50%)

548-50	1¢-5¢ (3 varieties, complete)	75.00	48.00	37.00	34.75	19.00	16.00
548	1¢ green	9.50	6.50	4.75	7.00	3.75	2.50
549	2¢ carmine rose	12.00	7.50	4.50	4.50	2.50	2.00
550	5¢ deep blue . .	65.00	40.00	32.00	37.00	20.00	18.00

FOR YOUR CONVENIENCE IN ORDERING, COMPLETE SETS ARE LISTED BEFORE SINGLE STAMP LISTINGS.

551, 653
Nathan Hale

552, 575, 578, 581,
594, 596, 597,
604, 632
Franklin

553, 576, 582, 598,
605, 631, 633
Harding

554, 577, 579, 583,
595, 599-99A, 606,
634-34A
Washington

555, 584, 600, 635
Lincoln

556, 585, 601, 636
Martha Washington

557, 586, 602, 637
Roosevelt

558, 587, 638, 723
Garfield

559, 588, 639
McKinley

560, 589, 640
Grant

561, 590, 641
Jefferson

562, 591, 603, 642
Monroe

563, 692
Hayes

564, 693
Cleveland

565, 695
American Indian

566, 696
Statue of Liberty

567, 698
Golden Gate

568, 699
Niagara Falls

569, 700
Bison

570, 701
Arlington Amphitheatre

571
Lincoln Memorial

572
U.S. Capitol

573
"America"

SCOTT NO.	DESCRIPTION	UNUSED O.G. VF	F	AVG	USED VF	F	AVG
	THE 1922-25 ISSUE Flat Plate Printings Perf. 11 (NH + 60%)						
551-73	1/2¢-$5 (23 varieties, complete)	1120.00	750.00	550.00	53.75	33.50	22.00
551	1/2¢ olive brown (1925) .60	.50	.25		.25	.20	.15
552	1¢ deep green (1923)	4.25	3.00	2.25	.25	.20	.15
552a	1¢ booklet pane of 6	17.50	12.75	8.75	....	....	....
553	1-1/2¢ yellow brown (1925).	5.25	3.25	2.50	2.00	1.35	.95
554	2¢ carmine (1923)	4.50	3.00	2.50	.25	.20	.15
554c	2¢ booklet pane of 6	12.00	8.75	5.50	....	....	....
555	3¢ violet (1923)	32.50	23.00	15.00	2.00	1.50	1.00
556	4¢ yellow brown (1923).	33.50	24.00	15.00	.75	.50	.35
557	5¢ dark blue . . .	33.50	24.00	15.00	.30	.20	.15
558	6¢ red orange. .	55.00	35.00	26.00	2.75	1.75	1.25
559	7¢ black (1923)	17.50	12.00	9.00	2.25	1.25	.90
560	8¢ olive green (1923)	62.00	42.00	30.00	2.00	1.25	.95
561	9¢ rose (1923) . .	26.50	16.00	10.50	4.00	2.25	1.50
562	10¢ orange (1923)	35.00	23.00	15.00	.30	.20	.15
563	11¢ light blue . .	4.25	3.00	2.00	.75	.50	.30
564	12¢ brown violet (1923).	15.00	8.00	5.00	.75	.50	.40
565	14¢ blue (1923)	9.00	5.00	3.00	2.50	2.00	1.25
566	15¢ gray	40.00	23.00	18.00	.25	.20	.15
567	20¢ carmine rose (1923).	40.00	25.00	20.00	.25	.20	.15
568	25¢ yellow green	33.50	21.00	15.00	2.25	1.50	1.25
569	30¢ olive brown (1923).	50.00	35.00	25.00	1.00	.60	.40
570	50¢ lilac	90.00	52.50	42.50	.50	.25	.20
571	$1 violet black (1923)	67.50	45.00	34.00	2.00	1.25	.75
572	$2 deep blue (1923)	165.00	105.00	88.00	18.00	11.00	6.50
573	$5 carmine & blue (1923).	350.00	255.00	185.00	29.00	17.50	12.00
	1923-25 Imperforate						
575	1¢ green	16.50	12.00	9.00	14.00	8.00	5.50
576	1-1/2¢ yellow brown (1925).	3.25	2.00	1.25	4.00	2.15	1.75
577	2¢ carmine	3.25	2.20	1.35	3.00	1.75	1.25
	Rotary Press Printings 1923 Perf. 11 x 10 (†) (NH + 60%)						
578	1¢ green	155.00	92.00	63.00	250.00	150.00	110.00
579	2¢ carmine . . .	155.00	90.00	65.00	225.00	135.00	92.50
	1923-26 Perf. 10 (†)						
581-91	1¢-10¢ (11 varieties, complete)	285.00	175.00	122.00	25.00	16.25	10.75
581	1¢ green	18.25	12.00	7.50	1.25	.85	.60
582	1-1/2¢ brown (1925)	6.00	4.00	3.00	1.25	.90	.65
583	2¢ carmine (1924)	4.00	2.00	1.25	.25	.20	.15
583a	2¢ booklet pane of 6 (1924).	110.00	70.00	50.00	....	....	....
584	3¢ violet (1925)	40.00	24.00	17.00	5.00	3.50	2.00
585	4¢ yellow brown (1925).	24.00	16.00	11.00	.80	.60	.40
586	5¢ blue (1925) .	24.00	16.00	11.00	.75	.50	.30
587	6¢ red orange (1925)	18.50	10.00	6.50	1.50	.90	.60
588	7¢ black (1926)	25.00	16.00	10.50	18.00	12.00	8.00
589	8¢ olive green (1926)	40.00	24.00	15.00	13.00	8.50	5.00
590	9¢ rose (1926)	8.00	4.00	3.00	5.00	2.50	1.65
591	10¢ orange (1925)	90.00	55.00	42.00	.55	.45	.35
	Perf. 11 (†)						
594	1¢ green	....	21500.00	15500.00	....	7500.00	6000.00
595	2¢ carmine	425.00	240.00	185.00	650.00	375.00	250.00
	Perf. 11						
596	1¢ green	....	....	....	....	90000.00	50000.00

PLATE BLOCKS (6)

SCOTT NO.		UNUSED NH VF	F	AVG.	UNUSED OG VF	F	AVG.
551	1/2¢ olive brown (1923)......	12.00	9.00	7.00	8.50	6.00	4.50
552	1¢ deep green (1923)..........	52.00	30.00	25.00	32.50	20.00	14.00
553	1-1/2¢ yellow brown (1923)	65.00	47.50	35.00	45.00	35.00	25.00
554	2¢ carmine (1923)	50.00	30.00	22.50	32.50	21.50	15.00
555	3¢ violet (1923)	350.00	225.00	180.00	195.00	150.00	110.00
556	4¢ yellow brown (1923)......	350.00	225.00	180.00	195.00	150.00	110.00
557	5¢ dark blue	375.00	240.00	200.00	210.00	160.00	125.00
558	6¢ red orange	750.00	450.00	400.00	500.00	350.00	250.00
559	7¢ black (1923)	150.00	100.00	70.00	100.00	65.00	45.00
560	8¢ olive green (1923)	1100.00	740.00	650.00	750.00	500.00	375.00
561	9¢ rose (1923)	340.00	225.00	160.00	195.00	160.00	130.00
562	10¢ orange (1923)..............	400.00	290.00	200.00	300.00	200.00	160.00
563	11¢ light blue	55.00	38.00	32.00	45.00	28.00	18.50
564	12¢ brown violet (1923)......	225.00	132.00	92.50	160.00	90.00	75.00
565	14¢ blue (1923)	120.00	80.00	57.50	85.00	52.50	42.50
566	15¢ grey	500.00	350.00	240.00	350.00	225.00	175.00
567	20¢ carmine rose (1923) ...	475.00	320.00	240.00	400.00	220.00	190.00
568	25¢ yellow green	420.00	260.00	200.00	325.00	190.00	125.00
569	30¢ olive brown (1923).......	550.00	375.00	295.00	325.00	225.00	160.00
570	50¢ lilac	1350.00	1000.00	750.00	850.00	600.00	450.00
571	$1 violet black (1923).........	800.00	520.00	400.00	550.00	400.00	300.00
572	$2 deep blue (1923)	1750.00	1300.00	1000.00	1100.00	850.00	650.00
573	$5 carmine + blue (1923) ...	5000.00	3750.00	2800.00	3500.00	2250.00	1750.00

SCOTT NO.		CENTER LINE BLOCKS F/NH	F/OG	AVG/OG	ARROW BLOCKS F/NH	F/OG	AVG/OG
571	$1 violet black	....	....	....	310.00	210.00	140.00
572	$2 deep blue	....	....	....	650.00	450.00	360.00
573	$5 carmine & blue	1050.00	900.00	750.00	1050.00	900.00	750.00
575	1¢ imperforate	58.00	50.00	40.00	55.00	47.50	38.00
576	1-1/2¢ imperforate.............	19.50	15.00	10.50	11.00	8.00	5.00
577	2¢ imperforate	22.50	17.50	12.00	12.00	9.00	7.00

PLATE BLOCKS

SCOTT NO.		UNUSED NH VF	F	AVG.	UNUSED OG VF	F	AVG.
575 (6)	1¢ green	160.00	110.00	75.00	110.00	70.00	50.00
576 (6)	1-1/2¢ yellow brown (1925)	50.00	33.00	25.00	35.00	22.00	16.00
577 (6)	2¢ carmine	50.00	34.00	25.00	42.00	25.00	18.00
578	1¢ green	1350.00	875.00	675.00	1000.00	625.00	495.00
579	2¢ carmine	1100.00	700.00	525.00	695.00	450.00	350.00
581	1¢ green	225.00	140.00	100.00	160.00	100.00	70.00
582	1-1/2¢ brown (1925)	85.00	55.00	35.00	60.00	38.00	25.00
583	2¢ carmine (1923)	75.00	45.00	28.50	55.00	33.00	20.00
584	3¢ violet (1925)	400.00	260.00	190.00	260.00	190.00	150.00
585	4¢ yellow green (1925).......	275.00	190.00	150.00	210.00	160.00	115.00
586	5¢ blue (1925)	375.00	240.00	170.00	275.00	170.00	120.00
587	6¢ red orange (1925)	225.00	145.00	95.00	150.00	95.00	65.00
588	7¢ black (1926)	250.00	155.00	100.00	175.00	110.00	70.00
589	8¢ olive green (1926)	400.00	260.00	190.00	275.00	190.00	125.00
590	9¢ rose (1926)...................	115.00	70.00	45.00	80.00	50.00	30.00
591	10¢ orange (1925)..............	1050.00	700.00	500.00	650.00	475.00	380.00

SCOTT NO.	DESCRIPTION	UNUSED VF	F	AVG	USED VF	F	AVG
		1923-29 Rotary Press Coil Stamps (NH + 50%)					
597/606	597-99, 600-06 (10 varieties)..	34.25	23.50	15.50	3.50	2.45	1.65
		Perf. 10 Vertically					
597	1¢ green......	.60	.25	.25	.25	.20	.15
598	1-1/2¢ deep brown (1925).......	1.35	1.00	.75	.30	.20	.15
599	2¢ carmine (I) (1923)	.60	.50	.25	.25	.20	.15
599A	2¢ carmine (II) (1929).......	200.00	110.00	70.00	22.00	13.50	8.50
600	3¢ violet (1924)	13.75	9.25	5.50	.35	.25	.15
601	4¢ yellow brown	8.25	5.75	4.25	1.50	.75	.45
602	5¢ dark blue (1924)	2.95	1.75	1.25	.50	.35	.20
603	10¢ orange (1924)	7.25	5.00	3.50	.50	.25	.20
		Perf. 10 Horizontally					
604	1¢ yellow green (1924)	.60	.50	.25	.25	.20	.15
605	1-1/2¢ yellow brown (1925).......	.75	.50	.25	.50	.35	.25
606	2¢ carmine	.65	.50	.25	.50	.40	.30

NOTE: For further details on the various types of similar appearing stamps please refer to our U.S. Stamp Identifier.

UNUSED OG (NH + 40%)

SCOTT NO.		COIL LINE PAIRS VF	F	AVG.	COIL PAIRS VF	F	AVG.
597	1¢ green	2.55	1.95	1.40	1.10	.65	.45
598	1-1/2¢ brown (1925)	6.75	5.25	4.00	2.10	1.45	1.10
599	2¢ carmine (I)	2.15	1.65	1.20	1.25	.85	.55
599A	2¢ carmine (II) (1929).........	850.00	575.00	385.00	425.00	225.00	150.00
600	3¢ deep violet (1924)	34.50	26.50	20.50	28.00	17.00	8.00
601	4¢ yellow brown	35.75	27.50	22.00	16.50	12.00	8.00
602	5¢ dark blue (1924)	11.75	9.00	6.00	6.25	4.25	2.75
603	10¢ orange (1924)..............	28.50	22.00	16.00	15.00	10.00	6.50
604	1¢ green (1924)..................	3.40	2.60	1.65	1.25	.75	.50
605	1-1/2¢ yellow brown (1925)	4.25	3.00	2.00	1.50	1.00	.75
606	2¢ carmine	2.75	2.00	1.35	1.25	.75	.50

610-613
Harding

SCOTT NO.	DESCRIPTION	UNUSED VF	F	AVG	USED VF	F	AVG
		1923 HARDING MEMORIAL ISSUE (NH + 50%)					
610	2¢ black, perf 11 flat	1.50	1.00	.75	.25	.20	.15
611	2¢ black, imperf	17.50	10.50	8.00	10.50	7.00	5.50
612	2¢ black, perf 10 rotary ..	27.00	14.00	12.00	6.00	3.50	2.50
613	2¢ black perf 11 rotary	......	......	......	......	27000.00	21500.00

614
Ship "New Netherlands"

615
Landing at Fort Orange

616
Monument at Mayport, Fla.

1924 HUGUENOT-WALLOON ISSUE (NH + 40%)

SCOTT NO.	DESCRIPTION	UNUSED VF	F	AVG	USED VF	F	AVG
614-16	1¢-5¢ (3 varieties, complete)	69.00	49.00	36.00	30.00	21.00	15.00
614	1¢ dark green..	6.50	4.75	3.50	5.50	3.25	2.50
615	2¢ carmine rose	10.00	6.00	4.00	5.50	3.75	2.75
616	5¢ dark blue...	60.00	47.00	36.50	37.00	28.50	20.00

617
Washington at Cambridge

618
Birth of Liberty

619
The Minute Man

1925 LEXINGTON-CONCORD SESQUICENTENNIAL (NH + 40%)

SCOTT NO.	DESCRIPTION	UNUSED VF	F	AVG	USED VF	F	AVG
617-19	1¢-5¢ (3 varieties, complete)	76.00	56.00	42.25	28.50	20.75	14.50
617	1¢ deep green .	8.75	5.50	4.75	4.00	2.50	1.75
618	2¢ carmine rose	13.50	9.00	6.00	10.50	8.00	6.00
619	5¢ dark blue...	60.00	45.00	34.50	29.00	21.50	14.00

SCOTT NO.	DESCRIPTION	UNUSED O.G. VF	F	AVG	USED VF	F	AVG

620
Sloop
"Restaurationen"

621
Viking Ship

1925 NORSE-AMERICAN ISSUE (NH + 40%)

SCOTT NO.	DESCRIPTION	VF	F	AVG	VF	F	AVG
620-21	2¢-5¢ (2 varieties, complete)	45.00	28.50	19.25	21.25	14.25	10.00
620	2¢ carmine & black	10.25	7.00	5.50	8.00	6.00	4.50
621	5¢ dark blue & black	39.50	24.25	15.75	36.00	23.50	17.00

622, 694
Harrison

623, 697
Wilson

616 1925-26 Flat Plate Printings, Perf. 11

622	13¢ green (1926)	25.00	15.75	11.50	1.25	.75	.60
623	17¢ black	31.50	19.25	14.50	.75	.50	.40

SCOTT NO.	PLATE BLOCKS	UNUSED NH VF	F	AVG	UNUSED OG VF	F	AVG.
610 (6)	2¢ black perf 11 flat	45.00	30.00	22.00	33.00	23.00	18.00
611 (6)	2¢ black imperf.	210.00	140.00	90.00	160.00	105.00	80.00
611 (4)	2¢ black center line block . . .	110.00	85.00	60.00	77.50	60.00	45.00
611 (4)	2¢ black arrow block	58.00	45.00	32.50	45.00	35.00	25.00
612 (4)	2¢ black perf 10 rotary	500.00	370.00	300.00	390.00	275.00	210.00
614 (6)	1¢ dark green	80.00	54.00	40.00	60.00	39.00	25.00
615 (6)	2¢ carmine rose	150.00	90.00	65.00	110.00	75.00	55.00
616 (6)	5¢ dark blue	620.00	450.00	350.00	510.00	325.00	250.00
617 (6)	1¢ deep green	90.00	50.00	40.00	65.00	40.00	30.00
618 (6)	2¢ carmine rose	160.00	95.00	75.00	115.00	72.00	55.00
619 (6)	5¢ dark blue	510.00	395.00	300.00	410.00	315.00	220.00
620 (8)	2¢ carmine black	325.00	250.00	175.00	235.00	180.00	125.00
621 (8)	5¢ dark blue+black	1050.00	800.00	550.00	815.00	625.00	435.00
622 (6)	13¢ green (1926)	280.00	215.00	150.00	190.00	145.00	105.00
623 (6)	17¢ black	325.00	250.00	175.00	255.00	195.00	136.50

627
Liberty Bell

628
John Ericsson Statue

629, 630
Hamilton's Battery

1926-27 COMMEMORATIVES (NH + 40%)

SCOTT NO.	DESCRIPTION	VF	F	AVG	VF	F	AVG
627/644	627-29, 643-44 (5 varieties, complete)	20.75	15.75	11.25	13.45	10.15	6.85

1926 COMMEMORATIVES

627	2¢ Sesquicentennial	5.75	4.25	3.25	1.00	.80	.55
628	5¢ Ericsson Memorial	16.25	12.50	9.00	7.00	5.00	3.50
629	2¢ White Plains	3.75	2.75	2.00	3.25	2.50	1.50
630	White Plains Sheet of 25	750.00	575.00	450.00	725.00	620.00	515.00
630V	2¢ Dot over "S" variety	650.00	500.00	400.00	600.00	525.00	450.00

Rotary Press Printings Designs of 1922-25 1926 Imperforate

631	1-1/2¢ yellow brown	4.95	3.75	2.75	4.50	3.25	2.25
631	1-1/2¢ center line block	26.00	20.00	13.50	. . . . . .	. . . . . .	. . . . . .
631	1-1/2¢ arrow block	12.25	9.50	6.50	. . . . . .	. . . . . .	. . . . . .

SCOTT NO.	DESCRIPTION	UNUSED O.G. VF	F	AVG	USED VF	F	AVG

1926-28 Perf. 11 x 10 1/2

632/42	1¢-10¢ (632-34, 635-42 11 varieties) . . .	40.25	30.75	23.25	2.60	2.10	1.55
632	1¢ green (1927)	.50	.25	.25	.25	.20	.15
632a	1¢ booklet pane of 6	7.00	5.00	3.50	. . . . . .	. . . . . .	. . . . . .
633	1-1/2¢ yellow brown (1927)	3.75	2.75	2.00	.25	.20	.15
634	2¢ carmine (I) . .	.40	.25	.25	.25	.20	.15
634	Electric Eye Plate	5.50	4.25	2.75	. . . . . .	. . . . . .	. . . . . .
634d	2¢ booklet pane of 6	2.15	1.75	1.25	. . . . . .	. . . . . .	. . . . . .
634A	2¢ carmine (II) (1928)	550.00	400.00	255.00	25.00	16.50	11.00
635	3¢ violet (1927)	1.00	.75	.50	.25	.20	.15
636	4¢ yellow brown (1927)	4.25	3.25	2.75	.50	.30	.25
637	5¢ dark blue (1927)	3.95	3.00	2.25	25	.20	.15
638	6¢ red orange (1927)	6.25	4.75	3.50	25	.20	.15
639	7¢ black (1927)	5.50	4.25	3.00	25	.20	.15
640	8¢ olive green (1927)	5.50	4.25	3.00	25	.20	.15
641	9¢ orange red (1931)	4.50	3.50	2.50	25	.20	.15
642	10¢ orange (1927)	6.75	5.50	4.00	.25	.20	.15

643

644

1927 COMMEMORATIVES

643	2¢ Vermont. . . .	3.25	2.50	1.75	2.75	2.15	1.50
644	2¢ Burgoyne. . .	6.95	5.50	3.75	5.00	3.95	2.50

645

646

647

648

649

650

1928 COMMEMORATIVES (NH + 40%)

645-50	6 varieties, complete	36.00	25.75	18.00	32.50	23.50	16.00
645	2¢ Valley Forge	2.50	2.00	1.50	1.50	1.10	.80
646	2¢ Molly Pitcher	2.35	2.00	1.50	2.35	1.90	1.25
647	2¢ Hawaii	7.75	5.00	3.25	7.50	6.00	3.50
648	5¢ Hawaii	37.00	26.50	19.00	33.00	25.00	17.00
649	2¢ Aeronautics .	4.00	2.50	2.00	4.00	2.25	1.50
650	5¢ Aeronautics .	13.50	9.25	7.00	9.00	5.00	3.75

651

654-656

657

1929 COMMEMORATIVES
(NH + 40%)

651/81	651, 654-55, 657, 680-81 (6 varieties) . . .	10.25	8.25	5.25	5.00	3.70	2.75
651	2¢ George R. Clark	2.25	1.25	1.25	1.75	1.10	.90
	Same, arrow block of 4	4.50	3.35	2.35	. . . . . .	. . . . . .	. . . . . .

1929 Design of 1922-25
Rotary Press Printing Perf. 11x10-1/2

653	1/2¢ olive brown	.60	.50	.50	.25	.20	.15

1929 COMMEMORATIVES

SCOTT NO.	DESCRIPTION	UNUSED O.G. VF	F	AVG	USED VF	F	AVG
654	2¢ Edison, Flat, Perf 11	2.15	1.75	1.25	1.75	1.40	1.00
655	2¢ Edison, Rotary, 11x10-1/2	1.50	1.25	1.00	.50	.45	.30
656	2¢ Edison, Rotary Press Coil, Perf. 10 Vertically	28.50	22.00	15.00	3.00	2.35	1.50
657	2¢ Sullivan Expedition	1.60	1.25	1.00	1.50	1.20	.95

1929. 632-42 Overprinted Kansas
(NH + 50%)

SCOTT NO.	DESCRIPTION	UNUSED O.G. VF	F	AVG	USED VF	F	AVG
658-68	1¢-10¢ (11 varieties, complete)	400.00	244.00	179.00	245.00	160.00	120.00
658	1¢ green	5.00	3.00	2.25	4.75	3.00	2.00
659	1-1/2¢ brown . .	6.50	4.50	2.75	6.00	3.65	3.50
660	2¢ carmine	6.50	4.25	2.75	2.00	1.25	.80
661	3¢ violet	35.00	23.75	16.25	30.00	19.00	14.75
662	4¢ yellow brown	48.50	31.00	23.00	42.00	27.50	16.00
663	5¢ deep blue . .	23.50	14.00	11.00	20.00	11.85	9.00
664	6¢ red orange. .	45.00	25.00	20.00	35.00	22.75	16.75
665	7¢ black	45.00	28.00	21.00	40.00	26.50	20.50
666	8¢ olive green . .	147.50	85.00	65.00	115.00	75.00	57.50
667	9¢ light rose . . .	21.00	15.00	10.00	17.50	11.50	8.00
668	10¢ orange yellow	38.50	26.50	20.00	25.00	17.50	13.00

1929. 632-42 Overprinted Nebraska
(NH + 50%)

SCOTT NO.	DESCRIPTION	UNUSED O.G. VF	F	AVG	USED VF	F	AVG
669-79	1¢-10¢, 11 varieties, complete	545.00	365.00	254.00	220.00	140.00	97.50
669	1¢ green.	6.00	4.00	2.50	5.00	3.00	2.25
670	1-1/2¢ brown . .	6.00	3.75	2.25	5.00	2.85	2.00
671	2¢ carmine	6.00	3.75	2.25	2.50	1.40	.90
672	3¢ violet	24.50	18.00	12.00	21.50	15.00	10.75
673	4¢ yellow brown	37.00	23.00	18.00	24.00	17.00	12.00
674	5¢ deep blue . .	33.50	23.00	16.00	30.00	18.75	12.75
675	6¢ red orange. .	83.50	58.00	43.00	49.00	30.00	21.00
676	7¢ black	50.00	32.50	23.00	49.00	30.00	22.00
677	8¢ olive green . .	67.00	42.00	26.00	60.00	37.50	26.00
678	9¢ light rose . . .	80.00	49.00	34.00	38.50	23.00	15.75
679	10¢ orange yellow	185.00	125.00	85.00	78.00	47.50	34.00

PLATE BLOCKS

SCOTT NO.	DESCRIPTION	UNUSED NH VF	F	AVG.	UNUSED OG VF	F	AVG.
627 (6)	Sesquicentennial.	65.00	50.00	35.00	49.50	38.00	26.00
628 (6)	5¢ Ericsson Memorial.	145.00	110.00	77.50	110.00	85.00	60.00
629 (6)	2¢ White Plains	67.50	52.00	35.00	52.00	40.00	30.00
631	1-1/2¢ yellow brown	93.00	71.50	50.00	70.00	55.00	40.00
632	1¢ green	3.25	2.50	1.75	2.60	2.00	1.40
633	1-1/2¢ yellow brown (1927)	120.00	92.50	65.00	90.00	70.00	48.00
634	2¢ carmine (1)	2.60	1.95	1.40	2.10	1.70	1.25
635	3¢ violet	15.00	12.50	9.00	10.50	7.50	4.50
636	4¢ yellow brown (1927)	130.00	95.00	70.00	105.00	80.00	55.00
637	5¢ dark blue (1927)	29.50	22.50	15.75	22.75	17.50	12.75
638	6¢ red orange (1927)	29.50	22.50	15.75	22.75	17.50	12.75
639	7¢ black (1927)	29.50	22.50	15.75	22.75	17.50	12.75
640	8¢ olive green (1927)	29.50	22.50	15.75	22.75	17.50	12.75
641	9¢ orange red (1931)	30.00	23.00	16.00	23.00	18.00	13.00
642	10¢ orange (1927)	43.50	33.50	23.00	34.00	26.00	18.25
643 (6)	2¢ Vermont	65.00	50.00	35.00	58.00	42.00	28.00
644 (6)	2¢ Burgoyne	80.00	57.00	42.00	60.00	45.00	30.00
645 (6)	2¢ Valley Forge	58.00	40.00	28.00	41.00	30.00	19.50
646	2¢ Molly Pitcher	60.00	42.50	32.00	42.00	33.00	25.00
647	2¢ Hawaii	205.00	140.00	110.00	145.00	110.00	77.00
648	5¢ Hawaii	425.00	315.00	225.00	335.00	260.00	185.00
649 (6)	2¢ Aeronautics	24.00	18.00	12.00	19.50	14.00	10.00
650 (6)	5¢ Aeronautics	115.00	90.00	65.00	85.00	65.00	47.50
651 (6)	2¢ George R. Clark	19.50	15.00	10.00	14.50	11.00	7.50
653	1/2¢ olive brown	2.75	2.00	1.25	1.95	1.50	.95
654 (6)	2¢ Edison	51.00	39.50	28.00	40.00	31.50	22.50
655	2¢ Edison	70.00	55.00	40.00	58.00	45.00	30.50
657 (6)	2¢ Sullivan Expedition.	45.00	35.00	26.50	39.50	30.00	22.50

LINE PAIR

SCOTT NO.	DESCRIPTION	VF	F	AVG.	VF	F	AVG.
656	2¢ Edison, coil.	125.00	95.00	65.00	80.00	62.50	45.00

PLATE BLOCKS

SCOTT NO.	DESCRIPTION	UNUSED NH VF	F	AVG.	UNUSED OG VF	F	AVG.
658	1¢ green.	65.00	40.00	30.00	45.00	30.00	20.00
659	1-1/2¢ brown	80.00	50.00	35.00	60.00	38.00	25.00
660	2¢ carmine	80.00	50.00	35.00	60.00	38.00	25.00
661	3¢ violet.	375.00	225.00	150.00	250.00	165.00	115.00
662	4¢ yellow brown	375.00	225.00	150.00	250.00	165.00	115.00
663	5¢ deep blue	275.00	165.00	125.00	185.00	120.00	90.00
664	6¢ red orange.	850.00	550.00	400.00	525.00	325.00	225.00
665	7¢ black.	850.00	550.00	400.00	525.00	325.00	225.00
666	8¢ olive green	1500.00	900.00	750.00	1000.00	625.00	475.00
667	9¢ light rose	450.00	300.00	200.00	295.00	200.00	125.00
668	10¢ orange yellow	650.00	425.00	295.00	425.00	285.00	195.00
669	1¢ green.	85.00	50.00	40.00	55.00	35.00	25.00
670	1-1/2¢ brown	100.00	50.00	40.00	60.00	35.00	25.00
671	2¢ carmine	80.00	50.00	35.00	55.00	35.00	25.00
672	3¢ violet.	350.00	200.00	140.00	225.00	135.00	95.00
673	4¢ yellow brown	475.00	300.00	200.00	325.00	200.00	140.00
674	5¢ deep blue	500.00	300.00	200.00	350.00	210.00	150.00
675	6¢ red orange.	1000.00	550.00	450.00	650.00	375.00	265.00
676	7¢ black.	550.00	325.00	225.00	335.00	215.00	155.00
677	8¢ olive green	750.00	450.00	315.00	475.00	350.00	250.00
678	9¢ light rose	1000.00	550.00	400.00	600.00	375.00	265.00
679	10¢ orange yellow	2000.00	1200.00	850.00	1200.00	750.00	550.00

	680	681

1929 COMMEMORATIVES
(NH + 30%)

SCOTT NO.	DESCRIPTION	UNUSED O.G. VF	F	AVG	USED VF	F	AVG
680	2¢ Fallen Timbers	2.50	2.00	1.25	2.00	1.50	1.00
681	2¢ Ohio River Canal	1.50	1.25	1.00	1.25	1.00	.75

682	683	684, 686	685, 687

1930-31 COMMEMORATIVES

SCOTT NO.	DESCRIPTION	VF	F	AVG	VF	F	AVG
682/703	(682-83, 688-90, 702-03) 7 varieties, complete	5.50	4.10	3.10	5.35	4.15	2.85

1930 COMMEMORATIVES

682	2¢ Massachusetts Bay	1.50	1.25	1.00	1.25	1.00	.65
683	2¢ Carolina-Charleston	2.50	2.00	1.50	2.50	2.00	1.35

1930 Rotary Press Printing Perf. 11 x 10-1/2
(NH + 30%)

684	1-1/2¢ Harding .	.75	.50	.50	.25	.20	.15
685	4¢ Taft	1.50	1.25	.75	.25	.20	.15

1930 Rotary Press Coil Stamps Perf. 10 Vertically

686	1-1/2¢ Harding .	2.95	2.25	1.50	.25	.20	.15
687	4¢ Taft	4.75	3.75	2.50	1.00	.75	.50

688	689	690

1930 COMMEMORATIVES

688	2¢ Braddock's Field	1.95	1.50	1.00	1.85	1.30	.95
689	2¢ Von Steuben	1.10	1.00	.75	1.10	.80	.60

1931 COMMEMORATIVES

690	2¢ Pulaski	.75	.50	.50	.50	.40	.30

SCOTT NO.	PLATE BLOCKS UNUSED NH			UNUSED OG		
	VF	F	AVG.	VF	F	AVG.
680 (6) 2¢ Fallen Timbers..............	48.00	35.00	22.50	36.00	27.50	21.00
681 (6) 2¢ Ohio River Canal..........	33.75	25.00	15.75	26.00	20.00	12.00
682 (6) 2¢ Massachusetts Bay.......	58.50	40.00	27.00	39.00	30.00	18.00
683 (6) 2¢ Carolina-Charleston......	85.00	60.00	40.00	64.50	49.50	36.00
684 1-1/2¢ Harding	3.65	2.50	1.70	2.90	2.25	1.65
685 4¢ Taft..............................	17.00	12.00	9.00	13.00	10.00	6.00
688 (6) 3¢ Braddock's Field..........	71.50	47.50	33.00	52.00	40.00	24.00
689 (6) 2¢ Von Steuben..............	40.00	31.50	18.00	32.50	25.00	15.00
690 (6) 2¢ Pulaski......................	23.50	17.00	10.75	18.25	14.00	8.50
LINE PAIR						
686 1-1/2¢ Harding	15.00	10.75	7.50	10.00	8.00	6.00
687 4¢ Taft..............................	30.00	22.50	15.00	20.00	15.00	10.00

SCOTT NO.	DESCRIPTION	UNUSED			USED		
		VF	F	AVG	VF	F	AVG

1931 Designs of 1922-26. Rotary Press Printing.
(NH + 35%)

692-701	11¢ to 50¢ (10 varieties, complete)	184.00	140.00	105.00	3.25	2.50	1.80

Perf. 11 x 10-1/2

692	11¢ light blue . .	5.50	4.25	3.50	.25	.20	.15
693	12¢ brown violet	10.50	8.00	5.50	.25	.25	.20
694	13¢ yellow green	4.00	3.00	2.25	.50	.40	.25
695	14¢ dark blue . .	10.50	8.00	5.50	2.00	1.65	1.25
696	15¢ gray.	16.00	12.00	9.00	.25	.20	.15

Perf. 10-1/2 x 11

697	17¢ black	12.50	9.50	6.50	.50	.40	.30
698	20¢ carmine rose	16.50	13.00	9.00	.25	.20	.15
699	25¢ blue green . .	16.00	12.50	8.75	.25	.20	.15
700	30¢ brown	36.50	28.00	21.00	.25	.20	.15
701	50¢ lilac	65.00	50.00	41.00	.25	.20	.15

702   703

1931 COMMEMORATIVES
(NH + 30%)

702	2¢ Red Cross. .	.50	.25	.25	.25	.25	.20
702	2¢ arrow block .	1.50	1.00	.65			
703	2¢ Yorktown . . .	.60	.50	.50	.50	.35	.25
703	2¢ center line block	3.00	2.15	1.75	....	....	....
703	2¢ arrow block .	2.75	1.95	1.45	....	....	....

1932 WASHINGTON BICENTENNIAL ISSUE

Planning for this set, which celebrated the 200th anniversary of the birth of George Washington, began more than eight years before its release. Despite many suggestions that a pictorial series be created, the final set depicted 12 portraits of Washington at various stages of his life. For reasons of economy, the stamps were produced in single colors and in the same size as regular issues. Nevertheless, the set was an instant success and it was reported that more than a million covers were mailed from Washington, D.C. on January 1, 1932, the first day of issue.

704   705   706   707

708   709   710   711

712   713   714   715

SCOTT NO.	DESCRIPTION	UNUSED			USED		
		VF	F	AVG	VF	F	AVG

(NH + 40%)

704-15	1/2¢ to 10¢ (12 varieties, complete)	55.75	41.00	30.00	4.00	3.05	2.40
704	1/2¢ olive brown	.35	.25	.25	.25	.20	.15
705	1¢ green.	.40	.25	.25	.25	.20	.15
706	1-1/2¢ brown . .	.75	.50	.25	.25	.25	.20
707	2¢ carmine rose		.40	.25	.25	.20	.15
708	3¢ deep violet. .	1.15	1.00	.50	.25	.20	.15
709	4¢ light brown. .	.75	.50	.50	.25	.25	.20
710	5¢ blue.	4.50	3.50	2.50	.30	.20	.15
711	6¢ red orange. .	8.50	6.50	5.00	.25	.20	.15
712	7¢ black.	.95	.75	.50	.75	.60	.50
713	8¢ olive bistre. .	10.00	6.25	5.00	2.75	2.00	1.75
714	9¢ pale red	7.15	5.00	3.50	.50	.40	.35
715	10¢ orange yellow	25.00	19.00	13.00	.25	.20	.15

716   717   718   719

1932 COMMEMORATIVES
(NH + 30%)

716/25	(716-19, 724-25) 6 varieties	12.75	9.50	7.50	2.10	1.55	1.25
716	2¢ Winter Olympics	.95	.75	.50	.50	.40	.35
717	2¢ Arbor Day . .	.40	.25	.25	.25	.20	.15
718	3¢ Summer Olympics	4.00	3.00	2.50	.25	.20	.15
719	5¢ Summer Olympics	6.00	4.50	3.50	.75	.50	.40

720-722   723

724   725   726

1932 Rotary Press

720	3¢ deep violet. .	.50	.25	.25	.25	.20	.15
720b	3¢ booklet pane of 6	60.00	40.00	28.00	....	....	....
721	3¢ deep violet coil perf 10 vertically	3.95	3.00	2.00	.25	.20	.15
722	3¢ deep violet coil perf 10 horizontally	2.95	2.25	1.50	1.00	.80	.65
723	6¢ Garfield, coil perf 10 vertically	17.50	13.00	9.00	.30	.30	.25

1932 COMMEMORATIVES

| 724 | 3¢ Penn . . . . . . | 1.10 | .75 | .50 | .50 | .30 | .25 |
| 725 | 3¢ Webster. . . . | 1.30 | .75 | .50 | .55 | .40 | .30 |

SCOTT NO.		UNUSED OG (NH + 30%)					
		COIL LINE PAIRS			COIL PAIRS		
		VF	F	AVG.	VF	F	AVG.
686	1-1/2¢ Harding	10.00	8.00	5.50	4.50	3.50	2.25
687	4¢ Taft...............................	20.00	15.00	10.00	9.00	7.00	4.75
721	3¢ deep violet perf 10 vertically	10.75	8.25	5.50	7.50	6.00	4.00
722	3¢ deep violet perf 10 horizontally	7.75	6.00	4.15	4.00	3.00	2.00
723	6¢ Garfield perf 10 vertically	71.50	55.00	33.00	27.50	21.00	14.00

727, 752   728, 730, 766   729, 731, 767

1933 COMMEMORATIVES (NH + 30%)

SCOTT NO.	DESCRIPTION	UNUSED VF	F	AVG	USED VF	F	AVG
726/34	(726-29, 732-34) 7 varieties	3.40	2.65	2.00	2.40	1.90	1.40
726	3¢ Oglethorpe .	1.30	.75	.75	.30	.30	.20
727	3¢ Washington's Headquarters . .	.50	.50	.25	.25	.20	.15
728	1¢ Fort Dearborn .	.60	.50	.25	.25	.20	.15
729	3¢ Federal Building	.80	.75	.50	.25	.20	.15

Special Printing for A.P.S. Convention
Imperforate: Without Gum

730	1¢ yellow green, sheet of 25	....	42.50	....	....	45.00	....
730a	1¢ yellow green single	1.25	1.10	.65	.75	.60	.40
731	3¢ violet, sheet of 25	....	33.50	....	....	38.50	....
731a	3¢ violet, single	1.25	1.15	.85	.60	.50	.35

732   733, 735, 753, 768   734   736

732	3¢ N.R.A.	.40	.25	.25	.25	.20	.15
733	3¢ Byrd.	1.50	1.25	1.00	1.50	1.00	.80
734	5¢ Kosciuszko .	1.50	1.25	1.00	1.50	1.25	.90

1934 NATIONAL PHILATELIC EXHIBITION
Imperforate Without Gum

735	3¢ dark blue, sheet of 6	....	18.50	....	....	26.50	....
735a	3¢ dark blue, single	4.50	4.25	....	2.75	2.10	....

737, 738, 754   739, 755

1934 COMMEMORATIVES (NH + 30%)

736-39	4 varieties	1.95	1.45	.85	1.15	.90	.75
736	3¢ Maryland . . .	.55	.50	.25	.30	.30	.25
737	3¢ Mother's Day, rotary, perf 11 x 10-1/2	.50	.25	.25	.30	.25	.20
738	3¢ Mother's Day, flat, perf 11	.60	.50	.25	.50	.35	.30
739	3¢ Wisconsin . .	.60	.50	.25	.30	.25	.20

FOR YOUR CONVENIENCE IN ORDERING, COMPLETE SETS ARE LISTED BEFORE SINGLE STAMP LISTINGS.

741, 757

743, 759

740, 751, 756, 769

742, 750, 758, 770

745, 761

744, 760

747, 763

746, 762

748, 764   749, 765

1934 NATIONAL PARKS ISSUE (NH + 30%)

SCOTT NO.	DESCRIPTION	UNUSED VF	F	AVG	USED VF	F	AVG
740-49	1¢-10¢ (10 varieties, complete)	22.25	16.00	12.75	9.25	7.10	4.80
740	1¢ Yosemite . . .	.30	.25	.25	.25	.20	.15
741	2¢ Grand Canyon	.30	.25	.25	.25	.20	.15
742	3¢ Mt. Rainier. .	.50	.25	.25	.25	.20	.15
743	4¢ Mesa Verde.	1.60	1.25	1.00	.75	.65	.45
744	5¢ Yellowstone .	2.00	1.45	1.15	1.75	1.35	.95
745	6¢ Crater Lake .	3.35	2.25	1.75	2.50	1.95	1.25
746	7¢ Acadia	1.75	1.25	1.00	2.00	1.65	1.10
747	8¢ Zion.	4.50	3.50	2.50	4.35	3.35	2.30
748	9¢ Glacier.	4.25	3.00	2.50	1.75	1.35	.90
749	10¢ Great Smoky Mountains	6.50	4.75	4.00	2.50	2.00	1.25

Special Printing for the A.P.S. Convention & Exhibition of Atlantic City
Imperforate Souvenir Sheet
(NH + 30%)

750	3¢ deep violet, sheet of 6	....	45.00	....	....	65.00	....
750a	3¢ deep violet, single	7.25	6.00	....	6.00	5.00	....

Special Printing for Trans-Mississippi Philatelic Exposition and Convention at Omaha
Imperforate Souvenir Sheet
(NH + 30%)

751	1¢ green, sheet of 6	....	16.50	....	....	20.00	....
751a	1¢ green, single	3.25	2.65	....	2.75	2.25	

SCOTT NO.		PLATE BLOCKS UNUSED NH			UNUSED OG		
		VF	F	AVG.	VF	F	AVG.
692	11¢ light blue	22.50	16.50	10.00	16.50	12.75	9.50
693	12¢ brown violet	47.50	32.50	20.00	33.00	25.00	19.75
694	13¢ yellow green	21.50	16.50	10.00	16.50	12.75	9.50
695	14¢ dark blue	42.00	28.00	18.00	30.00	20.00	12.50
696	15¢ grey	65.00	50.00	35.00	49.75	36.00	27.00
697	17¢ black	65.00	47.50	30.00	40.00	30.00	20.00
698	20¢ carmine rose	75.00	55.00	40.00	55.00	43.00	30.00
699	25¢ blue green	75.00	60.00	40.00	55.00	45.00	30.00
700	30¢ brown	145.00	100.00	75.00	105.00	75.00	55.00
701	50¢ lilac	350.00	275.00	155.00	250.00	195.00	115.00
702	2¢ Red Cross	4.00	3.00	2.00	3.00	2.50	1.75
703	2¢ Yorktown (4)	5.75	4.00	2.70	4.25	3.35	2.65
704-15	Washington Bicentennial	590.00	435.00	290.00	445.00	335.00	248.50
704	1/2¢ olive brown	7.50	5.00	3.50	5.50	4.00	3.00
705	1¢ green	7.50	5.00	3.50	5.75	4.50	3.25
706	1-1/2¢ brown	34.50	23.50	17.00	25.00	18.00	13.25
707	2¢ carmine rose	3.00	2.00	1.25	2.25	1.60	1.10
708	3¢ deep violet	25.00	18.50	12.50	21.00	15.00	10.50
709	4¢ light brown	11.50	8.00	6.00	8.50	6.00	4.50
710	5¢ blue	30.00	22.00	16.00	23.50	18.00	14.00
711	6¢ red orange	105.00	80.00	49.50	78.00	60.00	46.50
712	7¢ black	12.00	8.50	6.00	9.00	7.00	5.50
713	8¢ olive bistre	105.00	80.00	49.50	78.00	60.00	40.00
714	9¢ pale red	80.00	55.00	40.00	57.50	42.50	30.00
715	10¢ orange yellow	200.00	150.00	100.00	155.00	115.00	90.00
716 (6)	2¢ Winter Olympics	22.00	16.00	11.00	16.95	13.00	9.50
717	2¢ Arbor Day	14.00	10.50	6.50	10.75	8.25	6.00
718	3¢ Summer Olympics	30.00	22.50	15.00	21.00	15.00	11.00
719	5¢ Summer Olympics	45.00	35.00	25.00	35.00	28.00	20.00
720	3¢ deep violet	2.95	2.00	1.40	2.15	1.65	1.10
724 (6)	3¢ Penn	20.00	14.00	9.50	14.00	11.00	9.00
725 (6)	3¢ Daniel Webster	35.75	26.00	14.00	28.00	22.00	16.00
726 (6)	3¢ Oglethorpe	23.50	16.50	11.00	18.00	14.00	10.00
727	3¢ Washington Hdqrs	10.00	7.00	4.50	7.95	6.00	4.50
728	1¢ Fort Dearborn	3.55	2.75	1.65	2.95	2.25	1.65
729	3¢ Federal Building	6.00	4.00	2.75	4.25	3.35	2.25
732	3¢ N.R.A.	2.95	2.00	1.40	2.55	1.95	1.40
733 (6)	3¢ Byrd	27.50	20.00	13.00	21.00	16.00	13.00
734 (6)	5¢ Kosciuszko	60.00	45.00	28.00	42.95	33.00	25.00
736 (6)	3¢ Maryland	17.50	12.50	8.25	13.00	10.00	8.25
737	3¢ Mother's Day, rotary perf. 11 x 10-1/2	2.95	2.00	1.30	2.40	1.75	1.40
738 (6)	3¢ Mother's Day, flat, perf. 11	8.50	6.50	3.95	6.50	5.00	3.85
739 (6)	3¢ Wisconsin	9.50	7.50	5.00	7.00	5.50	4.00
740-49	10 varieties complete	210.00	160.00	96.50	160.00	125.00	94.00
740 (6)	1¢ Yosemite	2.55	1.80	1.15	2.00	1.55	1.10
741 (6)	2¢ Grand Canyon	2.65	1.95	1.25	2.15	1.65	1.20
742 (6)	3¢ Mt. Rainier	3.50	2.75	1.65	3.00	2.30	1.55
743 (6)	4¢ Mesa Verde	15.50	12.00	7.25	13.00	10.00	7.00
744 (6)	5¢ Yellowstone	19.50	15.00	9.00	14.00	11.00	8.25
745 (6)	6¢ Crater Lake	33.50	26.00	15.50	26.50	20.50	15.50
746 (6)	7¢ Acadia	21.50	16.50	10.00	17.25	13.25	10.00
747 (6)	8¢ Zion	33.50	26.00	15.50	26.50	20.50	15.50
748 (6)	9¢ Glacier	33.50	26.00	15.50	26.50	20.50	15.50
749 (6)	10¢ Great Smoky Mountains	53.50	41.25	24.75	39.00	30.00	23.50

SELECTED U.S. COMMEMORATIVE MINT SHEETS

SCOTT NO.	F/NH SHEET	SCOTT NO.	F/NH SHEET
610 (100)	145.00	709 (100)	40.00
614 (50)	300.00	710 (100)	235.00
615 (50)	500.00	711 (100)	490.00
617 (50)	375.00	712 (100)	40.00
618 (50)	575.00	713 (100)	500.00
620 (100)	900.00	714 (100)	400.00
627 (50)	275.00	715 (100)	1750.00
628 (50)	650.00	716 (100)	67.50
629 (100)	350.00	717 (100)	26.00
643 (100)	300.00	718 (100)	195.00
644 (50)	290.00	719 (100)	305.00
645 (100)	235.00	724 (100)	50.00
646 (100)	220.00	725 (100)	82.50
647 (100)	750.00	726 (100)	55.00
648 (100)	2925.00	727 (100)	22.00
649 (50)	130.00	728 (100)	15.00
650 (50)	500.00	729 (100)	22.00
651 (50)	80.00	732 (100)	14.00
654 (100)	175.00	733 (50)	50.00
655 (100)	145.00	734 (100)	110.00
657 (100)	140.00	736 (100)	33.00
680 (100)	200.00	737 (50)	9.00
681 (100)	125.00	738 (50)	15.00
682 (100)	135.00	739 (50)	15.00
683 (100)	220.00	740-49 set	665.00
688 (100)	175.00	740 (50)	6.50
689 (100)	100.00	741 (50)	9.00
690 (100)	65.00	742 (50)	13.00
702 (100)	37.50	743 (50)	33.50
703 (50)	28.00	744 (50)	55.00
704-15 set	4500.00	745 (50)	85.00
704 (100)	25.00	746 (50)	46.50
705 (100)	30.00	747 (50)	120.00
706 (100)	71.50	748 (50)	115.00
707 (100)	30.00	749 (50)	215.00
708 (100)	95.00		

THE FARLEY PERIOD

The 1933-35 period was one of great excitement for the hobby. With a stamp collector in the White House, in the person of President Franklin Delano Roosevelt, it was a period during which special Souvenir Sheets were issued for the A.P.S. Convention in 1933 (catalog #730) and the National Philatelic Exhibition in 1934 (#735). Collectors gloried in the limelight.

But there was a darker side, in the form of rare imperforate sheets that were being released to then Postmaster General James A. Farley, President Roosevelt himself, and a few other prominent personages. The protests against the practice grew to unmanageable proportions when word got around that one of the imperforate sheets of the 1934 Mother's Day issue had been offered to a stamp dealer for $20,000. Adding insult to injury, it was learned shortly thereafter that not only were there individual sheets floating around, but full, uncut sheets also had been presented as gifts to a fortunate few.

The outcry that followed could not be stifled. Congress had become involved in the affair and the demands were mounting that the gift sheets be recalled and destroyed. This being deemed impractical or undesirable, another solution was found—one that comes down to us today in the form of "The Farleys".

The solution was to let everyone "share the wealth", so to speak. Instead of recalling the few sheets in existence, additional quantities of the imperforates were issued in the same full sheet form as the gift sheets. Naturally, this step substantially reduced the value of the original, very limited edition, but it satisfied most collectors and left as its legacy "The Farley Issues".

The Farleys were issued March 15, 1935, and consisted of reprints of 20 issues. They remained on sale for three months, a relatively short time by most standards, but more than enough time for collectors who really cared. Although purists felt then—and some still do now—that President Roosevelt would have saved collectors a considerable sum by having the first few sheets destroyed, the issue has provided us with a wondrous selection of Gutters and Lines, arrow blocks, single sheets and full panes.

The collector on a limited budget can fill the spaces in an album with single imperforates. But the Farleys are such an interesting study that owning and displaying at least one of each variety of any one issue is a must. We illustrate here one of the full sheets of the 1 cent Century of Progress Farley Issue. The full sheets consisted of nine panes of 25 stamps each. The individual panes were separated by wide horizontal (**A**) or vertical (**B**) gutters and the gutters of four adjacent sheets formed a cross gutter (**C**).

NOTE: For #s 753-765 and 771, lines separated the individual panes. The lines ended in arrows at the top, bottom and side margins.

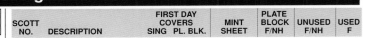

1935 "FARLEY SPECIAL PRINTINGS"
Designs of 1933-34 Imperforate (#752, 753 Perf.) Without Gum

SCOTT NO.		PLATE BLOCK	CENTER LINE BLOCK	ARROW BLOCK T OR B	L OR R	PAIR WITH V. LINE	H. LINE	FINE UNUSED	USED
752-71	20 varieties, complete ..	....	470.00	....	....	135.00	91.50	35.00	29.75
752	3¢ Newburgh	22.50	50.00	16.50	9.50	7.50	4.50	.45	.40
753	3¢ Byrd	(6)19.00	95.00	90.00	4.00	42.50	1.65	.75	.75
754	3¢ Mother's Day	(6)19.00	9.50	4.00	4.25	1.65	1.75	.75	.65
755	3¢ Wisconsin	(6)19.00	9.50	4.00	4.25	1.65	1.75	.75	.65
756-65	1¢-10¢ Parks (10 varieties, complete)..	295.00	150.00	140.00	140.00	42.25	43.50	19.50	17.00
756	1¢ Yosemite	(6) 5.00	4.00	1.40	1.10	.60	.50	.30	.25
757	2¢ Grand Canyon....	(6) 6.50	5.50	1.55	1.45	.65	.85	.40	.30
758	3¢ Mt. Rainier	(6)16.50	6.50	3.60	4.00	1.55	1.75	.75	.65
759	4¢ Mesa Verde	(6)22.00	11.00	6.00	7.00	2.50	3.10	1.50	1.35
760	5¢ Yellowstone	(6)27.50	16.50	12.00	10.50	5.25	4.75	2.50	2.00
761	6¢ Crater Lake	(6)45.00	22.00	15.00	16.50	6.50	7.50	3.00	2.75
762	7¢ Acadia	(6)36.00	18.00	10.50	12.25	4.50	5.50	2.25	2.00
763	8¢ Zion	(6)45.00	20.00	14.50	12.00	6.25	5.35	2.75	2.25
764	9¢ Glacier ..	(6)50.00	22.00	13.00	5.75	5.75	6.50	3.00	2.50
765	10¢ Great Smoky Mountains ..	(6)57.50	33.00	25.00	22.00	11.00	10.00	5.00	4.25
766a-70a	5 varieties, complete ..	....	95.00	....	....	40.00	35.50	9.45	7.75
766a	1¢ Fort Dearborn	20.00	....	....	....	9.00	6.50	.75	.45
767a	3¢ Federal Building....	....	21.50	....	....	9.00	6.50	.75	.45
768a	3¢ Byrd ..	....	19.00	....	....	7.75	6.50	3.00	2.75
769a	1¢ Yosemite	....	12.00	....	....	5.25	5.00	1.85	1.50
770a	3¢ Mt. Rainier	....	28.00	....	....	11.50	13.00	3.60	3.05
771	16¢ Air Post Special Delivery....	(6)80.00	82.50	15.00	16.50	6.75	7.50	3.50	3.20

U.S. FARLEY ISSUE COMPLETE MINT SHEETS

SCOTT NO.	F/NH SHEET	SCOTT NO.	F/NH SHEET
752-71 set	7500.00	761 (200)...................	650.00
752 (400).................	400.00	762 (200)...................	500.00
753 (200).................	635.00	763 (200)...................	550.00
754 (200).................	190.00	764 (200)...................	600.00
755 (200).................	190.00	765 (200)...................	1000.00
756-65 set	4100.00	766 (225)...................	400.00
756 (200).................	67.50	767 (225)...................	400.00
757 (200).................	75.00	768 (150)...................	550.00
758 (200).................	160.00	769 (120)...................	240.00
759 (200).................	280.00	770 (120)...................	600.00
760 (200).................	450.00	771 (200)...................	725.00

772, 778a

773, 778b

774

775, 778c

1935-36 COMMEMORATIVES

SCOTT NO.	DESCRIPTION	FIRST DAY COVERS SING	PL. BLK.	MINT SHEET	PLATE BLOCK F/NH	UNUSED F/NH	USED F
772/84	(772-77, 782-84) 9 varieties.......	....	....	....		3.60	1.70
772	3¢ Connecticut........	12.00	19.50	16.50 (50)	2.25	.40	.20
773	3¢ San Diego..........	12.00	19.50	16.50 (50)	1.85	.40	.20
774	3¢ Boulder Dam........	12.00	19.50	16.50 (50)	(6)2.75	.60	.20
775	3¢ Michigan...........	12.00	19.50	16.50 (50)	1.85	.60	.20

776, 778d

777

1936 COMMEMORATIVE

SCOTT NO.	DESCRIPTION	FIRST DAY COVERS SING	PL. BLK.	MINT SHEET	PLATE BLOCK F/NH	UNUSED F/NH	USED F
776	3¢ Texas	15.00	25.00	16.50 (50)	1.85	.60	.20
777	3¢ Rhode Island	12.00	19.50	25.00 (50)	3.00	.60	.20

778

782

783

784

1936 THIRD INTERNATIONAL PHILATELIC EXHIBITION
"TIPEX" Imperforate Souvenir Sheet
Designs of 772, 773, 775, 776

SCOTT NO.	DESCRIPTION	FIRST DAY COVERS SING	PL. BLK.	MINT SHEET	PLATE BLOCK F/NH	UNUSED F/NH	USED F
778	red violet, sheet of 4	16.50	....	....	....	4.00	4.00
778a	3¢ Connecticut.........	....	....	....	....	1.00	.95
778b	3¢ San Diego..........	....	....	....	....	1.00	.95
778c	3¢ Michigan...........	....	....	....	....	1.00	.95
778d	3¢ Texas	....	....	....	....	1.00	.95
782	3¢ Arkansas Statehood ..	12.00	19.50	20.00 (50)	1.95	.60	.20
783	3¢ Oregon Territory	12.00	19.50	14.50 (50)	1.75	.50	.20
784	3¢ Suffrage for Women ..	12.00	19.50	30.00 (100)	1.75	.40	.20

FIRST DAY COVERS:

First Day Covers are envelopes cancelled on the "First Day of Issue" of the stamp used on an envelope. Usually they also contain a picture (cachet) on the left side designed to go with the theme of the stamp. From 1935 to 1949, prices listed are for cacheted, addressed covers. From 1950 to date, prices are for cacheted, unaddressed covers.

SCOTT NO.	DESCRIPTION	FIRST DAY COVERS SING	FIRST DAY COVERS PL. BLK.	MINT SHEET	PLATE BLOCK F/NH	UNUSED F/NH	USED F

785

786

787

788

789

1936-37 ARMY AND NAVY ISSUE

| 785-94 | 10 varieties, complete | 57.50 | ...... | ...... | 59.00 | 5.50 | 2.30 |

ARMY COMMEMORATIVES

785	1¢ green	6.00	12.00	15.00 (50)	1.60	.40	.20
786	2¢ carmine	6.00	12.00	15.00 (50)	1.60	.40	.20
787	3¢ purple	6.00	12.00	25.00 (50)	2.75	.60	.20
788	4¢ gray	6.00	14.50	40.00 (50)	12.00	.60	.30
789	5¢ ultramarine	7.00	14.50	50.00 (50)	13.50	1.00	.30

790

791

792

793

794

NAVY COMMEMORATIVES

790	1¢ green	6.00	12.00	9.00 (50)	1.40	.25	.20
791	2¢ carmine	6.00	12.00	14.00 (50)	1.60	.35	.20
792	3¢ purple	6.00	12.00	18.50 (50)	2.50	.50	.20
793	4¢ gray	6.00	14.50	45.00 (50)	12.00	.75	.30
794	5¢ ultramarine	7.00	14.50	50.00 (50)	13.50	1.00	.35

SCOTT NO.	DESCRIPTION	FIRST DAY COVERS SING	FIRST DAY COVERS PL. BLK.	MINT SHEET	PLATE BLOCK F/NH	UNUSED F/NH	USED F

795

796

1937 COMMEMORATIVES

795/802	(795-96, 798-802) 7 varieties	......	......	......	......	3.00	1.40
795	3¢ Northwest Ordinance	8.50	16.00	16.50 (50)	1.80	.45	.20
796	5¢ Virginia Dare	8.50	16.00	25.00 (48)	10.00(6)	.45	.30

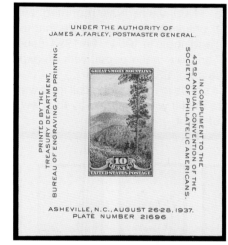
797

1937 S.P.A. CONVENTION ISSUE
Design of 749 Imperforate Souvenir Sheet

| 797 | 10¢ blue green | 8.50 | ...... | ...... | ...... | 1.10 | .80 |

798

799

800

801

802

798	3¢ Constitution	10.00	16.00	37.50 (50)	4.00	.95	.20
799	3¢ Hawaii	10.00	16.00	12.50 (50)	1.85	.50	.20
800	3¢ Alaska	10.00	16.00	12.50 (50)	1.85	.50	.20
801	3¢ Puerto Rico	10.00	16.00	12.50 (50)	1.85	.35	.20
802	3¢ Virgin Islands	10.00	16.00	12.50 (50)	1.85	.35	.20

1938 Presidential Series

In 1938 a new set of definitive stamps was issued honoring the first 29 presidents, Ben Franklin, Martha Washington, and the White House. These were regular issues that effectively replaced the previous definitive issues of the 1922-25 series.

The "Presidential Series" contained 32 denominations ranging from 1/2¢-$5.00. It is an interesting series because various printing methods were employed. The 1/2¢-50¢ values were printed in single colors on rotary presses using both normal and "electric eye" plates. The $1.00 to $5.00 values were printed in two colors on flat plate presses.

The $1.00 value was reprinted twice, once in 1951 on revenue paper watermarked "USIR" (#832b) and again in 1954. The 1954 issue was "dry printed" on thick white paper, with an experimental colorless gum (832c).

This series in regular and coil form was used for 16 years until it was replaced by the new definitive issues of 1954.

823	824	825	826
827	828	829	
830	831		
832	833	834	

803

804, 839, 848

805, 840, 849

806, 841, 850

807, 842, 851

808, 843

809, 844

810, 845

811, 846

812

813

814

815, 847

816

817

818

819

820

821

822

SCOTT NO.	DESCRIPTION	FIRST DAY COVERS SING	FIRST DAY COVERS PL. BLK.	MINT SHEET	PLATE BLOCK F/NH	UNUSED F/NH	USED F
		1938 PRESIDENTIAL SERIES					
803-34	1/2¢-$5, 32 varieties, complete.	520.00	. . . . . .	. . . . . .	900.00	200.00	17.50
803-31	1/2¢-50¢, 29 varieties	110.00	. . . . . .	. . . . . .	225.00	50.00	5.90
803	1/2¢ Franklin	2.50	5.50	15.00(100)	1.00	.20	.15
804	1¢ G. Washington . . .	2.50	5.50	20.00(100)	1.00	.25	.15
804b	1¢ booklet pane of 6 .	14.00	. . . . . .	. . . . . .	. . . . . .	2.25	. . . . . .
805	1-1/2¢ M. Washington	2.50	5.50	20.00(100)	1.00	.25	.15
806	2¢ J. Adams.	2.50	5.50	20.00(100)	1.00	.25	.15
806	E.E. Plate Block of 10	. . . . . .	. . . . . .	. . . . . .	7.00	. . . . . .	. . . . . .
806b	2¢ booklet pane of 6 .	14.00	. . . . . .	. . . . . .	. . . . . .	4.50	. . . . . .
807	3¢ Jefferson.	2.50	5.50	20.00(100)	1.00	.25	.15
807	E.E. Plate Block of 10	. . . . . .	. . . . . .	. . . . . .	50.00	. . . . . .	. . . . . .
807a	3¢ booklet pane of 6 .	14.00	. . . . . .	. . . . . .	. . . . . .	8.25	. . . . . .
808	4¢ Madison	2.50	5.50	110.00(100)	5.25	1.10	.15
809	4-1/2¢ White House. .	2.50	5.50	25.00(100)	1.60	.30	.20
810	5¢ J. Monroe	2.50	5.50	30.00(100)	1.75	.35	.15
811	6¢ J.Q. Adams.	2.50	5.50	47.50(100)	2.25	.55	.15
812	7¢ A. Jackson	2.50	5.50	47.50(100)	3.00	.55	.15
813	8¢ Van Buren.	2.50	5.50	47.50(100)	2.35	.55	.15
814	9¢ Harrison	2.50	5.50	50.00(100)	2.50	.55	.15
815	10¢ Tyler	2.50	5.50	50.00(100)	2.00	.45	.15
816	11¢ Polk.	3.75	6.75	55.00(100)	3.00	1.00	.15
817	12¢ Taylor	3.75	6.75	130.00(100)	7.00	2.00	.15
818	13¢ Fillmore.	3.75	6.75	185.00(100)	8.50	2.00	.15
819	14¢ Pierce	3.75	6.75	130.00(100)	7.00	2.00	.15
820	15¢ Buchanan.	3.75	6.75	65.00(100)	3.50	.75	.15
821	16¢ Lincoln	4.50	8.25	140.00(100)	8.25	2.00	.55
822	17¢ Johnson	4.50	8.25	140.00(100)	7.00	2.00	.20
823	18¢ Grant.	4.50	8.25	350.00(100)	17.00	4.00	.20
824	19¢ Hayes	4.50	8.25	210.00(100)	9.00	2.50	.75
825	20¢ Garfield.	4.75	11.25	110.00(100)	5.50	1.25	.15
826	21¢ Arthur	5.25	11.25	250.00(100)	12.00	2.75	.25
827	22¢ Cleveland	5.25	11.25	165.00(100)	13.50	2.00	.75
828	24¢ B. Harrison	6.25	11.25	550.00(100)	22.00	6.00	.25
829	25¢ McKinley	6.25	13.75	130.00(100)	5.50	1.20	.20
830	30¢ T. Roosevelt	8.50	13.75	650.00(100)	32.50	7.50	.20
831	50¢ Taft	15.00	30.00	950.00(100)	45.00	10.00	.20
		Flat Plate Printing Perf. 11					
832	$1 Wilson.	70.00	150.00	1150.00(100)	55.00	12.00	.20
832	$1 center line block . .	. . . . . .	. . . . . .	. . . . . .	55.00	. . . . . .	. . . . . .
832	$1 arrow block.	. . . . . .	. . . . . .	. . . . . .	50.00	. . . . . .	. . . . . .
832b	$1 Watermarked "USIR"	. . . . . .	. . . . . .	. . . . . .	. . . . . .	325.00	70.00
832c	$1 dry print thick paper (1954)	35.00	75.00	725.00(100)	32.50	8.00	.20
833	$2 Harding	135.00	275.00	. . . . . .	140.00	26.00	6.50
833	$2 center line block . .	. . . . . .	. . . . . .	. . . . . .	115.00	. . . . . .	. . . . . .
833	$2 arrow block.	. . . . . .	. . . . . .	. . . . . .	110.00	. . . . . .	. . . . . .
834	$5 Coolidge	225.00	400.00	. . . . . .	525.00	120.00	6.00
834	$5 center line block . .	. . . . . .	. . . . . .	. . . . . .	525.00	. . . . . .	. . . . . .
834	$5 arrow block.	. . . . . .	. . . . . .	. . . . . .	500.00	. . . . . .	. . . . . .

835   836

837   838

857   858

1939 COMMEMORATIVES

SCOTT NO.	DESCRIPTION	FIRST DAY COVERS SING	FIRST DAY COVERS PL. BLK.	MINT SHEET	PLATE BLOCK F/NH	UNUSED F/NH	USED F
857	3¢ Printing	12.00	19.50	30.00(50)	2.50	.40	.20
858	3¢ Four States	10.00	14.50	40.00(50)	4.50	.90	.20

859   860   861

1938-39 COMMEMORATIVES

SCOTT NO.	DESCRIPTION	FIRST DAY COVERS SING	FIRST DAY COVERS PL. BLK.	MINT SHEET	PLATE BLOCK F/NH	UNUSED F/NH	USED F
835-58	(835-38, 852-58) 11 varieties, complete	. . . . . .	. . . . . .	. . . . . .	. . . . . .	7.00	2.15
835	3¢ Ratification	10.00	14.00	35.00(50)	6.00	.80	.20
836	3¢ Swedes-Finns. . . .	10.00	14.00	14.00(48)	(6)4.00	.35	.20
837	3¢ Northwest Territory	10.00	14.00	35.00(100)	11.50	.35	.20
838	3¢ Iowa Territory	10.00	14.00	24.00(50)	8.00	.80	.20

1939 PRESIDENTIALS ROTARY PRESS COIL

SCOTT NO.	DESCRIPTION	FIRST DAY COVERS SING	FIRST DAY COVERS LINE PAIR	MINT SHEET	PLATE BLOCK LINE PAIR	UNUSED F/NH	USED F
839-51	13 varieties, complete	67.50	120.00	. . . . . .	148.50	36.75	5.30

Perforated 10 Vertically

839	1¢ G. Washington . . .	5.00	8.50	. . . . . .	1.75	.40	.15
840	1-1/2¢ M. Washington	5.00	8.50	. . . . . .	1.65	.40	.15
841	2¢ J. Adams.	5.00	8.50	. . . . . .	1.75	.40	.15
842	3¢ T. Jefferson	5.00	8.50	. . . . . .	2.00	.70	.15
843	4¢ J. Madison	5.75	10.50	. . . . . .	32.50	8.00	.75
844	4-1/2¢ White House. .	5.75	10.50	. . . . . .	6.25	.70	.50
845	5¢ J. Monroe	5.75	11.00	. . . . . .	30.00	5.50	.50
846	6¢ J.Q. Adams.	5.75	11.00	. . . . . .	8.00	1.75	.40
847	10¢ J. Tyler	8.50	16.00	. . . . . .	50.00	12.00	.90

Perforated 10 Horizontally

848	1¢ G. Washington . . .	5.00	8.50	. . . . . .	3.75	1.10	.25
849	1-1/2¢ M. Washington	5.00	8.50	. . . . . .	5.00	1.50	.65
850	2¢ J. Adams.	5.00	8.50	. . . . . .	9.00	3.00	.90
851	3¢ T. Jefferson	5.00	8.50	. . . . . .	7.00	2.75	.75

862   863

1940 FAMOUS AMERICANS ISSUES

SCOTT NO.	DESCRIPTION	FIRST DAY COVERS SING	FIRST DAY COVERS PL. BLK.	MINT SHEET	PLATE BLOCK F/NH	UNUSED F/NH	USED F
859-93	35 varieties, complete	130.00	. . . . . .	. . . . . .	500.00	50.00	23.50

American Authors

859	1¢ Washington Irving .	3.00	4.00	20.00(70)	1.75	.35	.20
860	2¢ James F. Cooper .	3.00	4.00	20.00(70)	1.75	.35	.20
861	3¢ Ralph W. Emerson	3.00	4.00	22.50(70)	1.85	.35	.20
862	5¢ Louisa May Alcott .	4.00	6.00	40.00(70)	13.00	.50	.35
863	10¢ Samuel L. Clemens	7.50	13.50	180.00(70)	52.50	2.50	2.00

852   853   854

855   856

864   865   866

867   868

1939 COMMEMORATIVES

852	3¢ Golden Gate	12.00	19.50	25.00(50)	3.00	.60	.20
853	3¢ World's Fair.	12.00	19.50	20.00(50)	2.75	.40	.20
854	3¢ Inauguration	12.00	19.50	55.00(50)	(6)8.00	.90	.20
855	3¢ Baseball	37.50	60.00	150.00(50)	14.00	3.00	.30
856	3¢ Panama Canal . . .	17.50	25.00	25.00(50)	(6)5.00	.60	.20

American Poets

864	1¢ Henry W. Longfellow	3.00	4.00	30.00(70)	4.00	.35	.20
865	2¢ John Whittier.	3.00	4.00	20.00(70)	4.00	.35	.20
866	3¢ James Lowell	3.00	4.00	22.50(70)	4.00	.35	.20
867	5¢ Walt Whitman	4.00	6.00	60.00(70)	18.00	.80	.35
868	10¢ James Riley	7.50	11.50	225.00(70)	35.00	3.50	2.50

SCOTT NO.	DESCRIPTION	FIRST DAY COVERS SING	FIRST DAY COVERS PL. BLK.	MINT SHEET	PLATE BLOCK F/NH	UNUSED F/NH	USED F

869   870   871

872   873

American Educators

SCOTT NO.	DESCRIPTION	SING	PL. BLK.	MINT SHEET	PLATE BLOCK F/NH	UNUSED F/NH	USED F
869	1¢ Horace Mann	3.00	4.00	20.00(70)	3.50	.35	.20
870	2¢ Mark Hopkins	3.00	4.00	20.00(70)	1.75	.35	.20
871	3¢ Charles W. Eliot . .	3.00	4.00	22.50(70)	4.00	.40	.20
872	5¢ Frances Willard. . .	4.00	6.00	70.00(70)	17.50	.75	.35
873	10¢ Booker T. Washington	9.50	13.50	300.00(70)	42.50	3.50	2.00

874   875   876

877   878

American Scientists

SCOTT NO.	DESCRIPTION	SING	PL. BLK.	MINT SHEET	PLATE BLOCK F/NH	UNUSED F/NH	USED F
874	1¢ John J. Audubon. .	3.00	4.00	20.00(70)	1.75	.35	.20
875	2¢ Dr. Crawford Long	3.00	4.00	20.00(70)	1.75	.35	.20
876	3¢ Luther Burbank. . .	3.00	4.00	22.50(70)	1.85	.40	.20
877	5¢ Dr. Walter Reed . .	4.00	6.00	35.00(70)	9.00	.45	.35
878	10¢ Jane Addams . . .	6.00	11.50	145.00(70)	30.00	2.25	1.60

879   880   881

882   883

American Composers

SCOTT NO.	DESCRIPTION	SING	PL. BLK.	MINT SHEET	PLATE BLOCK F/NH	UNUSED F/NH	USED F
879	1¢ Stephen Foster. . .	3.00	4.00	20.00(70)	1.75	.35	.20
880	2¢ John Philip Sousa. .	3.00	4.00	20.00(70)	1.75	.35	.20
881	3¢ Victor Herbert	3.00	4.00	20.00(70)	1.75	.35	.20
882	5¢ Edward A. MacDowell	4.00	6.00	60.00(70)	14.00	.75	.35
883	10¢ Ethelbert Nevin. .	6.00	11.50	370.00(70)	50.00	6.00	2.10

884   885   886

887   888

American Artists

SCOTT NO.	DESCRIPTION	SING	PL. BLK.	MINT SHEET	PLATE BLOCK F/NH	UNUSED F/NH	USED F
884	1¢ Gilbert Stuart	3.00	4.00	20.00(70)	1.75	.40	.20
885	2¢ James Whistler. . .	3.00	4.00	20.00(70)	1.75	.35	.20
886	3¢ A. Saint-Gaudens .	3.00	4.00	22.50(70)	1.75	.40	.20
887	5¢ Daniel C. French. .	4.00	6.00	55.00(70)	12.50	1.00	.35
888	10¢ Frederic Remington	6.00	11.50	195.00(70)	40.00	3.00	2.00

889   890   891

892   893

American Inventors

SCOTT NO.	DESCRIPTION	SING	PL. BLK.	MINT SHEET	PLATE BLOCK F/NH	UNUSED F/NH	USED F
889	1¢ Eli Whitney	3.00	4.00	35.00(70)	3.00	.40	.20
890	2¢ Samuel Morse . . .	3.00	4.00	50.00(70)	3.00	.70	.20
891	3¢ Cyrus McCormick .	3.00	4.00	32.50(70)	2.50	.55	.20
892	5¢ Elias Howe	4.00	6.00	120.00(70)	20.00	1.75	.45
893	10¢ Alexander G. Bell	8.00	20.00	1150.00(70)	105.00	18.00	3.50

894   895

1940 COMMEMORATIVES

SCOTT NO.	DESCRIPTION	SING	PL. BLK.	MINT SHEET	PLATE BLOCK F/NH	UNUSED F/NH	USED F
894-902	9 varieties, complete	. . . .	. . . .			3.80	1.80
894	3¢ Pony Express	7.00	11.00	24.00(50)	4.50	.60	.25
895	3¢ Pan Am Union. . . .	5.00	11.00	24.00(50)	4.50	.45	.20

MINT SHEETS: From 1935 to date, we list prices for standard size Mint Sheets in Fine, Never Hinged condition. The number of stamps in each sheet is noted in ( ).

FAMOUS AMERICANS: Later additions to the Famous American series include #945 Edison, #953 Carver, #960 White, #965 Stone, #975 Rogers, #980 Harris, #986 Poe, and #988 Gompers.

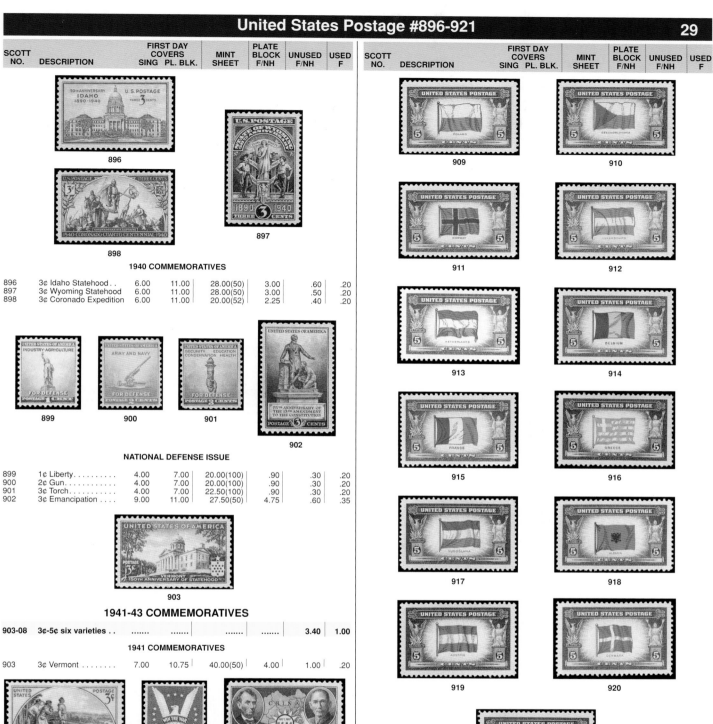

SCOTT NO.	DESCRIPTION	FIRST DAY COVERS SING	PL. BLK.	MINT SHEET	PLATE BLOCK F/NH	UNUSED F/NH	USED F

896, 897, 898

1940 COMMEMORATIVES

SCOTT NO.	DESCRIPTION	FIRST DAY COVERS SING	PL. BLK.	MINT SHEET	PLATE BLOCK F/NH	UNUSED F/NH	USED F
896	3¢ Idaho Statehood ..	6.00	11.00	28.00(50)	3.00	.60	.20
897	3¢ Wyoming Statehood	6.00	11.00	28.00(50)	3.00	.50	.20
898	3¢ Coronado Expedition	6.00	11.00	20.00(52)	2.25	.40	.20

899, 900, 901, 902

NATIONAL DEFENSE ISSUE

899	1¢ Liberty..........	4.00	7.00	20.00(100)	.90	.30	.20
900	2¢ Gun............	4.00	7.00	20.00(100)	.90	.30	.20
901	3¢ Torch...........	4.00	7.00	22.50(100)	.90	.30	.20
902	3¢ Emancipation	9.00	11.00	27.50(50)	4.75	.60	.35

903

1941-43 COMMEMORATIVES

903-08	3¢-5¢ six varieties ..	....	......	......	......	3.40	1.00

1941 COMMEMORATIVES

903	3¢ Vermont	7.00	10.75	40.00(50)	4.00	1.00	.20

904, 905, 906

1942 COMMEMORATIVES

904	3¢ Kentucky........	5.00	10.75	18.00(50)	1.85	.35	.20
905	3¢ Win The War.....	4.50	7.50	24.00(100)	1.20	.30	.20
906	5¢ China Resistance .	12.00	20.00	80.00(50)	20.00	1.75	.35

907, 908

1943 COMMEMORATIVES

907	2¢ Allied Nations	6.00	7.50	15.00(100)	1.00	.30	.20
908	1¢ Four Freedoms ...	6.00	10.50	15.00(100)	1.00	.30	.20

909, 910, 911, 912, 913, 914, 915, 916, 917, 918, 919, 920

921

1943-44 OVERRUN COUNTRIES SERIES

SCOTT NO.	DESCRIPTION	FIRST DAY COVERS SING	PL. BLK.	MINT SHEET	PLATE BLOCK F/NH	UNUSED F/NH	USED F
909-21	13 varieties, complete	50.00	......	......	72.50	6.50	3.25
909	5¢ Poland	5.00	10.00	21.50(50)	9.00	.40	.25
910	5¢ Czechoslovakia ..	5.00	10.00	17.50(50)	4.00	.40	.25
911	5¢ Norway	5.00	10.00	15.00(50)	2.75	.40	.25
912	5¢ Luxembourg	5.00	10.00	15.00(50)	1.85	.40	.25
913	5¢ Netherlands	5.00	10.00	15.00(50)	1.85	.40	.25
914	5¢ Belgium.........	5.00	10.00	15.00(50)	1.85	.40	.25
915	5¢ France	5.00	10.00	15.00(50)	1.85	.40	.25
916	5¢ Greece	5.00	10.00	45.00(50)	17.50	1.10	.40
917	5¢ Yugoslavia	5.00	10.00	27.50(50)	8.00	.60	.30
918	5¢ Albania	5.00	10.00	25.00(50)	8.00	.60	.30
919	5¢ Austria.	5.00	10.00	20.00(50)	6.00	.60	.30
920	5¢ Denmark........	5.00	10.00	27.50(50)	8.00	.60	.30
921	5¢ Korea (1944).....	5.00	10.00	30.00(50)	7.00	.60	.30

SCOTT NO.	DESCRIPTION	FIRST DAY COVERS SING	FIRST DAY COVERS PL. BLK.	MINT SHEET	PLATE BLOCK F/NH	UNUSED F/NH	USED F

922

923

924

925

926

927

1944 COMMEMORATIVES

SCOTT NO.	DESCRIPTION	SING	PL. BLK.	MINT SHEET	PLATE BLOCK F/NH	UNUSED F/NH	USED F
922-26	5 varieties........	....	....	....	....	1.90	1.00
922	3¢ Railroad	9.00	12.00	20.00(50)	2.25	.40	.25
923	3¢ Steamship......	9.00	12.00	20.00(50)	2.25	.40	.25
924	3¢ Telegraph	9.00	12.00	15.00(50)	1.75	.40	.20
925	3¢ Corregidor......	9.00	12.00	17.50(50)	1.75	.40	.25
926	3¢ Motion Picture....	9.00	12.00	20.00(50)	1.75	.40	.20

928

929

1945-46 COMMEMORATIVES

SCOTT NO.	DESCRIPTION	SING	PL. BLK.	MINT SHEET	PLATE BLOCK F/NH	UNUSED F/NH	USED F
927-38	1¢-5¢ (12 varieties, complete)	....	....	....	....	4.00	2.25
927	3¢ Florida.........	10.00	15.00	32.00(50)	3.00	.75	.20
928	5¢ Peace Conference	10.00	15.00	15.00(50)	1.00	.30	.20
929	3¢ Iwo Jima	17.00	20.00	20.00(50)	3.50	.50	.20

930

931

932

933

930	1¢ FDR & Hyde Park	4.00	6.00	6.00(50)	1.00	.30	.20
931	2¢ FDR & "Little White House"..	4.00	6.00	8.50(50)	1.00	.30	.20
932	3¢ FDR & White House	4.00	6.00	10.00(50)	1.25	.30	.20
933	5¢ FDR & Globe (1946)	4.00	6.00	15.00(50)	1.25	.35	.20

934

935

936

937

938

934	3¢ Army	10.00	14.00	12.50(50)	1.25	.30	.20
935	3¢ Navy	10.00	14.00	15.00(50)	1.25	.30	.20
936	3¢ Coast Guard....	10.00	14.00	12.00(50)	1.25	.30	.20
937	3¢ Al Smith	10.00	14.00	22.00(100)	1.25	.30	.20
938	3¢ Texas Statehood..	10.00	14.00	18.00(50)	1.75	.50	.20

939

940

941

942

943

944

1946-47 COMMEMORATIVES

SCOTT NO.	DESCRIPTION	SING	PL. BLK.	MINT SHEET	PLATE BLOCK F/NH	UNUSED F/NH	USED F
939/52	(939-47, 949-52) 13 varieties........	....	....	....	....	4.50	2.50
939	3¢ Merchant Marine..	10.00	12.00	10.00(50)	1.30	.30	.20
940	3¢ Honorable Discharge	10.00	12.00	22.00(100)	1.30	.30	.20
941	3¢ Tennessee Statehood	3.00	5.00	15.00(50)	1.30	.30	.20
942	3¢ Iowa Statehood...	3.00	5.00	12.50(50)	1.50	.40	.20
943	3¢ Smithsonian Institute	3.00	5.00	12.50(50)	1.50	.40	.20
944	3¢ Kearny Expedition	3.00	5.00	12.00(50)	1.50	.40	.20

945

946

947

1947 COMMEMORATIVES

945	3¢ Thomas A. Edison	3.00	5.00	17.50(70)	1.25	.30	.20
946	3¢ Joseph Pulitzer...	3.00	5.00	12.50(50)	1.25	.30	.20
947	3¢ Stamp Centenary .	3.00	5.00	10.00(50)	1.25	.30	.20

SCOTT NO.	DESCRIPTION	FIRST DAY COVERS SING	FIRST DAY COVERS PL. BLK.	MINT SHEET	PLATE BLOCK F/NH	UNUSED F/NH	USED F

"CIPEX" SOUVENIR SHEET

948	5¢ & 10¢ Sheet of 2..	4.00	....	....	....	1.50	1.00
948a	5¢ blue, single stamp.	....	....	....	....	.65	.50
948b	10¢ brown orange, single stamp	....	....	....	....	.65	.50

949

950

951

952

953

949	3¢ Doctors.........	8.00	12.00	12.00(50)	1.20	.30	.20
950	3¢ Utah Centennial ..	3.00	5.00	20.00(50)	1.80	.50	.20
951	3¢ "Constitution"	8.00	12.00	12.00(50)	1.20	.30	.20
952	3¢ Everglades National Park.......	4.00	6.00	18.00(50)	2.00	.45	.20

954

955

956

957

1948 COMMEMORATIVES

953-80	3¢-5¢ (28 varieties, complete)	....	....	....	....	9.25	5.25
953	3¢ George Washington Carver	6.00	10.00	19.00(70)	1.60	.35	.20
954	3¢ Gold Rush.......	2.40	5.00	18.00(50)	1.60	.35	.20
955	3¢ Mississippi Territory	2.40	5.00	18.00(50)	1.60	.35	.20
956	3¢ Chaplains	3.00	5.00	18.00(50)	1.60	.35	.20
957	3¢ Wisconsin Statehood	2.40	5.00	20.00(50)	2.00	.45	.20

958

959

960

961

962

963

958	5¢ Swedish Pioneer..	2.40	5.00	12.50(50)	1.25	.35	.20
959	3¢ Women's Progress	2.40	5.00	18.00(50)	1.75	.40	.20
960	3¢ William White	2.40	5.00	18.00(70)	1.25	.35	.20
961	3¢ U.S.-Canada Friendship	2.40	5.00	12.50(50)	1.25	.35	.20
962	3¢ Francis S. Key ...	2.40	5.00	12.50(50)	1.25	.35	.20
963	3¢ Salute to Youth ...	2.40	5.00	12.50(50)	1.25	.35	.20

964

965

966

967

968

969

970

964	3¢ Oregon Territory ..	2.40	5.00	20.00(50)	2.00	.50	.20
965	3¢ Harlan Stone.....	2.40	5.00	12.50(70)	1.25	.35	.20
966	3¢ Mt. Palomar	3.00	5.00	20.00(70)	1.80	.35	.20
967	3¢ Clara Barton.....	3.00	5.00	12.50(50)	1.25	.35	.20
968	3¢ Poultry	2.40	5.00	12.50(50)	1.25	.35	.20
969	3¢ Gold Star Mothers	2.40	5.00	12.50(50)	1.25	.35	.20
970	3¢ Fort Kearny......	2.40	5.00	12.50(50)	1.60	.35	.20

PLATE BLOCKS: are portions of a sheet of stamps adjacent to the number(s) indicating the printing plate number used to produce that sheet. Flat plate issues are usually collected in plate blocks of six (number opposite middle stamp) while rotary issues are normally corner blocks of four.

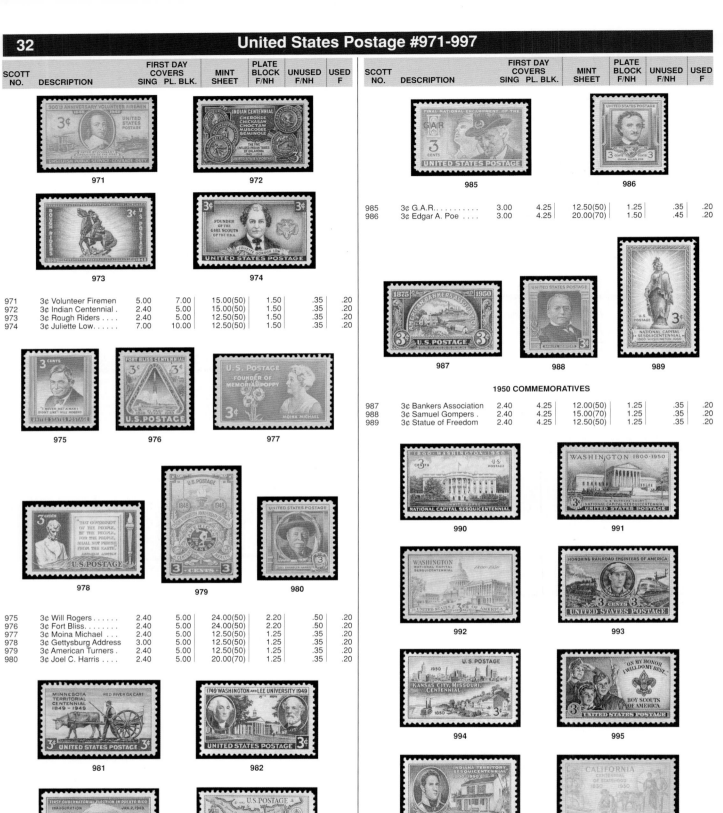

SCOTT NO.	DESCRIPTION	FIRST DAY COVERS SING	FIRST DAY COVERS PL. BLK.	MINT SHEET	PLATE BLOCK F/NH	UNUSED F/NH	USED F
971	3¢ Volunteer Firemen	5.00	7.00	15.00(50)	1.50	.35	.20
972	3¢ Indian Centennial .	2.40	5.00	15.00(50)	1.50	.35	.20
973	3¢ Rough Riders	2.40	5.00	12.50(50)	1.50	.35	.20
974	3¢ Juliette Low.	7.00	10.00	12.50(50)	1.50	.35	.20
975	3¢ Will Rogers	2.40	5.00	24.00(50)	2.20	.50	.20
976	3¢ Fort Bliss.	2.40	5.00	24.00(50)	2.20	.50	.20
977	3¢ Moina Michael . . .	2.40	5.00	12.50(50)	1.25	.35	.20
978	3¢ Gettysburg Address	3.00	5.00	12.50(50)	1.25	.35	.20
979	3¢ American Turners .	2.40	5.00	12.50(50)	1.25	.35	.20
980	3¢ Joel C. Harris	2.40	5.00	20.00(70)	1.25	.35	.20

1949-50 COMMEMORATIVES

981-97	17 varieties, complete	....	....	....	....	5.70	3.20
981	3¢ Minnesota Territory	2.40	4.25	20.00(50)	2.00	.50	.20
982	3¢ Washington & Lee University.	2.40	4.25	12.50(50)	1.25	.35	.20
983	3¢ Puerto Rico.	3.00	4.25	12.50(50)	1.25	.35	.20
984	3¢ Annapolis	3.00	4.25	12.50(50)	1.25	.35	.20

SCOTT NO.	DESCRIPTION	FIRST DAY COVERS SING	FIRST DAY COVERS PL. BLK.	MINT SHEET	PLATE BLOCK F/NH	UNUSED F/NH	USED F
985	3¢ G.A.R.	3.00	4.25	12.50(50)	1.25	.35	.20
986	3¢ Edgar A. Poe	3.00	4.25	20.00(70)	1.50	.45	.20

1950 COMMEMORATIVES

987	3¢ Bankers Association	2.40	4.25	12.00(50)	1.25	.35	.20
988	3¢ Samuel Gompers .	2.40	4.25	15.00(70)	1.25	.35	.20
989	3¢ Statue of Freedom	2.40	4.25	12.50(50)	1.25	.35	.20
990	3¢ Executive Mansion	2.40	4.25	12.50(50)	1.25	.35	.20
991	3¢ Supreme Court . . .	2.40	4.25	12.50(50)	1.25	.35	.20
992	3¢ United States Capitol	2.40	4.25	12.50(50)	1.25	.35	.20
993	3¢ Railroad	4.00	5.25	12.50(50)	1.25	.35	.20
994	3¢ Kansas City	2.40	4.25	15.00(50)	1.60	.35	.20
995	3¢ Boy Scouts	7.00	10.00	12.50(50)	1.25	.35	.20
996	3¢ Indiana Territory . .	2.40	4.25	15.00(50)	1.50	.50	.20
997	3¢ California Statehood	2.40	4.25	25.00(50)	3.00	.70	.20

Buy Complete Sets and Save

SCOTT NO.	DESCRIPTION	FIRST DAY COVERS SING	PL. BLK.	MINT SHEET	PLATE BLOCK F/NH	UNUSED F/NH	USED F

998   999

1000   1001

1002   1003

1951-52 COMMEMORATIVES

998-1016 19 varieties, complete		......	......	......	......	6.40	3.50
998	3¢ Confederate Veterans	3.00	4.25	17.50(50)	1.75	.40	.20
999	3¢ Nevada Settlement	2.00	4.25	19.00(50)	1.75	.35	.20
1000	3¢ Landing of Cadillac	2.00	4.25	17.00(50)	1.50	.35	.20
1001	3¢ Colorado Statehood	2.00	4.25	17.00(50)	1.50	.35	.20
1002	3¢ Chemical Society	2.00	4.25	12.50(50)	1.25	.35	.20
1003	3¢ Battle of Brooklyn	2.00	4.25	12.50(50)	1.25	.35	.20

1004   1005

1006   1007   1008

1009   1010

1952 COMMEMORATIVES

1004	3¢ Betsy Ross	2.50	5.50	12.00(50)	1.20	.40	.20
1005	3¢ 4-H Club	6.00	10.00	17.50(50)	1.75	.50	.20
1006	3¢ B. & O. Railroad	4.00	6.50	17.50(50)	2.50	.40	.20
1007	3¢ AAA	2.00	4.25	14.00(50)	1.60	.40	.20
1008	3¢ NATO	2.00	4.25	22.00(100)	1.25	.35	.20
1009	3¢ Grand Coulee Dam	2.00	4.25	20.00(50)	1.75	.35	.20
1010	3¢ Lafayette	2.00	4.25	17.50(50)	1.50	.40	.20

SCOTT NO.	DESCRIPTION	FIRST DAY COVERS SING	PL. BLK.	MINT SHEET	PLATE BLOCK F/NH	UNUSED F/NH	USED F

1011   1012

1013   1014

1015   1016

1011	3¢ Mt. Rushmore	2.00	4.25	25.00(50)	2.50	.60	.20
1012	3¢ Civil Engineers	2.00	4.25	12.50(50)	1.25	.35	.20
1013	3¢ Service Women	2.25	4.25	12.50(50)	1.25	.35	.20
1014	3¢ Gutenburg Press	2.00	4.25	12.50(50)	1.25	.35	.20
1015	3¢ Newspaper Boys	2.00	4.25	12.50(50)	1.25	.35	.20
1016	3¢ Red Cross	3.00	6.25	12.50(50)	1.25	.35	.20

1017   1018

1019   1020

1021   1022

1953-54 COMMEMORATIVES

1017/63	(1017-29, 1060-63) 17 varieties, complete	......	......	......	......	5.55	3.20
1017	3¢ National Guard	2.00	4.25	12.50(50)	1.25	.35	.20
1018	3¢ Ohio Statehood	2.00	4.25	17.50(70)	1.25	.35	.20
1019	3¢ Washington Territory	2.00	4.25	18.00(50)	2.00	.50	.20
1020	3¢ Louisiana Purchase	4.00	6.00	12.50(50)	1.25	.35	.20
1021	5¢ Opening of Japan	3.00	4.25	14.00(50)	1.50	.40	.20
1022	3¢ American Bar Association	5.00	6.25	17.50(50)	1.50	.40	.20

SCOTT NO.	DESCRIPTION	FIRST DAY COVERS SING	PL. BLK.	MINT SHEET	PLATE BLOCK F/NH	UNUSED F/NH	USED F
1023	3¢ Sagamore Hill....	2.00	4.25	12.50(50)	1.25	.35	.20
1024	3¢ Future Farmers...	2.00	4.25	12.50(50)	1.25	.35	.20
1025	3¢ Trucking Industry .	2.50	4.50	12.50(50)	1.25	.35	.20
1026	3¢ Gen. George S. Patton	3.00	4.75	12.50(50)	1.25	.35	.20
1027	3¢ New York City....	2.00	4.25	12.50(50)	1.25	.35	.20
1028	3¢ Gadsden Purchase	2.00	4.25	17.00(50)	1.60	.35	.20

1029

1954 COMMEMORATIVE

1029	3¢ Columbia University	2.00	4.25	12.50(50)	1.25	.35	.20

1030   **1031, 1054**   **1031A, 1054A**   **1032**

1033, 1055   **1034, 1056**   **1035, 1057, 1075a**   **1036, 1058**

1037, 1059   **1038**   **1039**   **1040**

1041, 1075b   **1042**   **1042A**   **1043**

1044   **1044A**   **1045**   **1046**

1047   **1048, 1059A**   **1049**   **1050**

1051   **1052**   **1053**

1954-68 LIBERTY SERIES

SCOTT NO.	DESCRIPTION	FIRST DAY COVERS SING	PL. BLK.	MINT SHEET	PLATE BLOCK F/NH	UNUSED F/NH	USED F
1030-53	1/2¢-$5, 27 varieties, complete.........	110.00	235.00	....	525.00	120.00	14.50
1030-51	1/2¢-50¢, 25 varieties	55.00	115.00	....	70.00	17.25	3.50
1030	1/2¢ Benjamin Franklin (1955)	2.00	4.25	9.25(100)	.80	.25	.25
1031	1¢ George Washington	2.00	4.25	8.00(100)	.80	.25	.25
1031A	1-1/4¢ Palace of Governors (1960) ...	2.00	4.25	8.00(100)	.80	.25	.25
1032	1-1/2¢ Mount Vernon.	2.00	4.25	22.00(100)	2.50	.25	.25
1033	2¢ Thomas Jefferson.	2.00	4.25	14.00(100)	.80	.25	.25
1034	2-1/2¢ Bunker Hill (1959)	2.00	4.25	22.00(100)	1.00	.25	.25
1035	3¢ Statue of Liberty ..	2.00	4.25	13.50(100)	.80	.25	.25
1035a	3¢ booklet pane of 6 .	3.50	....	....	....	5.00	....
1036	4¢ Abraham Lincoln..	2.00	4.25	27.00(100)	.80	.25	.25
1036a	4¢ booklet pane of 6 .	3.00	....	....	....	3.50	....
1037	4-1/2¢ Hermitage (1959)	2.00	4.25	27.00(100)	1.35	.30	.25
1038	5¢ James Monroe ...	2.00	4.25	27.00(100)	1.35	.30	.25
1039	6¢ T. Roosevelt (1955)	2.00	4.25	40.00(100)	2.10	.60	.25
1040	7¢ Woodrow Wilson (1956)	2.00	4.25	30.00(100)	1.60	.40	.25
1041	8¢ Statue of Liberty (flat plate).	2.00	4.25	35.00(100)	2.50	.40	.25
1041B	8¢ Statue of Liberty ..	2.00	4.25	50.00(100)	4.00	.60	.25
1042	8¢ Liberty re-engraved (1958)	2.00	4.25	35.00(100)	1.60	.40	.25
1042A	8¢ John J. Pershing (1961)	2.25	5.00	35.00(100)	1.60	.40	.25
1043	9¢ Alamo (1956)	2.25	5.00	55.00(100)	2.25	.50	.25
1044	10¢ Independence Hall (1956)	2.25	5.00	45.00(100)	2.25	.50	.25
1044A	11¢ Statue of Liberty (1961)	2.25	5.00	45.00(100)	2.25	.50	.25
1045	12¢ Benjamin Harrison (1959)	2.25	5.00	60.00(100)	2.25	.60	.25
1046	15¢ John Jay (1958) .	2.50	5.25	120.00(100)	4.95	1.10	.25
1047	20¢ Monticello (1956)	2.50	5.25	90.00(100)	4.00	.95	.25
1048	25¢ Paul Revere (1958)	2.50	5.25	175.00(100)	9.00	2.10	.25
1049	30¢ Robert E. Lee (1955)	3.75	6.00	175.00(100)	79.00	2.00	.25
1050	40¢ John Marshall (1955)	3.75	7.00	295.00(100)	12.50	3.00	.25
1051	50¢ Susan B. Anthony (1955)	5.50	8.50	225.00(100)	10.50	3.00	.25
1052	$1 Patrick Henry (1955)	9.25	17.50	....	32.50	7.50	.25
1053	$5 Alexander Hamilton (1956)	50.00	110.00	....	500.00	105.00	12.50

1954-65 COIL STAMPS
Perf. 10 Vertically or Horizontally

SCOTT NO.	DESCRIPTION	FIRST DAY COVERS SING	LINE PAIR PL. BLK.	MINT SHEET	LINE PAIR PLATE BLOCK F/NH	UNUSED F/NH	USED F
1054-59A	1¢-25¢ (8 varieties, complete).........	16.00	29.75	....	29.75	4.65	2.40
1054	1¢ George Washington	2.00	3.75	....	1.25	.30	.20
1054A	1-1/4¢ Palace of Governors(1960)....	2.00	3.75	....	3.00	.30	.20
1055	2¢ Thomas Jefferson(1957)	2.00	3.75	....	.75	.30	.20
1056	2-1/2¢ Bunker Hill Mon. (1959)	2.00	3.75	....	5.50	.45	.30
1057	3¢ Statue of Liberty(1956)	2.00	3.75	....	.85	.25	.20
1058	4¢ Abraham Lincoln (1958)	2.00	3.75	....	.85	.25	.20
1059	4-1/2¢ Hermitage (1959)	2.00	3.75	....	18.00	3.00	2.00
1059A	25¢ Paul Revere (1965)	2.50	5.00	....	3.00	.95	.20

NOTE: Pairs of the above can be priced at two times the single price.

SCOTT NO.	DESCRIPTION	FIRST DAY COVERS SING	FIRST DAY COVERS PL. BLK.	MINT SHEET	PLATE BLOCK F/NH	UNUSED F/NH	USED F

1060   1061

1062   1063

1954 COMMEMORATIVES

1060	3¢ Nebraska Territory	2.00	4.25	16.00(50)	1.50	.35	.20
1061	3¢ Kansas Territory . .	2.00	4.25	20.00(50)	2.00	.50	.20
1062	3¢ George Eastman .	2.00	4.25	15.00(70)	1.50	.35	.20
1063	3¢ Lewis & Clark	4.00	6.00	25.00(50)	2.50	.60	.20

1064   1065

1066

1067

1069   1068

1955 COMMEMORATIVES

1064-72	3¢-8¢ (9 varieties, complete)	....	....	....	....	2.95	1.50
1064	3¢ Pennsylvania Academy	2.00	4.25	15.00(50)	1.75	.40	.20
1065	3¢ Land Grant Colleges	2.50	4.50	22.00(50)	2.00	.50	.20
1066	8¢ Rotary International	5.00	7.00	27.00(50)	2.75	.70	.20
1067	3¢ Armed Forces Reserve	2.00	4.25	12.50(50)	1.25	.35	.20
1068	3¢ Great Stone Face .	2.00	4.25	15.00(50)	1.75	.40	.20
1069	3¢ Soo Locks.	2.00	4.25	18.00(50)	1.50	.50	.20

1070   1071   1072

1070	3¢ Atoms for Peace . .	2.00	4.25	12.50(50)	1.25	.35	.20
1071	3¢ Fort Ticonderoga .	2.00	4.25	12.50(50)	1.25	.35	.20
1072	3¢ Andrew Mellon . . .	2.00	4.25	22.50(70)	1.75	.40	.20

SCOTT NO.	DESCRIPTION	FIRST DAY COVERS SING	FIRST DAY COVERS PL. BLK.	MINT SHEET	PLATE BLOCK F/NH	UNUSED F/NH	USED F

1073   1074

1075

1956 COMMEMORATIVES

1073/85	(1073-74, 1076-85) 12 varieties.	....	....	....	....	3.80	2.00
1073	3¢ Benjamin Franklin.	2.00	4.25	14.00(50)	1.40	.35	.20
1074	3¢ Booker T. Washington	3.50	5.50	14.00(50)	1.40	.35	.20
1075	3¢ & 8¢ FIPEX Sheet of 2	6.00	....	....	....	3.25	3.25
1075a	3¢ deep violet, single.	....	....	....	....	1.25	1.05
1075b	8¢ violet blue & carmine, single	....	....	....	....	1.75	1.25

1076   1077

1078   1079

1076	3¢ FIPEX.	2.00	4.25	12.50(50)	1.25	.35	.20
1077	3¢ Wild Turkey.	2.75	4.50	20.00(50)	2.00	.35	.20
1078	3¢ Antelope	2.75	4.50	12.50(50)	1.25	.35	.20
1079	3¢ Salmon	2.75	4.50	16.00(50)	1.50	.35	.20

PLATE BLOCKS: are portions of a sheet of stamps adjacent to the number(s) indicating the printing plate number used to produce that sheet. Flat plate issues are usually collected in plate blocks of six (number opposite middle stamp) while rotary issues are normally corner blocks of four.

SCOTT NO.	DESCRIPTION	FIRST DAY COVERS SING	FIRST DAY COVERS PL. BLK.	MINT SHEET	PLATE BLOCK F/NH	UNUSED F/NH	USED F

1080

1081

1082

1080	3¢ Pure Food & Drug Act	2.00	4.25	13.50(50)	1.35	.35	.20
1081	3¢ "Wheatland"	2.00	4.25	13.50(50)	1.35	.35	.20
1082	3¢ Labor Day.	2.00	4.25	13.50(50)	1.35	.35	.20

1083

1084

1085

1083	3¢ Nassau Hall	2.00	4.25	13.50(50)	1.35	.35	.20
1084	3¢ Devil's Tower.	2.00	4.25	15.00(50)	1.50	.35	.20
1085	3¢ Children of the World	2.00	4.25	15.00(50)	1.50	.35	.20

1086

1087

1088

1089

1090

1091

1086-99	14 varieties, complete	. . . . . .	. . . . . .	. . . . . .	. . . . . .	4.35	2.65
1086	3¢ Alexander Hamilton	2.00	4.25	12.50(50)	1.25	.35	.20
1087	3¢ Polio	2.25	4.50	12.50(50)	1.25	.35	.20
1088	3¢ Coast & Geodetic Survey	2.00	4.25	12.50(50)	1.25	.35	.20
1089	3¢ Architects	2.00	4.25	12.50(50)	1.25	.35	.20
1090	3¢ Steel Industry	2.00	4.25	12.50(50)	1.25	.35	.20
1091	3¢ International Naval Review.	2.00	4.25	12.50(50)	1.25	.30	.20

1092

1093

1094

1095

1096

1097

1092	3¢ Oklahoma Statehood	2.00	4.25	20.00(50)	2.00	.50	.20
1093	3¢ School Teachers . .	2.25	4.50	12.50(50)	1.25	.35	.20
1094	4¢ 48-Star Flag	2.00	4.25	12.50(50)	1.25	.35	.20
1095	3¢ Shipbuilding Anniversary	2.00	4.25	20.00(70)	1.25	.35	.20
1096	8¢ Ramon Magsaysay	2.50	4.25	14.00(48)	1.40	.35	.20
1097	3¢ Birth of Lafayette .	2.00	4.25	12.50(50)	1.25	.35	.20

1098

1099

1100

| 1098 | 3¢ Whooping Cranes. | 2.25 | 4.50 | 12.50(50) | 1.25 | .35 | .20 |
| 1099 | 3¢ Religious Freedom | 2.00 | 4.25 | 12.50(50) | 1.25 | .35 | .20 |

1104

1105

1106

1107

1100-23	21 varieties, complete	. . . . . .	. . . . . .	. . . . . .	. . . . . .	7.00	4.00
1100	3¢ Gardening & Horticulture.	2.00	4.25	12.50(50)	1.25	.35	.20
1104	3¢ Brussels Exhibition	2.00	4.25	12.50(50)	1.25	.35	.20
1105	3¢ James Monroe . . .	2.00	4.25	18.00(70)	1.25	.35	.20
1106	3¢ Minnesota Statehood	2.00	4.25	18.00(50)	1.70	.35	.20
1107	3¢ Int'l. Geophysical Year	2.00	4.25	12.50(50)	1.25	.35	.20

SCOTT NO.	DESCRIPTION	FIRST DAY COVERS SING	PL. BLK.	MINT SHEET	PLATE BLOCK F/NH	UNUSED F/NH	USED F

1108

1109

1110, 1111

1112

1108	3¢ Gunston Hall.....	2.00	4.25	12.50(50)	1.25	.35	.20
1109	3¢ Mackinac Bridge..	2.00	4.25	18.00(50)	1.75	.40	.20
1110	4¢ Simon Bolivar....	2.00	4.25	14.00(70)	1.25	.35	.20
1111	8¢ Simon Bolivar....	2.00	4.50	19.50(72)	1.85	.35	.20
1112	4¢ Atlantic Cable Centenary.........	2.00	4.25	12.50(50)	1.25	.35	.20

1113

1114

1115

1116

1113	1¢ Abraham Lincoln (1959)	2.00	4.25	5.00(50)	.75	.30	.20
1114	3¢ Bust of Lincoln (1959)	2.00	4.25	15.00(50)	1.75	.40	.20
1115	4¢ Lincoln-Douglas Debates............	2.00	4.25	17.50(50)	1.75	.40	.25
1116	4¢ Statue of Lincoln (1959)	2.00	4.25	15.00(50)	1.75	.40	.25

1117, 1118

1119

1120

1117	4¢ Lajos Kossuth....	2.00	4.25	18.00(70)	1.25	.35	.20
1118	8¢ Lajos Kossuth....	2.00	4.50	19.50(72)	1.60	.35	.20
1119	4¢ Freedom of Press.	2.00	4.25	12.50(50)	1.25	.35	.20
1120	4¢ Overland Mail....	2.00	4.25	12.50(50)	1.25	.35	.20

1121

1122

1123

1121	4¢ Noah Webster....	2.00	4.25	14.00(70)	1.25	.35	.20
1122	4¢ Forest Conservation	2.00	4.25	12.50(50)	1.25	.35	.20
1123	4¢ Fort Duquesne ...	2.00	4.25	12.50(50)	1.25	.35	.20

1124

1125, 1126

1127

1128

1129

1959 COMMEMORATIVES

1124-38	4¢-8¢, 15 varieties ..	......	....	....	....	4.95	2.85
1124	4¢ Oregon Statehood	2.00	4.25	20.00(50)	2.20	.35	.20
1125	4¢ José de San Martin	2.00	4.25	14.00(70)	1.25	.35	.20
1126	8¢ José de San Martin	2.00	4.25	19.50(72)	1.40	.35	.20
1127	4¢ NATO	2.00	4.25	12.50(70)	1.25	.35	.20
1128	4¢ Arctic Exploration .	2.00	4.25	12.50(50)	1.25	.35	.20
1129	8¢ World Peace & Trade	2.00	4.25	16.00(50)	1.75	.40	.20

1130

1131

1132

1133

1134

1135

Plate blocks will be blocks of 4 stamps unless otherwise noted.

SCOTT NO.	DESCRIPTION	FIRST DAY COVERS SING	PL. BLK.	MINT SHEET	PLATE BLOCK F/NH	UNUSED F/NH	USED F

1136, 1137   1138

1130	4¢ Silver Centennial .	2.00	4.25	24.00(50)	2.00	.50	.20
1131	4¢ St. Lawrence Seaway	2.00	4.25	12.50(50)	1.25	.35	.20
1132	4¢ 49-Star Flag	2.00	4.25	12.50(50)	1.25	.35	.20
1133	4¢ Soil Conservation .	2.00	4.25	18.00(50)	1.50	.35	.20
1134	4¢ Petroleum.	2.00	4.25	15.00(50)	1.25	.40	.20
1135	4¢ Dental Health	5.00	7.00	15.00(50)	1.40	.40	.20
1136	4¢ Ernst Reuter	2.00	4.25	14.00(70)	1.25	.35	.20
1137	8¢ Ernst Reuter	2.00	4.25	19.50(72)	1.50	.35	.20
1138	4¢ Dr. Ephraim McDowell	2.00	4.25	19.50(70)	1.50	.35	.20

1139   1140

1141   1142

1143   1144

1960-61 CREDO OF AMERICA SERIES

1139-44	6 varieties, complete	....	....	....	....	1.85	1.15
1139	4¢ Credo—Washington	2.00	4.25	12.50(50)	1.25	.35	.20
1140	4¢ Credo—Franklin . .	2.00	4.25	12.50(50)	1.25	.35	.20
1141	4¢ Credo—Jefferson .	2.00	4.25	12.50(50)	1.25	.35	.20
1142	4¢ Credo—Key	2.00	4.25	12.50(50)	1.25	.35	.20
1143	4¢ Credo—Lincoln. . .	2.00	4.25	12.50(50)	1.25	.35	.20
1144	4¢ Credo—Henry (1961)	2.00	4.25	12.50(50)	1.25	.35	.20

1145   1146   1147, 1148

1149   1150

1151   1152   1153

1960 COMMEMORATIVES

1145-73	4¢-8¢, 29 varieties . .	....	....	....	....	8.85	5.25
1145	4¢ Boy Scouts	8.50	10.50	17.50(50)	1.75	.40	.20
1146	4¢ Winter Olympics . .	2.00	4.25	12.50(50)	1.00	.35	.20
1147	4¢ Thomas Masaryk . .	2.00	4.25	14.00(70)	1.00	.35	.20
1148	8¢ Thomas Masaryk .	2.00	4.25	21.00(72)	1.40	.40	.20
1149	4¢ World Refugee Year	2.00	4.25	12.50(50)	1.00	.35	.20
1150	4¢ Water Conservation	2.00	4.25	12.50(50)	1.00	.35	.20
1151	4¢ SEATO	2.00	4.25	25.00(70)	1.75	.35	.20
1152	4¢ American Women .	2.00	4.25	12.50(50)	1.00	.35	.20
1153	4¢ 50-Star Flag	2.00	4.25	12.50(50)	1.00	.35	.20

1154   1155   1156

1157   1158   1159, 1160

1161   1162   1163

1154	4¢ Pony Express	2.00	4.25	19.50(50)	2.00	.45	.20
1155	4¢ Employ the Handicapped.	2.00	4.25	12.00(50)	1.25	.30	.20
1156	4¢ World Forestry Congress.	2.00	4.25	12.00(50)	1.25	.30	.20
1157	4¢ Mexican Independence	2.00	4.25	12.00(50)	1.25	.30	.20
1158	4¢ U.S.-Japan Treaty.	2.00	4.25	12.00(50)	1.25	.30	.20
1159	4¢ Ignacy Paderewski	2.00	4.25	17.00(70)	1.75	.30	.20
1160	8¢ Ignacy Paderewski	2.00	4.25	19.50(72)	1.75	.35	.20
1161	4¢ Robert A. Taft	2.00	4.25	19.00(70)	1.75	.30	.20
1162	4¢ Wheels of Freedom	2.00	4.25	17.00(50)	1.75	.30	.20
1163	4¢ Boys' Club of America	2.25	4.25	15.00(50)	1.75	.30	.20

Buy Complete Sets and Save

SCOTT NO.	DESCRIPTION	FIRST DAY COVERS SING	FIRST DAY COVERS PL. BLK.	MINT SHEET	PLATE BLOCK F/NH	UNUSED F/NH	USED F

1164

1165, 1166

1167

1168, 1169

1170

1171

1172

1173

1164	4¢ Automated Post Office	2.00	4.25	20.00(50)	1.75	.45	.20
1165	4¢ Gustaf Mannerheim	2.00	4.25	14.00(70)	1.00	.30	.20
1166	8¢ Gustaf Mannerheim	2.00	4.25	19.50(72)	1.40	.35	.20
1167	4¢ Camp Fire Girls	5.00	7.25	23.00(50)	2.50	.60	.20
1168	4¢ Giuseppe Garibaldi	2.00	4.25	14.00(70)	1.00	.30	.20
1169	8¢ Giuseppe Garibaldi	2.00	4.25	19.50(72)	1.40	.35	.20
1170	4¢ Walter George	2.00	4.25	29.00(70)	2.50	.75	.20
1171	4¢ Andrew Carnegie	2.00	4.25	17.50(70)	1.25	.35	.20
1172	4¢ John Foster Dulles	2.00	4.25	17.50(70)	1.25	.35	.20
1173	4¢ "ECHO I" Satellite	3.00	6.50	15.00(50)	1.40	.70	.20

1174, 1175

1176

1177

1961 COMMEMORATIVES

1174/90	(1174-77, 1183-90) 12 varieties	....	....	....	....	4.00	2.25
1174	4¢ Mahatma Gandhi	2.00	4.25	16.00(70)	1.25	.50	.20
1175	8¢ Mahatma Gandhi	2.00	4.25	19.50(72)	1.75	.50	.20
1176	4¢ Range Conservation	2.00	4.25	17.00(50)	1.75	.50	.20
1177	4¢ Horace Greeley	2.00	4.25	20.00(70)	1.75	.50	.20

1178

1179

1180

1181

SCOTT NO.	DESCRIPTION	FIRST DAY COVERS SING	FIRST DAY COVERS PL. BLK.	MINT SHEET	PLATE BLOCK F/NH	UNUSED F/NH	USED F

1182

1183

1961-65 CIVIL WAR CENTENNIAL SERIES

1178-82	4¢-5¢, 5 varieties, complete	....	....	....	....	2.75	.80
1178	4¢ Fort Sumter	7.50	10.00	27.50(50)	2.50	.60	.20
1179	4¢ Shiloh (1962)	7.50	10.00	17.50(50)	1.75	.40	.20
1180	5¢ Gettysburg (1963)	7.50	10.00	17.50(50)	1.75	.60	.20
1181	5¢ Wilderness (1964)	7.50	10.00	17.50(50)	1.75	.55	.20
1181	Zip Code Block	....	....	....	1.40	....	....
1182	5¢ Appomattox (1965)	7.50	10.00	40.00(50)	4.00	.75	.20
1182	Zip Code Block	....	....	....	3.50	....	....

1184

1185

1186

1187

1188

1189

1190

1961 COMMEMORATIVES

1183	4¢ Kansas Statehood	2.00	4.25	30.00(50)	2.75	.60	.20
1184	4¢ George W. Norris	2.00	4.25	12.00(50)	1.30	.35	.20
1185	4¢ Naval Aviation	2.00	4.25	12.00(50)	1.30	.35	.20
1186	4¢ Workmen's Compensation	2.00	4.25	18.00(50)	1.75	.35	.20
1187	4¢ Frederic Remington	2.00	4.25	15.00(50)	1.30	.35	.20
1188	4¢ Sun Yat-sen	6.00	10.00	15.00(50)	1.30	.35	.20
1189	4¢ Basketball	9.00	12.00	15.00(50)	1.30	.75	.20
1190	4¢ Nursing	13.50	20.00	15.00(50)	1.30	.75	.20

NOTE: To determine the VF price on stamps issued from 1941 to date, add 20% to the F/NH or F (used) price (minimum .03 per item). All VF unused stamps from 1941 date priced as NH.

SCOTT NO.	DESCRIPTION	FIRST DAY COVERS SING	PL. BLK.	MINT SHEET	PLATE BLOCK F/NH	UNUSED F/NH	USED F

1191

1192

1193

1194

1962 COMMEMORATIVES

1191-1207	17 varieties	....	....	....	....	5.40	3.40
1191	4¢ New Mexico Statehood	1.75	4.00	17.00(50)	1.25	.40	.20
1192	4¢ Arizona Statehood	1.75	4.00	14.00(50)	1.25	.30	.20
1193	4¢ Project Mercury	5.00	7.50	14.00(50)	1.25	.30	.20
1194	4¢ Malaria Eradication	1.75	4.00	14.00(50)	1.25	.30	.20

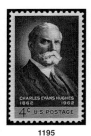

1195

1196

1197

1195	4¢ Charles Evans Hughes	2.00	4.00	13.00(50)	1.25	.30	.20
1196	4¢ Seattle World's Fair	2.00	4.00	13.00(50)	1.25	.30	.20
1197	4¢ Louisiana Statehood	2.00	4.00	17.00(50)	1.50	.40	.20

1198

1199

1200

1201

1202

1203

1205

1206

1207

1198	4¢ Homestead Act.	2.00	4.00	14.00(50)	1.25	.35	.20
1199	4¢ Girl Scouts	7.00	10.00	14.00(50)	1.25	.35	.20
1200	4¢ Brien McMahon	2.00	4.00	14.00(50)	1.25	.35	.20
1201	4¢ Apprenticeship .	2.00	4.00	14.00(50)	1.25	.35	.20
1202	4¢ Sam Rayburn . .	2.00	4.00	17.00(50)	1.50	.35	.20
1203	4¢ Dag Hammarskjold	2.00	4.00	10.00(50)	1.00	.35	.20
1204	same, yellow inverted	5.00	10.25	10.00(50)	1.50	.35	.20
1205	4¢ Christmas 1962	2.00	4.00	17.00(50)	1.00	.35	.20
1206	4¢ Higher Education	2.00	4.00	10.00(50)	1.00	.35	.20
1207	4¢ Winslow Homer	2.00	4.00	12.50(50)	1.25	.35	.20

1208

1209, 1225

1213, 1229

1962-66 REGULAR ISSUE

1208	5¢ Flag & White House (1963)	2.00	4.25	27.50(100)	1.35	.30	.15
1209	1¢ Andrew Jackson (1963)	2.00	4.00	10.00(100)	.75	.20	.15
1213	5¢ Washington . . .	2.00	4.00	27.50(100)	1.35	.30	.15
1213a	5¢ b. pane of 5—Slog. I	2.50	....	....	....	6.50	
1213a	5¢ b. pane of 5—Slog. II (1963)	....	....	....	....	20.00	
1213a	5¢ b. pane of 5—Slog. III (1964)	....	....	....	....	3.50	
1213c	5¢ Tagged pane of 5 Slogan II (1963)	....	....	....	....	....	
	....					90.00	
1213c	5¢ b. p. of 5—Slog. III (1963)	....	....	....	....	2.50	

Slogan I—Your Mailman Deserves Your Help • Keep Harmful Objects Out of…
Slogan II—Add Zip to Your Mail • Use Zone Numbers for Zip Code.
Slogan III—Add Zip to Your Mail • Always Use Zip Code.

1962-66 COIL STAMPS Perf. 10 Vertically

SCOTT NO.	DESCRIPTION	SING	LINE PAIRS		LINE PAIRS	F/NH	F
1225	1¢ Andrew Jackson (1963)	2.00	3.00	....	3.00	.20	.15

1230

1231

1232

1233

1963 COMMEMORATIVES

1230-41	12 varieties.	....	....	....	....	3.85	2.00
1230	5¢ Carolina Charter	2.00	4.00	14.00(50)	1.50	.40	.20
1231	5¢ Food for Peace.	2.00	4.00	12.00(50)	1.25	.30	.20
1232	5¢ West Virginia Statehood	2.00	4.00	20.00(50)	2.00	.50	.20
1233	5¢ Emancipation Proclamation.	4.00	6.00	12.50(50)	1.25	.35	.20

SCOTT NO.	DESCRIPTION	FIRST DAY COVERS SING	PL. BLK.	MINT SHEET	PLATE BLOCK F/NH	UNUSED F/NH	USED F

1234

1235

1236

1237

1238

1239

1240

1241

1242

1243

1963 COMMEMORATIVES

1234	5¢ Alliance for Progress	2.00	4.00	10.00(50)	1.00	.30	.20
1235	5¢ Cordell Hull. . . .	2.00	4.00	17.50(50)	1.75	.40	.20
1236	5¢ Eleanor Roosevelt	2.00	4.00	12.50(50)	1.25	.35	.20
1237	5¢ The Sciences . .	2.00	4.00	10.00(50)	1.00	.30	.20
1238	5¢ City Mail Delivery	2.00	4.00	10.00(50)	1.00	.30	.20
1239	5¢ International Red Cross.	2.00	4.00	10.00(50)	1.00	.30	.20
1240	5¢ Christmas 1963	2.00	4.00	25.00(100)	1.50	.35	.20
1241	5¢ John J. Audubon	2.00	4.00	10.00(50)	1.00	.30	.20

SCOTT NO.	DESCRIPTION	FIRST DAY COVERS SING	PL. BLK.	MINT SHEET	PLATE BLOCK	UNUSED F/NH	USED

1244

1245

1964 COMMEMORATIVES

1242-60	19 varieties.	....	....	....	....	6.95	3.50
1242	5¢ Sam Houston	4.00	6.00	25.00(50)	2.75	.70	.20
1243	5¢ Charles M. Russell	2.00	4.00	17.50(50)	1.75	.35	.20
1244	5¢ New York World's Fair	2.00	4.00	12.50(50)	1.25	.35	.20
1245	5¢ John Muir	2.00	4.00	20.00(50)	2.00	.50	.20

SCOTT NO.	DESCRIPTION	FIRST DAY COVERS SING	PL. BLK.	MINT SHEET	PLATE BLOCK	UNUSED F/NH	USED

1246

1247

| 1246 | 5¢ John F. Kennedy. . | 2.50 | 5.00 | 25.00(50) | 2.50 | .75 | .20 |
| 1247 | 5¢ New Jersey Tercentenary . . . . | 1.75 | 4.00 | 15.00(50) | 1.25 | .35 | .20 |

1248

1249

1250

1251

1252

1248	5¢ Nevada Statehood	2.00	4.00	17.00(50)	1.50	.35	.20
1249	5¢ Register and Vote .	2.00	4.00	12.00(50)	1.20	.30	.20
1250	5¢ Shakespeare	2.00	4.00	12.00(50)	1.20	.30	.20
1251	5¢ Mayo Brothers . . .	5.00	7.00	25.00(50)	2.75	.60	.20
1252	5¢ American Music . .	2.00	4.00	12.00(50)	1.20	.30	.20

1253

1254

1255

1256

1257

1253	5¢ Homemakers	2.00	4.00	12.00(50)	1.20	.30	.20
1254-57	5¢ Christmas, 4 varieties, attached .	5.25	7.50	42.00(100)	2.50	2.00	1.50
1254	5¢ Holly	2.75	....	....	....	.40	.20
1255	5¢ Mistletoe	2.75	....	....	....	.40	.20
1256	5¢ Poinsettia	2.75	....	....	....	.40	.20
1257	5¢ Pine Cone.	2.75	....	....	....	.40	.20

COMMEMORATIVES: Commemorative stamps are special issues released to honor or recognize persons, organizations, historical events or landmarks. They are usually issued in the current first class denomination to supplement regular issues.

SCOTT NO.	DESCRIPTION	FIRST DAY COVERS SING	FIRST DAY COVERS PL. BLK.	MINT SHEET	PLATE BLOCK	UNUSED F/NH	USED

1258   1259   1260

1258	5¢ Verrazano-Narrows. Bridge	2.00	4.00	12.50(50)	1.25	.35	.20
1259	5¢ Modern Art	2.00	4.00	12.00(50)	1.20	.30	.20
1260	5¢ Radio Amateurs . . .	8.00	10.00	25.00(50)	2.50	.60	.20

1261   1262   1263

1264   1265

1965 COMMEMORATIVES

1261-76	5¢-11¢, 16 varieties . .	....	....	....	....	5.15	3.00
1261	5¢ Battle of New Orleans	2.00	4.00	22.50(50)	2.25	.50	.20
1262	5¢ Physical Fitness . . .	2.00	4.00	12.00(50)	1.20	.30	.20
1263	5¢ Crusade Against Cancer.	4.00	6.00	12.00(50)	1.20	.30	.20
1264	5¢ Winston Churchill . .	2.00	4.00	17.50(50)	1.75	.40	.20
1265	5¢ Magna Carta.	2.00	4.00	8.00(50)	1.20	.30	.20

1266   1267   1268

1269   1270

1271   1272   1273

1266	5¢ International Cooperation Year.	2.00	4.00	12.50(50)	1.25	.30	.20
1267	5¢ Salvation Army	3.00	4.00	12.50(50)	1.25	.30	.20
1268	5¢ Dante Alighieri	2.00	4.00	12.50(50)	1.25	.30	.20
1269	5¢ Herbert Hoover. . . .	2.00	4.00	18.00(50)	1.75	.50	.20
1270	5¢ Robert Fulton	2.00	4.00	12.00(50)	1.20	.45	.20
1271	5¢ Florida Settlement .	2.00	4.00	18.00(50)	1.75	.40	.20
1272	5¢ Traffic Safety.	2.00	4.00	18.00(50)	1.75	.40	.20
1273	5¢ John S. Copley. . . .	2.00	4.00	18.00(50)	1.75	.30	.20

1274   1275   1276

1274	11¢ Telecom- munication	2.00	4.00	30.00(50)	7.00	.75	.40
1275	5¢ Adlai Stevenson . . .	2.00	4.00	12.00(50)	1.20	.30	.15
1276	5¢ Christmas 1965 . . .	2.00	4.00	22.00(100)	1.20	.30	.15

Stamp History

Thatcher Ferry Bridge

In 1962, during the regular course of business H.E. Harris purchases, at their 4 cent face value, a pane of 50 stamps honoring the Canal Zone's Thatcher Ferry Bridge. Due to a printing error, the silver bridge has been omitted. Harris discovers that his is the only pane from the sheet of 200 printed that has reached the public. Because a recent error in a Dag Hammerskjold stamp prompted the U.S. Postal Service to reprint thousands in order to make the error worthless, Harris questions how the Canal Zone will handle the bridge error. Flooding the market, he insists, would blunt the fun and excitement of stamp collecting. When the Canal Zone says it will reprint the error, Harris sues.

March 25, 1965, The Federal District Court in Washington rules in Harris' favor, stopping the Canal Zone authorities from reprinting the stamp error. Viewed as a precedent-setting event in philately, the effort won Harris the respect and awards of his fellow collectors.

SCOTT NO.	DESCRIPTION	FIRST DAY COVERS SING	PL. BLK.	MINT SHEET	PLATE BLOCK	UNUSED F/NH	USED

1278, 1299   1279   1280   1281, 1297

1282, 1303   1283, 1304   1283B, 1304C   1284, 1298

1285   1286   1286A   1287

1288, 1288B, 1288d, 1305E, 1305Ei   1289   1290   1291

1292   1293   1294, 1305C

1295   1305

1965-78 PROMINENT AMERICAN SERIES

Scott	Description	FDC Sing	FDC Pl.Blk.	Mint Sheet	Plate Block	Unused F/NH	Used
1278-95	1¢-$5, 20 varieties, complete (No #1288B or 1288d)	91.50	....	....	150.00	32.50	7.75
1278	1¢ T. Jefferson (1968)	1.75	4.00	12.00(100)	.75	.20	.15
1278a	1¢ bklt.pane of 8	2.50	....	....	....	1.00	....
1278ae	1¢ test gum	90.00	....	....	....	2.00	....
1278b	1¢ bklt pane of 4 (1971)	18.00	....	....	....	1.00	....
1279	1¼¢ A. Gallatin (1967)	1.75	4.00	20.00(100)	12.00	.20	.15
1280	2¢ F.L. Wright (1966)	1.75	4.00	15.00(100)	.90	.20	.15
1280a	2¢ bklt pane of 5 (1968)	2.50	....	....	....	1.00	....
1280c	2¢ bklt pane of 6 (1971)	18.00	....	....	....	1.00	....
1280ce	2¢ test gum	125.00	....	....	....	1.00	....
1281	3¢ F. Parkman (1967)	1.75	4.00	14.00(100)	.95	.25	.15
1282	4¢ A. Lincoln	1.75	4.00	29.00(100)	.95	.25	.15
1283	5¢ G. Washington (1966)	1.75	4.00	19.00(100)	.95	.25	.15
1283B	5¢ Washington, redrawn (1967)	1.75	4.00	18.00(100)	1.00	.30	.15
1284	6¢ F. D. Roosevelt(1966)	1.75	4.00	29.00(100)	1.10	.35	.15
1284b	6¢ bklt pane of 8 (1967)	3.00	....	....	....	1.75	....
1284c	6¢ bklt pane of 5 (1968)	150.00	....	....	....	1.60	....
1285	8¢ A. Einstein (1966)	4.00	6.00	50.00(100)	2.25	.50	.15
1286	10¢ A. Jackson (1967)	2.00	4.25	50.00(100)	2.25	.50	.15
1286A	12¢ H. Ford (1968)	2.00	4.25	50.00(100)	2.25	.50	.15
1287	13¢ J.F. Kennedy (1967)	2.50	4.50	67.50(100)	3.50	.70	.20
1288	15¢ O.W. Holmes, die I (1968)	2.25	4.50	55.00(100)	2.25	.60	.15
1288d	15¢ Holmes, die II (1979)	....	....	90.00(100)	14.00	1.10	.15

SCOTT NO.	DESCRIPTION	FIRST DAY COVERS SING	PL. BLK.	MINT SHEET	PLATE BLOCK	UNUSED F/NH	USED
1288B	same, from bklt pane (1978)	2.25	....	....	....	.60	.15
1288Bc	15¢ bklt pane of 8	3.75	....	....	....	4.75	....
1289	20¢ G.C. Marshall (1967)	2.25	4.50	85.00(100)	5.00	.70	.15
1290	25¢ F. Douglass (1967)	5.00	6.00	110.00(100)	5.00	1.20	.15
1291	30¢ J. Dewey (1968)	2.50	5.00	165.00(100)	5.50	1.25	.15
1292	40¢ T. Paine (1968)	2.50	5.00	155.00(100)	6.00	1.50	.15
1293	50¢ L. Stone (1968)	3.75	7.25	210.00(100)	8.00	2.00	.20
1294	$1 E. O'Neil (1967)	6.00	12.50	395.00(100)	17.00	5.00	.15
1295	$5 J. B. Moore (1966)	50.00	115.00	....	60.00	16.00	5.00

BOOKLET PANE SLOGANS

Slogan IV : Mail Early in the Day.   #1278b–Slogans IV and V
Slogan V: Use Zip Code.   #1280a, 1284c–Slogans IV or V

1966-81 COIL STAMPS

Scott	Description	FDC Sing	FDC Pl.Blk.	LINE PAIR	Mint	LINE PAIR / Plate	Unused F/NH	Used
1297-1305C	1¢-$1, 9 varieties, (No #1305Ei)	....	....		....	15.00	6.80	2.75

Perf. 10 Horizontally

1297	3¢ F. Parkman (1975)	1.75	2.75	....	.70	.20	.15
1298	6¢ F.D. Roosevelt (1967)	1.75	2.75	....	1.55	.40	.15

Perf. 10 Vertically

1299	1¢ T. Jefferson (1968)	1.75	2.75	....	.45	.60	.15
1303	4¢ A. Lincoln	1.75	2.75	....	2.50	1.00	.15
1304	5¢ G. Washington	1.75	2.75	....	4.50	2.30	.15
1304C	5¢ Washington, redrawn (1981)	1.75	2.75	....	1.15	.25	.15
1305	6¢ F.D. Roosevelt (1968)	1.75	2.75	....	.85	.40	.15
1305E	15¢ O.W. Holmes, die I (1978)	2.00	3.25	....	1.40	.50	.15
1305Ei	15¢ O.W. Holmes, die II (1979)	....	....	....	3.00	.80	.30
1305C	$1 E. O'Neil (1973)	5.00	9.50	....	8.50	3.95	1.50

1306   1307

1308   1309   1310

1312   1313   1314

1966 COMMEMORATIVES

Scott	Description	FDC Sing	FDC Pl.Blk.	Mint Sheet	Plate Block	Unused F/NH	Used
1306/22	(1306-10, 1312-22) 16 varieties	....	....	....	....	5.10	3.00
1306	5¢ Migratory Bird Treaty	2.00	4.25	12.50(50)	1.20	.35	.20
1307	5¢ A.S.P.C.A.	2.00	4.00	12.50(50)	1.20	.35	.20
1308	5¢ Indiana Statehood	2.00	4.00	19.50(50)	2.25	.35	.20
1309	5¢ American Circus	3.00	4.25	20.00(50)	2.25	.35	.20
1310	5¢ SIPEX (single)	2.00	4.00	12.50(50)	1.20	.35	.20
1311	5¢ SIPEX, Imperf Souvenir Sheet	2.00				.35	.20
1312	5¢ Bill of Rights	2.25	4.00	12.50(50)	1.20	.35	.20
1313	5¢ Polish Millennium	2.00	4.00	12.50(50)	1.20	.35	.20
1314	5¢ National Park Service	2.00	4.00	12.50(50)	1.20	.35	.20

SCOTT NO.	DESCRIPTION	FIRST DAY COVERS SING	FIRST DAY COVERS PL. BLK.	MINT SHEET	PLATE BLOCK	UNUSED F/NH	USED

1315 1316 1317

1318 1319 1320

SCOTT NO.	DESCRIPTION	SING	PL. BLK.	MINT SHEET	PLATE BLOCK	UNUSED F/NH	USED
1315	5¢ Marine Corps Reserve	2.00	4.00	12.50(50)	1.25	.30	.20
1316	5¢ Women's Clubs. . .	2.00	4.00	12.50(50)	1.25	.30	.20
1317	5¢ Johnny Appleseed.	2.00	4.00	17.50(50)	1.50	.40	.20
1318	5¢ Beautification	2.00	4.00	12.50(50)	.80	.30	.20
1319	5¢ Great River Road .	2.00	4.00	21.00(50)	2.10	.40	.20
1320	5¢ Servicemen– Bonds.	2.00	4.00	12.50(50)	1.20	.30	.20

1321 1322 1323

| 1321 | 5¢ Christmas 1966 . . | 1.75 | 4.00 | 24.00(100) | 1.50 | .30 | .20 |
| 1322 | 5¢ Mary Cassatt . . . . | 1.75 | 4.00 | 12.00(50) | 1.20 | .30 | .20 |

1324 1325

1326 1327

1967 COMMEMORATIVES

1323-37	15 varieties, complete.	. . . .	. . . .	. . . .	. . . .	7.50	3.20
1323	5¢ National Grange . .	2.00	4.00	12.00(50)	1.25	.35	.20
1324	5¢ Canada Centennial.	2.00	4.00	12.00(50)	1.25	.30	.20
1325	5¢ Erie Canal.	2.00	4.00	12.00(50)	1.25	.30	.20
1326	5¢ Search for Peace . .	2.00	4.00	12.00(50)	1.25	.30	.20
1327	5¢ Henry D. Thoreau . .	2.00	4.00	17.50(50)	1.50	.40	.20

1328 1330 1329

SCOTT NO.	DESCRIPTION	FIRST DAY COVERS SING	FIRST DAY COVERS PL. BLK.	MINT SHEET	PLATE BLOCK	UNUSED F/NH	USED
1328	5¢ Nebraska Statehood	2.00	4.00	17.00(50)	1.50	.30	.20
1329	5¢ Voice of America. . .	4.00	6.00	12.00(50)	1.00	.30	.20
1330	5¢ Davy Crockett.	2.50	4.25	17.50(50)	1.50	.50	.20

1331 1332

1331-32	5¢ Space, attached, 2 varieties	12.50	25.00	60.00(50)	5.75	3.75	1.80
1331	5¢ Astronaut	4.00	. . . .	. . . .	. . . .	1.50	.40
1332	5¢ Gemini 4 Capsule . .	4.00	. . . .	. . . .	. . . .	1.50	.40

1333 1334

| 1333 | 5¢ Urban Planning. . . . | 2.00 | 4.00 | 12.00(50) | 1.20 | .30 | .20 |
| 1334 | 5¢ Finland Independence . . . . | 2.00 | 4.00 | 12.00(50) | 1.20 | .30 | .20 |

1335 1336 1337

1335	5¢ Thomas Eakins . . .	2.00	4.00	12.00(50)	1.20	.30	.20
1336	5¢ Christams 1967 . . .	2.00	4.00	12.00(50)	1.20	.30	.20
1337	5¢ Mississippi Statehood	2.00	4.00	22.50(50)	2.25	.50	.20

FOR YOUR CONVENIENCE IN ORDERING, COMPLETE SETS ARE LISTED BEFORE SINGLE STAMP LISTINGS.

1338, 1338A, 1338D

1338F, 1338G

SCOTT NO.	DESCRIPTION	FIRST DAY COVERS SING	FIRST DAY COVERS PL. BLK.	MINT SHEET	PLATE BLOCK	UNUSED F/NH	USED

GIORI PRESS
1868 Design size: 18½ x 22 mm Perf. 11

| 1338 | 6¢ Flag & White House | 1.75 | 4.00 | 24.00(100) | 1.20 | .30 | .15 |

HUCK PRESS Design size: 18 x 21 mm
1969 Coil Stamp Perf. 10 Vertically

| 1338A | 6¢ Flag & White House | 1.75 | .... | .... | .... | .30 | .15 |

1970 Perf. 11 x 10½

| 1338D | 6¢ Flag & White House | 2.00 | 4.25 | 17.00(100) | 4.00(20) | .30 | .15 |

1971 Perf. 11 x 10½

| 1338F | 8¢ Flag & White House | 2.00 | 4.25 | 21.50(100) | 4.75(20) | .30 | .15 |

Coil Stamp Perf. 10 Vertically

| 1338G | 8¢ Flag & White House | 2.00 | .... | .... | .... | .30 | .15 |

1339

1340

1968 COMMEMORATIVES

1339/64	(1339-40, 1342-64) 25 varieties........	....	....	....	....	12.45	6.95
1339	6¢ Illinois Statehood..	2.00	4.00	22.50(50)	2.25	.50	.20
1340	6¢ Hemisfair '68......	2.00	4.00	12.00(50)	1.20	.30	.20

1341

| 1341 | $1 Airlift to Servicemen | 8.50 | 17.50 | 175.00(50) | 15.00 | 3.95 | 2.75 |

1342

1343

1344

1342	6¢ Support our Youth..	2.00	4.00	12.00(50)	1.20	.30	.20
1343	6¢ Law and Order....	4.00	6.00	19.50(50)	2.25	.50	.20
1344	6¢ Register and Vote..	2.00	4.00	12.00(50)	1.20	.30	.20

1345

1346

1347

1348

1349

1350

1351

1352

1353

1354

1968 HISTORIC AMERICAN FLAGS

SCOTT NO.	DESCRIPTION	FIRST DAY COVERS SING	FIRST DAY COVERS PL. BLK.	MINT SHEET	PLATE BLOCK	UNUSED F/NH	USED
1345-54	10 varieties, complete, attached..........	10.00	....	25.00(50)	12.00	6.00	....
1345-54	Same, set of singles.	57.50	....	....	....	5.25	4.25
1345	6¢ Fort Moultrie Flag..	6.00	....	....	....	.55	.45
1346	6¢ Fort McHenry Flag.	6.00	....	....	....	.55	.45
1347	6¢ Washington's Cruisers	6.00	....	....	....	.55	.45
1348	6¢ Bennington Flag...	6.00	....	....	....	.55	.45
1349	6¢ Rhode Island Flag.	6.00	....	....	....	.55	.45
1350	6¢ First Stars & Stripes	6.00	....	....	....	.55	.45
1351	6¢ Bunker Hill Flag...	6.00	....	....	....	.55	.45
1352	6¢ Grand Union Flag..	6.00	....	....	....	.55	.45
1353	6¢ Philadelphia Light Horse	6.00	....	....	....	.55	.45
1354	6¢ First Navy Jack....	6.00	....	....	....	.55	.45

NOTE: All ten varieties of 1345-54 were printed on the same sheet; therefore, plate and regular blocks are not available for each variety separately. Plate blocks of four will contain two each of #1346, with number adjacent to #1345 only; Zip blocks will contain two each of #1353 and #1354, with inscription adjacent to #1354 only; Mail Early blocks will contain two each of #1347-49 with inscription adjacent to #1348 only. A plate strip of 20 stamps, with two of each variety will be required to have all stamps in plate block form and will contain all marginal inscription.

1355

1356

SCOTT NO.	DESCRIPTION	FIRST DAY COVERS SING	FIRST DAY COVERS PL. BLK.	MINT SHEET	PLATE BLOCK	UNUSED F/NH	USED

1357   1358

1359   1360   1361

1968 COMMEMORATIVES

Scott	Description	Sing	Pl. Blk.	Mint Sheet	Plate Block	Unused F/NH	Used
1355	6¢ Walt Disney	40.00	50.00	55.00(50)	5.00	1.50	.30
1356	6¢ Father Marquette .	2.00	4.00	19.50(50)	2.25	.50	.20
1357	6¢ Daniel Boone	2.00	4.00	17.50(50)	1.50	.50	.20
1358	6¢ Arkansas River . . .	2.00	4.00	29.00(50)	2.25	.60	.20
1359	6¢ Leif Erikson	2.00	4.00	12.00(50)	1.25	.50	.20
1360	6¢ Cherokee Strip . . .	2.00	4.00	14.00(50)	1.25	.40	.20
1361	6¢ Trumbull Art	4.00	6.00	17.50(50)	1.50	.50	.20

1362   1363   1364

Scott	Description	Sing	Pl. Blk.	Mint Sheet	Plate Block	Unused F/NH	Used
1362	6¢ Waterfowl Conservation	2.00	4.00	22.00(50)	2.50	.50	.20
1363	6¢ Christmas 1968 . . .	2.00	. . . .	12.00(50)	2.10(10)	.30	.20
1364	6¢ Chief Joseph	2.00	4.00	20.00(50)	2.25	.50	.20

1365   1366

1367   1368

1969 COMMEMORATIVES

Scott	Description	Sing	Pl. Blk.	Mint Sheet	Plate Block	Unused F/NH	Used
1365-86	**22 varieties, complete**	. . . .	. . . .	. . . .	. . . .	13.00	4.50
1365-68	Beautification, 4 varieties, attached	6.00	8.50	32.50(50)	4.25	3.75	3.00
1365	6¢ Azaleas & Tulips . .	3.00	. . . .	. . . .	. . . .	1.00	.25
1366	6¢ Daffodils	3.00	. . . .	. . . .	. . . .	1.00	.25
1367	6¢ Poppies	3.00	. . . .	. . . .	. . . .	1.00	.25
1368	6¢ Crabapple Trees . .	3.00	. . . .	. . . .	. . . .	1.00	.25

1369   1370   1371

Scott	Description	Sing	Pl. Blk.	Mint Sheet	Plate Block	Unused F/NH	Used
1369	6¢ American Legion . . .	2.00	4.00	12.00(50)	1.20	.30	.20
1370	6¢ Grandma Moses . . .	2.00	4.00	12.00(50)	1.20	.30	.20
1371	6¢ Apollo 8 Moon Orbit	2.50	5.00	18.00(50)	1.75	.50	.20

1372   1373

1374   1375

Scott	Description	Sing	Pl. Blk.	Mint Sheet	Plate Block	Unused F/NH	Used
1372	6¢ W.C. Handy–Musician	3.50	5.00	18.00(50)	1.75	.50	.20
1373	6¢ California Settlement	2.00	4.00	18.00(50)	1.75	.30	.20
1374	6¢ Major J.W. Powell . .	2.00	4.00	17.50(50)	1.75	.40	.20
1375	6¢ Alabama Statehood	2.00	4.00	17.50(50)	1.75	.40	.20

1376   1377

1378   1379

Scott	Description	Sing	Pl. Blk.	Mint Sheet	Plate Block	Unused F/NH	Used
1376-79	Bontanical Congress, 4 varieties, attached . .	7.00	9.50	35.00(50)	4.50	3.75	3.00
1376	6¢ Douglas Fir	3.00	. . . .	. . . .	. . . .	1.00	.25
1377	6¢ Lady's-slipper	3.00	. . . .	. . . .	. . . .	1.00	.25
1378	6¢ Ocotillo	3.00	. . . .	. . . .	. . . .	1.00	.25
1379	6¢ Franklinia	3.00	. . . .	. . . .	. . . .	1.00	.25

AVERAGE QUALITY: From 1935 to date, deduct 20% from the Fine price to determine the price for an Average quality stamp.

MINT SHEETS: From 1935 to date, we list prices for standard size Mint Sheets in Fine, Never Hinged condition. The number of stamps in each sheet is noted in ( ).

SCOTT NO.	DESCRIPTION	FIRST DAY COVERS SING	PL. BLK.	MINT SHEET	PLATE BLOCK	UNUSED F/NH	USED

1380

1381

1382

1383

1380	6¢ Dartmouth College .	2.00	4.00	17.50(50)	1.75	.40	.20
1381	6¢ Professional Baseball	16.00	25.00	65.00(50)	6.50	1.50	.20
1382	6¢ College Football . . .	7.00	13.50	27.50(50)	2.25	.75	.20
1383	6¢ Eisenhower.	2.00	4.00	12.00(32)	1.75	.40	.20

1384

1385

1386

1384	6¢ Christmas 1969 . . .	2.00	. . . .	14.00(50)	3.50(10)	.30	.20
1384a	6¢ precancelled set of 4 cities	. . . .	. . . .	225.00(50)	125.00(10)	3.00	. . . .
1385	6¢ Rehabilitation	2.00	4.00	12.00(50)	1.20	.30	.20
1386	6¢ William M. Harnett .	2.00	4.00	8.00(32)	1.20	.30	.20

1387

1388

1389

1390

1391

1392

1970 COMMEMORATIVES

SCOTT NO.	DESCRIPTION	FIRST DAY COVERS SING	PL. BLK.	MINT SHEET	PLATE BLOCK	UNUSED F/NH	USED
1387/1422	(1387-92, 1405-22) 24 varieties, (No precancels). . . .	. . . .	. . . .		. . . .	11.85	5.75
1387-90	Natural History, 4 varieties, attached . .	5.00	7.00	12.00(32)	2.25	1.95	1.50
1387	6¢ Bald Eagle	2.50	. . . .			.50	.20
1388	6¢ Elephant Herd.	2.50	. . . .			.50	.20
1389	6¢ Haida Canoe.	2.50	. . . .			.50	.20
1390	6¢ Reptiles.	2.50	. . . .			.50	.20
1391	6¢ Maine Statehood . .	2.00	4.00	17.50(50)	1.75	.40	.20
1392	6¢ Wildlife—Buffalo. . . .	2.00	4.00	17.50(50)	1.75	.40	.20

1393, 1401

1393D

1394

1395, 1402

1396

1397

1398

1399

1400

1970-74 REGULAR ISSUE

1393/1400	6¢-21¢, 8 varieties, complete (No #1395)	. . . .	. . . .		. . . .	3.85	1.30
1393	6¢ D. Eisenhower	1.75	4.00	20.00(100)	1.50	.30	.15
1393a	6¢ bklt pane of 8	2.75	. . . .			1.95	. . . .
1393ae	6¢ test gum	90.00	. . . .			1.90	. . . .
1393b	6¢ bklt pane of 5— Slogan IV or V	3.75	. . . .			1.75	. . . .
1393D	7¢ B. Franklin (1972). .	1.75	4.00	25.00(100)	1.50	.30	.15
1394	8¢ Ike—black, blue, red (1971)	1.75	4.00	29.00(100)	1.50	.30	.15
1395	same, deep claret bklt single (1971)	2.50				.45	.15
1395a	8¢ bklt pane of 8	2.50	. . . .			2.40	. . . .
1395b	8¢ bklt pane of 6	2.25	. . . .			1.90	. . . .
1395c	8¢ bklt pane of 4, VI & VII (1972)	2.00	. . . .			1.70	. . . .
1395d	8¢ bklt pane of 7 II or V (1972)	2.50	. . . .			2.50	. . . .
1396	8¢ Postal Service Emblem (1971)	1.75	4.00	34.00(100)	3.25(12)	.35	.15
1397	14¢ F. LaGuardia (1972)	1.75	4.00	50.00(100)	3.50	.75	.15
1398	16¢ E. Pyle (1971)	2.50	4.50	85.00(100)	4.50	.75	.15
1399	18¢ E. Blackwell (1974)	2.00	4.25	60.00(100)	3.50	.75	.20
1400	21¢ A.P. Giannini (1973)	2.50	4.50	70.00(100)	3.75	.75	.30

1970-71 COIL STAMPS—Perf. 10 Vertically

			LINE PAIR		LINE PAIR		
1401	6¢ D. Eisenhower	1.75	2.75	. . . .	.65	.30	.15
1402	8¢ Eisenhower, claret (1971)	1.75	2.75	. . . .	.80	.35	.15

SCOTT NO.	DESCRIPTION	FIRST DAY COVERS SING	FIRST DAY COVERS PL. BLK.	MINT SHEET	PLATE BLOCK	UNUSED F/NH	USED

1405

1406

1407

1408

1409

1970 COMMEMORATIVES

SCOTT NO.	DESCRIPTION	SING	PL. BLK.	MINT SHEET	PLATE BLOCK	UNUSED F/NH	USED
1405	6¢ E.L. Master–Poet . .	2.00	4.00	17.50(50)	1.75	.40	.20
1406	6¢ Woman Suffrage. . .	2.00	4.00	12.00(50)	1.20	.30	.20
1407	6¢ South Carolina Tercentenary	2.00	4.00	20.00(50)	2.25	.50	.20
1408	6¢ Stone Mountain Memorial	2.00	4.00	15.00(50)	1.50	.50	.20
1409	6¢ Fort Snelling	2.00	4.00	22.00(50)	2.25	.55	.20

1412   1413

1410   1411

SCOTT NO.	DESCRIPTION	SING	PL. BLK.	MINT SHEET	PLATE BLOCK	UNUSED F/NH	USED
1410-13	Anti-Pollution, 4 varieties, attached . .	5.00	7.00	20.00(50)	6.00(10)	3.00	2.40
1410	6¢ Globe & Wheat. . . .	2.50	....	....	....	.75	.25
1411	6¢ Globe & City	2.50	....	....	....	.75	.25
1412	6¢ Globe & Bluegill . . .	2.50	....	....	....	.75	.25
1413	6¢ Globe & Seagull . . .	2.50	....	....	....	.75	.25

1414

SCOTT NO.	DESCRIPTION	SING	PL. BLK.	MINT SHEET	PLATE BLOCK	UNUSED F/NH	USED
1414	6¢ Nativity	1.75	....	12.00(50)	1.75(8)	.30	.20

1415   1416

1417   1418

SCOTT NO.	DESCRIPTION	SING	PL. BLK.	MINT SHEET	PLATE BLOCK	UNUSED F/NH	USED
1415-18	Christmas Toys, 4 varieties, attached . .	5.50	....	30.00(50)	6.25(8)	3.00	2.25
1415	6¢ Locomotive	3.00	....	....	....	1.00	.25
1416	6¢ Horse	3.00	....	....	....	1.00	.25
1417	6¢ Tricycle	3.00	....	....	....	1.00	.25
1418	6¢ Doll Carriage.	3.00	....	....	....	1.00	.25

Precancelled

SCOTT NO.	DESCRIPTION	SING	PL. BLK.	MINT SHEET	PLATE BLOCK	UNUSED F/NH	USED
1414a	6¢ Nativity (precancelled)	4.00	....	14.00(50)	2.75(8)	.30	.15
1415a-18a	Christmas Toys, precancelled, 4 varieties attached . .	45.00	....	45.00(50)	9.50(8)	4.25	3.75
1415a	6¢ Locomotive	7.00	....	....	....	1.50	.20
1416a	6¢ Horse	7.00	....	....	....	1.50	.20
1417a	6¢ Tricycle	7.00	....	....	....	1.50	.20
1418a	6¢ Doll Carriage.	7.00	....	....	....	1.50	.20

NOTE: Unused precancels are with original gum, while used are without gum.

1419

1420

SCOTT NO.	DESCRIPTION	SING	PL. BLK.	MINT SHEET	PLATE BLOCK	UNUSED F/NH	USED
1419	6¢ U.N. 25th Anniversary	2.00	4.00	12.00(50)	1.20	.30	.20
1420	6¢ Pilgrim Landing. . . .	2.00	4.00	12.00(50)	1.20	.30	.20

1421   1422

SCOTT NO.	DESCRIPTION	SING	PL. BLK.	MINT SHEET	PLATE BLOCK	UNUSED F/NH	USED
1421-22	D.A.V. Servicemen, 2 varieties, attached . .	3.00	5.00	15.00(50)	2.25	.60	.35
1421	6¢ Disabled Veterans .	2.00	....	....	....	.30	.20
1422	6¢ Prisoners of War. . .	2.00	....	....	....	.30	.20

FIRST DAY COVERS: First Day Covers are envelopes cancelled on the "First Day of Issue" of the stamp used on the envelope. Usually they also contain a picture (cachet) on the left side designed to go with the theme of the stamp. From 1935 to 1949, prices listed are for cacheted, addressed covers. From 1950 to date, prices are for cacheted, unaddressed covers.

SE-TENANTS: Beginning with the 1964 Christmas issue (#1254-57), the United States has issued numerous Se-Tenant stamps covering a wide variety of subjects. Se-Tenants are issues where two or more different stamp designs are produced on the same sheet in pair, strip or block form. Mint stamps are usually collected in attached blocks, etc.; used are generally saved as single stamps.

SCOTT NO.	DESCRIPTION	FIRST DAY COVERS SING	FIRST DAY COVERS PL. BLK.	MINT SHEET	PLATE BLOCK	UNUSED F/NH	USED

1423

1424

1425

1426

1971 COMMEMORATIVES

1423-45	6¢-8¢, 23 varieties complete	. . . . . .	. . . . . .	. . . . . .	. . . . . .	8.75	4.95
1423	6¢ Sheep	1.75	4.00	20.00(50)	2.00	.50	.20
1424	6¢ General D. MacArthur	1.75	4.00	24.00(50)	2.25	.50	.20
1425	6¢ Blood Donors	1.75	4.00	12.00(50)	1.20	.30	.20
1426	8¢ Missouri Statehood.	1.75	4.00	20.00(50)	5.75(12)	.50	.20

1427

1428

1429

1430

1427-30	Wildlife Conservation, 4 varieties, attached . .	5.00	9.00	12.50(32)	2.50	2.00	1.50
1427	8¢ Trout	2.50	. . . . . .	. . . . . .	. . . . . .	.40	.25
1428	8¢ Alligator.	2.50	. . . . . .	. . . . . .	. . . . . .	.40	.25
1429	8¢ Polar Bear.	2.50	. . . . . .	. . . . . .	. . . . . .	.40	.25
1430	8¢ Condor	2.50	. . . . . .	. . . . . .	. . . . . .	.40	.25

1431

1432

1433

1431	8¢ Antarctic Treaty. . . .	2.00	4.00	11.50(50)	1.25	.35	.20
1432	8¢ American Revolution	2.00	4.00	11.50(50)	1.40	.40	.20
1433	8¢ John Sloan–Artist . .	2.00	4.00	11.50(50)	1.25	.35	.20

SCOTT NO.	DESCRIPTION	FIRST DAY COVERS SING	FIRST DAY COVERS PL. BLK.	MINT SHEET	PLATE BLOCK	UNUSED F/NH	USED

1434

1435

1434-35	Space Achievements, . 2 varieties, attached . .	3.50	4.50	13.50(50)	1.75	.75	.55
1434	8¢ Moon, Earth, Sun & Landing Craft	2.00	. . . . . .	. . . . . .	. . . . . .	.45	.30
1435	8¢ Lunar Rover	2.00	. . . . . .	. . . . . .	. . . . . .	.45	.30

1436

1437

1438

1439

1436	8¢ Emily Dickinson . . .	2.00	4.00	17.50(50)	1.75	.40	.20
1437	8¢ San Juan	2.00	4.00	17.50(50)	1.75	.35	.20
1438	8¢ Drug Addiction	2.00	4.00	11.25(50)	1.75(6)	.35	.20
1439	8¢ CARE	2.00	4.00	11.25(50)	2.20(8)	.35	.20

1440

1441

1442

1443

1440-43	Historic Preservation 4 varieties, attached . .	5.00	6.00	12.50(32)	2.00	1.75	1.00
1440	8¢ Decatur House	2.50	. . . . . .	. . . . . .	. . . . . .	.40	.25
1441	8¢ Whaling Ship	2.50	. . . . . .	. . . . . .	. . . . . .	.40	.25
1442	8¢ Cable Car	2.50	. . . . . .	. . . . . .	. . . . . .	.40	.25
1443	8¢ Mission	2.50	. . . . . .	. . . . . .	. . . . . .	.40	.25

SCOTT NO.	DESCRIPTION	FIRST DAY COVERS SING	PL. BLK.	MINT SHEET	PLATE BLOCK	UNUSED F/NH	USED

1444

1445

| 1444 | 8¢ Christmas Nativity. . | 2.00 | 4.00 | 11.25(50) | 3.00(12) | .35 | .20 |
| 1445 | 8¢ Christmas Patridge . | 2.00 | 4.00 | 11.25(50) | 3.00(12) | .35 | .20 |

1446

1447

1972 COMMEMORATIVES

1446/74	29 varieties, complete.	. . . . . .	. . . . . .	. . . . . .	. . . . . .	10.15	5.50
1446	8¢ Sidney Lanier–Poet	2.00	4.00	17.50(50)	2.25	.50	.20
1447	8¢ Peace Corps.	2.00	4.00	12.50(50)	1.80(6)	.35	.20

1448   1449

1452

1450   1451

1454

1453

1972 NATIONAL PARKS CENTENNIAL

1448-54	2¢-15¢, 7 varieties, complete	. . . . . .	. . . . . .	. . . . . .	. . . . . .	2.50	1.50
1448-51	Cape Hatteras, 4 varieties, attached.	6.00	7.00	11.00(100)	1.00	1.00	.65
1448	2¢ Ship's Hull.	. . . . . .	. . . . . .	. . . . . .	. . . . . .	.25	.15
1449	2¢ Lighthouse	. . . . . .	. . . . . .	. . . . . .	. . . . . .	.25	.15
1450	2¢ Three Seagulls	. . . . . .	. . . . . .	. . . . . .	. . . . . .	.25	.15
1451	2¢ Two Seagulls	. . . . . .	. . . . . .	. . . . . .	. . . . . .	.25	.15
1452	6¢ Wolf Trap Farm Park	2.00	4.00	15.00(50)	1.75	.40	.20
1453	8¢ Yellowstone Park . .	2.00	4.00	12.00(32)	1.50	.40	.20
1454	15¢ Mount McKinley . .	2.00	4.00	25.00(50)	2.75	.60	.35

1455

1972 COMMEMORATIVES

| 1455 | 8¢ Family Planning . . . | 2.00 | 4.00 | 11.25(50) | 1.25 | .35 | .20 |

1456   1457

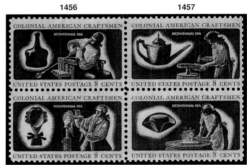

1458   1459

1456-59	Colonial Craftsmen, 4 varieties, attached . .	3.75	4.75	15.00(50)	1.75	1.50	1.20
1456	8¢ Glassmaker	2.25	. . . . . .	. . . . . .	. . . . . .	.45	.25
1457	8¢ Silversmith	2.25	. . . . . .	. . . . . .	. . . . . .	.45	.25
1458	8¢ Wigmaker	2.25	. . . . . .	. . . . . .	. . . . . .	.45	.25
1459	8¢ Hatter	2.25	. . . . . .	. . . . . .	. . . . . .	.45	.25

1460

1461

1462

1460	6¢ Olympics–Cycling . .	2.10	4.25	12.00(50)	2.50(10)	.30	.20
1461	8¢ Olympics–Bob Sled Racing	2.10	4.25	12.25(50)	2.80(10)	.35	.20
1462	15¢ Olympics–Foot Racing	2.10	4.25	22.00(50)	4.75(10)	.50	.45

1463

| 1463 | 8¢ Parent Teacher Association . . . . | 2.00 | 4.00 | 17.50(50) | 1.50 | .40 | .20 |
| 1463a | Same, Reversed Plate Number . . . . | 2.00 | 4.00 | 17.50(50) | 1.50 | . . . . . . | . . . . . . |

SCOTT NO.	DESCRIPTION	FIRST DAY COVERS SING	FIRST DAY COVERS PL. BLK.	MINT SHEET	PLATE BLOCK	UNUSED F/NH	USED

1464   1465

1476   1477

1466   1467

1478   1479

1973 COMMEMORATIVES

1475-1508	**34 varieties, complete**	....	....	....	....	12.00	7.25
1475	8¢ "Love"	2.25	5.00	12.00(50)	1.50(6)	.35	.20

COLONIAL COMMUNICATIONS

1476	8¢ Pamphlet Printing . .	2.00	4.00	15.00(50)	1.75	.40	.20
1477	8¢ Posting Broadside .	2.00	4.00	15.00(50)	1.75	.40	.20
1478	8¢ Colonial Post Rider.	2.00	4.00	15.00(50)	1.75	.40	.20
1479	8¢ Drummer & Soldiers	2.00	4.00	15.00(50)	1.75	.40	.20

1464-67	Wildlife Conservation, 4 varieties, attached . .	4.00	6.00	15.00(32)	2.50	2.00	1.50
1464	8¢ Fur Seal	2.00	....	....	....	.50	.25
1465	8¢ Cardinal	2.00	....	....	....	.50	.25
1466	8¢ Brown Pelican.....	2.00	....	....	....	.50	.25
1467	8¢ Bighorn Sheep	2.00	....	....	....	.50	.25

1480   1481

1482   1483

1468

1469   1470

1468	8¢ Mail Order Business	2.00	4.00	17.50(50)	4.50(12)	.40	.20
1469	8¢ Osteopathic Medicine	2.00	4.25	20.00(50)	2.75(6)	.50	.20
1470	Tom Sawyer–Folklore .	2.00	4.00	20.00(50)	2.25	.50	.20

1480-83	Boston Tea Party, 4 varieties, attached . .	4.50	6.50	17.00(50)	1.75	1.50	1.10
1480	8¢ Throwing Tea	2.25	....	....	....	.45	.25
1481	8¢ Ship	2.25	....	....	....	.45	.25
1482	8¢ Rowboats	2.25	....	....	....	.45	.25
1483	8¢ Rowboat & Dock...	2.25	....	....	....	.45	.25

1471   1472   1473

1471	8¢ Christmas–Virgin Mother	1.75	4.00	14.00(50)	3.50(12)	.35	.20
1472	8¢ Christmas–Santa Claus	1.75	4.00	14.00(50)	3.50(12)	.40	.20
1473	8¢ Pharmacy	8.00	10.00	19.50(50)	2.25(4)	.50	.20

1484   1485

Copernicus 1473-1973

1488

1474   1475

1474	8¢ Stamp Collecting ..	2.00	4.25	9.50(40)	1.25(4)	.35	.20

1486   1487

SCOTT NO.	DESCRIPTION	FIRST DAY COVERS SING	PL. BLK.	MINT SHEET	PLATE BLOCK	UNUSED F/NH	USED
	AMERICAN ARTS						
1484	8¢ George Gershwin–Composer	2.00	4.00	10.25(40)	3.75(12)	.35	.20
1485	8¢ Robinson Jeffers–Poet	2.00	4.00	10.25(40)	3.75(12)	.35	.20
1486	8¢ Henry O. Tanner–Artist	5.00	6.00	10.25(40)	3.75(12)	.35	.20
1487	8¢ Willa Cather–Novelist	2.00	4.00	15.00(40)	5.00(12)	.50	.20
1488	8¢ Nicolaus Copernicus	2.00	4.00	12.25(40)	1.50	.35	.20

1489

1490

1491

1492

1493

1494

1495

1496

1497

1498

1973 POSTAL SERVICE EMPLOYEES

SCOTT NO.	DESCRIPTION	SING	PL. BLK.	MINT SHEET	PLATE BLOCK	UNUSED	USED
1489-98	10 varieties, complete, attached	6.50	....	18.00(50)	9.00(20)	4.50	3.50
1489-98	Set of singles, complete	22.00	....	....	....	4.25	2.50
1489	8¢ Window Clerk	2.25	....	....	....	.45	.25
1490	8¢ Mail Pickup	2.25	....	....	....	.45	.25
1491	8¢ Conveyor Belt	2.25	....	....	....	.45	.25
1492	8¢ Sacking Parcels	2.25	....	....	....	.45	.25
1493	8¢ Mail Cancelling	2.25	....	....	....	.45	.25
1494	8¢ Manual Sorting	2.25	....	....	....	.45	.25
1495	8¢ Machine Sorting	2.25	....	....	....	.45	.25
1496	8¢ Loading Truck	2.25	....	....	....	.45	.25
1497	8¢ Letter Carrier	2.25	....	....	....	.45	.25
1498	8¢ Rural Delivery	2.25	....	....	....	.45	.25

1499

1500

1501

1502

1503

1973 COMMEMORATIVES

SCOTT NO.	DESCRIPTION	SING	PL. BLK.	MINT SHEET	PLATE BLOCK	UNUSED	USED
1499	8¢ Harry S. Truman	2.00	4.00	14.00(32)	2.25	.50	.20
1500	6¢ Electronics	2.00	4.00	12.00(50)	1.20	.35	.20
1501	8¢ Electronics	2.00	4.00	11.50(50)	1.25	.35	.20
1502	15¢ Electronics	2.00	4.00	25.00(50)	2.50	.60	.40
1503	8¢ Lyndon B. Johnson	2.00	4.00	15.00(32)	5.50(12)	.50	.20

1504

1505

1506

1973-74 RURAL AMERICA

SCOTT NO.	DESCRIPTION	SING	PL. BLK.	MINT SHEET	PLATE BLOCK	UNUSED	USED
1504	8¢ Angus Cattle	2.00	4.00	17.00(50)	1.75	.35	.20
1505	10¢ Chautauqua (1974)	2.00	4.00	14.00(50)	1.50	.35	.20
1506	10¢ Winter Wheat (1974)	2.00	4.00	21.00(50)	2.00	.35	.20

1507

1508

1973 CHRISTMAS

SCOTT NO.	DESCRIPTION	SING	PL. BLK.	MINT SHEET	PLATE BLOCK	UNUSED	USED
1507	8¢ Madonna	2.25	3.25	14.50(50)	3.50(12)	.35	.20
1508	8¢ Christmas Tree	2.25	3.25	14.50(50)	3.50(12)	.35	.20

SCOTT NO.	DESCRIPTION	FIRST DAY COVERS SING	FIRST DAY COVERS PL. BLK.	MINT SHEET	PLATE BLOCK	UNUSED F/NH	USED

1509, 1519

1510, 1520

1511

1518

1973-74 REGULAR ISSUES

SCOTT NO.	DESCRIPTION	SING	PL. BLK.	MINT SHEET	PLATE BLOCK	UNUSED F/NH	USED
1509	10¢ Crossed Flags . . .	2.25	4.00	33.25(100)	7.25(20)	.35	.15
1510	10¢ Jefferson Memorial	2.25	4.00	30.00(100)	1.50	.35	.15
1510b	10¢ bklt pane of 5– Slogan VIII	2.25	....	....	....	1.85	....
1510c	10¢ bklt pane of 8	2.25	....	....	....	2.50	....
1510d	10¢ bklt pane of 6 (1974)	2.25	....	....	....	8.75	....
1511	10¢ Zip Code Theme (1974)	2.25	4.00	29.50(100)	2.75(8)	.35	.15

BOOKLET PANE SLOGANS

VI–Stamps in This Book....
VII– This Book Contains 25....   VIII–Paying Bills....

COIL STAMPS Perf.10 Vertically

SCOTT NO.	DESCRIPTION	LINE	PAIR	LINE	PAIR	UNUSED F/NH	USED
1518	6.3¢ Liberty Bell.	2.25	2.75	....	.70	.40	.25
1519	10¢ Crossed Flags . . .	2.25	....	....	....	.40	.15
1520	10¢ Jefferson Memorial	2.25	2.75	....	1.00	.35	.15

1525

1526

1527

1528

1529

1974 COMMEMORATIVES

SCOTT NO.	DESCRIPTION	SING	PL. BLK.	MINT SHEET	PLATE BLOCK	UNUSED F/NH	USED
1525-52	28 varieties, complete.	....	....	....	....	11.00	6.00
1525	10¢ Veterans of Foreign Wars	2.25	4.00	14.00(50)	1.40	.35	.20
1526	10¢ Robert Frost	2.25	4.00	21.00(50)	2.00	.35	.20
1527	10¢ Environment– EXPO '74.	2.25	4.00	20.00(40)	7.00(12)	.50	.20
1528	10¢ Horse Racing	2.25	4.00	19.50(50)	5.00(12)	.50	.20
1529	10¢ Skylab Project. . . .	2.25	4.00	14.25(50)	1.40	.35	.20

1530

1531

1532

1533

1534

1535

1536

1537

1974 UNIVERSAL POSTAL UNION

SCOTT NO.	DESCRIPTION	SING	PL. BLK.	MINT SHEET	PLATE BLOCK	UNUSED F/NH	USED
1530-37	8 varieties, attached .	6.00	....	15.00(32)	7.50(16)	3.50(8)	2.95
1530-37	Set of singles, complete	17.50	....	....	....	3.25	2.25
1530	10¢ Raphael	2.75	....	....	....	.50	.35
1531	10¢ Hokusai.	2.75	....	....	....	.50	.35
1532	10¢ J.F. Peto	2.75	....	....	....	.50	.35
1533	10¢ J.E. Liotard	2.75	....	....	....	.50	.35
1534	10¢ G. Terborch.	2.75	....	....	....	.50	.35
1535	10¢ J.B.S. Chardin . . .	2.75	....	....	....	.50	.35
1536	10¢ T. Gainsborough . .	2.75	....	....	....	.50	.35
1537	10¢ F. de Goya	2.75	....	....	....	.50	.35

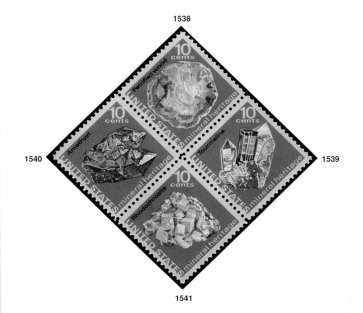
1538
1540
1539
1541

1974 COMMEMORATIVES

SCOTT NO.	DESCRIPTION	SING	PL. BLK.	MINT SHEET	PLATE BLOCK	UNUSED F/NH	USED
1538-41	Mineral Heritage, 4 varieties, attached . .	3.50	5.00	20.00(48)	2.00	1.75	1.25
1538	10¢ Petrified Wood . . .	2.25	....	....	....	.50	.25
1539	10¢ Tourmaline	2.25	....	....	....	.50	.25
1540	10¢ Amethyst.	2.25	....	....	....	.50	.25
1541	10¢ Rhodochrosite . . .	2.25	....	....	....	.50	.25

SCOTT NO.	DESCRIPTION	FIRST DAY COVERS SING	PL. BLK.	MINT SHEET	PLATE BLOCK	UNUSED F/NH	USED

1542

| 1542 | 10¢ Fort Harrod Bicentennial........ | 2.25 | 4.00 | 20.00(50) | 2.00 | .60 | .20 |

1543   1544

1545   1546

1543-46	Continental Congress, 4 varieties, attached ..	4.50	6.00	18.00(50)	2.00	1.75	1.25
1543	10¢ Carpenter's Hall ..	2.25	....	....	....	.40	.20
1544	10¢ Quote–First Congress	2.25	....	....	....	.40	.20
1545	10¢ Quote–Declaration– of Independence	2.25	....	....	....	.40	.20
1546	10¢ Independence Hall	2.25	....	....	....	.40	.20

1547   1548   1549

1547	10¢ Energy Conservation	2.25	4.00	21.00(50)	2.00	.45	.20
1548	10¢ Sleepy Hollow....	2.25	4.00	15.00(50)	1.50	.40	.20
1549	10¢ Retarded Children	2.25	4.00	15.00(50)	1.50	.40	.20

1550   1551   1552

1550	10¢ Christmas–Angel .	2.25	4.00	14.00(50)	4.00(10)	.35	.15
1551	10¢ Christmas–Currier & Ives.............	2.25	4.00	14.00(50)	4.50(12)	.35	.15
1552	10¢ Christams– Dove of Peace.......	2.25	4.00	20.00(50)	9.00(20)	.40	.30
1552	same	....	....	....	4.75(12)	....	....

1553   1554

1555

1975 COMMEMORATIVES

1553-80	8¢-10¢, 28 varieties, complete...........	....	....	....	....	12.00	5.25
1553	10¢ Benjamin West– Arts	2.25	4.00	20.00(50)	5.00(10)	.45	.20
1554	10¢ Paul Dunbar–Arts .	2.25	4.00	20.00(50)	5.00(10)	.45	.20
1555	10¢ D.W. Griffith–Arts .	2.25	4.00	20.00(50)	2.00	.45	.20

1556   1557

1558

1556	10¢ Pioneer 10	2.25	4.00	17.00(50)	2.00	.45	.20
1557	10¢ Mariner 10	2.25	4.00	17.00(50)	2.00	.45	.20
1558	10¢ Collective Bargaining	2.25	4.00	14.50(50)	3.00(8)	.40	.20

1559   1560

1561   1562

1559	8¢ Sybil Ludington....	2.25	4.00	14.00(50)	4.00(10)	.35	.20
1560	10¢ Salem Poor......	2.25	4.00	20.00(50)	5.00(10)	.45	.20
1561	10¢ Haym Salomon...	2.25	4.00	20.00(50)	5.00(10)	.45	.20
1562	18¢ Peter Francisco ..	2.25	4.00	27.50(50)	7.50(10)	.70	.40

1563   1564

| 1563 | 10¢ Lexington-Concord | 2.25 | 4.00 | 15.00(40) | 5.50(12) | .45 | .20 |
| 1564 | 10¢ Battle of Bunker Hill | 2.25 | 4.00 | 15.00(40) | 5.50(12) | .45 | .20 |

SCOTT NO.	DESCRIPTION	FIRST DAY COVERS SING	FIRST DAY COVERS PL. BLK.	MINT SHEET	PLATE BLOCK	UNUSED F/NH	USED

1565   **1566**   **1567**   **1568**

SCOTT NO.	DESCRIPTION	SING	PL. BLK.	MINT SHEET	PLATE BLOCK	UNUSED F/NH	USED
1565-68	Military Uniforms, 4 varieties, attached ..	4.00	6.00	15.00(50)	5.00(12)	1.75	1.30
1565	10¢ Continental Army .	2.25	....	....	....	.50	.20
1566	10¢ Continental Navy .	2.25	....	....	....	.50	.20
1567	10¢ Continental Marines	2.25	....	....	....	.50	.20
1568	10¢ American Militia ..	2.25	....	....	....	.50	.20

1569

1570

1569-70	Apollo-Soyuz Mission, .. 2 varieties, attached ..	3.00	4.50	8.00(24)	5.00(12)	.95	.55
1569	10¢ Docked	2.25	....	....	....	.50	.20
1570	10¢ Docking.	2.25	....	....	....	.50	.20

1571

1571	10¢ International Women's Year	2.25	4.00	14.00(50)	2.10(6)	.35	.20

1572   **1573**

1574   **1575**

1572-75	Postal Service Bicentennial, 4 varieties, attached ..	4.00	5.00	15.00(50)	5.00(12)	1.85	1.50
1572	10¢ Stagecoach & Trailer	2.25	....	....	....	.50	.20
1573	10¢ Locomotives	2.25	....	....	....	.50	.20
1574	10¢ Airplanes.	2.25	....	....	....	.50	.20
1575	10¢ Satellite.	2.25	....	....	....	.50	.20

1576

1577   **1578**

1576	10¢ World Peace through Law	2.25	4.00	18.00(50)	2.00	.45	.20
1577-78	Banking & Commerce, 2 varieties, attached ..	2.50	3.75	18.00(40)	2.00	1.00	.70
1577	10¢ Banking.	2.25	....	....	....	.60	.20
1578	10¢ Commerce	2.25	....	....	....	.60	.20

1579   **1580**

1579	(10¢) Madonna	2.25	4.00	18.00(50)	5.00(12)	.45	.20
1580	(10¢) Christams Card .	2.25	4.00	18.00(50)	5.00(12)	.45	.20
1580b	(10¢) Christmas Card, perf. 10 1/2 x 11	....	....	48.50(50)	15.00(12)	1.00	.50

1581, 1811   **1582**   **1584**   **1585**

1590, 1591, 1616   **1592, 1617**   **1593**   **1594, 1816**

1595, 1618   **1596**   **1597, 1598, 1618C**   **1599, 1619**

1603   **1604**   **1605**   **1606**

SCOTT NO.	DESCRIPTION	FIRST DAY COVERS SING	FIRST DAY COVERS PL. BLK.	MINT SHEET	PLATE BLOCK	UNUSED F/NH	USED

1608

1610

1611

1612

1975-81 AMERICANA ISSUE

SCOTT NO.	DESCRIPTION	SING	PL. BLK.	MINT SHEET	PLATE BLOCK	UNUSED F/NH	USED
1581/1612	1¢-$5, (No #1590, 1590a, 1595, or 1598) 19 varieties, complete	51.50	....	....	155.00	33.50	6.95
1581	1¢ Inkwell & Quill (1977)	2.25	4.00	7.00(100)	.70	.20	.15
1582	2¢ Speaker's Stand (1977)	2.25	4.00	8.25(100)	.70	.20	.15
1584	3¢ Ballot Box (1977)	2.25	4.00	11.50(100)	.70	.20	.15
1585	4¢ Books & Eyeglasses (1977)	2.25	4.00	13.00(100)	.85	.20	.15
1590	9¢ Capitol, from bklt pane (1977)	15.00	....	....	....	1.25	1.00
1590a	same, perf 10 (1977)	....	....	....	....	31.50	....
1590,1623	Attached pair, from bklt pane	....	....	....	....	1.75	....
1590a, 1623b	Attached pair, perf. 10	....	....	....	....	35.00	....
1591	9¢ Capitol, grey paper	2.25	4.00	30.00(100)	1.50	.40	.15
1592	10¢ Justice (1977)	2.25	4.00	32.00(100)	1.50	.40	.15
1593	11¢ Printing Press	2.25	4.00	40.00(100)	1.75	.50	.15
1594	12¢ Torch (1981)	2.25	4.00	42.50(100)	2.25	.50	.15
1595	13¢ Liberty Bell from bklt pane	2.25				.50	.15
1595a	13¢ bklt pane of 6	2.25				3.25	
1595b	13¢ bklt pane of 7– Slogan VIII	2.50				3.50	
1595c	13¢ bklt pane of 8	2.50				3.50	
1595d	13¢ bklt pane of 5– Slogan IX (1976)	2.25				3.50	

VIII–Paying Bills... IX–Collect Stamps...

SCOTT NO.	DESCRIPTION	SING	PL. BLK.	MINT SHEET	PLATE BLOCK	UNUSED F/NH	USED
1596	13¢ Eagle & Shield	2.25	4.00	45.00(100)	6.00(12)	.50	.15
1597	15¢ Fort McHenry Flag (1978)	2.25	4.00	43.00(100)	9.50(20)	.50	.15
1598	same, from bklt pane (1978)	2.25				.90	.15
1598a	15¢ bklt pane of 8	3.00				8.50	
1599	16¢ Statue of Liberty (1978)	2.25	4.00	55.00(100)	3.00	.60	.30
1603	24¢ Old North Church	2.25	4.00	80.00(100)	4.00	.95	.20
1604	28¢ Fort Nisqually (1978)	2.25	4.00	90.00(100)	5.00	1.10	.20
1605	29¢ Lighthouse (1978)	2.25	4.00	100.00(100)	5.00	1.20	.50
1606	30¢ School House (1979)	2.25	4.00	100.00(100)	5.00	1.20	.20
1608	50¢ "Betty" Lamp (1979)	2.50	5.25	180.00(100)	8.25	2.00	.30
1610	$1 Rush Lamp (1979)	3.50	17.50	350.00(100)	14.50	3.50	.20
1610c	Same, candle flame inverted	....	....	....	....	14500.00	....
1611	$2 Kerosene Lamp (1978)	7.00	14.50	600.00(100)	27.00	6.25	.70
1612	$5 Conductor's Lantern (1979)	15.00	31.50	1400.00(100)	70.00	15.00	3.00

1613

1614

1615

1615C

1975-79 COIL STAMPS Perforated Vertically

SCOTT NO.	DESCRIPTION	SING	PL. BLK.		LINE PR.	UNUSED F/NH	USED
1613-19	3.1¢-16¢, 9 varieties, complete	....	....	....	12.50	3.75	1.80
1613	3.1¢ Guitar (1979)	2.25	2.75	....	1.20	.45	.20
1614	7.7¢ Saxhorns (1976)	2.25	2.75	....	1.30	.60	.40
1615	7.9¢ Drum (1976)	2.25	2.75	....	1.20	.60	.40
1615C	8.4¢ Piano (1978)	2.25	2.75	....	3.75	.60	.40
1616	9¢ Capitol (1976)	2.25	2.75	....	1.30	.60	.40
1617	10¢ Justice (1977)	2.25	2.75	....	1.10	.50	.20
1618	13¢ Liberty Bell	2.25	2.75	....	1.00	.60	.30
1618C	15¢ Fort McHenry Flag (1978)	2.25				.65	.20
1619	16¢ Statue of Liberty (1978)	2.25	2.75	....	2.50	.75	.60

COIL LINE PAIRS: are two connected coil stamps with a line the same color as the stamps printed between the two stamps. This line usually appears every 20 to 30 stamps on a roll depending on the issue.

1622, 1625

1623, 1623b

1975-77 REGULAR ISSUES

SCOTT NO.	DESCRIPTION	SING	PL. BLK.	MINT SHEET	PLATE BLOCK	UNUSED F/NH	USED
1622	13¢ Flag & Independence Hall, 11 x 10½	2.25	4.00	48.00(100)	12.00(20)	.55	.15
1622c	same, perf. 11 (1981)	....	....	180.00(100)	90.00(20)	1.20	....
1623	13¢ Flag & Capitol from bklt pane, perf 11 x 10½ (1977)	3.00	....	....	....	.50	.50
1623a	bklt pane of 8 (one–1590, seven–1623)	30.00	....	....	....	3.75	3.75
1623b	13¢ Flag & Capitol from bklt pane, perf. 10	2.25				.90	.75
1623c	bklt pane of 8 (one–1590a, seven–1623b)	17.00				40.00	....

1975 COIL STAMP

SCOTT NO.	DESCRIPTION	SING	PL. BLK.	MINT SHEET	PLATE BLOCK	UNUSED F/NH	USED
1625	13¢ Flag & Independence Hall	2.25			3.75	.55	.15

1629   1630   1631

1632

1976 COMMEMORATIVES

SCOTT NO.	DESCRIPTION	SING	PL. BLK.	MINT SHEET	PLATE BLOCK	UNUSED F/NH	USED
1629/1703	(1629-32, 1683-85, 1690-1703) 21 varieties	....	....	....	....	12.80	3.50
1629-31	Spirit of '76, 3 varieties, attached	3.00	6.00	19.00(50)	6.00(12)	1.75	1.25
1629	13¢ Boy Drummer	2.00	....	....	....	.50	.20
1630	13¢ Older Drummer	2.00	....	....	....	.50	.20
1631	13¢ Fifer	2.00	....	....	....	.50	.20
1632	13¢ Interphil	2.25	4.00	18.75(50)	1.75	.45	.20

1633

1682

1976 BICENTENNIAL STATE FLAGS
Complete Set Printed in One Sheet of 50 Stamps

1633	Delaware	1650	Louisiana	1667	West Virginia
1634	Pennsylvania	1651	Indiana	1668	Nevada
1635	New Jersey	1652	Mississippi	1669	Nebraska
1636	Georgia	1653	Illinois	1670	Colorado
1637	Connecticut	1654	Alabama	1671	North Dakota
1638	Massachusetts	1655	Maine	1672	South Dakota
1639	Maryland	1656	Missouri	1673	Montana
1640	South Carolina	1657	Arkansas	1674	Washington
1641	New Hampshire	1658	Michigan	1675	Idaho
1642	Virginia	1659	Florida	1676	Wyoming
1643	New York	1660	Texas	1677	Utah
1644	North Carolina	1661	Iowa	1678	Oklahoma
1645	Rhode Island	1662	Wisconsin	1679	New Mexico
1646	Vermont	1663	California	1680	Arizona
1647	Kentucky	1664	Minnesota	1681	Alaska
1648	Tennessee	1665	Oregon	1682	Hawaii
1649	Ohio	1666	Kansas		

SCOTT NO.	DESCRIPTION	FIRST DAY COVERS SING	FIRST DAY COVERS PL. BLK.	MINT SHEET	PLATE BLOCK	UNUSED F/NH	USED

1976 BICENTENNIAL STATE FLAGS
Complete Set Printed in One Sheet of 50 Stamps
Continued

1633-82	13¢ State Flags, 50 varieties, attached.	....	....	32.00(50)	....	32.00	....
	Set of 50 singles	95.00	....	....	....	....	18.75
	Singles of above	2.50	....	....	....	1.00	.50

1683

1684

1685

1683	13¢ Telephone.	2.25	4.00	20.00(50)	2.10	.60	.20
1684	13¢ Aviation.	2.25	4.00	32.00(50)	8.50(10)	.75	.20
1685	13¢ Chemistry	2.25	4.00	25.00(50)	7.50(12)	.60	.20

1686

1687

1976 BICENNTENNIAL SOUVENIR SHEETS

1686-89	4 varieties, complete . .	32.50	....	....	....	30.00	27.00
1686	13¢ Cornwallis Surrender	6.00	....	....	....	5.00	4.75
1686a-e	13¢ singles, each.	3.50	....	....	....	1.20	1.10
1687	18¢ Independence.	7.50	....	....	....	7.00	6.50
1687a-e	18¢ singles, each.	3.75	....	....	....	1.60	1.50
1688	24¢ Washington Crossing Delaware	9.50	....	....	....	8.75	8.25
1688a-e	24¢ singles, each.	4.25	....	....	....	1.90	1.80
1689	31¢ Washington at Valley Forge.	11.50	....	....	....	11.00	10.50
1689a-e	31¢ singles, each.	5.25	....	....	....	2.40	2.30

SCOTT NO.	DESCRIPTION	FIRST DAY COVERS SING	FIRST DAY COVERS PL. BLK.	MINT SHEET	PLATE BLOCK	UNUSED F/NH	USED

1690

1691   **1692**   **1693**   **1694**

1690	13¢ Benjamin Franklin.	2.25	4.00	24.00(50)	2.20	.50	.20
1691-94	Declaration of Independence, 4 varieties, attached . .	5.00	10.00	36.00(50)	14.50(16)	4.00	3.00
1691	13¢ Delegation members	2.25	....	....	....	1.10	.25
1692	13¢ Adams, etc.	2.25	....	....	....	1.10	.25
1693	13¢ Jefferson, Franklin, etc.	2.25	....	....	....	1.10	.25
1694	13¢ Hancock, Thomson, etc.	2.25	....	....	....	1.10	.25

1695   **1696**   **1697**   **1698**

1695-98	Olympic Games, 4 varieties, attached . .	4.00	6.00	23.50(50)	6.75(12)	2.40	1.95
1695	13¢ Diving	2.25	....	....	....	.75	.25
1696	13¢ Skiing	2.25	....	....	....	.75	.25
1697	13¢ Running	2.25	....	....	....	.75	.25
1698	13¢ Skating	2.25	....	....	....	.75	.25

1699   **1700**

| 1699 | 13¢ Clara Maass . . . . . | 2.25 | 4.00 | 20.00(40) | 7.00(12) | .60 | .20 |
| 1700 | 13¢ Adolph S. Ochs. . . | 2.25 | 4.00 | 16.00(32) | 2.25 | .60 | .20 |

1701   **1702, 1703**

1701	13¢ Nativity	2.25	....	20.00(50)	6.00(12)	.55	.20
1702	13¢ "Winter Pastime" (Andreati).	2.25	....	20.00(50)	5.25(10)	.55	.20
1703	13¢ "Winter Pastime" (Gravure Int.)	2.25	....	20.00(50)	10.00(20)	.55	.20

SCOTT NO.	DESCRIPTION	FIRST DAY COVERS SING	PL. BLK.	MINT SHEET	PLATE BLOCK	UNUSED F/NH	USED

1705

1704

1977 COMMEMORATIVES

SCOTT NO.	DESCRIPTION	SING	PL. BLK.	MINT SHEET	PLATE BLOCK	F/NH	USED
1704-30	**27 varieties, complete**	....	....	....	....	13.00	5.00
1704	13¢ Princeton	2.25	4.00	20.00(40)	5.50(10)	.60	.20
1705	13¢ Sound Recording .	2.25	4.00	25.00(50)	2.25	.60	.20

1708   1709

1706   1707

1706-09	Pueblo Art, 4 varieties, attached . .	4.00	....	18.00(40)	5.75(10)	3.00	2.50
1706	13¢ Zia.	2.25	....	....	....	.75	.25
1707	13¢ San Ildefonso	2.25	....	....	....	.75	.25
1708	13¢ Hopi	2.25	....	....	....	.75	.25
1709	13¢ Acoma.	2.25	....	....	....	.75	.25

1710

1711

1710	13¢ Transatlantic Flight	3.00	5.00	28.00(50)	7.50(12)	.60	.20
1711	13¢ Colorado Statehood	2.25	4.00	28.00(50)	7.50(12)	.60	.20

1712

1713

SCOTT NO.	DESCRIPTION	FIRST DAY COVERS SING	PL. BLK.	MINT SHEET	PLATE BLOCK	UNUSED F/NH	USED

1714   1715

1716

1712-15	Butterflies, 4 varieties, attached . .	4.00	6.00	25.00(50)	7.50(12)	3.00	2.50
1712	13¢ Swallowtail	2.25	....	....	....	.60	.20
1713	13¢ Checkerspot	2.25	....	....	....	.60	.20
1714	13¢ Dogface	2.25	....	....	....	.60	.20
1715	13¢ Orange-Tip	2.25	....	....	....	.60	.20
1716	13¢ Lafayette.	2.25	6.00	17.00(40)	1.90	.50	.20

1717   1718

1719   1720

1717-20	Skilled Hands, 4 varieties, attached . .	4.00	....	22.00(50)	6.50(12)	2.50	2.00
1717	13¢ Seamstress.	2.25	....	....	....	.60	.20
1718	13¢ Blacksmith	2.25	....	....	....	.60	.20
1719	13¢ Wheelwright	2.25	....	....	....	.60	.20
1720	13¢ Leatherworker. . . .	2.25	....	....	....	.60	.20

1721   1722

1723   1724

1721	13¢ Peace Bridge	2.25	4.00	24.00(50)	3.00	.50	.20
1722	13¢ Herkimer at Oriskany	2.25	4.00	17.50(40)	4.75(10)	.50	.20
1723-24	Energy, 2 varieties, attached . .	2.50	....	20.00(40)	6.00(12)	1.10	.85
1723	13¢ Conservation	2.25	....	....	....	.60	.20
1724	13¢ Development	2.25	....	....	....	.60	.20

SCOTT NO.	DESCRIPTION	FIRST DAY COVERS SING	PL. BLK.	MINT SHEET	PLATE BLOCK	UNUSED F/NH	USED

1799
1800

1979 COMMEMORATIVES

| 1799 | 15¢ Christmas–Madonna | 2.25 | .... | 42.00(100) | 6.25(12) | .55 | .15 |
| 1800 | 15¢ Christmas–Santa Claus | 2.25 | .... | 42.00(100) | 6.25(12) | .55 | .15 |

1801
1802

| 1801 | 15¢ Will Rogers | 3.00 | .... | 25.00(50) | 7.00(12) | .55 | .20 |
| 1802 | 15¢ Vietnam Veterans | 3.00 | 5.25 | 30.00(50) | 7.00(10) | .55 | .75 |

1803
1804

1980 COMMEMORATIVES

1795/1843	(1795-98, 1803-10, 1821-43) 35 varieties, complete	....	....	....	....	21.50	6.80
1803	15¢ W.C. Fields	2.25	4.00	25.00(50)	6.50(12)	.55	.20
1804	15¢ Benjamin Banneker	2.25	4.00	35.00(50)	9.50(12)	.85	.20

1805
1806, 1808, 1810
1807
1809

1805-10	6 varieties, attached	4.50	....	35.00(60)	24.00(36)	4.25	2.75
1805-06	2 varieties, attached	2.50	....	....	....	....	....
1807-08	2 varieties, attached	2.50	....	....	....	....	....
1809-10	2 varieties, attached	2.50	....	....	....	....	....
1805	15¢ "Letters Preserve Memories"	2.25				.75	.30
1806	15¢ claret & multicolor	2.25				.75	.30
1807	15¢ "Letters Lift Spirits"	2.25				.75	.30
1808	15¢ green & multicolor	2.25				.75	.25
1809	15¢ "Letters Shape Opinions"	2.25				.75	.30
1810	15¢ red, white & blue	2.25				.75	.30

1813
1818, 1819, 1820

1980-81 Coil Stamps, Perf. 10 Vertically

SCOTT NO.	DESCRIPTION	FIRST DAY COVERS SING	PL. BLK. LINE PR.	MINT SHEET	PLATE BLOCK LINE PR.	UNUSED F/NH	USED
1811	1¢ Inkwell & Quill	2.25	2.75	....	.50	.20	.15
1813	3.5¢ Two Violins	2.25	2.75	....	1.40	.30	.25
1816	12¢ Torch (1981)	2.25	2.75	....	2.25	.50	.40
1818	(18¢) "B" definitive	2.50	3.50	55.00(100)	3.00	.70	.15
1819	(18¢) "B" definitive, from bklt pane	2.25	....	....	....	1.00	.15
1819a	(18¢) "B" bklt pane of 8	4.00	....	....	....	7.00	....

1981 Coil Stamp Perf. Vertically

| 1820 | (18¢) "B" definitive | 2.25 | 2.75 | .... | 2.00 | .75 | .15 |

1821
1822
1823

1824
1825
1826

1821	15¢ Frances Perkins	2.25	4.00	25.00(50)	2.50	.60	.20
1822	15¢ Dolley Madison	2.25	4.00	70.00(150)	2.50	.60	.20
1823	15¢ Emily Bissell	2.25	4.00	25.00(50)	2.50	.60	.20
1824	15¢ Helen Keller & Anne Sullivan	2.25	4.00	35.00(50)	3.25	.80	.20
1825	15¢ Veterans Administration	2.25	4.00	25.00(50)	2.50	.60	.20
1826	15¢ General Bernardo deGalvez	2.25	4.00	37.00(50)	3.50	.60	.20

1827
1828
1829
1830

1827-30	Coral Reefs, 4 varieties, attached	5.00	....	22.50(50)	7.00(12)	2.50	2.00
1827	15¢ Brain Coral, Virgin Is.	2.25	....	....	....	.80	.20
1828	15¢ Elkhorn Coral, Florida	2.25	....	....	....	.80	.20
1829	15¢ Chalice Coral, American Samoa	2.25	....	....	....	.80	.20
1830	15¢ Finger Coral, Hawaii	2.25	....	....	....	.80	.20

1831
1832
1833

1831	15¢ Organized Labor	2.25	4.00	35.00(50)	10.00(12)	.80	.20
1832	15¢ Edith Wharton	2.25	4.00	27.50(50)	2.75	.65	.20
1833	15¢ Education	2.25	4.00	30.00(50)	3.75(6)	.65	.20

SCOTT NO.	DESCRIPTION	FIRST DAY COVERS SING	PL. BLK.	MINT SHEET	PLATE BLOCK	UNUSED F/NH	USED

1834 1835

1836 1837

1834-37	American Folk Art, 4 varieties, attached	5.00	....	27.00(40)	9.00(10)	3.25	2.00
1834	15¢ Bella Bella Tribe	2.25	....	....	....	1.00	.20
1835	15¢ Chilkat Tlingit Tribe	2.25	....	....	....	1.00	.20
1836	15¢ Tlingit Tribe	2.25	....	....	....	1.00	.20
1837	15¢ Bella Coola Tribe	2.25	....	....	....	1.00	.20

1838 1839

1840 1841

1838-41	American Architecture, 4 varieties, attached	4.00	5.00	25.00(40)	3.50	3.00	2.00
1838	15¢ Smithsonian Inst.	2.25	....	....	....	.90	.20
1839	15¢ Trinity Church	2.25	....	....	....	.90	.20
1840	15¢ Penn Academy	2.25	....	....	....	.90	.20
1841	15¢ Lyndhurst	2.25	....	....	....	.90	.20

1842 1843

| 1842 | 15¢ Madonna | 2.25 | 4.00 | 22.50(50) | 6.50(12) | .55 | .15 |
| 1843 | 15¢ Christmas Wreath & Toy | 2.25 | 4.00 | 23.50(50) | 11.75(20) | .55 | .15 |

SE-TENANTS: Beginning with the 1964 Christmas issue (#1254-57), the United States has issued numerous Se-Tenant stamps covering a wide variety of subjects. Se-Tenants are issues where two or more different stamp designs are produced on the same sheet in pair, strip or block form. Mint stamps are usually collected in attached blocks, etc.; used are generally saved as single stamps.

1844 1845 1846 1847

1848 1849 1850 1851

1852 1853 1854 1855

1856 1857 1858 1859

1860 1861 1862 1863

1864 1865 1866 1867

1868 1869

1980-85 GREAT AMERICANS

SCOTT NO.	DESCRIPTION	FIRST DAY COVERS SING	PL. BLK.	MINT SHEET	PLATE BLOCK	UNUSED F/NH	USED
1844-69	1¢-50¢, 26 varieties, complete	....	....		....	16.50	5.40
1844	1¢ Dorothea Dix (1983)	2.25	4.00	10.00(100)	3.25(20)	.25	.20
1844a	same, Bullseye perf.	....	....		2.25(20)	.25	....
1845	2¢ Igor Stravinsky (1982)	2.25	4.00	10.00(100)	.80	.25	.20
1846	3¢ Henry Caly (1983)	2.25	4.00	11.25(100)	.80	.25	.20
1847	4¢ Carl Schurz (1983)	2.25	4.00	15.00(100)	.80	.25	.20
1848	5¢ Pearl Buck (1983)	2.25	4.00	70.00(100)	3.00	.70	.20
1849	6¢ Walter Lippmann (1985)	2.25	4.00	17.50(100)	3.75(20)	.25	.25
1850	7¢ Abraham Baldwin (1985)	2.25	4.00	30.00(100)	5.50(20)	.60	.20
1851	8¢ Henry Knox (1985)	2.25	4.00	27.00(100)	1.25	.30	.20
1852	9¢ Sylvanus Thayer (1985)	2.25	4.00	35.00(100)	7.00(20)	.40	.25
1853	10¢ Richard Russell (1984)	2.25	4.00	50.00(100)	8.50(20)	.60	.20
1854	11¢ Partridge (1985)	2.25	4.00	60.00(100)	3.00	.45	.20
1855	13¢ Crazy Horse (1982)	2.25	4.00	57.00(100)	3.00	.50	.40
1856	14¢ Sinclair Lewis (1985)	2.25	4.00	70.00(100)	17.00(20)	.80	.20
1857	17¢ Rachel Carson (1981)	2.25	4.00	50.00(100)	2.50	.60	.20
1858	18¢ George Mason (1981)	2.25	4.00	55.00(100)	3.75	.60	.20
1859	19¢ Sequoyah	2.25	4.00	65.00(100)	3.50	.75	.40
1860	20¢ Ralph Bunche (1982)	2.25	4.00	70.00(100)	4.00	.80	.20
1861	20¢ T. H. Gallaudet (1983)	2.25	4.00	70.00(100)	4.25	1.00	.20

SCOTT NO.	DESCRIPTION	FIRST DAY COVERS SING	PL. BLK.	MINT SHEET	PLATE BLOCK	UNUSED F/NH	USED
1862	20¢ Harry Truman (1984)	2.25	4.00	65.00(100)	15.00(20)	.80	.20
1862a	same, Bullseye perf. .	....	....	....	4.50	.80	....
1863	22¢ J. Audubon (1985)	2.25	4.00	75.00(100)	16.00(20)	.80	.20
1863a	same, Bullseye perf. .	....	....	....	5.50	.80	....
1864	30¢ F.C. Laubach (1984)	2.25	4.00	90.00(100)	20.00(20)	1.00	.20
1864a	same, Bullseye perf. .	....	....	....	5.00	1.00	....
1865	35¢ Charles Drew (1981)	2.25	4.50	140.00(100)	7.00	4.50	.40
1866	37¢ Robert Millikan (1982)	2.25	4.50	125.00(100)	6.00	1.20	.20
1867	39¢ Grenville Clark(1985)	2.25	4.50	125.00(100)	24.00(20)	1.20	.20
1867a	same, Bullseye perf. .	....	....	....	6.25	1.20	....
1868	40¢ Lillian Gilbreth (1984)	2.25	4.50	110.00(100)	25.00(20)	1.35	.20
1868a	same, Bullseye perf. .	....	....	....	6.25	1.35	....
1869	50¢ Chester Nimitz (1985)	2.25	4.50	145.00(100)	10.00	1.60	.20
1869a	same, Bullseye perf. .	....	....	....	10.00	1.60	....

1874

1875

1981 COMMEMORATIVES

1874/1945	(1874-79, 1910-45) 42 varieties, complete	....	....	....	....	32.00	8.75
1874	15¢ Everett Dirksen...	2.25	4.00	22.00(50)	2.10	.55	.20
1875	15¢ Whitney Moore Young	2.25	4.00	30.00(50)	3.00	.65	.20

1876   1877

1878   1879

1876-79	Flowers, 4 varieties, attached ..	5.00	6.00	32.50(48)	3.50	3.25	2.60
1876	18¢ Rose...........	2.25	....	....	....	.80	.25
1877	18¢ Camellia........	2.25	....	....	....	.80	.25
1878	18¢ Dahlia.........	2.25	....	....	....	.80	.25
1879	18¢ Lily...........	2.25	....	....	....	.80	.25

1880   1881   1882   1883   1884

1885   1886   1887   1888   1889

1981 WILDLIFE DEFINITIVES

1880-89	Wildlife, set of singles .	17.00	....	....	....	10.50	1.90
1880	18¢ Bighorned Sheep .	2.25	....	....	....	1.10	.20
1881	18¢ Puma..........	2.25	....	....	....	1.10	.20
1882	18¢ Seal..........	2.25	....	....	....	1.10	.20
1883	18¢ Bison.........	2.25	....	....	....	1.10	.20
1884	18¢ Brown Bear......	2.25	....	....	....	1.10	.20
1885	18¢ Polar Bear.......	2.25	....	....	....	1.10	.20
1886	18¢ Elk...........	2.25	....	....	....	1.10	.20
1887	18¢ Moose..........	2.25	....	....	....	1.10	.20
1888	18¢ White-tailed Deer .	2.25	....	....	....	1.10	.20
1889	18¢ Pronghorned Antelope	2.25	....	....	....	1.10	.20
1889a	Wildlife, bklt pane of 10 .	6.50	....	....	....	11.25	....

1890   1891   1892

1893   1894, 1895, 1896

1981 FLAG AND ANTHEM ISSUE

SCOTT NO.	DESCRIPTION	FIRST DAY COVERS SING	PL. BLK.	MINT SHEET	PLATE BLOCK	UNUSED F/NH	USED
1890	18¢ "Waves of Grain"..	2.25	4.00	67.00(100)	14.50(20)	.75	.15

1981 Coil Stamp Perf. 10 Vertically

			PLATE#		PLATE#		
		STRIP 3	STRIP 3		STRIP 3	PLATE# STRIP 3	
1891	18¢ "Shining Sea"	2.25	....	....	6.00	.60	.15

1981

1892	6¢ Stars, from bklt pane	2.25	....	....	....	1.75	1.25
1893	18¢ "Purple Mountains" from bklt pane	2.25	....	....	....	.75	.15
1892-93	6¢ & 18¢ as above, attached pair	....	....	....	....	2.75	....
1893a	2-1892, 6-1893 bklt pane of 8........	5.25	....	....	....	7.50	....

			PLATE BLOCK		PLATE BLOCK		
1894	20¢ Flag & Supreme Court	2.25	4.00	110.00(100)	22.50(20)	1.10	.15

			PLATE# STRIP 3		PLATE# STRIP 3		
1895	20¢ Flag & Supreme Court	2.25	5.00	....	4.50	.65	.15
1896	20¢ Flag & Supreme Court, from bklt pane	2.25	....	....	....	.80	.15
1896a	20¢ bklt pane of 6	3.50	....	....	....	4.25	....
1896b	20¢ bklt pane of 10 ...	5.50	....	....	....	7.00	....

Note: For plate number strips of 5, see page 149

1897

1897A

1898

1898A

1899

1900

1901

1902

1903

1904

1905

1906

SCOTT NO.	DESCRIPTION	FIRST DAY COVERS SING	FIRST DAY COVERS PL. BLK.	MINT SHEET	PLATE BLOCK	UNUSED F/NH	USED

1907

1908

NOTE: #1898A—"Stagecoach 1890s" is 19-1/2 mm long.

1981-84 Perf. 10 Vertically TRANSPORTATION COILS

1897-1908 1¢-20¢, 14 varieties, complete		PLATE# STRIP 3 29.50		PLATE# STRIP 3		4.25	2.60
1897	1¢ Omnibus (1983) . . .	2.25	17.50	....	.70	.20	.20
1897A	2¢ Locomotive (1982) .	2.25	25.00	....	.75	.20	.20
1898	3¢ Handcar (1983). . . .	2.25	25.00	....	1.05	.20	.20
1898A	4¢ Stagecoach (1982) .	2.25	22.50	....	1.80	.20	.20
1899	5¢ Motorcycle (1983). .	2.25	25.00	....	1.25	.20	.20
1900	5.2¢ Sleigh (1983) . . .	2.25	37.50	....	7.00	.30	.20
1901	5.9¢ Bicycle (1982) . . .	2.25	37.50	....	8.00	.50	.40
1902	7.4¢ Baby Buggy (1984)	2.25	25.00	....	9.50	.50	.40
1903	9.3¢ Mail Wagon	2.25	42.50	....	4.00	.30	.20
1904	10.9¢ Hansom Cab (1982)	2.25	40.00	....	8.00	.50	.40
1905	11¢ Caboose (1984) . .	2.25	40.00	....	4.00	.40	.20
1906	17¢ Electric Car.	2.25	37.50	....	3.75	.60	.20
1907	18¢ Surrey.	2.25	55.00	....	4.00	.65	.20
1908	20¢ Fire Pumper	2.25	55.00	....	3.75	.65	.20

NOTE: Plate # Strips of 3 and 5 have plate number under center stamp. Some issues have lines between two of the stamps.

PRECANCELLED COILS

The following are for precancelled, unused, never hinged stamps.
Stamps without gum sell for less.

SCOTT NO.		PL# STRIP 3	UNUSED
1895b	20¢ Supreme Court	90.00	1.00
1898Ab	4¢ Stagecoach.	8.50	.35
1900a	5.2¢ Sleigh	10.00	.30
1901a	5.9¢ Bicycle	50.00	.45
1902a	7.4¢ Baby Buggy	6.25	.40
1903a	9.3¢ Mail Wagon	4.50	.40
1904a	10.9¢ Hansom Cab	40.00	.50
1905a	11¢ Caboose	4.50	.45
1906a	17¢ Electric Car	6.00	.55

1909

1983 EXPRESS MAIL BOOKLET SINGLE

1909	$9.35 Eagle & Moon . .	75.00	....	....	....	35.00	27.00
1909a	$9.35 bklt pane of 3. . .	200.00	....	....	....	95.00	....

1910

1911

1981 COMMEMORATIVES (Continued)

1910	18¢ American Red Cross	2.25	4.00	27.75(50)	3.25	.60	.20
1911	18¢ Savings & Loans Assoc.	2.25	4.00	25.75(50)	2.75	.60	.20

SCOTT NO.	DESCRIPTION	FIRST DAY COVERS SING	FIRST DAY COVERS PL. BLK.	MINT SHEET	PLATE BLOCK	UNUSED F/NH	USED

1912

1913

1914

1915

1916

1917

1918

1919

1912-19	Space Achievement, 8 varieties, attached . .	6.00	9.00	34.50(48)	7.00(8)	5.00	5.50
1912-19	same, set of singles. . .	15.50	....	....	....	....	1.80
1912	18¢ Exploring the Moon	2.00	....	....	....	.80	.25
1913	18¢ Releasing Boosters	2.00	....	....	....	.80	.25
1914	18¢ Cooling Electric Systems.	2.00	....	....	....	.80	.25
1915	18¢ Understanding the Sun	2.00	....	....	....	.80	.25
1916	18¢ Probing the Planets	2.00	....	....	....	.80	.25
1917	18¢ Shuttle and Rockets	2.00	....	....	....	.80	.25
1918	18¢ Landing.	2.00	....	....	....	.80	.25
1919	18¢ Comprehending the Universe	2.00	....	....	....	.80	.25

1920

1920	18¢ Professional Management	2.25	4.00	26.50(50)	2.75	.60	.20

1921

1922

1923

1924

1921-24	Wildlife Habitats, 4 varieties, attached . .	5.00	6.00	48.00(50)	5.00	4.00	3.00
1921	18¢ Blue Heron	2.25	....	....	....	.90	.25
1922	18¢ Badger	2.25	....	....	....	.90	.25
1923	18¢ Grizzly Bear	2.25	....	....	....	.90	.25
1924	18¢ Ruffled Grouse . . .	2.25	....	....	....	.90	.25

SCOTT NO.	DESCRIPTION	FIRST DAY COVERS SING	PL. BLK.	MINT SHEET	PLATE BLOCK	UNUSED F/NH	USED

1925   **1926**   **1927**

1925	18¢ Disabled Persons .	2.25	4.00	26.00(50)	2.75	.75	.20
1926	18¢ Edna St. Vincent Millay	2.25	4.00	26.00(50)	2.75	.75	.20
1927	18¢ Alcoholism	4.50	7.00	60.00(50)	47.50(20)	.75	.20

1928   **1929**

1930   **1931**

1928-31	American Architecture, 4 varieties, attached . .	5.00	6.00	32.50(40)	4.25	3.75	3.00
1928	18¢ New York Univ. Library	2.25	....	....	....	1.00	.25
1929	18¢ Biltmore House . . .	2.25	....	....	....	1.00	.25
1930	18¢ Palace of the Arts .	2.25	....	....	....	1.00	.25
1931	18¢ National Farmers Bank	2.25	....	....	....	1.00	.25

1932   **1933**

| 1932 | 18¢ Babe Zaharias . . . | 12.00 | 15.00 | 38.00(50) | 4.50 | .90 | .30 |
| 1933 | 18¢ Bobby Jones . . . . . | 15.00 | 18.00 | 80.00(50) | 8.25 | 1.75 | .30 |

1934

1935   **1936**

SCOTT NO.	DESCRIPTION	FIRST DAY COVERS SING	PL. BLK.	MINT SHEET	PLATE BLOCK	UNUSED F/NH	USED

1937   **1938**

1934	18¢ Coming Through the Rye	2.25	4.50	38.00(50)	3.75	.80	.20
1935	18¢ James Hoban	2.25	4.00	26.00(50)	2.75	.60	.20
1936	20¢ James Hoban	2.25	4.00	26.00(50)	3.00	.60	.20
1937-38	Yorktown/Virginia Capes, 2 varieties, attached . .	2.00	4.00	29.00(50)	3.35	1.75	1.25
1937	18¢ Yorktown	2.25	....	....	....	1.00	.30
1938	18¢ Virginia Capes . . .	2.25	....	....	....	1.00	.30

1939   **1940**   **1941**

1939	(20¢) Madonna & Child	2.25	4.00	52.00(100)	2.75	.60	.15
1940	(20¢) Christmas Toy . .	2.25	4.00	27.00(50)	2.75	.60	.15
1941	20¢ John Hanson	2.25	4.00	29.50(50)	3.00	.70	.15

1943

1942   **1944**   **1945**

1942-45	Desert Plants, 4 varieties, attached . .	5.00	6.00	32.50(40)	4.00	3.75	3.00
1942	20¢ Barrel Cactus	2.25	....	....	....	1.00	.25
1943	20¢ Agave	2.25	....	....	....	1.00	.25
1944	20¢ Beavertail Cactus .	2.25	....	....	....	1.00	.25
1945	20¢ Saguaro	2.25	....	....	....	1.00	.25

1946, 1947, 1948   **1949**

1981-1982 Regular Issues

| 1946 | (20¢) "C" Eagle, 11x10½ | 2.25 | 4.00 | 65.00(100) | 3.00 | .60 | .15 |

			LINE PAIR		LINE PAIR		
1947	(20¢) "C" Eagle, coil. . .	2.25	2.75	....	2.25	.80	.15
1948	(20¢) "C" Eagle, from pane	2.25	....	....	....	.80	.15
1948a	same, bklt pane of 10 .	6.00	....	....	....	7.50	....
1949	20¢ Bighorned Sheep, blue, from bklt pane (1982) .	2.25	....	....	....	.75	.15
1949a	same, bklt pane of 10 .	6.00	....	....	....	7.50	....
1949c	Type II, from bklt pane.	....	....	....	....	16.00	.40
1949d	same, bklt pane of 10 .	....	....	....	....	16.00	....

SCOTT NO.	DESCRIPTION	FIRST DAY COVERS SING	PL. BLK.	MINT SHEET	PLATE BLOCK	UNUSED F/NH	USED

1950

1951

1952

1982 COMMEMORATIVES

SCOTT NO.	DESCRIPTION	SING	PL. BLK.	MINT SHEET	PLATE BLOCK	UNUSED F/NH	USED
1950/2030	(1950-52, 2003-04, 2006-30) 30 varieties	....	....	....	....	24.00	5.75
1950	20¢ Franklin D. Roosevelt	2.25	4.00	30.50(48)	2.90	.80	.20
1951	20¢ LOVE, perf. 11 . . .	1.85	4.25	30.50(50)	2.90	.65	.20
1951a	same, perf. 11x 10½ . .	....	....	51.75(50)	5.50	1.10	.35

NOTE: Perforations will be mixed on Used #1951.

| 1952 | 20¢ George Washington | 2.25 | 4.00 | 40.00(50) | 3.75 | .80 | .20 |

1982 STATE BIRDS AND FLOWERS

1953

1953	Alabama	1978	Montana
1954	Alaska	1979	Nebraska
1955	Arizona	1980	Nevada
1956	Arkansas	1981	New Hampshire
1957	California	1982	New Jersey
1958	Colorado	1983	New Mexico
1959	Connecticut	1984	New York
1960	Delaware	1985	North Carolina
1961	Florida	1986	North Dakota
1962	Georgia	1987	Ohio
1963	Hawaii	1988	Oklahoma
1964	Idaho	1989	Oregon
1965	Illinois	1990	Pennsylvania
1966	Indiana	1991	Rhode Island
1967	Iowa	1992	South Carolina
1968	Kansas	1993	South Dakota
1969	Kentucky	1994	Tennessee
1970	Louisiana	1995	Texas
1971	Maine	1996	Utah
1972	Maryland	1997	Vermont
1973	Massachusetts	1998	Virginia
1974	Michigan	1999	Washington
1975	Minnesota	2000	West Virginia
1976	Mississippi	2001	Wisconsin
1977	Missouri	2002	Wyoming

1973

1966

2002

Perf. 10½ x 11

1953-2002	20¢, 50 varieties, attached.......	....		45.00(50)	....	45.00	....
	set of singles.	86.00	....	....	....	....	25.00
	singles of above	2.00	....	....	....	1.10	.65
1953a-2002a	same, perf. 11.	....	....	47.50(50)	....	47.50	....
	singles of above	....	....	....	....	1.25	....

NOTE: Used singles will not be sorted by perf. sizes.

2003

2004

2005

| 2003 | 20¢ USA/Netherlands . | 2.25 | 4.00 | 34.50(50) | 17.00(20) | .70 | .20 |
| 2004 | 20¢ Library of Congress | 2.25 | 4.00 | 28.00(50) | 2.75 | .60 | .20 |

		PLATE# STRIP 3		PLATE# STRIP 3			
2005	20¢ Consumer Education, Coil	2.25	60.00	....	28.50	1.20	.15

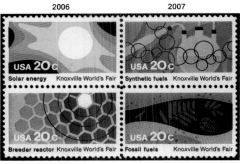
2006   2007   2008   2009

2006-09	World's Fair, 4 varieties, attached . .	5.00	6.00	42.50(50)	4.50	4.00	2.00
2006	20¢ Solar Energy.	2.25	....	....	....	1.00	.20
2007	20¢ Synthetic Fuels . .	2.25	....	....	....	1.00	.20
2008	20¢ Breeder Reactor . .	2.25	....	....	....	1.00	.20
2009	20¢ Fossil Fuels	2.25	....	....	....	1.00	.20

2010

2011

2012

2010	20¢ Horatio Alger.	2.25	4.00	27.00(50)	2.75	.60	.20
2011	20¢ Aging Together . . .	2.25	4.00	27.00(50)	2.75	.60	.20
2012	20¢ Barrymores.	2.25	4.00	30.00(50)	2.75	.60	.20

2013

2014

2015

2013	20¢ Dr. Mary Walker . .	2.25	4.00	29.50(50)	3.00	.60	.20
2014	20¢ Peace Garden . . .	2.25	4.00	60.00(50)	6.00	1.20	.20
2015	20¢ America's Libraries	2.25	4.00	27.00(50)	2.75	.60	.20

2016

2017

2018

2016	20¢ Jackie Robinson . .	7.00	13.50	110.00(50)	11.00	2.50	.20
2017	20¢ Touro Synagogue .	3.00	4.00	40.00(50)	18.00(20)	.85	.20
2018	20¢ Wolf Trap Farm. . .	2.25	4.00	27.00(50)	2.50	.60	.20

PLATE BLOCKS: are portions of a sheet of stamps adjacent to the number(s) indicating the printing plate number used to produce that sheet. Flat plate issues are usually collected in plate blocks of six (number opposite middle stamp) while rotary issues are normally corner blocks of four.

SCOTT NO.	DESCRIPTION	FIRST DAY COVERS SING	PL. BLK.	MINT SHEET	PLATE BLOCK	UNUSED F/NH	USED

2019 **2020**

2021 **2022**

2019-22	American Architecture, 4 varieties, attached ..	5.00	6.00	35.00(40)	4.50	4.00	3.25
2019	20¢ Fallingwater Mill Run	2.25	....	....	....	1.25	.25
2020	20¢ Illinois Inst. Tech ..	2.25	....	....	....	1.25	.25
2021	20¢ Gropius House ...	2.25	....	....	....	1.25	.25
2022	20¢ Dulles Airport	2.25	....	....	....	1.25	.25

2023 **2024**

2025 **2026**

2023	20¢ St. Francis of Assisi	2.25	4.00	30.00(50)	3.00	.65	.20
2024	20¢ Ponce de Leon ...	2.25	4.00	47.00(50)	21.00(20)	1.00	.20
2025	13¢ Kitten & Puppy, Christmas	2.25	4.00	19.50(50)	2.25	.50	.20
2026	20¢ Madonna & Child, Christmas	2.25	4.00	30.00(50)	16.50(20)	.65	.20

2027 **2028**

2029 **2030**

2027-30	Winter Scenes, Christmas, 4 varieties, attached ..	4.00	5.00	43.00(50)	5.00	4.25	3.50
2027	20¢ Sledding	2.25	....	....	....	1.25	.20
2028	20¢ Snowman	2.25	....	....	....	1.25	.20
2029	20¢ Skating	2.25	....	....	....	1.25	.20
2030	20¢ Decorating	2.25	....	....	....	1.25	.20

2031

1983 COMMEMORATIVES

| 2031-65 | 13¢-20¢, 35 varieties, complete.......... | .... | .... | .... | .... | 28.40 | 7.50 |
| 2031 | 20¢ Science & Industry | 2.25 | 4.00 | 27.00(50) | 2.75 | .60 | .20 |

2033

2032 **2034** **2035**

2032-35	20¢ Ballooning, 4 varieties, attached ..	5.00	6.00	27.00(40)	3.75	3.25	2.50
2032	20¢ Intrepid	2.25	....	....	....	1.10	.25
2033	20¢ Red, white, & blue balloon.............	2.25	....	....	....	1.10	.25
2034	20¢ Yellow, gold & green balloon.............	2.25	....	....	....	1.10	.25
2035	20¢ Explorer II	2.25	....	....	....	1.10	.25

  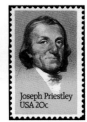

2036 **2037** **2038**

2036	20¢ USA/Sweden	2.25	4.00	27.00(50)	2.75	.65	.20
2037	20¢ Civilian Conservation Corps.............	2.25	4.00	27.00(50)	2.75	.65	.20
2038	20¢ Joseph Priestley ..	2.25	4.00	27.00(50)	2.75	.65	.20

2039

2040 **2041**

2039	20¢ Volunteerism.....	2.25	4.00	34.50(50)	18.00(20)	.65	.20
2040	20¢ German Immigrants	2.25	4.00	27.00(50)	2.75	.65	.20
2041	20¢ Brooklyn Bridge ..	3.00	5.00	30.00(50)	2.75	.65	.20

SCOTT NO.	DESCRIPTION	FIRST DAY COVERS SING	PL. BLK.	MINT SHEET	PLATE BLOCK	UNUSED F/NH	USED

2042

2043

2044

2042	20¢ Tennessee Valley Authority	2.25	4.00	34.50(50)	18.00(20)	.65	.80
2043	20¢ Physical Fitness . .	2.25	4.00	34.50(50)	18.00(20)	.65	.80
2044	20¢ Scott Joplin	2.25	4.00	35.00(50)	3.00	.75	1.00

2045

2046

2047

2045	20¢ Medal of Honor . . .	6.00	8.00	30.00(40)	3.75	.85	.20
2046	20¢ Babe Ruth	8.00	16.00	110.00(50)	10.00	2.50	.20
2047	20¢ Nathaniel Hawthorne	2.25	4.00	32.50(50)	3.25	.75	.20

2048   2049

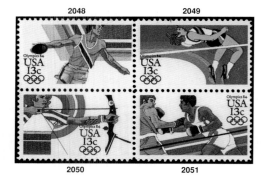

2050   2051

2048-51	Olympics, 4 varieties, attached . .	5.00	6.00	30.00(50)	4.00	3.50	2.75
2048	13¢ Discus	2.25	. . . .	. . . .	. . . .	1.00	.30
2049	13¢ High Jump	2.25	. . . .	. . . .	. . . .	1.00	.30
2050	13¢ Archery	2.25	. . . .	. . . .	. . . .	1.00	.30
2051	13¢ Boxing	2.25	. . . .	. . . .	. . . .	1.00	.30

2052

2053

2054

2052	20¢ Treaty of Paris . . .	2.25	4.00	24.00(40)	3.00	.65	.20
2053	20¢ Civil Service	2.25	4.00	34.50(50)	18.00(20)	.65	.20
2054	20¢ Metropolitan Opera	2.25	4.00	30.00(50)	3.00	.65	.20

2055   2056

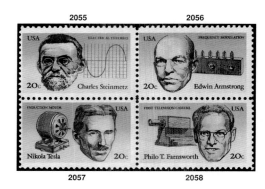

2057   2058

2055-58	Inventors, 4 varieties, attached . .	5.00	6.00	47.50(50)	5.75	5.00	3.50
2055	20¢ Charles Steinmetz	2.25	. . . .	. . . .	. . . .	1.35	.25
2056	20¢ Edwin Armstrong .	2.25	. . . .	. . . .	. . . .	1.35	.25
2057	20¢ Nikola Tesla	2.25	. . . .	. . . .	. . . .	1.35	.25
2058	20¢ Philo T. Farnsworth	2.25	. . . .	. . . .	1.35	.25	.25

2059   2060

2061   2062

2059-62	Streetcars, 4 varieties, attached . .	5.00	6.00	37.50(50)	4.75	4.00	3.00
2059	20¢ First Streetcar	2.25	. . . .	. . . .	. . . .	1.25	.25
2060	20¢ Electric Trolley . . .	2.25	. . . .	. . . .	. . . .	1.25	.25
2061	20¢ "Bobtail"	2.25	. . . .	. . . .	. . . .	1.25	.25
2062	20¢ St. Charles Streetcar	2.25	. . . .	. . . .	. . . .	1.25	.25

2064

2063

| 2063 | 20¢ Madonna . . . . | 2.25 | 4.00 | 27.00(50) | 2.75 | .60 | .20 |
| 2064 | 20¢ Santa Claus . . . . . | 2.25 | 4.00 | 34.50(50) | 18.00(20) | .60 | .20 |

2065

MINT SHEETS: From 1935 to date, we list prices for standard size Mint Sheets in Fine, Never Hinged condition. The number of stamps in each sheet is noted in ( ).

| 2065 | 20¢ Martin Luther . . . . | 2.25 | 4.00 | 27.00(50) | 2.75 | .60 | .20 |

SCOTT NO.	DESCRIPTION	FIRST DAY COVERS SING	FIRST DAY COVERS PL. BLK.	MINT SHEET	PLATE BLOCK	UNUSED F/NH	USED

2066

1984 COMMEMORATIVES

| 2066-2109 | 44 varieties, complete . . . . | . . . . | . . . . | . . . . | . . . . | 37.50 | 9.30 |
| 2066 | 20¢ Alaska Statehood . | 2.25 | 4.00 | 27.00(50) | 3.00 | 1.00 | .20 |

2067   **2068**   **2069**   **2070**

2067-70	Winter Olympics, 4 varieties, attached . .	5.00	6.00	39.00(50)	4.50	4.00	3.00
2067	20¢ Ice Dancing	2.25	. . . .	. . . .	. . . .	1.10	.30
2068	20¢ Downhill Skiing . . .	2.25	. . . .	. . . .	. . . .	1.10	.30
2069	20¢ Cross Country Skiing	2.25	. . . .	. . . .	. . . .	1.10	.30
2070	20¢ Hockey	2.25	. . . .	. . . .	. . . .	1.10	.30

2071   **2072**   **2073**   **2074**

2071	20¢ Federal Deposit Insurance Corporation	2.25	4.00	27.00(50)	2.75	.75	.20
2072	20¢ Love	1.95	4.00	34.50(50)	18.00(20)	.75	.20
2073	20¢ Carter G. Woodson	3.00	4.00	30.00(50)	2.00	.75	.20
2074	20¢ Conservatiion	2.25	4.00	27.00(50)	2.00	.75	.20

2076   **2077**

2075

2078   **2079**

2075	20¢ Credit Union	1.95	4.50	27.00(50)	2.75	.60	.20
2076-79	Orchids, 4 varieties, attd.	4.00	5.00	34.00(48)	3.75	3.25	2.75
2076	20¢ Wildpink	2.25	. . . .	. . . .	. . . .	.95	.25
2077	20¢ Lady's-slipper	2.25	. . . .	. . . .	. . . .	.95	.25
2078	20¢ Spreading Pogonia	2.25	. . . .	. . . .	. . . .	.95	.25
2079	20¢ Pacific Calypso . . .	2.25	. . . .	. . . .	. . . .	.95	.25

2080   **2081**

| 2080 | 20¢ Hawaii Statehood . | 2.25 | 4.00 | 30.00(50) | 3.00 | .70 | .20 |
| 2081 | 20¢ National Archives . | 2.25 | 4.00 | 30.00(50) | 3.00 | .70 | .20 |

2082   **2083**   **2084**   **2085**

2082-85	Olympics, 4 varieties, attached	5.00	6.00	51.75(50)	6.00	5.50	4.75
2082	20¢ Men's Diving	2.25	. . . .	. . . .	. . . .	1.50	.25
2083	20¢ Long Jump	2.25	. . . .	. . . .	. . . .	1.50	.25
2084	20¢ Wrestling	2.25	. . . .	. . . .	. . . .	1.50	.25
2085	20¢ Women's Kayak . .	2.25	. . . .	. . . .	. . . .	1.50	.25

2086   **2087**   **2088**

2086	20¢ Louisiana Exposition	2.25	4.00	37.50(40)	4.25	.95	.20
2087	20¢ Health Research . .	2.25	4.00	32.00(50)	3.50	.70	.20
2088	20¢ Douglas Fairbanks	2.25	4.00	65.00(50)	30.00(20)	1.30	.30

2089   **2090**   **2091**

2089	20¢ Jim Thorpe	4.50	8.00	65.00(50)	6.00	1.30	.30
2090	20¢ John McCormack .	3.00	4.00	30.00(50)	3.00	.65	.20
2091	20¢ St. Lawrence Seaway	3.00	4.00	30.00(50)	3.00	.65	.20

SE-TENANTS: Beginning with the 1964 Christmas issue (#1254-57), the United States has issued numerous Se-Tenant stamps covering a wide variety of subjects. Se-Tenants are issues where two or more different stamp designs are produced on the same sheet in pair, strip or block form. Mint stamps are usually collected in attached blocks, etc.—Used are generally saved as single stamps. Our Se-Tenant prices follow in this collecting pattern.

SCOTT NO.	DESCRIPTION	FIRST DAY COVERS SING	PL. BLK.	MINT SHEET	PLATE BLOCK	UNUSED F/NH	USED

2092

2093

2092	Preserving Wetlands . .	1.95	4.00	45.00(50)	5.00	1.10	.20
2093	Roanoke Voyages	2.25	4.00	40.00(50)	4.00	1.00	.20

2094 2095 2096 2097

2094	20¢ Herman Melville .	2.25	4.00	27.00(50)	2.75	.70	.20
2095	20¢ Horace Moses . .	2.25	4.00	40.00(50)	19.00(20)	1.20	.20
2096	20¢ Smokey Bear . . .	2.25	4.00	34.00(50)	3.50	1.20	.20
2097	20¢ Roberto Clemente	12.00	20.00	140.00(50)	13.50	2.00	.50

2098   2099

2100   2101

2098-2101	American Dogs, 4 varieties, attached .	5.00	6.00	37.50(40)	5.25	4.50	3.75
2098	20¢ Beagle, Boston Terrier	2.25	....	....	....	1.10	.25
2099	20¢ Chesapeake Bay Retriever, Cocker Spaniel	2.25	....	....	....	1.10	.25
2100	20¢ Alaskan Malamute, Collie	2.25	....	....	....	1.10	.25
2101	20¢ Black & Tan Coonhound, American Foxhound . .	2.25	....	....	....	1.10	.25

2102 2103 2104

2102	20¢ Crime Prevention .	2.25	4.00	27.00(50)	2.75	.60	.20
2103	20¢ Hispanic Americans	3.00	4.00	22.00(40)	2.75	.60	.20
2104	20¢ Family Unity	2.25	4.00	45.00(50)	22.00(20)	1.25	.20

2105 2106 2107

2105	20¢ Eleanor Roosevelt	2.25	4.00	26.00(40)	3.00	.70	.20
2106	20¢ Nation of Readers.	2.25	4.00	37.50(50)	4.00	1.10	.30
2107	20¢ Madonna & Child .	2.25	4.00	27.00(50)	2.75	.60	.20

2108

2109

2108	20¢ Santa Claus	1.35	4.00	27.00(50)	2.75	.60	.15
2109	20¢ Vietnam Veterans .	5.00	4.00	45.00(40)	5.50	1.50	.30

2110

1985 COMMEMORATIVES

2110/2166	(2110, 2137-47, 2152-66) 27 varieties	....	....	....	....	41.45	8.25
2110	22¢ Jerome Kern.	2.25	4.00	32.00(50)	3.25	.70	.20

2111-2113 2114, 2115 2116

1985 REGULAR ISSUES

2111	(22¢) "D" Eagle	2.25	4.00	100.00(100)	35.00(20)	.90	.15

			PLATE# STRIP 3		PLATE# STRIP 3		
2112	(22¢) "D" Eagle, coil. . .	2.25	21.00	....	6.75	.75	.15
2113	(22¢) "D" Eagle from bklt pane	2.25	....	....	....	1.25	.15
2113a	same, bklt pane of 10 .	7.50	....	....	....	12.00	

			PLATE BLOCK		PLATE BLOCK		
2114	22¢ Flag over Capitol	2.25	....	75.00(100)	4.00	.80	.15

			PLATE# STRIP 3		PLATE# STRIP 3		
2115	22¢ Flag over Capitol, coil	2.25	27.50	....	3.75	.70	.15
2115b	22¢ Flag "T" coil (1985-87)	2.90	....	....	5.50	.80	.15
2116	22¢ Flag over Capitol from bklt pane	2.25	....	....	....	1.00	.20
2116a	same, bklt pane of 5 . . .	2.90	....	....	....	4.75	....

SCOTT NO.	DESCRIPTION	FIRST DAY COVERS SING PL. BLK.	MINT SHEET	PLATE BLOCK	UNUSED F/NH	USED

2117

2118

2119

2120

2121

1985 SEASHELLS FROM BOOKLET PANE

Scott	Description	Sing				F/NH	Used
2117-21	Shells, strip of 5, attached	3.00	....	....	....	4.25	4.00
2117	22¢ Frilled Dogwinkle .	2.25	....	....	....	.90	.20
2118	22¢ Reticulated Helmet	2.25	....	....	....	.90	.20
2119	22¢ New England Neptune	2.25	....	....	....	.90	.20
2120	22¢ Calico Scallop....	2.25	....	....	....	.90	.20
2121	22¢ Lightning Whelk ..	2.25	....	....	....	.90	.20
2121a	22¢ Seashells, bklt pane of 10..............	7.50	....	....	....	8.00	6.50

2122

1985 EXPRESS MAIL STAMP FROM BOOKLET PANE

2122	$10.75 Eagle & Moon .	65.00	....	....	....	32.50	15.00
2122a	same, bklt pane of 3 ..	160.00	....	....	....	95.00	....
2122b	Type II, from bklt pane .	....	....	....	....	45.00	20.00
2122c	same, bklt pane of 3 ..	....	....	....	....	135.00	....

2123

2124

2125

2126

2127

2128

2129

2130

2131

2132

2133

2134

SCOTT NO.	DESCRIPTION	FIRST DAY COVERS SING PL. BLK.	MINT SHEET	PLATE BLOCK	UNUSED F/NH	USED

2135

2136

TRANSPORTATION COILS 1985-87 PERF. 10

Scott	Description	Sing	PLATE# STRIP 3		PLATE# STRIP 3	F/NH	Used
2123	3.4¢ School Bus	2.00	11.50	....	1.35	.25	.30
2124	4.9¢ Buckboard	2.00	14.00	....	1.25	.25	.30
2125	5.5¢ Star Route Truck (1986)	2.00	15.00	....	2.50	.25	.30
2126	6¢ Tricycle	2.00	14.00	....	2.00	.25	.30
2127	7.1¢ Tractor (1987) ..	2.00	15.00	....	3.15	.35	.30
2128	8.3¢ Ambulance.....	2.00	14.00	....	1.95	.35	.30
2129	8.5¢ Tow Truck (1987)	2.00	12.50	....	3.45	.35	.30
2130	10.1¢ Oil Wagon	2.00	12.50	....	2.75	.40	.30
2131	11¢ Stutz Bearcat ...	2.00	18.00	....	1.75	.40	.30
2132	12¢ Stanley Steamer.	2.00	15.00	....	2.35	.60	.30
2133	12.5¢ Pushcart	2.00	15.00	....	3.00	.40	.30
2134	14¢ Iceboat	2.00	15.00	....	2.30	.40	.30
2135	17¢ Dog Sled (1986) .	2.00	12.50	....	3.25	.70	.30
2136	25¢ Bread Wagon (1986)	2.00	15.00	....	4.00	.80	.20

Note: **For plate number strips of 5, see page 149**

PRECANCELLED COILS

The following are for precancelled, unused, never hinged stamps.
Stamps without gum sell for less.

SCOTT NO.		PL# STRIP 3	UNUSED
2123a	3.4¢ School Bus........................	7.50	.35
2124a	4.9¢ Buckboard	2.35	.35
2125a	5.5¢ Star Route Truck	2.35	.35
2126a	6¢ Tricycle	2.30	.35
2127a	7.1¢ Tractor	4.00	.35
2127b	7.1¢ Tractor, precancel (1989).............	2.75	.35
2128a	8.3¢ Ambulance	1.75	.35
2129a	8.5¢ Tow Truck.......................	4.00	.35
2130a	10.1¢ Oil Wagon	3.25	.35
2130b	10.1¢ Oil Wagon, red precancel (1988)	3.00	.35
2132a	12¢ Stanley Steamer....................	3.00	.60
2132b	12¢ Stanley Steamer "B" Press	28.00	1.85
2133a	12.5¢ Pushcart........................	4.00	.40

2137

1985 COMMEMORATIVES (continued)

2137	22¢ Mary Bethune	2.25	4.00	50.00(50)	5.00	1.00	.20

2138   2139

2140   2141

2138-41	Duck Decoys, 4 varieties, attached ..	5.00	6.00	80.00(50)	8.00	7.00	6.00
2138	22¢ Broadbill	2.25	....	....	....	2.75	1.50
2139	22¢ Mallard	2.25	....	....	....	2.75	1.50
2140	22¢ Canvasback	2.25	....	....	....	2.75	1.50
2141	22¢ Redhead........	2.25	....	....	....	2.75	1.50

SCOTT NO.	DESCRIPTION	FIRST DAY COVERS SING	FIRST DAY COVERS PL. BLK.	MINT SHEET	PLATE BLOCK	UNUSED F/NH	USED

2143

2142

2144

2145

2142	22¢ Winter Special Olympics	2.25	4.00	65.00(40)	7.00	1.70	.20
2143	22¢ "LOVE"	1.95	4.00	34.00(50)	3.25	1.00	.20
2144	22¢ Rural Electricity. . .	2.25	....	70.00(50)	35.00(20)	1.50	.20
2145	22¢ Ameripex '86.	2.25	4.00	29.00(48)	2.80	1.00	.20

2146

2147

| 2146 | 22¢ Abigail Adams. . . . | 2.25 | 4.00 | 30.00(50) | 3.75 | .85 | .20 |
| 2147 | 22¢ Frederic Bartholdi . | 2.25 | 4.00 | 29.00(50) | 3.00 | .65 | .20 |

2149

2150

1985 REGULAR ISSUE COILS

SCOTT NO.	DESCRIPTION	FIRST DAY COVERS SING	PLATE# STRIP 3		PLATE# STRIP 3	UNUSED F/NH	USED
2149	18¢ George Washington	2.25	50.00	....	4.50	.85	.30
2149a	18¢ George Washington, precancel.	....	....	....	4.25	.60	....
2150	21.1¢ Envelope	2.25	32.50	....	4.50	1.00	.75
2150a	21.1¢ Envelope, precancel	....	....	....	4.85	.75	.50

2152

2153

2154

2152	22¢ Korean War Veterans	3.00	4.00	41.50(50)	5.00	1.00	.20
2153	22¢ Social Security . . .	2.25	4.00	29.00(50)	3.50	1.00	.20
2154	22¢ World War I Veterans	3.00	4.00	41.50(50)	5.00	1.00	.20

2155   2156

2157   2158

2155-58	American Horses, 4 varieties, attached . .	5.00	6.00	125.00(40)	16.00	15.00	10.00
2155	22¢ Quarter Horse. . . .	2.25	....	....	....	3.50	.75
2156	22¢ Morgan	2.25	....	....	....	3.50	.75
2157	22¢ Saddlebred	2.25	....	....	....	3.50	.75
2158	22¢ Appaloosa.	2.25	....	....	....	3.50	.75

2160

2159

2161

2162

2163

2159	22¢ Public Education. .	2.25	4.00	60.00(50)	6.00	1.50	.20
2160-63	Youth Year, 4 varieties, attached . .	5.00	6.00	61.00(50)	8.00	6.00	4.50
2160	22¢ YMCA	2.25	....	....	....	1.75	.40
2161	22¢ Boy Scouts	2.25	....	....	....	1.75	.40
2162	22¢ Big Brothers & Big Sisters	2.25	....	....	....	1.75	.40
2163	22¢ Camp Fire.	2.25	....	....	....	1.75	.40

2164

2165

2166

2167

2164	22¢ Help End Hunger .	2.25	4.00	32.75(50)	3.00	.70	.20
2165	22¢ Madonna & Child .	2.25	4.00	29.00(50)	3.00	.60	.15
2166	22¢ Poinsettia	2.25	4.00	29.00(50)	3.00	.60	.15
2167	22¢ Arkansas Statehood	2.25	4.00	65.00(50)	6.00	1.20	.20

SCOTT NO.	DESCRIPTION	FIRST DAY COVERS SING	PL. BLK.	MINT SHEET	PLATE BLOCK	UNUSED F/NH	USED

2168 — 2169 — 2170 — 2171

2172 — 2173 — 2175 — 2176

2177 — 2178 — 2179 — 2180

2181 — 2182, 2197 — 2183 — 2184

2185 — 2186 — 2187 — 2188

2189 — 2190 — 2191 — 2192

2193 — 2194 — 2195 — 2196

1986-93 GREAT AMERICANS

SCOTT NO.	DESCRIPTION	FDC SING	FDC PL.BLK	MINT SHEET	PLATE BLOCK	UNUSED F/NH	USED
2168	1¢ Margaret Mitchell . .	5.00	6.00	10.00(100)	.75	.20	.15
2169	2¢ Mary Lyon (1987) . .	2.25	4.00	10.00(100)	.75	.20	.15
2170	3¢ Dr. Paul D. White . .	2.25	4.00	12.50(100)	.75	.20	.15
2171	4¢ Father Flanagan . . .	2.25	4.00	14.00(100)	.75	.20	.15
2172	5¢ Hugo L. Black	2.25	4.00	35.00(100)	2.00	.50	.15
2173	5¢ Luis Muñoz Marin (1990)	2.25	4.00	18.00(100)	1.10	.30	.15
2175	10¢ Red Cloud (1987) .	2.25	4.00	45.00(100)	2.50	.40	.15
2176	14¢ Julia Ward Howe (1987)	2.25	4.00	50.00(100)	2.75	1.00	.20
2177	15¢ Buffalo Bill Cody (1988)	2.25	4.00	90.00(100)	10.00	1.00	.20
2178	17¢ Belva Ann Lockwood	2.25	4.00	50.00(100)	3.00	1.00	.20
2179	20¢ Virginia Apgar (1994)	2.25	4.00	50.00(100)	3.10	1.00	.20
2180	21¢ Chester Carlson (1988)	2.25	4.00	60.00(100)	3.50	1.00	.50
2181	23¢ Mary Cassatt (1988)	2.25	4.00	65.00(100)	4.00	1.00	.20
2182	25¢ Jack London (1988)	2.25	4.00	70.00(100)	4.00	1.00	.20
2182a	as above bklt pane of 10	8.00	....	....	....	7.00	....
2183	28¢ Sitting Bull (1989) .	2.25	....	120.00(100)	7.00	1.30	.50
2184	29¢ Earl Warren (1992)	2.25	4.00	110.00(100)	6.00	1.00	.20
2185	29¢ Thomas Jefferson (1993)	2.25	4.75	110.00(100)	6.00(4)	1.00	.20
2185b	same, Plate Block of 8.	....	....	....	8.00(8)	....	....
2186	35¢ Dennis Chavez (1991)	2.25	4.00	100.00(100)	6.00	1.20	.50
2187	40¢ Claire Lee Chenault (1990)	3.00	5.00	120.00(100)	6.75	1.35	.25
2188	45¢ Dr. Harvey Cushing (1988)	1.85	4.25	130.00(100)	6.75	1.50	.25

SCOTT NO.	DESCRIPTION	FDC SING	FDC PL.BLK	MINT SHEET	PLATE BLOCK	UNUSED F/NH	USED
2189	52¢ Hubert Humphrey (1991)	2.00	4.50	160.00(100)	9.00	1.75	.25
2190	56¢ John Harvard	3.00	4.50	160.00(100)	9.00	1.75	.25
2191	65¢ H.H. Arnold (1988)	3.00	4.25	170.00(100)	9.50	2.00	.25
2192	75¢ Wendell Willkie (1992)	2.75	5.50	220.00(100)	12.00	2.00	.25
2193	$1 Dr. Bernard Revel . .	5.00	10.00	375.00(100)	19.00	4.00	.50
2194	$1 John Hopkins (1989)	5.00	10.00	60.00(20)	13.50	3.75	.50
2195	$2 William Jennings Bryan	8.00	10.00	525.00(100)	22.50	5.50	.80
2196	$5 Bret Harte (1987) . .	17.50	28.50	250.00(20)	52.50	15.00	5.00
2197	25¢ Jack London, bklt single (1988)	2.25	....	....	....	.90	.15
2197a	as above bklt pane (6), perf.10	5.00	....	....	....	5.25	....

2198 — 2199

2200

2201

1986 COMMEMORATIVES

SCOTT NO.	DESCRIPTION	FDC SING	FDC PL.BLK	MINT SHEET	PLATE BLOCK	UNUSED F/NH	USED
2167/2245	(2167, 2202-04, 2210-11, 2220-24, 2235-45) 22 varieties		....	....	....	23.30	5.75
2198	22¢ Cover & Handstamp	2.25	....	....	....	.90	.40
2199	22¢ Collector with Album	2.25	....	....	....	.90	.40
2200	22¢ No. 836 under magnifier	2.25	....	....	....	.90	.40
2201	22¢ President sheet. . .	2.25	....	....	....	.90	.40
2201a	Stamp Collecting bklt pane, 4 varieties, attached . .	6.00	....	....	....	3.50	2.60

2202

2203

2204

SCOTT NO.	DESCRIPTION	FDC SING	FDC PL.BLK	MINT SHEET	PLATE BLOCK	UNUSED F/NH	USED
2202	22¢ LOVE	1.95	4.25	39.00(50)	4.00	1.00	.20
2203	22¢ Sojourner Truth. . .	3.00	4.00	40.00(50)	4.25	1.00	.20
2204	22¢ Texas Republic. . .	3.00	4.00	57.00(50)	6.00	1.25	.20

BOOKLET PANE SINGLES: Traditionally, booklet panes have been collected only as intact panes since, other than the straight edged sides, they were identical to sheet stamps. However, starting with the 1971 8¢ Eisenhower stamp, many issues differ from the comparative sheet stamp or may even be totally different issues (e.g. #1738-42 Windmills). These newer issues are now collected as booklet singles or panes—both methods being acceptable.

SCOTT NO.	DESCRIPTION	FIRST DAY COVERS SING	FIRST DAY COVERS PL. BLK.	MINT SHEET	PLATE BLOCK	UNUSED F/NH	USED

2205

2206

2207

2208

2209

2205	22¢ Muskellunge	2.25	....	....	....	2.50	.25
2206	22¢ Altantic Cod	2.25	....	....	....	2.50	.25
2207	22¢ Largemouth Bass .	2.25	....	....	....	2.50	.25
2208	22¢ Bluefin Tuna	2.25	....	....	....	2.50	.25
2209	22¢ Catfish	2.25	....	....	....	2.50	.25
2209a	Fish, bklt pane, 5 varieties, attached.	6.50	....	....	....	12.50	9.00

2210

2211

| 2210 | 22¢ Public Hospitals . . | 2.25 | 4.00 | 34.00(50) | 3.50 | .75 | .20 |
| 2211 | 22¢ Duke Ellington . . . | 4.00 | 6.00 | 40.00(50) | 5.00 | 1.00 | .20 |

1986 PRESIDENTS MINIATURE SETS
Complete set printed on 4 miniature sheets of 9 stamps each.

2216a Washington
2216b Adams
2216c Jefferson
2216d Madison
2216e Monroe
2216f J.Q. Adams
2216g Jackson
2216h Van Buren
2216i W.H. Harrison
2217a Tyler
2217b Polk
2217c Taylor
2217d Fillmore
2217e Pierce
2217f Buchanan
2217g Lincoln
2217h A. Johnson
2217i Grant
2218a Hayes
2218b Garfield
2218c Arthur
2218d Cleveland
2218e B. Harrison
2218f McKinley
2218g T. Roosevelt
2218h Taft
2218i Wilson
2219a Harding
2219b Coolidge
2219c Hoover
2219d F.D. Roosevelt
2219e White House
2219f Truman
2219g Eisenhower
2219h Kennedy
2219i L.B. Johnson

Presidents of
the United States: I

AMERIPEX 86
International
Stamp Show
Chicago, Illinois
May 22-June 1, 1986

2216

1986 AMERIPEX '86 MINIATURE SHEETS

| 2216-19 | 22¢ 36 varieties complete in 4 minature sheets . . . . | 29.95 | .... | .... | .... | 49.00 | 28.00 |
| 2216a-19i | set of 36 singles. . . . . | 70.00 | .... | .... | .... | .... | 22.50 |

2220   2221

2222   2223

1986 COMMEMORATIVES

2220-23	Explorers, 4 varieties, attached . .	6.00	7.00	62.00(50)	7.50	6.75	5.00
2220	22¢ Elisha Kent Kane .	2.50	....	....	....	1.75	.50
2221	22¢ Adolphus W. Greely	2.50	....	....	....	1.75	.50
2222	22¢ Vilhjalmur Stefansson	2.50	....	....	....	1.75	.50
2223	22¢ R.E. Peary, M. Henson	2.50	....	....	....	1.75	.50

2224

| 2224 | 22¢ Statue of Liberty . . | 4.00 | 6.00 | 40.00(50) | 4.00 | .80 | .20 |

2225

2226

2228

1986-91 TRANSPORTATION COILS–"B" Press
Perf. 10 Vertically

SCOTT NO.	DESCRIPTION	FIRST DAY COVERS SING	PLATE# STRIP 3		PLATE# STRIP 3	UNUSED F/NH	USED
2225	1¢ Omnibus	2.25	6.50	....	.85	.20	.15
2225a	1¢ Omnibus, untagged (1991)				1.25	.20	.15
2226	2¢ Locomotive (1987) .	2.25	6.50	....	1.00	.20	.15
2226a	2¢ Locomative, untagged (1994)				1.10	.20	.15
2228	4¢ Stagecoach.	....	....	....	1.75	.20	.15
2228a	same, overall tagging (1990)	....	....	....	15.00	.75	.30
2231	8.3¢ Ambulance precancelled (1986) . . .	....	....	....	8.50	2.00	.60

Note: For plate number strips of 5, see page 149
#2225—"¢" sign eliminated. #1897 has "1¢".
#2226—inscribed "2 USA". #1897A inscribed "USA 2¢".
#2228—"Stagecoach 1890s" is 17 mm long.

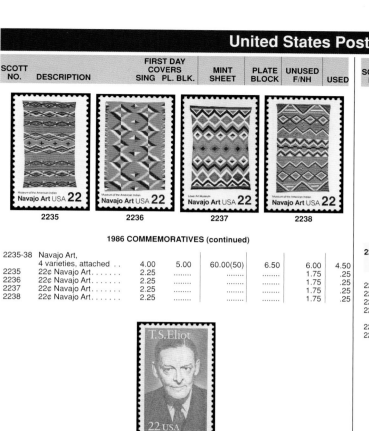

2235   2236   2237   2238

1986 COMMEMORATIVES (continued)

SCOTT NO.	DESCRIPTION	FIRST DAY COVERS SING	PL. BLK.	MINT SHEET	PLATE BLOCK	UNUSED F/NH	USED
2235-38	Navajo Art, 4 varieties, attached ..	4.00	5.00	60.00(50)	6.50	6.00	4.50
2235	22¢ Navajo Art......	2.25	....	....	....	1.75	.25
2236	22¢ Navajo Art......	2.25	....	....	....	1.75	.25
2237	22¢ Navajo Art......	2.25	....	....	....	1.75	.25
2238	22¢ Navajo Art......	2.25	....	....	....	1.75	.25

2239

2239	22¢ T.S. Eliot........	2.25	4.00	55.00(50)	5.50	1.20	.20

2240   2241   2242   2243

2240-43	Woodcarved Figurines, 4 varieties, attached ..	4.00	5.00	45.00(50)	5.00	4.25	3.50
2240	22¢ Highlander Figure .	2.25	....	....	....	1.10	.30
2241	22¢ Ship Figurehead..	2.25	....	....	....	1.10	.30
2242	22¢ Nautical Figure ...	2.25	....	....	....	1.10	.30
2243	22¢ Cigar Store Figure	2.25	....	....	....	1.10	.30

2244   2245

2244	22¢ Madonna.......	2.25	4.00	58.00(100)	3.00	.65	.15
2245	22¢ Village Scene	2.25	4.00	58.00(100)	3.00	.65	.15

2246

2247

2248

2249   2250   2251

1987 COMMEMORATIVES

SCOTT NO.	DESCRIPTION	FIRST DAY COVERS SING	PL. BLK.	MINT SHEET	PLATE BLOCK	UNUSED F/NH	USED
2246/2368	(2246-51, 2275, 2336-38, 2349-54, 2360-61, 2367-68) 20 varieties	....	....	....	....	19.40	5.00
2246	22¢ Michigan Statehood	2.25	4.00	65.00(50)	6.50	1.00	.20
2247	22¢ Pan American Games	2.25	4.00	30.00(50)	3.00	.80	.20
2248	22¢ LOVE	3.00	4.50	65.00(100)	4.00	.80	.20
2249	22¢ Jean Baptiste Pointe du Sable.....	2.25	4.00	33.00(50)	3.50	.80	.20
2250	22¢ Enrico Caruso....	2.25	4.00	33.00(50)	3.50	.80	.20
2251	22¢ Girls Scouts	2.25	4.00	35.00(50)	3.50	.80	.20

2252   2253   2254   2255

2256   2257   2258   2259

2260   2261   2262   2263

2264   2265   2266

1987-93 TRANSPORTATION COILS

SCOTT NO.	DESCRIPTION	FDC SING	PLATE# STRIP 3		PLATE# STRIP 3	UNUSED F/NH	USED
2252	3¢ Conestoga Wagon (1988)	2.25	9.00	....	1.25	.20	.20
2252a	same, untagged (1992)	....	9.00	....	1.75	.25	.20
2253	5¢ Milk Wagon.......	2.25	9.00	....	1.90	.25	.20
2254	5.3¢ Elevator, precancel ('88)	2.25	9.00	....	1.90	.40	.20
2255	7.6¢ Carreta, precancel ('88)	2.25	9.00	....	3.25	.40	.20
2256	8.4¢ Wheel Chair, precancel (1988)	2.25	9.00	....	3.25	.40	.20
2257	10¢ Canal Boat	2.25	9.00	....	3.25	.40	.20
2257a	same, overall tagging (1993)	....	9.00	....	12.00	3.00	.20
2258	13¢ Police Wagon, precancel (1988)	2.25	9.00	....	6.50	.80	.25
2259	13.2¢ Railroad Coal Car, precancel (1988)	2.25	9.00	....	3.50	.40	.20
2260	15¢ Tugboat (1988) ...	2.25	9.00	....	3.50	.50	.20
2260a	same, overall tagging (1990)	....	9.00	....	5.25	.75	.20
2261	16.7¢ Popcorn Wagon, precancel (1988)	2.25	9.00	....	4.25	.50	.20
2262	17.5¢ Racing Car.....	2.25	9.00	....	4.75	.70	.35
2262a	17.5¢ Racing Car, precancel (1988)	2.25	9.00	....	5.25	.70	.20
2263	20¢ Cable Car (1988) .	2.25	9.00	....	4.50	.70	.20
2263b	same, overall tagging (1990)	....	9.00	....	10.00	1.25	.20
2264	20.5¢ Fire Engine, precancel (1988)	2.25	9.00	....	8.00	1.25	.45
2265	21¢ Railroad Mail Car, precancel (1988)	2.25	9.00	....	5.50	.70	.45
2266	24.1¢ Tandem Bicycle, precancel (1988)	2.25	9.00	....	5.50	.85	.45

SCOTT NO.	DESCRIPTION	FIRST DAY COVERS SING	FIRST DAY COVERS PL. BLK.	MINT SHEET	PLATE BLOCK	UNUSED F/NH	USED

2267

2268

2269

2270

2271

2272

2273

2274

1987 SPECIAL OCCASIONS BOOKLET PANE

Scott	Description	Sing	Pl.Blk	Mint	Plate	Unused	Used
2267	22¢ Congratulations!..	2.25	....	....	....	2.25	.40
2268	22¢ Get Well!.......	2.25	....	....	....	2.25	.40
2269	22¢ Thank You!......	2.25	....	....	....	2.25	.40
2270	22¢ Love You, Dad!...	2.25	....	....	....	2.25	.40
2271	22¢ Best Wishes!.....	2.25	....	....	....	2.25	.40
2272	22¢ Happy Birthday!..	2.25	....	....	....	2.25	.40
2273	22¢ Love You, Mother!.	2.25	....	....	....	2.25	.40
2274	22¢ Keep in Touch!...	2.25	....	....	....	2.25	.40
2274a	Special Occasions bklt pane of 10, attached ..	17.00	....	....	....	18.50	....

NOTE: #2274a contains 1 each of #2268-71, 2273-74 and 2 each of #2267 and 2272.

2275

1987 COMMEMORATIVES (continued)

2275	22¢ United Way......	2.25	4.00	29.00(50)	3.00	1.00	.20

2276, 2276A

2277, 2279, 2282, 2282a

2278, 2285A, 2285Ac

1987-88 REGULAR ISSUE

2276	22¢ Flag & Fireworks..	2.25	4.00	58.00(100)	3.25	1.00	.15
2276a	bklt pane of 20......	12.50	....	....	....	13.50	....
2277	(25¢) "E" Earth (1988).	2.25	4.00	85.00(100)	4.25	.95	.15
2278	25¢ Flag with Clouds (1988)	2.25	4.00	70.00(100)	3.50	1.00	.15

2280

2281

2283, 2283a

2284

2285, 2285b

SCOTT NO.	DESCRIPTION	SING	PLATE # STRIP 3		PLATE# STRIP 3	UNUSED F/NH	USED
2279	(25¢) "E" Earth coil (1988)	2.25	7.50	....	4.50	.75	.15
2280	25¢ Flag over Yosemite, coil (1988)	2.25	7.50	....	4.50	.85	.15
2280a	25¢ Flag over Yosemite, phosphor (1989)	....	....	....	5.00	.95	.15
2281	25¢ Honey Bee, coil (1988)	2.25	7.50	....	4.00	.85	.15
2282	(25¢) "E" Earth, bklt single (1988)	2.25	....	....	....	.85	.20
2282a	(25¢) "E" Earth, bklt pane of 10	7.25	....	....	....	8.00	....
2283	25¢ Pheasant bklt single (1988)	2.25	....	....	....	.85	.15
2283a	25¢ Pheasant, bklt pane of 10	7.25	....	....	....	8.00	....
2283b	25¢ Pheasant, (red omitted) bklt single.	....	....	....	....	10.00	....
2283c	25¢ Pheasant, (red omitted) bklt pane of 10.......	....	....	....	....	95.00	....
2284	25¢ Grosbeak, bklt single (1988)	2.25	....	....	....	1.00	.15
2285	25¢ Owl bklt single ...	2.25	....	....	....	1.00	.15
2285b	25¢ Owl/Grosbeck, bklt pane of 10.......	7.25	....	....	....	7.00	....
2285A	25¢ Flag with Clouds, bklt single.	2.25	....	....	....	.90	.15
2285Ac	as above, bklt pane of 6 (1988)	4.00	....	....	....	5.75	....

2286

2310

2335

1987 AMERICAN WILDLIFE

2286	Barn Swallow	**2303**	Red-winged Blackbird	**2320**	Bison
2287	Monarch Butterfly	**2304**	American Lobster	**2321**	Snowy Egret
2288	Bighorn Sheep	**2305**	Black-tailed Jack Rabbit	**2322**	Gray Wolf
2289	Broad-tailed Hummingbird	**2306**	Scarlet Tanager	**2323**	Mountain Goat
2290	Cottontail	**2307**	Woodchuck	**2324**	Deer Mouse
2291	Osprey	**2308**	Roseate Spoonbill	**2325**	Black-tailed Prairie Dog
2292	Mountain Lion	**2309**	Bald Eagle	**2326**	Box Turtle
2293	Luna Moth	**2310**	Alaskan Brown Bear	**2327**	Wolverine
2294	Mule Deer	**2311**	Iiwi	**2328**	American Elk
2295	Gray Squirrel	**2312**	Badger	**2329**	California Sea Lion
2296	Armadillo	**2313**	Pronghorn	**2330**	Mockingbird
2297	Eastern Chipmunk	**2314**	River Otter	**2331**	Raccoon
2298	Moose	**2315**	Ladybug	**2332**	Bobcat
2299	Black Bear	**2316**	Beaver	**2333**	Black-footed Ferret
2300	Tiger Swallowtail	**2317**	White-tailed Deer	**2334**	Canada Goose
2301	Bobwhite	**2318**	Blue Jay	**2335**	Red Fox
2302	Ringtail	**2319**	Pika		

2286-2335	22¢, 50 varieties, attached..........	70.00	....	70.00(50)	....	70.00	....
	set of singles	86.00	....	....	....	....	30.00
	singles of above, each	2.00	....	....	....	....	1.00

2336

2337

2338

2339

SCOTT NO.	DESCRIPTION	FIRST DAY COVERS SING	PL. BLK.	MINT SHEET	PLATE BLOCK	UNUSED F/NH	USED

2340 — January 9, 1788 Connecticut

2341 — Feb 6, 1788 Massachusetts

2342 — April 28, 1788 Maryland

2343 — May 23, 1788 South Carolina

2344 — June 21, 1788 New Hampshire

2345 — June 25, 1788 Virginia

2346 — July 26, 1788 New York

2347 — November 21, 1789 North Carolina

2348 — May 29, 1790 Rhode Island

1987-90 COMMEMORATIVES

SCOTT NO.	DESCRIPTION	SING	PL. BLK.	MINT SHEET	PLATE BLOCK	UNUSED F/NH	USED
2336	22¢ Delaware Statehood	2.25	4.00	60.00(50)	6.50	1.50	.25
2337	22¢ Pennsylvania Statehood	2.25	4.00	60.00(50)	6.50	1.50	.25
2338	22¢ New Jersey Statehood	2.25	4.00	60.00(50)	6.50	1.50	.25
2339	22¢ Georgia Statehood (1988)	2.25	4.00	60.00(50)	6.50	1.50	.40
2340	22¢ Connecticut Statehood (1988)	2.25	4.00	60.00(50)	6.50	1.50	.25
2341	22¢ Massachusetts Statehood (1988)	2.25	4.00	60.00(50)	6.50	1.50	.60
2342	22¢ Maryland Statehood (1988)	2.25	4.00	60.00(50)	6.50	1.50	.40
2343	25¢ South Carolina Statehood (1988)	2.25	4.00	60.00(50)	6.50	1.50	.25
2344	25¢ New Hampshire Statehood (1988)	2.25	4.00	60.00(50)	6.50	1.50	.25
2345	25¢ Virginia Statehood (1988)	2.25	4.00	60.00(50)	6.50	1.50	.25
2346	25¢ New York Statehood (1988)	2.25	4.00	60.00(50)	6.50	1.50	.25
2347	25¢ North Carolina Statehood (1989)	2.25	4.00	60.00(50)	6.50	1.50	.25
2348	25¢ Rhode Island Statehood (1990)	2.25	9.00	60.00(50)	6.50	1.50	.25

2349 — Friendship with Morocco 1787-1987

2350 — William Faulkner

2349	22¢ Morocco	2.25	4.00	35.00(50)	3.50	.75	.20
2350	22¢ William Faulkner	2.25	4.00	50.00(50)	5.50	1.25	.20

SCOTT NO.	DESCRIPTION	FIRST DAY COVERS SING	PL. BLK.	MINT SHEET	PLATE BLOCK	UNUSED F/NH	USED

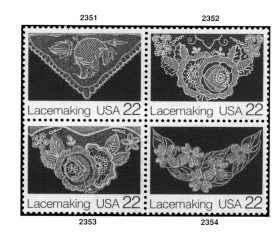

2351 2352
2353 2354

Lacemaking USA 22

2351-54	Lacemaking, 4 varieties, attached	4.00	5.00	40.00(40)	5.50	5.00	4.00
2351	22¢ Lace, Ruth Maxwell	2.25	....	....	....	1.25	.30
2352	22¢ Lace, Mary McPeek	2.25	....	....	....	1.25	.30
2353	22¢ Lace, Leslie K. Saari	2.25	....	....	....	1.25	.30
2354	22¢ Lace, Trenna Ruffner	2.25	....	....	....	1.25	.30

2355 — The Bicentennial of the Constitution of the United States of America 1787-1987 USA 22

2356 — We the people of the United States, in order to form a more perfect Union... Preamble, U.S. Constitution USA 22

2357 — Establish justice, insure domestic tranquility, provide for the common defense, promote the general welfare... Preamble, U.S. Constitution USA 22

2358 — And secure the blessings of liberty to ourselves and our posterity... Preamble, U.S. Constitution USA 22

2359 — Do ordain and establish this Constitution for the United States of America. Preamble, U.S. Constitution USA 22

2355	22¢ "The Bicentennial"	2.25	....	....	....	1.50	.30
2356	22¢ "We the people"	2.25	....	....	....	1.50	.30
2357	22¢ "Establish justice"	2.25	....	....	....	1.50	.30
2358	22¢ "And secure"	2.25	....	....	....	1.50	.30
2359	22¢ "Do ordain"	2.25	....	....	....	1.50	.30
2359a	Drafting of Constitution bklt pane, 5 varieties, attached	4.60	....	....	....	7.50	6.50

2360 — U.S. Constitution We the People 1787-1987 22 USA

2361 — CPA Certified Public Accountants 22 USA

2360	22¢ Signing of U.S. Constitution	2.25	4.00	55.00(50)	5.50	1.25	.20
2361	22¢ Certified Public Accountants	12.00	15.00	100.00(50)	10.00	2.00	.20

2362

2363

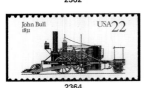
2364

2365

2366

LOCOMOTIVES ISSUE

SCOTT NO.	DESCRIPTION	FIRST DAY COVERS SING	PL. BLK.	MINT SHEET	PLATE BLOCK	UNUSED F/NH	USED
2362	22¢ "Strourbridge Lion, 1829"	2.25	....	....	....	1.25	.25
2363	22¢ "Best Friend of Charleston, 1830"	2.25	....	....	....	1.25	.25
2364	22¢ "John Bull, 1831" .	2.25	....	....	....	1.25	.25
2365	22¢ "Brother Jonathan, 1832"	2.25	....	....	....	1.25	.25
2366	22¢ "Gowan + Marx, 1839"	2.25	....	....	....	1.25	.25
2366a	Locomotives, bklt pane, 5 varieties, attached . .	4.60	....	....	....	6.00	4.75

2367

2368

| 2367 | 22¢ Madonna. . . . . . . | 2.25 | 4.00 | 58.00(100) | 3.00 | .90 | .15 |
| 2368 | 22¢ Ornament . . . . | 2.25 | 4.00 | 58.00(100) | 3.00 | .90 | .15 |

2369

2370

2371

2372 2373

Siamese Cat, Exotic Shorthair Cat
Abyssinian Cat, Himalayan Cat
Maine Coon Cat, Burmese Cat
American Shorthair Cat, Persian Cat

2374 2375

2376

2377

2378

1988 COMMEMORATIVES

SCOTT NO.	DESCRIPTION	FIRST DAY COVERS SING	PL. BLK.	MINT SHEET	PLATE BLOCK	UNUSED F/NH	USED
2339/2400	(2339-46, 2369-80, 2386-93, 2399-2400) 30 varieties	....	....	....	....	34.25	7.50
2369	22¢ Winter Olympics . .	2.25	4.00	80.00(50)	7.00	1.50	.20
2370	22¢ Australia Bicentennial	2.25	4.00	25.00(50)	3.00	.65	.20
2371	22¢ James Weldon Johnson	2.25	4.00	50.00(50)	5.00	1.00	.30
2372-75	Cats, 4 varieties, attached	8.00	12.00	40.00(40)	6.50	5.00	4.00
2372	22¢ Siamese, Exotic Shorthair	2.25	....	....	....	1.50	.60
2373	22¢ Abyssinian, Himalayan	2.25	....	....	....	1.50	.60
2374	22¢ Maine Coon, Burmese	2.25	....	....	....	1.50	.60
2375	22¢ American Shorthair, Persian	2.25	....	....	....	1.50	.60
2376	22¢ Knute Rockne. . . .	4.00	6.00	45.00(50)	4.75	1.20	.50
2377	25¢ Francis Ouimet . . .	8.00	10.00	60.00(50)	7.00	1.25	.30
2378	25¢ LOVE	2.25	4.00	68.00(100)	3.50	.75	.20

2379

2380

| 2379 | 45¢ LOVE . . . . | 2.25 | 4.00 | 67.50(50) | 7.00 | 1.50 | .25 |
| 2380 | 25¢ Summer Olympics | 2.25 | 4.00 | 40.00(50) | 3.75 | 1.00 | .20 |

2381

2382

2383

2384

2385

2381	25¢ Locomobile	2.25	....	....	....	2.25	.25
2382	25¢ Pierce-Arrow.	2.25	....	....	....	2.25	.25
2383	25¢ Cord	2.25	....	....	....	2.25	.25
2384	25¢ Packard	2.25	....	....	....	2.25	.25
2385	25¢ Duesenberg	2.25	....	....	....	2.25	.25
2385a	Classic Automobiles bklt pane , 5 varieties, attached	4.60	....	....	....	12.00	8.00

BOOKLET PANE SINGLES: Traditionally, booklet panes have been collected only as intact panes since, other than the straight edged sides, they were identical to sheet stamps. However, starting with the 1971 8¢ Eisenhower stamp, many issues differ from the comparative sheet stamp or may even be totally different issues (e.g. #1738-42 Windmills). These newer issues are now collected as booklet singles or panes—both methods being acceptable.

SCOTT NO.	DESCRIPTION	FIRST DAY COVERS SING	PL. BLK.	MINT SHEET	PLATE BLOCK	UNUSED F/NH	USED

2386 · 2387 · 2388 · 2389

SCOTT NO.	DESCRIPTION	SING	PL. BLK.	MINT SHEET	PLATE BLOCK	UNUSED F/NH	USED
2386-89	Antarctic Explorers, 4 varieties, attached . .	4.00	5.00	57.50(50)	6.75	5.75	4.50
2386	25¢ Nathaniel Palmer .	2.25	....	....	....	1.50	.40
2387	25¢ Lt. Charles Wilkes.	2.25	....	....	....	1.50	.40
2388	25¢ Richard E. Byrd . .	2.25	....	....	....	1.50	.40
2389	25¢ Lincoln Ellsworth. .	2.25	....	....	....	1.50	.40

2390 · 2391 · 2392 · 2393

2390-93	Carousel Animals, 4 varieties, attached . .	4.00	5.00	57.50(50)	6.75	6.00	4.75
2390	25¢ Deer	2.25	....	....	....	1.60	.30
2391	25¢ Horse	2.25	....	....	....	1.60	.30
2392	25¢ Camel.	2.25	....	....	....	1.60	.30
2393	25¢ Goat	2.25	....	....	....	1.60	.30

2394

2394	$8.75 Express Mail . . .	32.00	70.00	495.00(20)	120.00	27.00	12.00

2395 · 2396

2397 · 2398

2395-2398	Special Occasions, bklt singles.	7.00				4.50	1.20
2396a	Bklt pane (6) with gutter 3-#2395 + 3-#2396 . .	4.60	....	....	....	6.00	5.00
2398a	Bklt pane (6) with gutter 3-#2397 + 3-#2398 . .	4.60	....	....	....	6.00	5.00

2399

2400

2399	25¢ Madonna and Child	2.25	4.00	32.00(50)	3.25	1.00	.15
2400	25¢ One Horse Sleigh .	2.25	4.00	32.00(50)	3.25	1.00	.15

2401

2402

1989 COMMEMORATIVES

2347/2437	(2347, 2401-04, 2410-14, 2416-18, 2420-28, 2434-37) 26 varieties	....	....	....	....	27.70	5.75
2401	25¢ Montana Statehood	2.25	4.00	75.00(50)	7.00	1.50	.20
2402	25¢ A.P. Randolph	3.00	4.00	55.00(50)	5.00	1.20	.20

2403

2404

2403	25¢ North Dakota Statehood	2.25	4.00	75.00(50)	7.00	1.50	.20
2404	25¢ Washington Statehood	2.25	4.00	75.00(50)	7.00	1.50	.20

2405 · 2406

2407 · 2408

2409

2405	25¢ "Experiment,1788-90"	2.25	....	....	....	1.40	.25
2406	25¢ "Phoenix, 1809" . .	2.25	....	....	....	1.40	.25
2407	25¢ "New Orleans, 1812"	2.25	....	....	....	1.40	.25
2408	25¢ "Washington, 1816"	2.25	....	....	....	1.40	.25
2409	25¢ "Walk in the Water,1818"	2.25	....	....	....	1.40	.25
2409a	Steamboat, bklt pane, 5 varieties, attached . .	6.00	....	....	....	6.50	5.00
2409av	same, bklt pane, unfolded	....	....	....	....	10.00	

SCOTT NO.	DESCRIPTION	FIRST DAY COVERS SING	PL. BLK.	MINT SHEET	PLATE BLOCK	UNUSED F/NH	USED

2410

2411

| 2410 | 25¢ World Stamp Expo '89 | 2.25 | 4.00 | 35.00(50) | 3.75 | 1.00 | .20 |
| 2411 | 25¢ Arturo Toscanini .. | 2.25 | 4.00 | 35.00(50) | 3.75 | 1.00 | .20 |

2412   2413   2414   2415

2412	25¢ U.S. House of Representatives......	2.25	4.00	45.00(50)	4.50	1.00	.20
2413	25¢ U.S. Senate	2.25	4.00	57.00(50)	5.00	1.00	.20
2414	25¢ Executive Branch .	2.25	4.00	45.00(50)	5.00	1.00	.20
2415	25¢ U.S. Supreme Court (1990)	2.25	4.00	45.00(50)	4.75	1.00	.20

2416

| 2416 | 25¢ South Dakota Statehood .... | 2.25 | 4.00 | 80.00(50) | 8.00 | 2.00 | .20 |

2417   2418

| 2417 | 25¢ Lou Gehrig ...... | 5.00 | 8.00 | 55.00(50) | 6.00 | 1.20 | .30 |
| 2418 | 25¢ Ernest Hemingway | 2.25 | 4.00 | 42.50(50) | 4.50 | 1.00 | .20 |

2419

| 2419 | $2.40 Moon Landing .. | 7.50 | 15.75 | 160.00(20) | 40.00 | 12.00 | 7.50 |

SCOTT NO.	DESCRIPTION	FIRST DAY COVERS SING	PL. BLK.	MINT SHEET	PLATE BLOCK	UNUSED F/NH	USED

2420

2421

| 2420 | 25¢ Letter Carriers.... | 2.25 | 4.00 | 26.00(50) | 3.25 | 1.00 | .20 |
| 2421 | 25¢ Bill of Rights ..... | 2.25 | 4.00 | 55.00(50) | 5.75 | 1.25 | .20 |

2422   2423

2424   2425

2422-25	Prehistoric Animals, 4 attached	5.00	7.00	52.50(40)	6.25	6.25	4.50
2422	25¢ Tyrannosaurus Rex	2.50	....	....	....	1.50	.25
2423	25¢ Pteranodon......	2.50	....	....	....	1.50	.25
2424	25¢ Stegosaurus	2.50	....	....	....	1.50	.25
2425	25¢ Brontosaurus	2.50	....	....	....	1.50	.25

2426

| 2426 | 25¢ Kachina Doll ..... | 2.25 | 4.00 | 45.00(50) | 5.00 | 1.00 | .20 |

2427   2428, 2429   2431

2427	25¢ Madonna & Child .	1.75	4.00	40.00(50)	4.00	1.00	.15
2427a	same, bklt pane of 10 .	7.25	....	....	....	9.00	....
2427av	same, bklt pane, unfolded	....	....	....	....	10.00	....
2428	25¢ Sleigh full of Presents	2.25	4.00	40.00(50)	4.00	.75	.15
2429	25¢ Sleigh full of Presents, bklt single.	2.25	....	....	....	.90	.20
2429a	same, bklt pane of 10 .	7.25	....	....	....	8.00	....
2429av	same, bklt pane, unfolded	....	....	....	....	21.00	....
2431	25¢ Eagle & Shield, self-adhesive	1.95	....	....	....	1.25	.75
2431a	same, bklt pane of 18 .	32.00	....	....	....	19.50	....
2431	same, coil	....	....	....	3.00(3)	.85	....

SCOTT NO.	DESCRIPTION	FIRST DAY COVERS SING	PL. BLK.	MINT SHEET	PLATE BLOCK	UNUSED F/NH	USED

2433

| 2433 | $3.60 World Stamp Expo, Imperf. Souvenir Sheet | 15.00 | .... | .... | .... | 25.00 | 20.00 |

2434 **2435**

2436 **2437**

2434-37	Classic Mail Delivery, 4 attached	5.00	7.00	45.00(40)	6.25	5.50	4.00
2434	25¢ Stagecoach.	2.25	....	....	....	1.50	.40
2435	25¢ Paddlewheel Steamer	2.25	....	....	....	1.50	.40
2436	25¢ Biplane	2.25	....	....	....	1.50	.40
2437	25¢ Automobile	2.25	....	....	....	1.50	.40
2438	$1.00 Classic Mail Delivery Imperf. Souvenir Sheet	4.50	....	....	....	8.00	5.00

2439

2440, 2441

2442

1990 COMMEMORATIVES

| 2348/2515 | (2348, 2415, 2439-40, 2442, 2444-49, 2496-2500, 2506-15, 26 varieties, | .... | .... | .... | .... | 32.55 | 5.75 |

2439	25¢ Idaho Statehood . .	2.25	4.00	70.00(50)	7.00	1.50	.20
2440	25¢ LOVE	2.25	4.00	32.00(50)	3.25	1.50	.20
2441	25¢ LOVE, bklt single . .	2.25	....	....	....	1.25	.20
2441a	25¢ LOVE bklt pane of 10	8.65	....	....	....	12.00	....
2441av	same, bklt pane, unfolded	....	....	....	....	50.00	....
2442	25¢ Ida B. Wells	3.00	4.00	70.00(50)	7.00	1.50	.20

2443

2444

SCOTT NO.	DESCRIPTION	FIRST DAY COVERS SING	PL. BLK.	MINT SHEET	PLATE BLOCK	UNUSED F/NH	USED

2445

2449

2446

2447

2448

2443	15¢ Umbrella, bklt single	2.25	....	....	....	.70	.25
2443a	15¢ Umbrella, bklt pane of 10	5.75	....	....	....	5.00	3.40
2443av	same, bklt pane, unfolded	....	....	....	....	9.00	....
2444	25¢ Wyoming Statehood	8.00	10.00	70.00(50)	7.00	2.00	.20
2445-48	Classic Films, 4 varieties, attached . .	8.00	7.00	87.00(40)	12.00	10.00	7.50
2445	25¢ Wizard of OZ	4.00	....	....	....	2.75	.25
2446	25¢ Gone with the Wind	4.00	....	....	....	2.75	.25
2447	25¢ Beau Geste.	4.00	....	....	....	2.75	.25
2448	25¢ Stagecoach.	4.00	....	....	....	2.75	.25
2449	25¢ Marianne Craig Moore	2.25	4.00	55.00(50)	5.00	1.75	.20

2451

2452, 2452B, 2452D

2453, 2454

2457, 2458

2463

2464

2466

2468

1990-95 TRANSPORTATION COILS

SCOTT NO.	DESCRIPTION	SING	PLATE# STRIP 3		PLATE# STRIP 3	UNUSED F/NH	USED
2451	4¢ Steam Carriage (1991)	2.25	6.50	....	1.50	.20	.15
2451b	4¢ Steam Carriage, untagged	....	....	....	1.50	.20	.15
2452	5¢ Circus Wagon	2.25	6.50	....	1.75	.20	.15
2452a	5¢ Circus Wagon, untagged	....	....	....	1.85	.20	.20
2452B	5¢ Circus Wagon, Gravure (1992)	2.25	6.50	....	1.85	.20	.20
2452D	5¢ Circus Wagon, coil (Reissue, 1995 added)	3.00	10.00	....	1.85	.20	.20
2453	5¢ Canoe, precancel, brown (1991)	2.25	6.50	....	1.85	.20	.15
2454	5¢ Canoe, precancel, red (1991)	2.25	6.50	....	2.50	.20	.20
2457	10¢ Tractor Trailer (1991)	2.25	6.50	....	2.75	.45	.25
2458	10¢ Tractor Trailer, Gravure (1994)	2.25	6.50	....	3.25	.45	.25
2463	20¢ Cog Railway Car, coil	1.95	10.00	....	5.00	.50	.15
2464	23¢ Lunch Wagon (1991)	2.25	6.50	....	4.50	.75	.15
2466	32¢ Ferryboat, coil. . . .	1.95	10.00	....	7.00	1.00	.15
2468	$1 Seaplane, coil. . . .	3.00	10.00	....	13.00	3.00	1.00

NOTE: For plate number strips of 5, see page 149

Buy Complete Sets and Save

SCOTT NO.	DESCRIPTION	FIRST DAY COVERS SING	FIRST DAY COVERS PL. BLK.	MINT SHEET	PLATE BLOCK	UNUSED F/NH	USED

2470	2471	2472	2473	2474

2470	25¢ Admiralty Head Lighthouse..........	2.25	....	....	....	2.25	.25
2471	25¢ Cape Hatteras Lighthouse..........	2.25	....	....	....	2.25	.25
2472	25¢ West Quoddy Head Lighthouse.....	2.25	....	....	....	2.25	.25
2473	25¢ American Shoals Lighthouse..........	2.25	....	....	....	2.25	.25
2474	25¢ Sandy Hook Lighthouse..........	2.25	....	....	....	2.25	.25
2474a	Lighthouse, bklt pane, 5 varieties..........	4.60	....	....	....	9.00	7.00
2474av	Same, bklt pane, unfolded	....	....	....	....	14.50	....

2475

| 2475 | 25¢ ATM Plastic Stamp, single........ | 2.25 | .... | .... | .... | 2.00 | 1.25 |
| 2475a | Same, pane of 12 .... | 20.00 | .... | .... | .... | 13.00 | .... |

2476	2477	2478	2479

2480	2481	2482	2483

1990-95 REGULAR ISSUE

2476	1¢ Kestrel (1991).....	2.25	4.00	9.00(100)	.90	.20	.15
2477	1¢ Kestrel (redesign 1¢, 1995)	2.25	4.00	9.00(100)	.90	.20	.15
2478	3¢ Bluebird (1993)....	2.25	4.00	15.00(100)	1.50	.20	.15
2479	19¢ Fawn (1993)......	2.25	4.00	55.00(100)	5.00	.75	.15
2480	30¢ Cardinal (1993)...	2.25	4.00	85.00(100)	5.00	1.00	.80
2481	45¢ Pumpkinseed Sunfish (1992).......	2.00	4.50	135.00(100)	7.00	1.25	.75
2482	$2 Bobcat	6.00	14.00	105.00(20)	25.00	5.50	1.00
2483	20¢ Blue Jay, bklt single (1991)	1.95	....	....	....	.85	.30
2483a	same, bklt pane of 10 .	9.00	....	....	....	8.25	....
2483av	same, bklt pane, unfolded	....	....	....	....	9.00	....

2484, 2485	2486	2487, 2493, 2495	2488, 2494, 2495A

2489	2490	2491	2492

2484	29¢ Wood Duck, bklt single (BEP) (1991)	2.25	....	....	....	.95	.20
2484a	same, bklt pane of 10 (BEP)	9.00	....	....	....	8.00	....
2484av	same, bklt pane, unfolded	....	....	....	....	11.00	....
2485	29¢ Wood Duck, bklt single (KCS) (1991)	2.25	....	....	....	1.00	.20
2485a	same, bklt pane of 10 (KCS)	9.00	....	....	....	9.75	....
2485av	same, bklt pane, unfolded	....	....	....	....	12.50	....
2486	29¢ African Violet, bklt single..........	2.25	....	....	....	1.10	.20
2486a	same, bklt pane of 10 .	9.00	....	....	....	8.75	....
2486av	same, bklt pane, unfolded	....	....	....	....	9.75	....
2487	32¢ Peach, bklt single .	1.95	....	....	....	1.00	.25
2488	32¢ Pear, bklt single ..	1.95	....	....	....	1.00	.25
2488a	32¢ Peach & Pear, bklt pane of 10......	7.25	....	....	....	9.50	....
2488av	same, bklt pane, unfolded	....	....	....	....	10.75	....
2489	29¢ Red Squirrel, self-adhesive (1993)	2.25	....	....	....	.95	.45
2489a	same, bklt pane of 18 .	13.50	....	....	....	15.00	....
2489v	same, coil	....	....	....	3.00(3)	.95	....
2490	29¢ Rose, self-adhesive (1993)	2.25	....	....	....	.95	.40
2490a	same, bklt pane of 18 .	13.50	....	....	....	15.00	....
2491	29¢ Pine Cone, self-adhesive..........	2.25	....	....	....	.95	.40
2491a	same, bklt pane of 18 .	13.50	....	....	....	15.00	....
2492	32¢ Pink Rose, self-adhesive........	1.95	....	....	....	.95	.30
2492a	same, bklt pane of 20 .	14.50	....	....	....	20.00	....
2492b	same, bklt pane of 15 .	11.50	....	....	....	15.00	....
2493	32¢ Peach, self-adhesive........	1.95	....	....	....	.95	.30
2494	32¢ Pear, self-adhesive	1.95	....	....	....	.95	.30
2494a	32¢ Peach & Pear, self-adhesive, bklt pane of 20.......	14.50	....	....	....	20.00	....
2495	32¢ Peach, self-adhesive coil (1993)	1.95	....	....	7.00(3)	3.00	....
2495A	32¢ Pear, self-adhesive coil	1.95	....	....	....	3.00	....

2496	2497

2498	2499

2500

2496-2500	Olympians, strip of 5, attached..........	7.50	10.00	38.00(35)	13.00(10)	7.00	5.00
2496	25¢ Jesse Owens....	2.40	....	....	....	1.75	.50
2497	25¢ Ray Ewry	2.40	....	....	....	1.75	.50
2498	25¢ Hazel Wightman ..	2.40	....	....	....	1.75	.50
2499	25¢ Eddie Eagan.....	2.40	....	....	....	1.75	.50
2500	25¢ Helene Madison ..	2.40	....	....	....	1.75	.50

SCOTT NO.	DESCRIPTION	FIRST DAY COVERS SING	FIRST DAY COVERS PL. BLK.	MINT SHEET	PLATE BLOCK	UNUSED F/NH	USED

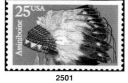
2501

2502

2503

2504

2505

2501	25¢ Assiniboine	2.40	. . . .	. . . .	. . . .	2.00	.25
2502	25¢ Cheyenne	2.40	. . . .	. . . .	. . . .	2.00	.25
2503	25¢ Comanche	2.40	. . . .	. . . .	. . . .	2.00	.25
2504	25¢ Flathead	2.40	. . . .	. . . .	. . . .	2.00	.25
2505	25¢ Shoshone	2.40	. . . .	. . . .	. . . .	2.00	.25
2505a	25¢ bklt pane of 10 . . .	7.85	. . . .	. . . .	. . . .	25.00	. . . .
2505av	same, bklt pane, unfolded	. . . .	. . . .	. . . .	. . . .	30.00	. . . .

2506   2507

2506-07	Micronesia + Marshall Islands 2 varieties, attached . .	5.00	6.00	48.00(50)	5.00	2.00	1.30
2506	25¢ Micronesia	2.50	. . . .	. . . .	. . . .	1.00	.25
2507	25¢ Marshall Islands . .	2.50	. . . .	. . . .	. . . .	1.00	.25

2508   2509

2510   2511

1990 REGULAR ISSUES

2508-11	Sea Creatures, ... 4 varieties, attached . .	5.00	6.00	40.00(40)	6.00	5.50	4.00
2508	25¢ Killer Whales	2.50	. . . .	. . . .	. . . .	1.25	.25
2509	25¢ Northern Sea Lions	2.50	. . . .	. . . .	. . . .	1.25	.25
2510	25¢ Sea Otter	2.50	. . . .	. . . .	. . . .	1.25	.25
2511	25¢ Common Dolphin .	2.50	. . . .	. . . .	. . . .	1.25	.25

SCOTT NO.	DESCRIPTION	FIRST DAY COVERS SING	FIRST DAY COVERS PL. BLK.	MINT SHEET	PLATE BLOCK	UNUSED F/NH	USED

2513

2514

2515, 2516

2512	25¢ Americas Issue (Grand Canyon)	2.25	4.00	50.00(50)	6.00	1.25	.20
2513	25¢ Dwight D. Eisenhower	2.25	4.00	43.00(40)	6.00	1.25	.20
2514	25¢ Madonna & Child– Antonello	2.25	4.00	32.50(50)	3.25	.85	.15
2514a	same, bklt pane of 10	6.50	. . . .	. . . .	. . . .	8.00	. . . .
2514av	same, bklt pane, unfolded	. . . .	. . . .	. . . .	. . . .	15.00	. . . .
2515	25¢ Christmas Tree . . .	2.25	4.00	32.50(50)	3.25	.75	.15
2516	25¢ Christmas Tree bklt single	2.25	. . . .	. . . .	. . . .	1.50	.15
2516a	same, bklt pane of 10 .	6.00	. . . .	. . . .	. . . .	12.00	. . . .
2516av	same, bklt pane, unfolded	. . . .	. . . .	. . . .	. . . .	19.50	. . . .

2517- 2519, 2520

1991 REGULAR ISSUES

| 2517 | (29¢) 'F' Flower . . . . . . | 2.25 | 4.25 | 85.00(100) | 4.25 | .95 | .15 |

			PLATE # STRIP 3		PLATE# STRIP 3		
2518	(29¢) "F" Flower, coil . .	2.25	10.00	. . . .	4.25	.85	.15
2519	(29¢) "F" Flower, bklt single (BEP)	2.25	. . . .	. . . .	. . . .	1.00	.15
2519a	same, bklt pane of 10 (BEP)	6.50	. . . .	. . . .	. . . .	10.00	. . . .
2520	(29¢) "F" Flower, bklt single (KCS)	3.00	. . . .	. . . .	. . . .	3.50	.70
2520a	same, bklt pane of 10 (KCS)	6.50	. . . .	. . . .	. . . .	27.50	. . . .

2521

2522

2521	(4¢) "F" Make-up Rate .	2.25	4.25	15.00(100)	1.00	.20	.15
2522	(29¢) "F" ATM Plastic Stamp, single	2.25	. . . .	. . . .	. . . .	1.75	.50
2522a	same, pane of 12	9.00	. . . .	. . . .	. . . .	18.00	. . . .

2523, 2523A

			PLATE# STRIP 3		PLATE# STRIP 3		
2523	29¢ Flag over Mt. Rushmore, coil	2.25	10.00	. . . .	6.00	1.20	.15
2523A	29¢ Falg over Mt. Rushmore, photogravure coil	2.25	10.00	. . . .	6.00	1.20	1.00

NOTE: For plate number strips of 5, see page 149

SCOTT NO.	DESCRIPTION	FIRST DAY COVERS SING	FIRST DAY COVERS PL. BLK.	MINT SHEET	PLATE BLOCK	UNUSED F/NH	USED

2524-27

| 2524 | 29¢ Flower. . . . . | 2.25 | 4.25 | 90.00(100) | 5.00 | 1.00 | .15 |
| 2524A | 29¢ Flower, perf. 13. . . | .... | .... | 125.00(100) | 12.00 | 1.20 | .50 |

				PLATE# STRIP 3		PLATE# STRIP 3	
2525	29¢ Flower, coil rouletted	2.25	10.00		5.50	1.00	.20
2526	29¢ Flower, coil, perf (1992)	2.25	10.00		5.50	1.00	.25
2527	29¢ Flower, bklt single	2.25	....		....	1.00	.20
2527a	same, bklt pane of 10 .	6.50	....		....	9.50	....
2527av	same, bklt pane, unfolded	....	....		....	9.75	....

2528   **2529, 2529C**   **2530**

2531   **2531A**

				PLATE# STRIP 3		PLATE# STRIP3	
2528	29¢ Flag with Olympic Rings, bklt single.	2.25	....	....	....	1.00	.15
2528a	same, bklt pane of 10 .	6.50	....	....	....	10.00	....
2528av	same, bklt pane, unfolded	....	....	....	....	9.00	....
2529	19¢ Fishing Boat Type I	2.25	10.00	....	4.50	.60	.15
2529a	same, Type II (1993) . .	....	....	....	4.50	.60	.40
2529C	19¢ Fishing Boat (reengraved)	2.25	10.00	....	7.00	1.10	.40
2530	19¢ Hot-Air Balloon bklt single.	2.25	....	....	....	.60	.25
2530a	same, bklt pane of 10 .	10.00	....	....	....	5.50	.20
2530av	same, bklt pane, unfolded	....	....	....	....	7.00	....
2531	29¢ Flags on Parade . .	2.25	4.25	95.00(100)	5.00	1.00	.20
2531A	29¢ Liberty Torch ATM Stamp	2.25	....	....	....	1.10	.30
2531Ab	same, pane of 18.	15.00	....	....	....	20.00	....

2532

1991 COMMEMORATIVES

2532/2579	(2532-35, 2537-38, 2550-51, 2553-61, 2567, 2578-79) 29 varieties	....	....	....	....	30.50	11.50
2532	50¢ Switzerland.	2.25	5.00	65.00(40)	7.50	1.75	.40

2533   **2534**   **2535, 2536**

2537   **2538**   **2539**

2533	29¢ Vermont Statehood	2.25	4.25	70.00(50)	7.50	1.50	.20
2534	29¢ Savings Bonds . . .	2.25	4.25	45.00(50)	4.50	1.00	.20
2535	29¢ Love	2.25	4.25	38.00(50)	4.00	1.00	.20
2536	29¢ Love, bklt single. .	2.25	....	....	....	1.00	.20
2536a	same, bklt pane of 10 .	6.50	....	....	....	8.50	....
2536av	same, bklt pane, unfolded	....	....	....	....	9.50	....
2537	52¢ Love	2.25	5.00	80.00(50)	7.00	1.50	.35
2538	29¢ William Saroyan . .	2.25	4.25	37.00(50)	3.75	1.00	.20
2539	$1 USPS/Olympic Rings	3.00	6.50	65.00(20)	15.00	3.50	1.50

2540

2540	$2.90 Eagle and Olympic Rings	10.00	16.50	185.00(20)	40.00	12.00	5.50

2541   **2542**

2541	$9.95 Express Mail . . .	27.00	50.00	600.00(20)	140.00	30.00	11.00
2542	$14.00 Express Mail . .	35.00	67.50	800.00(20)	200.00	45.00	22.00

2543   **2544**

2544A

2543	$2.90 Space Vechicle, priority mail	8.00	17.50	375.00(40)	45.00	10.00	2.75
2544	$3 Challenger Shuttle, priority mail (1995). . . .	8.00	17.50	165.00(20)	35.00	9.00	3.00
2544A	$10.75 Endeavour Shuttle, express mail (1995). . .	27.50	57.50	575.00(20)	130.00	30.00	10.00

SCOTT NO.	DESCRIPTION	FIRST DAY COVERS SING	FIRST DAY COVERS PL. BLK.	MINT SHEET	PLATE BLOCK	UNUSED F/NH	USED

2545

2546

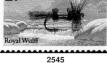
2547

2548

2549

2545	29¢ "Royal Wulff"	2.25	. . . . . .	. . . . . .		2.00	.25
2546	29¢ "Jock Scott"	2.25	. . . . . .	. . . . . .		2.00	.25
2547	29¢ "Apte Tarpon"	2.25	. . . . . .	. . . . . .		2.00	.25
2548	29¢ "Lefty's Deceiver" . .	2.25	. . . . . .	. . . . . .		2.00	.25
2549	29¢ "Muddler Minnow".	2.25	. . . . . .	. . . . . .		2.00	.25
2549a	Fishing Flies, bklt pane, 5 varieties, attached . .	4.50	. . . . . .	. . . . . .		11.00	9.00
2549av	same, bklt pane, unfolded	. . . . . .	. . . . . .	. . . . . .		16.00	. . . . . .

2550

2551, 2552

2550	29¢ Cole Porter	2.25	4.25	50.00(50)	4.50	1.10	.25
2551	29¢ Desert Storm	2.25	4.25	50.00(50)	4.50	1.10	.25
2552	29¢ Desert Storm, bklt single.	2.25	. . . . . .	. . . . . .	. . . . . .	2.50	.25
2552a	same, bklt pane of 5 . .	4.75	. . . . . .	. . . . . .	. . . . . .	5.50	. . . . . .
2552av	same, bklt pane, unfolded	. . . . . .	. . . . . .	. . . . . .	. . . . . .	7.50	. . . . . .

2553

2554

2555

2556

2557

2558

2553-57	Summer Olympics, 5 varieties, attached . .	4.50	. . . . . .	35.00(40)	10.50(10)	5.00	4.00
2553	29¢ Pole Vault	2.25	. . . . . .	. . . . . .	. . . . . .	1.10	.30
2554	29¢ Discus.	2.25	. . . . . .	. . . . . .	. . . . . .	1.10	.30
2555	29¢ Sprinters	2.25	. . . . . .	. . . . . .	. . . . . .	1.10	.30
2556	29¢ Javelin	2.25	. . . . . .	. . . . . .	. . . . . .	1.10	.30
2557	29¢ Hurdles.	2.25	. . . . . .	. . . . . .	. . . . . .	1.10	.30
2558	29¢ Numismatics	2.25	4.25	60.00(50)	6.00	1.30	.30

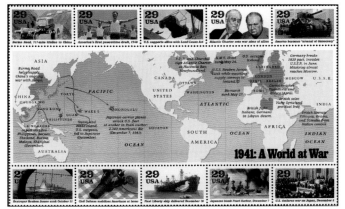
2559

2559	$2.90 World War II, 1941, souvenir sheet of 10 . .	14.00	. . . . . .	27.00(20)	. . . . . .	13.50	11.00
2559a	29¢ Burma Road	3.00	. . . . . .	. . . . . .	. . . . . .	1.35	.75
2559b	29¢ Peacetime Draft . .	3.00	. . . . . .	. . . . . .	. . . . . .	1.35	.75
2559c	29¢ Lend-Lease Act. . .	3.00	. . . . . .	. . . . . .	. . . . . .	1.35	.75
2559d	29¢ Atlantic Charter. . .	3.00	. . . . . .	. . . . . .	. . . . . .	1.35	.75
2559e	29¢ "Arsenal of Democracy"	3.00	. . . . . .	. . . . . .	. . . . . .	1.35	.75
2559f	29¢ Destroyer "Reuben James".	3.00	. . . . . .	. . . . . .	. . . . . .	1.35	.75
2559g	29¢ Civil Defense	3.00	. . . . . .	. . . . . .	. . . . . .	1.35	.75
2559h	29¢ Liberty Ship.	3.00	. . . . . .	. . . . . .	. . . . . .	1.35	.75
2559i	29¢ Pearl Harbor	3.00	. . . . . .	. . . . . .	. . . . . .	1.35	.75
2559j	29¢ Declaration of War on Japan	3.00	. . . . . .	. . . . . .	. . . . . .	1.35	.75

2560

| 2560 | 29¢ Basketball . . . . | 3.00 | 4.50 | 60.00(50) | 6.00 | 1.50 | .25 |

2561

| 2561 | 29¢ District of Columbia | 2.25 | 4.25 | 45.00(50) | 4.50 | 1.30 | .25 |

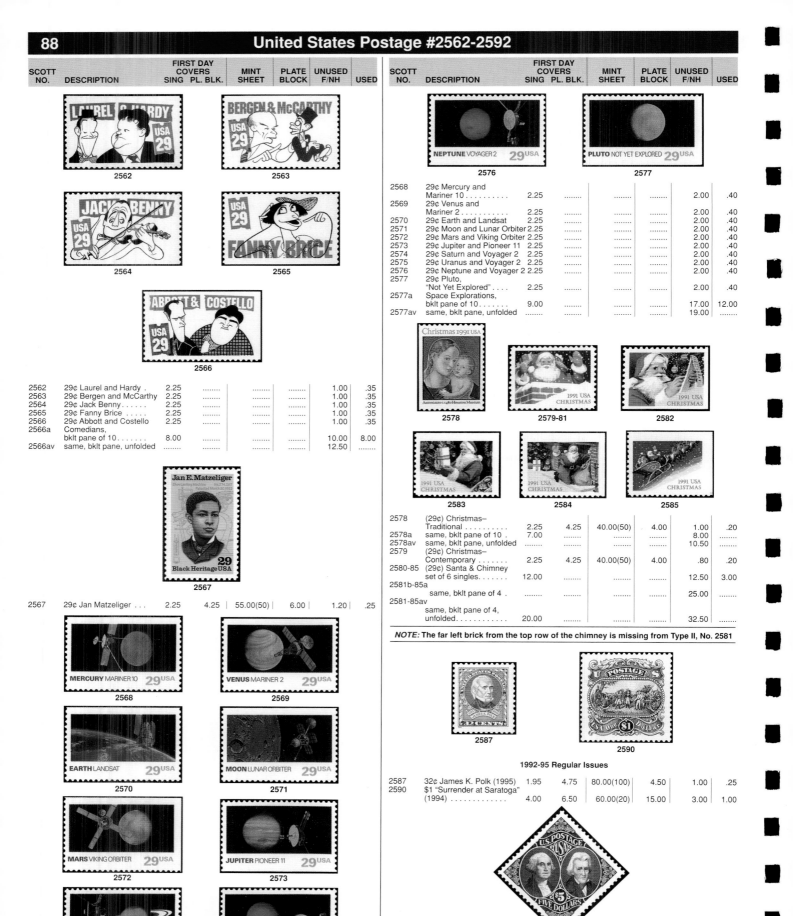

SCOTT NO.	DESCRIPTION	FIRST DAY COVERS SING	PL. BLK.	MINT SHEET	PLATE BLOCK	UNUSED F/NH	USED
2562	29¢ Laurel and Hardy .	2.25	....	....	....	1.00	.35
2563	29¢ Bergen and McCarthy	2.25	....	....	....	1.00	.35
2564	29¢ Jack Benny......	2.25	....	....	....	1.00	.35
2565	29¢ Fanny Brice	2.25	....	....	....	1.00	.35
2566	29¢ Abbott and Costello	2.25	....	....	....	1.00	.35
2566a	Comedians, bklt pane of 10	8.00	....	....	....	10.00	8.00
2566av	same, bklt pane, unfolded	....	....	....	....	12.50	....

| 2567 | 29¢ Jan Matzeliger . . . | 2.25 | 4.25 | 55.00(50) | 6.00 | 1.20 | .25 |

SCOTT NO.	DESCRIPTION	FIRST DAY COVERS SING	PL. BLK.	MINT SHEET	PLATE BLOCK	UNUSED F/NH	USED
2568	29¢ Mercury and Mariner 10	2.25	....	....	....	2.00	.40
2569	29¢ Venus and Mariner 2	2.25	....	....	....	2.00	.40
2570	29¢ Earth and Landsat	2.25	....	....	....	2.00	.40
2571	29¢ Moon and Lunar Orbiter	2.25	....	....	....	2.00	.40
2572	29¢ Mars and Viking Orbiter	2.25	....	....	....	2.00	.40
2573	29¢ Jupiter and Pioneer 11	2.25	....	....	....	2.00	.40
2574	29¢ Saturn and Voyager 2	2.25	....	....	....	2.00	.40
2575	29¢ Uranus and Voyager 2	2.25	....	....	....	2.00	.40
2576	29¢ Neptune and Voyager 2	2.25	....	....	....	2.00	.40
2577	29¢ Pluto, "Not Yet Explored"	2.25	....	....	....	2.00	.40
2577a	Space Explorations, bklt pane of 10	9.00	....	....	....	17.00	12.00
2577av	same, bklt pane, unfolded	....	....	....	....	19.00	....

2578	(29¢) Christmas– Traditional	2.25	4.25	40.00(50)	4.00	1.00	.20
2578a	same, bklt pane of 10 .	7.00	....	....	....	8.00	....
2578av	same, bklt pane, unfolded	....	....	....	....	10.50	....
2579	(29¢) Christmas– Contemporary	2.25	4.25	40.00(50)	4.00	.80	.20
2580-85	(29¢) Santa & Chimney set of 6 singles.	12.00	....	....	....	12.50	3.00
2581b-85a	same, bklt pane of 4 .	....	....	....	....	25.00	....
2581-85av	same, bklt pane of 4, unfolded.	20.00	....	....	....	32.50	....

NOTE: **The far left brick from the top row of the chimney is missing from Type II, No. 2581**

1992-95 Regular Issues

| 2587 | 32¢ James K. Polk (1995) | 1.95 | 4.75 | 80.00(100) | 4.50 | 1.00 | .25 |
| 2590 | $1 "Surrender at Saratoga" (1994) .... | 4.00 | 6.50 | 60.00(20) | 15.00 | 3.00 | 1.00 |

| 2592 | $5 Washington & Jackson (1994) .... | 22.00 | 30.00 | 275.00(20) | 60.00 | 14.00 | 4.00 |

SCOTT NO.	DESCRIPTION	FIRST DAY COVERS SING	PL. BLK.	MINT SHEET	PLATE BLOCK	UNUSED F/NH	USED

2593, 2594

SCOTT NO.	DESCRIPTION	FIRST DAY COVERS SING	PL. BLK.	MINT SHEET	PLATE BLOCK	UNUSED F/NH	USED
2593	29¢ Pledge of Allegiance (black) bklt single	2.25	....	....	....	1.00	.15
2593a	same, bklt pane of 10	7.00	....	....	....	9.50	....
2593av	same, bklt pane, unfolded	....	....	....	....	10.50	....
2594	29¢ Pledge of Allegiance (red) bklt single (1993)	2.25	....	....	....	1.50	.15
2594a	same, bklt pane of 10	7.00	....	....	....	12.00	....
2594av	same, bklt pane, unfolded	....	....	....	....	10.50	....

2595-97

2598

2599

1992-94 Self-Adhesive Stamps

SCOTT NO.	DESCRIPTION	SING	PL. BLK.	MINT SHEET	PLATE BLOCK	UNUSED F/NH	USED
2595	29¢ Eagle & Shield (brown) bklt single	2.25	....	....	....	1.20	.30
2595a	same, bklt pane of 17	12.00	....	....	....	16.50	....
2595v	same, coil	2.50	....	....	....	1.20	.30
2596	29¢ Eagle & Shield (green) bklt single	1.75	....	....	....	1.20	.30
2596a	same, bklt pane of 17	12.00	....	....	....	16.50	....
2596v	same, coil	2.50	....	....	....	1.20	.30
2597	29¢ Eagle & Shield (red) bklt single	2.25	....	....	....	1.20	.30
2597a	same, bklt pane of 17	12.00	....	....	....	16.50	....
2597v	same, coil	2.50	....	....	....	1.20	.30
2598	29¢ Eagle (1994)	2.25	....	....	....	1.20	.30
2598a	same, bklt pane of 18	13.50	....	....	....	16.50	....
2598v	29¢ Eagle, coil	2.50	....	....	5.00(3)	1.20	....
2599	29¢ Statue of Liberty (1994)	2.25	....	....	....	1.20	.30
2599a	same, bklt pane of 18	13.50	....	....	....	16.50	....
2599v	29¢ Statue of Liberty, coil	2.50	....	....	5.00(3)	1.20	....

2602

2603, 2604

2605

2606-08

2609

1991-93 Regular Issue

SCOTT NO.	DESCRIPTION	SING	PLATE# STRIP 3		PLATE# STRIP 3		USED
2602	(10¢) Eagle, Bulk-Rate coil	2.25	10.00	....	3.75	.30	.20
2603	(10¢) Eagle, Bulk-Rate coil (orange-yellow) (BEP)	2.25	10.00	....	4.25	.30	.20
2604	(10¢) Eagle, Bulk-Rate coil (Stamp Ventures) (gold) (1993)	2.25	10.00	....	3.00	.40	.20
2605	23¢ Flag, Presort First-Class	2.25	10.00	....	5.00	.70	.30
2606	23¢ USA, Presort First-Class (ABN) (1992)	2.25	10.00	....	5.75	.70	.30
2607	23¢ USA, Presort First-Class (BEP) (1992)	2.25	10.00	....	5.75	.75	.30
2608	23¢ USA, Presort First-Class (Stamp Ventures) (1993)	2.25	10.00	....	5.75	1.00	.30
2609	29¢ Flag over White House, coil (1992)	2.25	10.00	....	6.00	1.20	.15

NOTE: For plate number strips of 5, see page 149

2611

2612

2613

2614

2615

1992 COMMEMORATIVES

SCOTT NO.	DESCRIPTION	FIRST DAY COVERS SING	PL. BLK.	MINT SHEET	PLATE BLOCK	UNUSED F/NH	USED
2611/2720	(2611-23, 2630-41, 2697-2704, 2710-14, 2720) 48 varieties	....	....	....	....	50.00	16.50
2611-15	Winter Olympics, 5 varieties, attached	6.00	....	36.00(35)	10.50(10)	5.00	4.00
2611	29¢ Hockey	2.25	....	....	....	1.30	.25
2612	29¢ Figure Skating	2.25	....	....	....	1.30	.25
2613	29¢ Speed Skating	2.25	....	....	....	1.30	.25
2614	29¢ Skiing	2.25	....	....	....	1.30	.25
2615	29¢ Bobsledding	2.25	....	....	....	1.30	.25

2616

2617

SCOTT NO.	DESCRIPTION	SING	PL. BLK.	MINT SHEET	PLATE BLOCK	UNUSED F/NH	USED
2616	29¢ World Columbian Expo	2.25	4.25	42.00(50)	4.50	1.50	.25
2617	29¢ W.E.B. Du Bois	3.00	4.25	55.00(50)	5.50	1.50	.25

2618

2619

SCOTT NO.	DESCRIPTION	SING	PL. BLK.	MINT SHEET	PLATE BLOCK	UNUSED F/NH	USED
2618	29¢ Love	2.25	4.25	45.00(50)	4.00	.85	.25
2619	29¢ Olympic Baseball	3.75	5.50	57.50(50)	5.50	1.25	.25

SCOTT NO.	DESCRIPTION	FIRST DAY COVERS SING	PL. BLK.	MINT SHEET	PLATE BLOCK	UNUSED F/NH	USED

2620 2621

2622 2623

2620-23	First Voyage of Columbus	4.00	5.00	37.50(40)	5.25	4.25	4.00
2620	29¢ Seeking Isabella's Support	2.25	....	....	....	1.25	.25
2621	29¢ Crossing the Atlantic	2.25	....	....	....	1.25	.25
2622	29¢ Approaching Land.	2.25	....	....	....	1.25	.25
2623	29¢ Coming Ashore . . .	2.25	....	....	....	1.25	.25

2624

2625

2626

2627

2628

2629

| 2624-29 | 1¢-$5 Columbian Souvenir Sheets (6). . . | 55.00 | .... | .... | .... | 45.00 | 40.00 |
| 2624a-29a | same, set of 16 singles | 105.00 | .... | .... | .... | 42.00 | 37.00 |

SCOTT NO.	DESCRIPTION	FIRST DAY COVERS SING	PL. BLK.	MINT SHEET	PLATE BLOCK	UNUSED F/NH	USED

2630

| 2630 | 29¢ NY Stock Exchange | 4.00 | 6.00 | 35.00(40) | 4.00 | .75 | .25 |

2631 2632 2633 2634

2631-34	Space, US/Russian Joint Issue	4.00	5.00	45.00(50)	5.50	5.00	3.50
2631	29¢ Cosmonaut & Space Shuttle	2.50	....	....	....	1.30	.30
2632	29¢ Astronaut & Mir Space Station	2.50	....	....	....	1.30	.30
2633	29¢ Apollo Lunar Module & Sputnik	2.50	....	....	....	1.30	.30
2634	29¢ Soyuz, Mercury & Gemini Space Craft . . .	2.50	....	....	....	1.30	.30

2635 2636

| 2635 | 29¢ Alaska Highway . . | 2.25 | 4.75 | 45.00(50) | 4.50 | 1.20 | .25 |
| 2636 | 29¢ Kentucky Statehood | 2.25 | 4.75 | 37.50(50) | 3.75 | 1.20 | .25 |

2637

2638 2639

2640 2641

SCOTT NO.	DESCRIPTION	FIRST DAY COVERS SING	FIRST DAY COVERS PL. BLK.	MINT SHEET	PLATE BLOCK	UNUSED F/NH	USED

2642   2643   2644

2645   2646

Scott No.	Description	Sing	Pl. Blk.	Mint Sheet	Plate Block	Unused F/NH	Used
2637-41	Summer Olympics, 5 varieties, attached	5.50	....	32.50(35)	10.50(10)	5.00	3.50
2637	29¢ Soccer	2.25	....	....	....	1.30	.50
2638	29¢ Women's Gymnastics	2.25	....	....	....	1.30	.50
2639	29¢ Volleyball	2.25	....	....	....	1.30	.50
2640	29¢ Boxing	2.25	....	....	....	1.30	.50
2641	29¢ Swimming	2.25	....	....	....	1.30	.50
2642	29¢ Ruby-throated Hummingbird	2.25	....	....	....	1.30	.50
2643	29¢ Broad-billed Hummingbird	2.25	....	....	....	1.30	.50
2644	29¢ Costa's Hummingbird	2.25	....	....	....	1.30	.50
2645	29¢ Rufous Hummingbird	2.25	....	....	....	1.30	.50
2646	29¢ Calliope Hummingbird	2.25	....	....	....	1.30	.50
2646a	29¢ Hummingbirds, bklt pane, 5 vareities, attached	5.00	....	....	....	5.00	....
2646av	same, bklt pane, unfolded	....	....	....	....	6.00	....

2647   2648   2649

1992 WILDFLOWERS

2647	*Indian Paintbrush*	2664	*Harlequin Lupine*	2681	*Turk's Cap Lily*
2648	*Fragrant Water Lily*	2665	*Twinflower*	2682	*Dutchman's Breeches*
2649	*Meadow Beauty*	2666	*Common Sunflower*	2683	*Trumpet Honeysuckle*
2650	*Jack-in-the-Pulpit*	2667	*Sego Lily*	2684	*Jacob's Ladder*
2651	*California Poppy*	2668	*Virginia Bluebells*	2685	*Plains Prickly Pear*
2652	*Large-Flowered Trillium*	2669	*Ohi'a Lehua*	2686	*Moss Campion*
2653	*Tickseed*	2670	*Rosebud Orchid*	2687	*Bearberry*
2654	*Shooting Star*	2671	*Showy Evening Primrose*	2688	*Mexican Hat*
2655	*Stream Violet*	2672	*Fringed Gentian*	2689	*Harebell*
2656	*Bluets*	2673	*Yellow Lady's Slipper*	2690	*Desert Five Spot*
2657	*Herb Robert*	2674	*Passionflower*	2691	*Smooth Solomon's Seal*
2658	*Marsh Marigold*	2675	*Bunchberry*	2692	*Red Maids*
2659	*Sweet White Violet*	2676	*Pasqueflower*	2693	*Yellow Skunk Cabbage*
2660	*Claret Cup Cactus*	2677	*Round-lobed Hepatica*	2694	*Rue Anemone*
2661	*White Mountain Avens*	2678	*Wild Columbine*	2695	*Standing Cypress*
2662	*Sessile Bellwort*	2679	*Fireweed*	2696	*Wild Flax*
2663	*Blue Flag*	2680	*Indian Pond Lily*		

Scott No.	Description	Sing	Pl. Blk.	Mint Sheet	Plate Block	Unused F/NH	Used
2647-96	29¢ Wildflowers, 50 varieties, attached	70.00	....	60.00(50)	....	60.00	....
	set of singles	86.00	....	....	....	....	27.50
	singles of above, each	1.75	....	....	....	1.50	.75

2697

Scott No.	Description	Sing	Pl. Blk.	Mint Sheet	Plate Block	Unused F/NH	Used
2697	$2.90 World War II (1942) Souvenir Sheet of 10	12.00	....	27.00(20)	....	13.50	11.00
2697a	29¢ Tokyo Raid	2.50	....	....	....	1.35	.75
2697b	29¢ Commodity Rationing	2.50	....	....	....	1.35	.75
2697c	29¢ Battle of Coral Sea	2.50	....	....	....	1.35	.75
2697d	29¢ Fall of Corregidor	2.50	....	....	....	1.35	.75
2697e	29¢ Japan Invades Aleutians	2.50	....	....	....	1.35	.75
2697f	29¢ Allies Break Codes	2.50	....	....	....	1.35	.75
2697g	29¢ USS Yorktown Lost	2.50	....	....	1.35	.75	
2697h	29¢ Women Join War Effort	2.50	....	....	....	1.35	.75
2697i	29¢ Marines on Guadalcanal	2.50	....	....	....	1.35	.75
2697j	29¢ Allies Land in North Africa	2.50	....	....	....	1.35	.75

2698   2699

Scott No.	Description	Sing	Pl. Blk.	Mint Sheet	Plate Block	Unused F/NH	Used
2698	29¢ Dorothy Parker	2.25	4.75	40.00(50)	4.00	1.50	.25
2699	29¢ Dr. T. von Karman	2.25	4.75	40.00(50)	4.00	1.50	.25

2700   2701

2704

2702   2703

Scott No.	Description	Sing	Pl. Blk.	Mint Sheet	Plate Block	Unused F/NH	Used
2700-03	Minerals, 4 varieties, attached	5.00	4.00	60.00(40)	7.00	6.00	4.00
2700	29¢ Azurite	2.25	....	....	....	1.20	.30
2701	29¢ Copper	2.25	....	....	....	1.20	.30
2702	29¢ Variscite	2.25	....	....	....	1.20	.30
2703	29¢ Wulfenite	2.25	....	....	....	1.20	.30
2704	29¢ Juan Rodriguez Cabrillo	2.25	4.75	45.00(50)	4.50	1.00	.25

SCOTT NO.	DESCRIPTION	FIRST DAY COVERS SING	FIRST DAY COVERS PL. BLK.	MINT SHEET	PLATE BLOCK	UNUSED F/NH	USED

Giraffe
2705

Giant Panda
2706

Flamingo
2707

King Penguins
2708

White Bengal Tiger
2709

2705	29¢ Giraffe.........	2.25	....	....	....	1.10	.25
2706	29¢ Giant Panda.....	2.25	....	....	....	1.10	.25
2707	29¢ Flamingo........	2.25	....	....	....	1.10	.25
2708	29¢ King Penguins ...	2.25	....	....	....	1.10	.25
2709	29¢ White Bengal Tiger	2.25	....	....	....	1.10	.25
2709a	29¢ Wild Animals, bklt pane of 5........	5.00	....	....	....	5.00	4.50
2709av	same, bklt pane , unfolded	....	....	....	....	6.75	....

CHRISTMAS
Bellini c. 1490 National Gallery
2710

2710	29¢ Christmas–Traditional	2.25	4.75	36.00(50)	3.75	1.00	.20
2710a	same, bklt pane of 10 .	9.00	....	....	....	7.75	....
2710av	same, bklt pane, unfolded	....	....	....	....	9.50	....

2711, 2715   2712, 2716, 2719

2713, 2717   2714, 2718

2711-14	Christmas Toys, 4 varieties, attached ..	4.00	5.00	55.00(50)	4.75	5.50	4.50
2711	29¢ Hobby Horse.....	2.25	....	....	....	1.50	.20
2712	29¢ Locomotive......	2.25	....	....	....	1.50	.20
2713	29¢ Fire Engine......	2.25	....	....	....	1.50	.20
2714	29¢ Steamboat	2.25	....	....	....	1.50	.20
2715	29¢ Hobby Horse (gravure) bklt single...........	2.25	....	....	....	1.50	.20
2716	29¢ Locomotive (gravure) bklt single...........	2.25	....	....	....	1.50	.20
2717	29¢ Fire Engine (gravure) bklt single...........	2.25	....	....	....	1.50	.20
2718	29¢ Steamboat (gravure) bklt single...........	2.25	....	....	....	1.50	.20
2718a	29¢ Christmas Toys (gravure) bklt pane of 4........	9.00	....	....	....	6.50	5.50
2718av	same, bklt pane, unfolded	....	....	....	....	7.00	....
2719	29¢ Locomotive ATM, self-adhesive	2.25	....	....	....	1.20	.75
2719a	same, bklt pane of 18 .	13.50	....	....	....	21.00	....

SCOTT NO.	DESCRIPTION	FIRST DAY COVERS SING	FIRST DAY COVERS PL. BLK.	MINT SHEET	PLATE BLOCK	UNUSED F/NH	USED

2720

| 2720 | 29¢ Happy New Year.. | 3.00 | 4.75 | 22.50(20) | 5.50 | 1.20 | .20 |

2721   2722

2723

1993 COMMEMORATIVES

2721/2806	(2721-30, 2746-59, 2765-66, 2771-74, 2779-89, 2791-94, 2804-06) 57 varieties	....	....	....	....	68.50	21.50
2721	29¢ Elvis Presley.....	2.00	5.00	35.00(40)	4.50	1.00	.25
2722	29¢ "Oklahoma!".....	2.25	4.75	35.00(40)	4.00	1.00	.25
2723	29¢ Hank Williams....	2.25	4.75	60.00(40)	7.00	2.00	.25
2723a	29¢ Hank Williams, perf. 11.2 x 11.4......	....	....	950.00(40)	150.00	25.00	15.00

2724, 2731

2725, 2732   2726, 2733

2727, 2734   2728, 2735

2729, 2736   2730, 2737

SCOTT NO.	DESCRIPTION	FIRST DAY COVERS SING	PL. BLK.	MINT SHEET	PLATE BLOCK	UNUSED F/NH	USED
2724-30	Rock & Roll/Rhythm & Blues, 7 varieties, attached . .	12.00	....	45.00(35)	12.00(8)	10.00	7.50
2724-30	same, Top Plate Block of 10	....	....		16.00(10)	....	
2724	29¢ Elvis Presley	3.00	....	....	....	1.50	.50
2725	29¢ Bill Haley	3.00	....	....	....	1.50	.50
2726	29¢ Clyde McPhatter . .	3.00	....	....	....	1.50	.50
2727	29¢ Ritchie Valens	3.00	....	....	....	1.50	.50
2728	29¢ Otis Redding	3.00	....	....	....	1.50	.50
2729	29¢ Buddy Holly	3.00	....	....	....	1.50	.50
2730	29¢ Dinah Washington	3.00	....	....	....	1.50	.50
2731	29¢ Elvis Presley, bklt single	3.00	....	....	....	1.25	.40
2732	29¢ Bill Haley, bklt single	3.00	....	....	....	1.25	.40
2733	29¢ Clyde McPhatter, bklt single	3.00	....	....	....	1.25	.40
2734	29¢ Ritchie Valens, bklt single	3.00	....	....	....	1.25	.40
2735	29¢ Otis Redding, bklt single	3.00	....	....	....	1.25	.40
2736	29¢ Buddy Holly, bklt single	3.00	....	....	....	1.25	.40
2737	29¢ Dinah Washington, bklt single	3.00	....	....	....	1.25	.40
2737a	same, bklt pane of 8 . .	10.00	....	....	....	7.00	....
2737av	same, bklt pane, unfolded	....	....	....	....	9.00	....
2737b	same, bklt pane of 4 . .	5.00	....	....	....	5.00	....
2737bv	same, bklt pane, unfolded	....	....	....	....	5.50	....

2741

2742

2743

2744

2745

2741	29¢ Saturn & 3 Rockets	2.25	....	....	....	1.00	.30
2742	29¢ 2 Flying Saucers . .	2.25	....	....	....	1.00	.30
2743	29¢ 3 Rocketeers	2.25	....	....	....	1.00	.30
2744	29¢ Winged Spaceship	2.25	....	....	....	1.00	.30
2745	29¢ 3 Space Ships . . .	2.25	....	....	....	1.00	.30
2745a	29¢ Space Fantasy, bklt pane of 5	4.50	....	....	....	4.75	4.00
2745av	same, bklt pane, unfolded	....	....	....	....	6.00	....

2746

2747

2748

2749

2752   2753

2750   2751

2746	29¢ Percy Lavon Julian	3.00	4.75	55.00(50)	5.00	1.00	.25
2747	29¢ Oregon Trail	2.25	4.75	60.00(50)	6.00	1.70	.25
2748	29¢ World University Games	2.25	4.75	38.00(50)	3.75	.85	.25
2749	29¢ Grace Kelly	3.00	4.75	38.00(50)	3.75	.85	.25
2750-53	Circus, 4 varieties, attached	5.00	6.00	42.50(40)	8.00(6)	5.00	4.00
2750	29¢ Clown	2.25	....	....	....	1.35	.30
2751	29¢ Ringmaster	2.25	....	....	....	1.35	.30
2752	29¢ Trapeze Artist	2.25	....	....	....	1.35	.30
2753	29¢ Elephant	2.25	....	....	....	1.35	.30

2754

2755

2754	29¢ Cherokee Strip . . .	2.25	4.75	25.00(20)	6.00	1.30	.25
2755	29¢ Dean Acheson . . .	2.25	4.75	45.00(50)	5.00	1.10	.25

2756   2757

2758   2759

2756-59	Sporting Horses, 4 varieties, attached . .	7.50	4.75	38.00(40)	5.00	4.50	3.50
2756	29¢ Steeplechase	3.00	....	....	....	1.25	.60
2757	29¢ Thoroughbred	3.00	....	....	....	1.25	.60
2758	29¢ Harness	3.00	....	....	....	1.25	.60
2759	29¢ Polo	3.00	....	....	....	1.25	.60

SCOTT NO.	DESCRIPTION	FIRST DAY COVERS SING	PL. BLK.	MINT SHEET	PLATE BLOCK	UNUSED F/NH	USED

2760

2761

2762

2763

2764

2760	29¢ Hyacinth	2.25	. . . . . .	. . . . . .	. . . . . .	1.05	.30
2761	29¢ Daffodil	2.25	. . . . . .	. . . . . .	. . . . . .	1.05	.30
2762	29¢ Tulip	2.25	. . . . . .	. . . . . .	. . . . . .	1.05	.30
2763	29¢ Iris	2.25	. . . . . .	. . . . . .	. . . . . .	1.05	.30
2764	29¢ Lilac	2.25	. . . . . .	. . . . . .	. . . . . .	1.05	.30
2764a	Garden Flowers, bklt pane of 5	4.50	. . . . . .	. . . . . .	. . . . . .	4.95	4.00
2764av	same, bklt pane, unfolded	. . . . . .	. . . . . .	. . . . . .	. . . . . .	6.00	. . . . . .

2765

2765	$2.90 World War II, 1943, Souvenir Sheet of 10 . .	12.00	. . . . . .	27.00(20)	. . . . . .	13.50	11.00
2765a	29¢ Allies battle U-boats	2.50	. . . . . .	. . . . . .		1.35	.75
2765b	29¢ Medics treat wounded	2.50	. . . . . .	. . . . . .		1.35	.75
2765c	29¢ Allies attack Sicily .	2.50	. . . . . .	. . . . . .		1.35	.75
2765d	29¢ B-24's hit Ploesti refineries	2.50	. . . . . .	. . . . . .		1.35	.75
2765e	29¢ V-Mail	2.50	. . . . . .	. . . . . .		1.35	.75
2765f	29¢ Italy invaded by Allies	2.50	. . . . . .	. . . . . .		1.35	.75
2765g	29¢ Bonds and Stamps help	2.50	. . . . . .	. . . . . .		1.35	.75
2765h	29¢ "Willie and Joe" . . .	2.50	. . . . . .	. . . . . .		1.35	.75
2765i	29¢ Gold Stars	2.50	. . . . . .	. . . . . .		1.35	.75
2765j	29¢ Marines assault Tarawa	2.50	. . . . . .	. . . . . .		1.35	.75

2766

| 2766 | 29¢ Joe Louis . . . . | 5.00 | 6.00 | 50.00(50) | 5.50 | 1.50 | .25 |

2767

2768

2769

2770

2767	29¢ "Show Boat"	2.50	. . . . . .	. . . . . .	. . . . . .	1.75	.30
2768	29¢ "Porgy & Bess" . . .	2.50	. . . . . .	. . . . . .	. . . . . .	1.75	.30
2769	29¢ "Oklahoma!"	2.50	. . . . . .	. . . . . .	. . . . . .	1.75	.30
2770	29¢ "My Fair Lady" . . .	2.50	. . . . . .	. . . . . .	. . . . . .	1.75	.30
2770a	Broadway Musicals, bklt pane of 4	6.00	. . . . . .	. . . . . .	. . . . . .	7.50	. . . . . .
2770av	same, bklt pane, unfolded	. . . . . .	. . . . . .	. . . . . .	. . . . . .	8.50	. . . . . .

2771, 2775

2772, 2777

2773, 2776

2774, 2778

2771-74	Country Music, 4 varieties, attached . .	6.00	7.00	25.00(20)	7.00	6.50	4.00
2771	29¢ Hank Williams	2.50	. . . . . .	. . . . . .	. . . . . .	1.50	.35
2772	29¢ Patsy Cline	2.50	. . . . . .	. . . . . .	. . . . . .	1.50	.35
2773	29¢ The Carter Family .	2.50	. . . . . .	. . . . . .	. . . . . .	1.50	.35
2774	29¢ Bob Wills	2.50	. . . . . .	. . . . . .	. . . . . .	1.50	.35
2775	29¢ Hank Williams, bklt single	2.50	. . . . . .	. . . . . .	. . . . . .	1.20	.30
2776	29¢ The Carter Family, bklt single	2.50	. . . . . .	. . . . . .	. . . . . .	1.20	.30
2777	29¢ Patsy Cline, bklt single	2.50	. . . . . .	. . . . . .	. . . . . .	1.20	.30
2778	29¢ Bob Wills, bklt single	2.50	. . . . . .	. . . . . .	. . . . . .	1.20	.30
2778a	Country Music, bklt pane of 4	5.00	. . . . . .	. . . . . .	. . . . . .	4.50	. . . . . .
2778av	same, bklt pane, unfolded	. . . . . .	. . . . . .	. . . . . .	. . . . . .	5.00	. . . . . .

2779   2780

2781   2782

2783   2784

SCOTT NO.	DESCRIPTION	FIRST DAY COVERS SING	PL. BLK.	MINT SHEET	PLATE BLOCK	UNUSED F/NH	USED
2779-82	National Postal Museum, 4 varieties, attached	4.00	5.00	25.00(20)	7.00	6.00	4.50
2779	29¢ Ben Franklin	2.25	....	....	....	1.50	.50
2780	29¢ Soldier & Drum	2.25	....	....	....	1.50	.50
2781	29¢ Lindbergh	2.25	....	....	....	1.50	.50
2782	29¢ Stamps & Bar Code	2.25	....	....	....	1.50	.50
2783-84	American Sign Language/ Deaf Communication, 2 varieties, attached	2.50	4.75	17.00(20)	4.25	2.00	1.25
2783	29¢ Mother/Child	2.25	....	....	....	1.10	.25
2784	29¢ Hand Sign	2.25	....	....	....	1.10	.25

2785   2786

2787   2788

SCOTT NO.	DESCRIPTION	FIRST DAY COVERS SING	PL. BLK.	MINT SHEET	PLATE BLOCK	UNUSED F/NH	USED
2785-88	Youth Classics, 4 varieties, attached	5.00	6.00	50.00(40)	7.00	6.00	4.50
2785	29¢ Rebecca of Sunnybrook Farm	2.25	....	....	....	1.60	.30
2786	29¢ Little House on the Prairie	2.25	....	....	....	1.60	.30
2787	29¢ Adventures of Huckleberry Finn	2.25	....	....	....	1.60	.30
2788	29¢ Little Women	2.25	....	....	....	1.60	.30

2789, 2790

2791, 2798, 2801   2792, 2797, 2802   2793, 2796, 2799, 2803   2794, 2795, 2800

SCOTT NO.	DESCRIPTION	FIRST DAY COVERS SING	PL. BLK.	MINT SHEET	PLATE BLOCK	UNUSED F/NH	USED
2789	29¢ Christmas–Traditional	2.25	4.75	36.00(50)	3.75	1.00	.20
2790	29¢ Christmas–Traditional, bklt single	2.25	....	....	....	1.00	.20
2790a	same, bklt pane of 4	3.00	....	....	....	3.50	....
2790av	same, bklt pane, unfolded	....	....	....	....	5.25	....
2791-94	Christmas–Contemporary, 4 varieties, attached	3.00	4.75	47.50(50)	5.00	4.25	3.00

SCOTT NO.	DESCRIPTION	FIRST DAY COVERS SING	PL. BLK.	MINT SHEET	PLATE BLOCK	UNUSED F/NH	USED
2791	29¢ Jack-in-the-Box	2.25	....	....	....	1.10	.20
2792	29¢ Red-Nosed Reindeer	2.25	....	....	....	1.10	.20
2793	29¢ Snowman	2.25	....	....	....	1.10	.20
2794	29¢ Toy Soldier Blowing Horn	2.25	....	....	....	1.10	.20
2795	29¢ Toy Soldier Blowing Horn, bklt single	2.25	....	....	....	1.25	.20
2796	29¢ Snowman, bklt single	2.25	....	....	....	1.25	.20
2797	29¢ Red-Nosed Reindeer, bklt single	2.25	....	....	....	1.25	.20
2798	29¢ Jack-in-the-Box, bklt single	2.25	....	....	....	1.25	.20
2798a	same, bkle pane of 10	7.00	....	....	....	9.75	....
2798av	same, bklt pane, unfolded	....	....	....	....	12.00	....
2799-2802v	29¢ Christmas–Contemporary, coil	....	....	....	11.00(8)	5.50(4)	....
2799	29¢ Snowman, self-adhesive (3 buttons)	2.25	....	....	....	1.20	.50
2800	29¢ Toy Soldier Blowing Horn, self-adhesive	2.25	....	....	....	1.20	.50
2801	29¢ Jack-in-the-Box, self-adhesive	2.25	....	....	....	1.20	.50
2802	29¢ Red-Nosed Reindeer, self-adhesive	2.25	....	....	....	1.20	.50
2802a	same, bklt pane of 12	9.00	....	....	....	13.00	....
2803	29¢ Snowman, self-adhesive (2 buttons)	2.25	....	....	....	1.20	.50
2803a	same, bklt pane of 18	13.50	....	....	....	20.00	....

2804   2805   2806

SCOTT NO.	DESCRIPTION	FIRST DAY COVERS SING	PL. BLK.	MINT SHEET	PLATE BLOCK	UNUSED F/NH	USED
2804	29¢ Commonwealth of North Mariana Islands	2.25	4.75	20.00(20)	5.00	1.00	.25
2805	29¢ Columbus Landing in Puerto Rico	2.25	4.75	60.00(50)	4.00	1.20	.25
2806	29¢ AIDS Awareness	2.25	4.75	41.00(50)	4.50	1.20	.25
2806a	29¢ AIDS Awareness, bklt single	2.25	....	....	....	1.00	.25
2806b	same, bklt pane of 5	9.00	....	....	....	4.75	....
2806bv	same, bklt pane, unfolded	....	....	....	....	6.00	....

2807   2808   2809

2810   2811

1994 COMMEMORATIVES

SCOTT NO.	DESCRIPTION	FIRST DAY COVERS SING	PL. BLK.	MINT SHEET	PLATE BLOCK	UNUSED F/NH	USED
2807/76	(2807-12, 2814C-28, 2834-36, 2838-39, 2841a, 2848-68, 2871-72, 2876) 60 varieties	....	....	....	....	78.00	25.50
2807-11	Winter Olympics, 5 varieties, attached	5.00	....	22.00(20)	12.00(10)	7.00	6.00
2807	29¢ Alpine Skiing	2.25	....	....	....	1.50	.50
2808	29¢ Luge	2.25	....	....	....	1.50	.50
2809	29¢ Ice Dancing	2.25	....	....	....	1.50	.50
2810	29¢ Cross Country Skiing	2.25	....	....	....	1.50	.50
2811	29¢ Ice Hockey	2.25	....	....	....	1.50	.50

SCOTT NO.	DESCRIPTION	FIRST DAY COVERS SING	FIRST DAY COVERS PL. BLK.	MINT SHEET	PLATE BLOCK	UNUSED F/NH	USED

2813

2814

2815

2812

1994 COMMEMORATIVES (continued)

Scott No.	Description	SING	PL. BLK.	MINT SHEET	PLATE BLOCK	UNUSED F/NH	USED
2812	29¢ Edward R. Murrow	2.25	4.75	70.00(50)	7.00	1.50	.25
2813	29¢ Love (sunrise), self-adhesive	2.25	....	....	....	1.10	.30
2813a	same, bklt pane of 18	13.50	....	....	....	17.50	....
2813v	29¢ Love (sunrise), self-adhesive coil	2.50	....	....	7.00(3)	1.40	....
2814	29¢ Love (dove), bklt single	2.25	....	....	....	1.10	.30
2814a	same, bklt pane of 10	7.00	....	....	....	10.00	....
2814av	same, bklt pane, unfolded	....	....	....	....	11.00	....
2814C	29¢ Love (dove)	2.25	4.75	45.00(50)	4.75	1.10	.20
2815	52¢ Love (dove)	2.00	4.50	70.00(50)	7.00(4)	1.50	.40
....	same, plate block of 10	....	....	....	16.00(10)	....	....

2816

2817

2818

Scott No.	Description	SING	PL. BLK.	MINT SHEET	PLATE BLOCK	UNUSED F/NH	USED
2816	29¢ Allison Davis	2.25	4.75	20.00(20)	5.00	1.20	.25
2817	29¢ Chinese New Year of the Dog	2.25	4.75	32.50(20)	9.00	2.25	.25
2818	29¢ Buffalo Soldiers	4.00	5.00	16.00(20)	6.50	1.50	.25

2819

2820

2821

2822

2823

2824

2825

2826

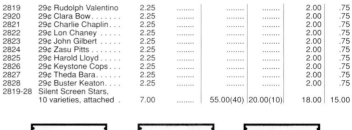

2827

2828

Scott No.	Description	SING	PL. BLK.	MINT SHEET	PLATE BLOCK	UNUSED F/NH	USED
2819	29¢ Rudolph Valentino	2.25	....	....	....	2.00	.75
2920	29¢ Clara Bow	2.25	....	....	....	2.00	.75
2821	29¢ Charlie Chaplin	2.25	....	....	....	2.00	.75
2822	29¢ Lon Chaney	2.25	....	....	....	2.00	.75
2823	29¢ John Gilbert	2.25	....	....	....	2.00	.75
2824	29¢ Zasu Pitts	2.25	....	....	....	2.00	.75
2825	29¢ Harold Lloyd	2.25	....	....	....	2.00	.75
2826	29¢ Keystone Cops	2.25	....	....	....	2.00	.75
2827	29¢ Theda Bara	2.25	....	....	....	2.00	.75
2828	29¢ Buster Keaton	2.25	....	....	....	2.00	.75
2819-28	Silent Screen Stars, 10 varieties, attached	7.00	....	55.00(40)	20.00(10)	18.00	15.00

2829

2830

2831

2832

2833

Scott No.	Description	SING	PL. BLK.	MINT SHEET	PLATE BLOCK	UNUSED F/NH	USED
2829	29¢ Lily	2.25	....	....	....	1.25	.30
2830	29¢ Zinnia	2.25	....	....	....	1.25	.30
2831	29¢ Gladiola	2.25	....	....	....	1.25	.30
2832	29¢ Marigold	2.25	....	....	....	1.25	.30
2833	29¢ Rose	2.25	....	....	....	1.25	.30
2833a	Summer Garden Flowers, bklt pane of 5	4.50	....	....	....	7.00	6.00
2833av	same, bklt pane, unfolded	....	....	....	....	7.00	....

2834

2835

2836

SCOTT NO.	DESCRIPTION	FIRST DAY COVERS SING	PL. BLK.	MINT SHEET	PLATE BLOCK	UNUSED F/NH	USED

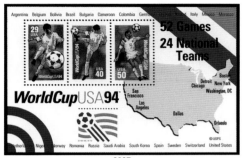

2837

2834	29¢ World Cup Soccer	2.25	4.75	20.00(20)	4.25	1.00	.50
2835	40¢ World Cup Soccer	2.25	4.75	25.00(20)	5.50	1.50	.75
2836	50¢ World Cup Soccer	2.25	5.50	34.50(20)	6.50	2.00	1.00
2837	29¢-50¢ World Cup Soccer Souvenir Sheet	3.50	....	....	....	6.00	4.00

2838

2838	$2.90 World War II, 1944, Souvenir Sheet of 10	12.00	....	50.00(20)	....	25.00	20.00
2838a	29¢ Allied forces retake New Guinea	2.50	....	....	....	2.50	1.00
2838b	29¢ P-51s escort B-17s on bombing raids	2.50	....	....	....	2.50	1.00
2838c	29¢ Allies in Normandy, D-Day, June 6	2.50	....	....	....	2.50	1.00
2838d	29¢ Airborne units spearhead attacks	2.50	....	....	....	2.50	1.00
2838e	29¢ Submarines shorten war in Pacific	2.50	....	....	....	2.50	1.00
2838f	29¢ Allies free Rome, June 4; Paris, August 25	2.50	....	....	....	2.50	1.00
2838g	29¢ U.S. troops clear Saipan bunkers	2.50	....	....	....	2.50	1.00
2838h	29¢ Red Ball Express speeds vital supplies	2.50	....	....	....	2.50	1.00
2838i	29¢ Battle for Leyte Gulf, October, 23-26	2.50	....	....	....	2.50	1.00
2838j	29¢ Bastogne and Battle of the Bulge, December	2.50	....	....	....	2.50	1.00

2839

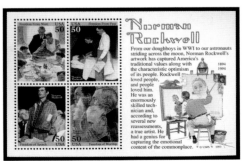

2840

| 2839 | 29¢ Norman Rockwell | 1.75 | 4.75 | 45.00(50) | 4.50 | 1.75 | .75 |
| 2840 | 50¢ "Four Freedoms" Souvenir Sheets | 5.00 | .... | .... | .... | 7.50 | 6.00 |

2841

| 2841 | 29¢ Moon Landing 25th Anniversary, Sheet of 12 | 12.00 | .... | .... | .... | 15.00 | .... |
| 2841a | 29¢ Moon Landing 25th Anniversary, single stamp | 1.75 | .... | .... | .... | 1.50 | .50 |

2842

| 2842 | $9.95 Moon Landing Express Mail Stamp | 27.00 | 50.00 | 750.00(20) | 175.00 | 40.00 | 18.00 |

2843

2844

2845   **2846**

2847

2843	29¢ Hudson's General	2.25	....	....	....	1.10	.30
2844	29¢ McQueen's Jupiter	2.25	....	....	....	1.10	.30
2845	29¢ Eddy's No. 242	2.25	....	....	....	1.10	.30
2846	29¢ Ely's No. 10	2.25	....	....	....	1.10	.30
2847	29¢ Buchanan's No. 999	2.25	....	....	....	1.10	.30
2847a	Locomotives, bklt pane of 5	4.50	....	....	....	5.50	4.25
2847av	same, bklt pane, unfolded	....	....	....	....	6.50	....

2848

| 2848 | 29¢ George Meany | 1.75 | 4.75 | 45.00(50) | 4.50 | 1.00 | .25 |

SCOTT NO.	DESCRIPTION	FIRST DAY COVERS SING	FIRST DAY COVERS PL. BLK.	MINT SHEET	PLATE BLOCK	UNUSED F/NH	USED

2849

2850

2851

2852

2853

2849-53	Popular Singers, 5 varieties, attached ..	8.00	....	30.00(20)	12.00(6)	7.75	6.00
2849	29¢ Al Jolson........	3.00	....	....	....	1.75	.75
2850	29¢ Bing Crosby	3.00	....	....	....	1.75	.75
2851	29¢ Ethel Waters.....	3.00	....	....	....	1.75	.75
2852	29¢ Nat "King" Cole...	3.00	....	....	....	1.75	.75
2853	29¢ Ethel Merman....	3.00	....	....	....	1.75	.75
....	same, Plate Block of 12	....	....	....	18.00(12)	....	....

2854

2855

2856

2857

2858

2859

2860

2861

2854-61	Blues & Jazz Singers, 8 varieties, attached .	12.00	....	45.00(35)	14.50(10)	13.50	7.50
....	same, Horizontal Plate Block of 10 w/Top Label	....	....	....	15.50(10)	....	....
2854	29¢ Bessie Smith....	3.00	....	....	....	1.75	.90
2855	29¢ Muddy Waters...	3.00	....	....	....	1.75	.90
2856	29¢ Billie Holiday....	3.00	....	....	....	1.75	.90
2857	29¢ Robert Johnson .	3.00	....	....	....	1.75	.90
2858	29¢ Jimmy Rushing..	3.00	....	....	....	1.75	.90
2859	29¢ "Ma" Rainey	3.00	....	....	....	1.75	.90
2860	29¢ Mildred Bailey...	3.00	....	....	....	1.75	.90
2861	29¢ Howlin' Wolf	3.00	....	....	....	1.75	.90

2862

| 2862 | 29¢ James Thurber . . . | 1.75 | 4.75 | 38.00(50) | 5.00 | 1.00 | .25 |

2863 2864

2865 2866

2863-66	Wonders of the Sea, 4 varieties, attached ..	5.00	6.00	27.50(24)	5.25	5.50	4.50
2863	29¢ Diver & Motorboat.	2.25	....	....	....	1.20	.30
2864	29¢ Diver & Ship	2.25	....	....	....	1.20	.30
2865	29¢ Diver & Ship's Wheel	2.25	....	....	....	1.20	.30
2866	29¢ Diver & Coral	2.25	....	....	....	1.20	.30

2867 2868

2867-68	Cranes.............	4.00	5.00	19.50(20)	5.00	2.25	1.50
2867	29¢ Black-Necked Crane	3.00	....	....	....	1.15	.25
2868	29¢ Whooping Crane..	3.00	....	....	....	1.15	.25

SCOTT NO.	DESCRIPTION	FIRST DAY COVERS SING	PL. BLK.	MINT SHEET	PLATE BLOCK	UNUSED F/NH	USED

2869

Legends of the West

2869a	Home on the Range	2869k	Nellie Cashman
2869b	Buffalo Bill Cody	2869l	Charles Goodnight
2869c	Jim Bridger	2869m	Geronimo
2869d	Annie Oakley	2869n	Kit Carson
2869e	Native American Culture	2869o	Wild Bill Hickok
2869f	Chief Joseph	2869p	Western Wildlife
2869g	Bill Pickett	2869q	Jim Beckwourth
2869h	Bat Masterson	2869r	Bill Tilghman
2869i	John Fremont	2869s	Sacagawea
2869j	Wyatt Earp	2869t	Overland Mail

2869g

2870g

SCOTT NO.	DESCRIPTION	SING	PL. BLK.	MINT SHEET	PLATE BLOCK	UNUSED F/NH	USED
2869	Legends of the West, 20 varieties, attached .	....	....	27.50(20)	....	27.50	25.00
....	set of singles	31.50	....	....	....	....	15.00
....	singles of above, each. .	....	....	....	....	....	.85
2869v	same as above, uncut sheet of 120 (6 panes)	....	100.00(120)	....	100.00	....	
....	block of 40 with vertical or horizontal, gutter between (2 panes)	....	....	27.50(40)	....	27.50	....
....	block of 24 with vertical gutter	....	....	20.75(24)	....	20.75	....
....	block of 25 with horizontal gutter	....	....	21.50(25)	....	21.50	....
....	cross gutter block of 20 .	....	....	....	....	31.00	....
....	cross gutter block of 4 .	....	....	....	....	17.00	....
....	vertical pair with horizontal gutter	....	....	....	....	2.75	....
....	horizontal pair with vertical gutter	....	....	....	....	2.75	....
2870	Legends of the West, (Recalled), 20 varieties, attached.	....	....	475.00(20)	....	475.00	....

2871

2872

2873

2874

SCOTT NO.	DESCRIPTION	FIRST DAY COVERS SING	PL. BLK.	MINT SHEET	PLATE BLOCK	UNUSED F/NH	USED
2871	29¢ Christmas–Traditional	2.25	4.75	45.00(50)	5.00	1.25	.20
2871a	29¢ Christmas–Traditional bklt single.	2.25	....	....	....	1.10	.20
2871b	same, bklt pane of 10 .	9.00	....	....	....	10.50	....
2871bv	same, bklt pane, unfolded	....	....	....	....	11.50	....
2872	29¢ Christmas Stocking	2.25	4.75	45.00(50)	5.00	1.25	.20
2872v	29¢ Christmas Stocking, bklt single.	2.25	....	....	....	1.25	.20
2872a	same, bklt pane of 20 .	....	....	....	....	17.00	....
2872av	same, bklt pane, unfolded	....	....	....	....	20.00	....
2873	29¢ Santa Claus, self-adhesive	2.25	....	....	....	1.20	.25
2873a	same, bklt pane of 12 .	9.00	....	....	....	13.50	....
2874	29¢ Cardinal in Snow, self-adhesive	2.25	....	....	....	1.50	1.20
2874a	same, bklt pane of 18 .	13.50	....	....	....	20.00	....

2875

2875	$2 B.E.P. Souvenir Sheet of 4 (Madison)	25.00	....	....	....	27.50	25.00
2875a	single from above ($2 Madison)	6.00	....	....	....	7.50	6.00

2876

2877, 2878

2876	29¢ Year of the Boar . .	3.00	4.75	22.50(20)	5.75	1.25	.25
2877	(3¢) "G" Make-up Rate (ABN, bright blue)	2.25	4.75	10.00(100)	1.00	.20	.15
2878	(3¢) "G" Make-up Rate (SVS, dark blue)	2.25	4.75	15.00(100)	1.25	.25	.15

SCOTT NO.	DESCRIPTION	FIRST DAY COVERS SING	FIRST DAY COVERS PL. BLK.	MINT SHEET	PLATE BLOCK	UNUSED F/NH	USED

2879, 2880 · **2881-85, 2889-92** · **2886, 2887** · **2888**

Old Glory

SCOTT NO.	DESCRIPTION	SING	PL. BLK.	MINT SHEET	PLATE BLOCK	UNUSED F/NH	USED
2879	(20¢) "G" Old Glory Postcard Rate (BEP, black "G")	2.25	4.75	65.00(100)	6.00	.75	.20
2880	(20¢) "G" Old Glory Postcard Rate (SVS, red "G")	2.25	4.75	110.00(100)	20.00	1.00	.20
2881	(32¢) "G" Old Glory (BEP, black "G")	2.25	4.75	300.00(100)	80.00	3.00	.50
2882	(32¢) "G" Old Glory (SVS, red "G")	2.25	4.75	90.00(100)	6.00	1.00	.25
2883	(32¢) "G" Old Glory, bklt single (BEP, black "G")	2.25				1.10	.25
2883a	same, bklt pane of 10	7.25				11.00	
2884	(32¢) "G" Old Glory, bklt single (ABN, blue "G")	2.25				1.25	.25
2884a	same, bklt pane of 10	7.25				12.50	
2885	(32¢) "G" Old Glory, bklt single (KCS, red "G")	2.25				1.50	.25
2885a	same, bklt pane of 10	7.25				15.00	
2886	(32¢) "G", self-adhesive	2.25				1.10	.30
2886a	same, bklt pane of 18	13.50				18.50	
2887	(32¢) "G" Old Glory, self-adhesive (blue shading)	2.25				1.40	.40
2887a	same, bklt pane of 18	13.50				22.00	

SCOTT NO.	DESCRIPTION	SING	PLATE# STRIP 3	MINT SHEET	PLATE# STRIP 3	UNUSED F/NH	USED
2888	(25¢) Old Glory First-Class Presort, coil	2.25	10.00		6.25	1.10	.35
2889	(32¢) "G" Old Glory, coil (BEP, black "G")	2.25	10.00		12.50	2.00	.35
2890	(32¢) "G" Old Glory, coil (ABN, blue "G")	2.25	10.00		6.25	1.10	.20
2891	(32¢) "G" Old Glory, coil (SVS, red "G")	2.25	10.00		11.00	2.00	.40
2892	(32¢) "G" Old Glory, coil (SVS, red "G") rouletted	2.25	10.00		10.00	1.25	.20

2893 · **2897, 2913-16, 2920, 2921** · **2902, 2902B** · **2903, 2904, 2904A, 2904B**

2905, 2906 · **2907** · **2908-10** · **2911, 2912, 2912A, 2912B**

1995-97 Regular Issues

SCOTT NO.	DESCRIPTION	SING	PL. BLK.	MINT SHEET	PLATE BLOCK	UNUSED F/NH	USED
2893	(5¢) "G" Old Glory, Nonprofit, coil	1.95	10.00		4.00	1.00	.40
2897	32¢ Flag over Porch	1.95	4.75	110.00(100)	6.00	1.50	.20

1995-97 Regular Issue Coils

SCOTT NO.	DESCRIPTION	SING	PLATE# STRIP 3	MINT SHEET	PLATE# STRIP 3	UNUSED F/NH	USED
2902	(5¢) Butte, Nonprofit, coil	1.95	10.00		2.00	.30	.20
2902B	(5¢) Butte, self-adhesive coil	1.95			2.75	.30	.20
2903	(5¢) Mountain, (BEP, violet 1996)	2.25	10.00		2.00	.30	.20
2904	(5¢) Mountain (SVS, blue 1996)	2.25	10.00		2.00	.30	.20
2904A	(5¢) Mountain, self-adhesive coil	2.25			2.75	.30	.20
2904B	(5¢) Mountain, self-adhesive coil (1997)	2.25			2.75	.30	.20
2905	(10¢) Automobile, Bulk Rate, coil	2.25	10.00		2.75	.30	.35
2906	(10¢) Automobile, self-adhesive coil	2.25			2.75	.30	.20
2907	(10¢) Eagle, bulk-rate, coil (1996)	2.25			4.00	.60	.35

SCOTT NO.	DESCRIPTION	SING	PLATE# STRIP 3	MINT SHEET	PLATE# STRIP 3	UNUSED F/NH	USED
2908	(15¢) Auto Tail Fin, Presorted First-Class Card, coil (BEP)	2.25	10.00		3.50	.50	.30
2909	(15¢) Auto Tail Fin, Presorted First-Class Card, coil (SVS)	2.25	10.00		3.50	.50	.30
2910	(15¢) Auto Tail Fin, self-adhesive coil	2.25			3.75	.55	.30
2911	(25¢) Juke Box, Presorted First-Class, coil (BEP)	2.25	10.00		5.75	.80	.40
2912	(25¢) Juke Box, Presorted First-Class, coil (SVS)	2.25	10.00		5.75	.80	.40
2912A	(25¢) Juke Box, self-adhesive coil	2.25			5.75	.80	.45
2912B	(25¢) Juke Box, self-adhesive coil (1997)	2.25			5.75	.80	.30
2913	32¢ Flag over Porch, coil (BEP, red date)	2.25	10.00		6.00	1.00	.25
2914	32¢ Flag over Porch, coil (SVS, blue date)	2.25	10.00		6.00	1.00	.25
2915	32¢ Flag over Porch, self-adhesive (Die Cut 8.7)	2.25			14.00	1.00	.30
2915A	32¢ Flag over Porch, self-adhesive (1996, Die Cut 9.8)	2.25			8.00	1.20	.30
2915B	32¢ Flag over Porch, self-adhesive coil (1996, Die Cut 11.5)	2.25			14.00	1.20	.25
2915C	32¢ Flag over Porch, self-adhesive coil (1996, Die Cut 10.9)	10.00			25.00	2.50	1.00
2915D	32¢ Flag over Porch, self adhesive coil (1997)	2.25			14.00	1.85	1.00

Note: For plate number strips of 5, see page 149

2919

1995-97 Booklet Panes

SCOTT NO.	DESCRIPTION	SING	PL. BLK.	MINT SHEET	PLATE BLOCK	UNUSED F/NH	USED
2916	32¢ Flag over Porch, bklt single	2.25				1.10	.20
2916a	same, bklt pane of 10	7.25				10.75	
2916av	same, bklt pane, unfolded					1.00	
2919	32¢ Flag over Field self-adhesive	2.25				1.10	.30
2919a	same, bklt pane of 18	13.50				17.00	
2920	32¢ Flag over Porch, self-adhesive (large "1995")	2.25				1.10	.30
2920a	same, bklt pane of 20	14.50				21.00	
2920b	32¢ Flag over Porch, self-adhesive (small "1995")	10.00				10.00	3.00
2920c	same, bklt pane of 20	50.00				170.00	
2920D	32¢ Flag over Porch ("1996" date) self-adhesive	2.25				2.00	1.00
2920e	same, Bklt pane of 10	9.00				10.75	
2921	32¢ Flag over Porch, self-adhesive (Red 1996, Die Cut 9.8)	2.25				1.10	.30
2921a	same, bklt pane of 10	7.00				10.75	
2921av	same, bklt pane, unfolded					14.00	
2921b	32¢ Flag over Porch, (Red 1997)	2.25				1.50	.30
2921c	same, bklt pane of 10	6.95				15.00	
2921d	same, bklt pane of 5	5.50				5.50	

2933 · **2934** · **2935**

2936 · **2938** · **2940**

SCOTT NO.	DESCRIPTION	FIRST DAY COVERS SING	PL. BLK.	MINT SHEET	PLATE BLOCK	UNUSED F/NH	USED

2941

2942

2943

1995-99 GREAT AMERICANS

2933	32¢ Milton S. Hershey .	2.25	4.75	100.00(100)	4.75	1.00	.30
2934	32¢ Carl Farley (1996).	2.25	4.75	100.00(100)	4.75	1.00	.50
2935	32¢ Henry R. Luce (1998)	2.25	4.75	16.00(20)	4.75	1.00	.50
2936	32¢ Lila & DeWitt Wallace (1998)	2.25	4.75	16.00(20)	4.75	1.00	.50
2938	46¢ Ruth Benedict . . .	2.25	5.00	110.00(100)	6.50	2.00	.90
2940	55¢ Alice Hamilton. . . .	2.25	5.00	120.00(100)	7.00	2.00	.35
2941	55¢ Justin Morrill (1999)	2.25	5.00	25.00(20)	7.00	2.00	1.25
2942	77¢ Mary Breckenridge (1998)	2.25	5.50	40.00(20)	10.00	2.50	.50
2943	78¢ Alice Paul	2.25	5.50	200.00(100)	10.00	2.50	.50

2948

2949

2950

1995 COMMEMORATIVES

2948/3023	(2948, 2950-58, 2961-68, 2974, 2976-92, 2998-99, 3001-07, 3019-23) 50 varieties					70.00	
25.75							
2948	(32¢) Love (Cherub) . .	2.25	4.75	40.00(50)	4.25	.95	.25
2949	(32¢) Love (Cherub), self-adhesive	2.25	. . . .	. . . .	. . . .	1.10	.25
2949a	same, bklt pane of 20 .	14.50	. . . .	. . . .	. . . .	20.00	. . . .
2950	32¢ Florida Statehood .	2.25	4.75	35.00(20)	8.00	1.20	.25

2951

2952

2953

2954

2951-54	Kids Care About Environment, 4 varieties, attached.	4.00	4.75	16.50(16)	5.00	4.50	3.50
2951	32¢ Earth in a Bathtub.	2.25	. . . .	. . . .	. . . .	1.20	.35
2952	32¢ Solar Energy.	2.25	. . . .	. . . .	. . . .	1.20	.35
2953	32¢ Tree Planting	2.25	. . . .	. . . .	. . . .	1.20	.35
2954	32¢ Beach Clean-Up . .	2.25	. . . .	. . . .	. . . .	1.20	.35

2955

2956

2957, 2959

2958

2960

2955	32¢ Richard M. Nixon .	2.25	4.75	55.00(50)	5.50	1.50	.25
2956	32¢ Bessie Coleman . .	2.25	4.75	70.00(50)	7.00	1.50	.25
2957	32¢ Love (Cherub) . . .	2.25	4.75	40.00(50)	3.95	.90	.25
2958	55¢ Love (Cherub). . . .	2.50	5.00	80.00(50)	8.00	1.75	.60
2959	32¢ Love (Cherub), bklt single.	2.25	. . . .	. . . .	. . . .	1.00	.25
2959a	same, bklt pane of 10 .	7.25	. . . .	. . . .	. . . .	9.75	. . . .
2959av	same, bklt pane, unfolded	. . . .	. . . .	. . . .	. . . .	10.50	. . . .
2960	55¢ Love (Cherub), self-adhesive	2.50	. . . .	. . . .	. . . .	1.75	.70
2960a	same, bklt pane of 20 .	23.50	. . . .	. . . .	. . . .	28.50	. . . .

2961

2962

2963

2964

2965

2961-65	Recreational Sports, 5 varieties, attached . .	7.00	. . . .	21.00(20)	12.00(10)	5.50	4.00
2961	32¢ Volleyball	3.00	. . . .	. . . .	. . . .	1.20	.50
2962	32¢ Softball	3.00	. . . .	. . . .	. . . .	1.20	.50
2963	32¢ Bowling	3.00	. . . .	. . . .	. . . .	1.20	.50
2964	32¢ Tennis	3.00	. . . .	. . . .	. . . .	1.20	.50
2965	32¢ Golf	3.00	. . . .	. . . .	. . . .	1.20	.50

2966

2967

2968

2966	32¢ POW & MIA	3.00	4.00	16.00(20)	3.95	1.20	.25
2967	32¢ Marilyn Monroe . . .	4.00	5.00	30.00(20)	6.50	2.00	.25
2967v	same as above, uncut sheet of 120 (6 panes)	. . . .	. . . .	180.00(120)	. . . .	. . . .	. . . .
. . . .	block of 8 with vertical gutter	. . . .	. . . .	. . . .	. . . .	50.00	. . . .
. . . .	cross gutter block of 8 .	. . . .	. . . .	. . . .	. . . .	65.00	. . . .
. . . .	vertical pair with horizontal gutter	. . . .	. . . .	. . . .	. . . .	5.50	. . . .
. . . .	horizontal pair with vertical gutter	. . . .	. . . .	. . . .	. . . .	9.50	. . . .
2968	32¢ Texas Statehood . .	3.00	4.75	28.00(20)	6.50	1.50	.25

SCOTT NO.	DESCRIPTION	FIRST DAY COVERS SING	PL. BLK.	MINT SHEET	PLATE BLOCK	UNUSED F/NH	USED

2969   2970   2971

2972   2973   2974

SCOTT NO.	DESCRIPTION	SING	PL. BLK.	MINT SHEET	PLATE BLOCK	UNUSED F/NH	USED
2969	32¢ Split Rock Lighthouse	2.25	....	....	....	1.50	.35
2970	32¢ St. Joseph Lighthouse	2.25	....	....	....	1.50	.35
2971	32¢ Spectacle Reef Lighthouse.........	2.25	....	....	....	1.50	.35
2972	32¢ Marblehead Lighthouse	2.25	....	....	....	1.50	.35
2973	32¢ Thirty Mile Point Lighthouse..........	2.25	....	....	....	1.50	.35
2973a	Great Lakes Lighthouses, bklt pane of 5.......	5.50	....	....	....	8.00	6.00
2973av	same, bklt pane, unfolded	....	....	....	....	9.00	....
2974	32¢ United Nations . . .	1.75	4.75	16.00(20)	3.95	.90	.25

SCOTT NO.	DESCRIPTION	FIRST DAY COVERS SING	PL. BLK.	MINT SHEET	PLATE BLOCK	UNUSED F/NH	USED
2975v	32¢ Civil War, uncut sheet of 120 (6 panes)	....	....	150.00(120)	....	150.00	....
....	cross gutter block of 20	....	....	....	....	55.00	....
....	cross gutter block of 4	....	....	....	....	27.50	....
....	vertical pair with horizontal gutter	....	....	....	....	6.00	....
....	horizontal pair with vertical gutter	....	....	....	....	6.00	....

2976   2977   2978   2979

Scott	Description	SING	PL. BLK.	MINT SHEET	PLATE BLOCK	UNUSED F/NH	USED
2976-79	Carousel Horses, 4 varieties, attached . .	4.00	4.75	21.50(20)	5.25	4.75	3.75
2976	32¢ Palamino.	2.25	....	....	....	1.20	.30
2977	32¢ Pinto Pony	2.25	....	....	....	1.20	.30
2978	32¢ Armored Jumper. .	2.25	....	....	....	1.20	.30
2979	32¢ Brown Jumper . . .	2.25	....	....	....	1.20	.30

2980

Scott	Description	SING	PL. BLK.	MINT SHEET	PLATE BLOCK	UNUSED F/NH	USED
2980	32¢ Women's Suffrage	1.95	4.75	40.00(40)	5.00	1.10	.30

2981

Scott	Description	SING	PL. BLK.	MINT SHEET	PLATE BLOCK	UNUSED F/NH	USED
2981	$3.20 World War II (1945) Souvenir Sheet of 10 . .	8.25	....	40.00(20)	....	25.00	20.00
2981a	32¢ Marines raise flag on Iwo Jima	2.25	....	....	....	2.00	1.00
2981b	32¢ Fierce fighting frees Manila	2.25	....	....	....	2.00	1.00
2981c	32¢ Okinawa, the last big battle	2.25	....	....	....	2.00	1.00
2981d	32¢ U.S. & Soviets link up at Elbe River	2.25	....	....	....	2.00	1.00
2981e	32¢ Allies liberate Holocaust survivors	2.25	....	....	....	2.00	1.00
2981f	32¢ Germany surrenders at Reims	2.25	....	....	....	2.00	1.00
2981g	32¢ By 1945, World War II has uprooted millions. .	2.25	....	....	....	2.00	1.00
2981h	32¢ Truman announces Japan's surrender	2.25	....	....	....	2.00	1.00
2981i	32¢ News of victory hits home	2.25	....	....	....	2.00	1.00
2981j	32¢ Hometowns honor their returning veterans	2.25	....	....	....	2.00	1.00

2975

CIVIL WAR

2975a	Monitor-Virginia	2975k	Harriet Tubman
2975b	Robert E. Lee	2975l	Stand Watie
2975c	Clara Barton	2975m	Joseph E. Johnston
2975d	Ulysses S. Grant	2975n	Winfield Hancock
2975e	Shiloh	2975o	Mary Chestnut
2975f	Jefferson Davis	2975p	Chancellorsville
2975g	David Farragut	2975q	William T. Sherman
2975h	Frederick Douglass	2975r	Phoebe Pember
2975i	Raphael Semmes	2975s	"Stonewall" Jackson
2975j	Abraham Lincoln	2975t	Gettysburg

Scott	Description	SING	PL. BLK.	MINT SHEET	PLATE BLOCK	UNUSED F/NH	USED
2975	32¢ Civil War, 20 varieties, attached .	....	....	60.00(20)	....	60.00	40.00
....	set of singles	35.00	....	....	....	....	20.00
....	singles of above, each.	....	....	....	....	....	1.00

SCOTT NO.	DESCRIPTION	FIRST DAY COVERS SING	FIRST DAY COVERS PL. BLK.	MINT SHEET	PLATE BLOCK	UNUSED F/NH	USED

2982

| 2982 | 32¢ Louis Armstrong .. | 1.95 | 4.75 | 30.00(20) | 6.00 | 1.50 | .50 |

2983   **2984**

2993   **2994**   **2995**   **2996**

2985

2987

2989

2991   2992

2997   **2998**   **2999**

2986

2988

2990

2993	32¢ Aster	2.25	....	....	....	1.25	.25
2994	32¢ Chrysanthemum ..	2.25	....	....	....	1.25	.25
2995	32¢ Dahlia	2.25	....	....	....	1.25	.25
2996	32¢ Hydrangea	2.25	....	....	....	1.25	.25
2997	32¢ Rudbeckia.	2.25	....	....	....	1.25	.25
2997a	Fall Garden Flowers, bklt pane of 5	5.50	....	....	....	5.25	4.00
2997av	same, bklt pane, unfolded					6.00	....
2998	60¢ Eddie Rickenbacker	2.25	5.00	80.00(50)	7.00	1.85	.40
2998a	same, large date (1999)	2.25	5.00	120.00(50)	15.00	2.00	.50
2999	32¢ Republic of Palau .	2.25	4.75	45.00(50)	5.00	1.20	.25

3000
COMIC STRIPS

3000a	*The Yellow Kid*		**3000k**	*Popeye*
3000b	*Katzenjammer Kids*		**3000l**	*Blondie*
3000c	*Little Nemo*		**3000m**	*Dick Tracy*
3000d	*Bringing Up Father*		**3000n**	*Alley Oop*
3000e	*Krazy Kat*		**3000o**	*Nancy*
3000f	*Rube Goldberg*		**3000p**	*Flash Gordon*
3000g	*Toonerville Folks*		**3000q**	*Li'l Abner*
3000h	*Gasoline Alley*		**3000r**	*Terry and the Pirates*
3000i	*Barney Google*		**3000s**	*Prince Valiant*
3000j	*Little Orphan Annie*		**3000t**	*Brenda Starr*

2983-92	Jazz Musicians, 10 varieties attached	8.25	....	35.00(20)	19.00(10)	17.00	15.00
2983	32¢ Coleman Hawkins.	2.25	....	....	....	2.00	1.00
2984	32¢ Louis Armstrong .	2.25	....	....	....	2.00	1.00
2985	32¢ James P. Johnson	2.25	....	....	....	2.00	1.00
2986	32¢ "Jelly Roll" Morton.	2.25	....	....	....	2.00	1.00
2987	32¢ Charlie Parker. . . .	2.25	....	....	....	2.00	1.00
2988	32¢ Eubie Blake	2.25	....	....	....	2.00	1.00
2989	32¢ Charles Mingus. . .	2.25	....	....	....	2.00	1.00
2990	32¢ Thelonius Monk . .	2.25	....	....	....	2.00	1.00
2991	32¢ John Coltrane. . . .	2.25	....	....	....	2.00	1.00
2992	32¢ Erroll Garner.	2.25	....	....	....	2.00	1.00

3000	32¢ Comic Strips, 20 varieties, attached .	....	....	25.00(20)	....	25.00	20.00
....	set of singles	50.00	....	....	....	....	12.50
....	single of above, each. .	....	....	....	....	....	.75

SCOTT NO.	DESCRIPTION	FIRST DAY COVERS SING	FIRST DAY COVERS PL. BLK.	MINT SHEET	PLATE BLOCK	UNUSED F/NH	USED

COMIC STRIPS (continued)

SCOTT NO.	DESCRIPTION	SING	PL. BLK.	MINT SHEET	PLATE BLOCK	UNUSED F/NH	USED
3000v	32¢ Comic Strips, uncut sheet of 120 (6 panes)	....	....	120.00(120)	....	120.00	....
....	cross gutter block of 20	....	....	....	....	40.00	....
....	cross gutter block of 4	....	....	....	....	18.50	....
....	vertical pair with horizontal gutter	....	....	....	....	4.50	....
....	horizontal pair with vertical gutter	....	....	....	....	4.50	....

3001

3002

| 3001 | 32¢ Naval Academy . . . | 2.25 | 4.75 | 18.00(20) | 4.50 | 1.00 | .25 |
| 3002 | 32¢ Tennessee Williams | 2.25 | 4.75 | 25.00(20) | 5.00 | 1.50 | .40 |

3003

3004, 3010, 3016   3005, 3009, 3015   3006, 3011, 3017   3007, 3008, 3014

3012, 3018

3003	32¢ Madonna & Child .	2.25	4.75	38.00(50)	3.75	.80	.20
3003a	32¢ Madonna & Child, bklt single.	2.25	....	....	....	1.10	.20
3003b	same, bklt pane of 10 .	7.25	....	....	....	10.50	....
3003bv	same, bklt pane, unfolded	....	....	....	....	11.50	....
3004-07	Santa & Children with Toys, 4 varieties, attached . .	4.00	4.75	60.00(50)	6.00	5.00	4.00
3004	32¢ Santa at Chimney .	2.25	....	....	....	1.30	.25
....	same, bklt single	2.25	....	....	....	1.30	.25
3005	32¢ Girl holding Jumping Jack.	2.25	....	....	....	1.30	.25
....	same, bklt single	2.25	....	....	....	1.30	.25
3006	32¢ Boy holding Toy Horse	2.25	....	....	....	1.30	.25
....	same, bklt single	2.25	....	....	....	1.30	.25
3007	32¢ Santa working on Sled	2.25	....	....	....	1.30	.25
....	same, bklt single	2.25	....	....	....	1.30	.25
3007b	32¢ Santa & Children with Toys, bklt pane of 10 (3 each of 3004-05) . . .	7.25	....	....	....	11.50	....
....	same, bklt pane unfolded	....	....	....	....	12.50	....
3007c	32¢ Santa & Children with Toys, bklt pane of 10 (3 each of 3006-07) . . .	7.25	....	....	....	11.50	....
....	same, bklt pane, unfolded	....	....	....	....	12.50	....
3008	32¢ Santa working on Sled, self-adhesive	2.25	....	....	....	1.25	.40
3009	32¢ Girl holding Jumping Jack, self-adhesive . . .	2.25	....	....	....	1.25	.40
3010	32¢ Santa at Chimney, self-adhesive	2.25	....	....	....	1.25	.40
3011	32¢ Boy holding Toy Horse, self-adhesive	2.25	....	....	....	1.25	.40
3011a	32¢ Santa & Children with Toys, self-adhesive, pane of 20	14.50	....	....	....	22.50	....
3012	32¢ Midnight Angel, self-adhesive	2.25	....	....	....	1.25	.45
3012a	same, bklt pane of 20 .	14.50	....	....	....	22.50	....

3013

3013	32¢ Children Sledding, self-adhesive	2.25	....	....	....	1.25	.50
3013a	same, bklt pane of 18 .	13.00	....	....	....	20.00	....
3014-17	Santa & Children with Toys, self-adhesive, coil strip of 4	....	....	....	....	5.50	....
3014	32¢ Santa working on Sled, self-adhesive coil	2.25	....	....	....	1.75	1.00
3015	32¢ Girl holding Jumping Jack, self-adhesive coil	2.25	....	....	....	1.75	1.00
3016	32¢ Santa at Chimney, self-adhesive coil	2.25	....	....	....	1.75	1.00
3017	32¢ Boy holding Toy Horse, self-adhesive coil	2.25	....	....	....	1.75	1.00
3018	32¢ Midnight Angel, self-adhesive coil	3.00	....	....	....	1.75	1.00

3019   3020

3021   3022

3023

3019-23	Antique Automobiles, 5 varieties, attached . .	5.50	....	30.00(25)	15.00(10)	7.50	6.50
3019	32¢ 1893 Duryea	2.25	....	....	....	1.50	.90
3020	32¢ 1894 Haynes	2.25	....	....	....	1.50	.90
3021	32¢ 1898 Columbia . . .	2.25	....	....	....	1.50	.90
3022	32¢ 1899 Winton	2.25	....	....	....	1.50	.90
3023	32¢ 1901 White	2.25	....	....	....	1.50	.90

3024

3025   3026   3027

3028

3029

1996 COMMEMORATIVES

SCOTT NO.	DESCRIPTION	FIRST DAY COVERS SING	PL. BLK.	MINT SHEET	PLATE BLOCK	UNUSED F/NH	USED
3024/3118	(3024, 3030, 3058-67, 3069-70, 3072-88, 3090-3104, 3106-11, 3118) 53 varieties		....	....	....	60.00	16.00
3024	32¢ Utah Statehood...	2.25	4.75	80.00(50)	8.00	1.75	.25
3025	32¢ Crocus	2.25	....			1.75	.25
3026	32¢ Winter Aconite ...	2.25	....			1.75	.25
3027	32¢ Pansy	2.25	....			1.75	.25
3028	32¢ Snowdrop	2.25	....			1.75	.25
3029	32¢ Anemone	2.25	....			1.75	.25
3029a	Winter Garden Flowers, bklt pane of 5........	5.50	....			5.50	4.00
3029av	same, bklt pane, unfolded					6.50	....

3030

3031, 3031A, 3044

3032, 3045

3033

3036, 3036a

3048, 3053

3049, 3054

3050, 3051, 3055

3052, 3052E

3030	32¢ Love (Cherub), self-adhesive	2.25	....	....	....	1.10	.20
3030a	same, bklt pane of 20 .	14.50	....	....	....	20.00	....
3030b	same, bklt pane of 15 .	11.50	....	....	....	15.00	....
3031	1¢ Kestrel, self-adhesive	2.25	....	8.00(50)	1.00	.20	.20
3031A	1¢ Kestrel, self-adhesive (2000)	1.95	....	8.00(50)	1.00	.20	.20
3032	2¢ Red-headed Woodpecker	2.25	4.75	11.00(100)	1.20	.20	.20
3033	3¢ Eastern Bluebird (redesign 3¢)	2.25	4.75	12.00(100)	1.30	.20	.20
3036	$1 Red Fox, self-adhesive	5.00	10.00	50.00(20)	10.00	2.25	.75
3036a	$1 Red Fox, 11.75 X 11(2002)	....	....	60.00(20)	15.00	3.00	.75
3044	1¢ Kestrel, coil......	2.25	5.00			.20	.20
3044a	1¢ Kestrel, large date, coil(1999)	2.25	5.00			.20	.20
3045	2¢ Red-headed Wood-pecker, coil..........	2.25	....		1.00	.20	.20
3048	20¢ Blue Jay, self-adhesive	2.25	....	....	....	.75	.20
3048a	same, bklt pane of 10 .	8.00	....	....	....	7.25	....
3049	32¢ Yellow Rose, self-adhesive	2.25	....	....	....	1.10	.20
3049a	same, bklt pane of 20 .	14.50	....	....	....	19.50	....
3050	20¢ Ring-necked Pheasant, self-adhesive	2.25	....	....	....	.70	.20
3050a	same, bklt pane of 10 .	9.00	....	....	....	6.75	....
3050b	20¢ Pheasant, die cut 11	2.25	....	....	....	.70	.20
3050c	same, bklt pane of 10 .	5.50	....	....	....	6.75	....
3051	20¢ Ring-necked Pheasant, die cut 10 1/2 x 11, self-adhesive	2.25	....	....	....	1.00	.30
3051A	same, sideways, die cut 10 1/2.......	2.25	....	....	....	6.50	1.50
3051b	same, bklt pane of 5, (4 #3051, 1 #3051a) ..	3.50	....	....	....	8.50	....
3052	33¢ Coral Pink Rose, self-adhesive	2.25	....	....	....	1.35	.30
3052a	same, bklt pane of 4 ..	3.00	....	....	....	5.25	....
3052b	same, bklt pane of 5 .	3.75	....	....	....	6.50	....

3052c	same, bklt pane of 6 ..	4.50	....	....	....	7.50	....
3052d	same, bklt pane of 20 .	14.50	....	....	....	22.50	....
3052E	33¢ Coral Pink Rose, die-cut 10.75 x 10.5, self-adhesive (2000)	2.25	....	....	....	1.00	.30
3052Ef	same, bklt pane of 20 .	14.50	....	....	....	18.00	....
3053	20¢ Blue Jay, self-adhesive, coil (1996)	2.25	....	....	8.00	1.00	.20
3054	32¢ Yellow Rose, self-adhesive coil (1997)	2.25	....	....	9.00	1.00	.20
3055	20¢ Ring-necked Pheasant, self-adhesive coil (1998)	2.25	....	....	5.00	.75	.20

3058

3059

3060

3058	32¢ Ernest Just	3.00	4.75	19.50(20)	5.00	1.20	.25
3059	32¢ Smithsonian Institution	2.25	4.75	19.50(20)	5.00	1.20	.25
3060	32¢ Year of the Rat ...	2.25	4.75	22.00(20)	5.50	1.40	.25

3061

3062

3063

3064

3061-64	Pioneers of Communication, 4 varieties, attached ..	4.00	4.75	18.00(20)	4.75	4.25	3.25
3061	32¢ Eadweard Muybridge	2.25	....	....	....	1.40	.50
3062	32¢ Ottmar Mergenthaler	2.25	....	....	....	1.40	.50
3063	32¢ Frederic E. Ives ..	2.25	....	....	....	1.40	.50
3064	32¢ William Dickson ..	2.25	....	....	....	1.40	.50

3065

3065	32¢ Fulbright Scholarships	2.25	4.75	85.00(50)	8.00	1.50	.25

3066

3067

3066	50¢ Jacqueline Cochran	2.25	5.00	75.00(50)	7.00	1.50	.50
3067	32¢ Marathon	3.00	4.75	17.00(20)	4.00	1.00	.25

SCOTT NO.	DESCRIPTION	FIRST DAY COVERS SING	PL. BLK.	MINT SHEET	PLATE BLOCK	UNUSED F/NH	USED

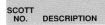

3068

1996 SUMMER OLYMPIC GAMES

3068a	Decathlon	3068k	Beach volleyball
3068b	Men's canoeing	3068l	Men's rowing
3068c	Women's running	3068m	Men's sprints
3068d	Women's diving	3068n	Women's swimming
3068e	Men's cycling	3068o	Women's softball
3068f	Freestyle wrestling	3068p	Men's hurdles
3068g	Women's gymnastics	3068q	Men's swimming
3068h	Women's sailboarding	3068r	Men's gymnastics
3068i	Men's shot put	3068s	Equestrian
3068j	Women's soccer	3068t	Men's basketball

SCOTT NO.	DESCRIPTION	FDC SING	MINT SHEET	UNUSED F/NH	USED
3068	32¢ Centennial Olympic Games, 20 varieties, attached .	....	25.00(20)	25.00	20.00
....	set of singles	35.00	....	....	14.00
....	single of above, each..	....	....	....	.90
3068v	same as above, uncut sheet of 120 (6 panes)	....	135.00(120)	135.00	....
....	cross gutter block of 20 .	....	....	35.00	....
....	cross gutter block of 4 .	....	....	19.50	....
....	vertical pair with horizontal gutter	....	....	4.50	....
....	horizontal pair with vertical gutter	....	....	4.50	....

3072

3073

3074

3075

3076

SCOTT NO.	DESCRIPTION	FDC SING	MINT SHEET	PLATE BLOCK	UNUSED F/NH	USED
3072-76	American Indian Dances, 5 varieties, attached . .	5.50	30.00(20)	18.00(10)	8.00	7.00
3072	32¢ Fancy Dance	2.25	....	....	1.25	.50
3073	32¢ Butterfly Dance...	2.25	....	....	1.25	.50
3074	32¢ Traditional Dance .	2.25	....	....	1.25	.50
3075	32¢ Raven Dance	2.25	....	....	1.25	.50
3076	32¢ Hoop Dance	2.25	....	....	1.25	.50

3077   **3078**

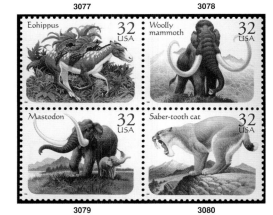

3079   **3080**

SCOTT NO.	DESCRIPTION	FDC SING	FDC PL.BLK.	MINT SHEET	PLATE BLOCK	UNUSED F/NH	USED
3077-80	Prehistoric Animals, 4 varieties, attached . .	4.00	4.75	20.00(20)	5.50	5.00	3.50
3077	32¢ Eohippus.	2.25	....	....	....	1.25	.40
3078	32¢ Woolly Mammoth .	2.25	....	....	....	1.25	.40
3079	32¢ Mastodon	2.25	....	....	....	1.25	.40
3080	32¢ Saber-tooth Cat . .	2.25	....	....	....	1.25	.40

3069

3070, 3071

SCOTT NO.	DESCRIPTION	FDC SING	FDC PL.BLK.	MINT SHEET	PLATE BLOCK	UNUSED F/NH	USED
3069	32¢ Georgia O'Keeffe	2.25	....	20.00(15)	5.50	1.50	.25
3070	32¢ Tennessee Statehood	2.25	4.75	50.00(50)	4.00	.80	.25
3071	32¢ Tennessee Statehood, self-adhesive	2.25	....	....	....	1.10	.40
3071a	same, bklt pane of 20 .	14.50	....	....	....	25.00	....

3081

3082

SCOTT NO.	DESCRIPTION	FDC SING	FDC PL.BLK.	MINT SHEET	PLATE BLOCK	UNUSED F/NH	USED
3081	32¢ Breast Cancer Awareness.	2.25	4.75	20.00(20)	5.00	1.10	.25
3082	32¢ James Dean	3.00	4.75	24.00(20)	6.00	1.25	.25
3082v	same as above, uncut sheet of 120 (6 panes)	....	....	175.00(120)	....	175.00(120)	....
....	block of 8 with vertical gutter.......	....	....	....	....	29.00	....
....	cross gutter block of 8 .	....	....	....	....	37.50	....
....	vertical pair with horizontal gutter	....	....	....	....	4.50	....
....	horizontal pair with vertical gutter	....	....	....	....	7.00	....

SCOTT NO.	DESCRIPTION	FIRST DAY COVERS SING	PL. BLK.	MINT SHEET	PLATE BLOCK	UNUSED F/NH	USED

3083   3084   3085   3086

SCOTT NO.	DESCRIPTION	SING	PL. BLK.	MINT SHEET	PLATE BLOCK	UNUSED F/NH	USED
3083-86	Folk Heroes, 4 varieties, attached . .	4.00	4.75	20.00(20)	5.25	4.75	3.50
3083	32¢ Mighty Casey	2.25	....	....	....	1.50	.50
3084	32¢ Paul Bunyan	2.25	....	....	....	1.50	.50
3085	32¢ John Henry	2.25	....	....	....	1.50	.50
3086	32¢ Pecos Bill	2.25	....	....	....	1.50	.50

3087   3088, 3089

3087	32¢ Olympic Discus Thrower	2.25	4.75	27.50(20)	7.00	1.50	.25
3088	32¢ Iowa Statehood. . .	2.25	4.75	70.00(50)	7.00	1.25	.25
3089	32¢ Iowa Statehood, self-adhesive	2.25	....	....	....	1.25	.30
3089a	same, bklt pane of 20 .	14.50	....	....	....	21.00	....

3090

3090	32¢ Rural Free Delivery	2.25	4.75	25.00(20)	6.00	1.50	.25

3091   3092

3093   3094

3095

3091-95	Riverboats, 5 varieties, attached . .	6.50	....	25.00(20)	12.50(10)	6.00	5.00
3091	32¢ Robt. E. Lee	2.25	....	....	....	1.20	.35
3092	32¢ Sylvan Dell	2.25	....	....	....	1.20	.35
3093	32¢ Far West	2.25	....	....	....	1.20	.35
3094	32¢ Rebecca Everingham	2.25	....	....	....	1.20	.35
3095	32¢ Bailey Gatzert. . . .	2.25	....	....	....	1.20	.35
3091-95b	32¢ Riverboats, special die cutting, 5 attached	....	....	....	170.00(10)	82.50	....
3095b	same, as above, pane of 20	....	....	325.00(20)	....	325.00	....

3098   3099

3096   3097

3096-99	Big Band Leaders, 4 varieties, attached . .	6.00	7.00	27.00(20)	7.00	5.50	4.50
3096	32¢ Count Basie	2.25	....	....	....	1.50	.50
3097	32¢ Tommy & Jimmy Dorsey	2.25	....	....	....	1.50	.50
3098	32¢ Glenn Miller	2.25	....	....	....	1.50	.50
3099	32¢ Benny Goodman. .	2.25	....	....	....	1.50	.50

3102   3103

3100   3101

3100-03	Songwriters, 4 varieties, attached . .	6.00	7.00	27.00(20)	7.00	5.50	4.50
3100	32¢ Harold Arlen	2.25	....	....	....	1.50	.50
3101	32¢ Johnny Mercer . . .	2.25	....	....	....	1.50	.50
3102	32¢ Dorothy Fields . . .	2.25	....	....	....	1.50	.50
3103	32¢ Hoagy Carmichael	2.25	....	....	....	1.50	.50

3104

3104	23¢ F. Scott Fitzgerald.	2.25	4.75	48.00(50)	5.00	1.00	.25

SE-TENANTS: Beginning with the 1964 Christmas issue (#1254-57), the United States has issued numerous Se-Tenant stamps covering a wide variety of subjects. Se-Tenants are issues where two or more different stamp designs are produced on the same sheet in pair, strip or block form. Mint stamps are usually collected in attached blocks, etc.—Used are generally saved as single stamps. Our Se-Tenant prices follow in this collecting pattern.

SCOTT NO.	DESCRIPTION	FIRST DAY COVERS SING	FIRST DAY COVERS PL. BLK.	MINT SHEET	PLATE BLOCK	UNUSED F/NH	USED

Endangered Species

National Stamp Collecting Month 1996 highlights these 15 species to promote awareness of endangered wildlife. Each generation must work to protect the delicate balance of nature, so that future generations may share a sound and healthy planet.

3105

ENDANGERED SPECIES

3105a	Black-footed ferret	**3105i**	California condor
3105b	Thick-billed parrot	**3105j**	Gila trout
3105c	Hawaiian monk seal	**3105k**	San Francisco garter snake
3105d	American crocodile	**3105l**	Woodland caribou
3105e	Ocelot	**3105m**	Florida panther
3105f	Schaus swallowtail butterfly	**3105n**	Piping plover
3105g	Wyoming toad	**3105o**	Florida manatee
3105h	Brown pelican		

SCOTT NO.	DESCRIPTION	SING	PL. BLK.	MINT SHEET	PLATE BLOCK	UNUSED F/NH	USED
3105	32¢ Endangered Species, 15 varieties, attached	15.00	....	22.00(15)	....	22.00	15.00
....	set of singles	27.50	....	....	....	....	12.00
....	singles of above, each.						1.00

3106

3107, 3112

SCOTT NO.	DESCRIPTION	SING	PL. BLK.	MINT SHEET	PLATE BLOCK	UNUSED F/NH	USED
3106	32¢ Computer Technology	2.25	4.75	35.00(40)	4.00	1.00	.25
3107	32¢ Madonna & Child	2.25	4.75	42.00(50)	4.25	1.00	.20

3108, 3113 3109, 3114 3110, 3115 3111, 3116

SCOTT NO.	DESCRIPTION	SING	PL. BLK.	MINT SHEET	PLATE BLOCK	UNUSED F/NH	USED
3108-11	Christmas Family Scenes, 4 varieties, attached	4.00	4.75	50.00(50)	5.50	5.00	4.00
3108	32¢ Family at Fireplace	2.25	....	....	....	1.25	.30
3109	32¢ Decorating Tree	2.25	....	....	....	1.25	.30
3110	32¢ Dreaming of SantaClaus	2.25	....	....	....	1.25	.30
3111	32¢ Holiday Shopping	2.25	....	....	....	1.25	.30
3112	32¢ Madonna & Child, self-adhesive	2.25	....	....	....	1.00	.30
3112a	same, bklt pane of 20	14.50	....	....	....	18.00	....
3113	32¢ Family at Fireplace, self-adhesive	2.25	....	....	....	1.20	.30
3114	32¢ Decorating Tree, self-adhesive	2.25	....	....	....	1.20	.30
3115	32¢ Dreaming of Santa Claus, self-adhesive	2.25	....	....	....	1.20	.30
3116	32¢ Holiday Shopping, self-adhesive	2.25	....	....	....	1.20	.30
3116a	Christams Family Scenes, self-adhesive, bklt pane of 20	14.50	....	....	....	18.00	....

3117

3118

SCOTT NO.	DESCRIPTION	SING	PL. BLK.	MINT SHEET	PLATE BLOCK	UNUSED F/NH	USED
3117	32¢ Skaters, self-adhesive	2.25	....	....	....	1.10	.40
3117a	same, bklt pane of 18	13.00	....	....	....	18.50	....
3118	32¢ Hanukkah, self-adhesive	2.25	....	17.00(20)	4.50	1.00	.25

3119

SCOTT NO.	DESCRIPTION	SING	PL. BLK.	MINT SHEET	PLATE BLOCK	UNUSED F/NH	USED
3119	50¢ Cycling, sheet of 2	4.00	....	....	....	3.25	3.00
3119a-b	same, set of 2 singles	5.00	....	....	....	3.00	2.50

3120

3121

1997 COMMEMORATIVES

SCOTT NO.	DESCRIPTION	SING	PL. BLK.	MINT SHEET	PLATE BLOCK	UNUSED F/NH	USED
3120/75	(3120-21, 3125, 3130-31, 3134-35, 3141, 3143-50, 3152-75) 40 varieties	....	....	....	....	43.50	15.00
3120	32¢ Year of the Ox	3.00	....	24.00(20)	5.00	1.20	.25
3121	32¢ Benjamin O. Davis, Sr.	3.00	4.75	24.00(20)	4.50	1.10	.25

3122

SCOTT NO.	DESCRIPTION	SING	PL. BLK.	MINT SHEET	PLATE BLOCK	UNUSED F/NH	USED
3122	32¢ Statue of Liberty, self-adhesive (1997)	2.25	....	....	....	1.35	.25
3122a	same, bklt pane of 20	14.50	....	....	....	20.00	....
3122b	same, bklt pane of 4	4.75	....	....	....	5.00	....
3122c	same, bklt pane of 5	5.00	....	....	....	6.00	....
3122d	same, bklt pane of 6	5.75	....	....	....	12.00	....
3122E	32¢ Statue of Liberty, die cut 11.5 x 11.8	....	....	....	....	2.00	1.00
3122Ef	same, bklt pane of 20	....	....	....	....	40.00	....
3122Eg	same, bklt pane of 6	....	....	....	....	11.00	....

3123

3124

SCOTT NO.	DESCRIPTION	SING	PL. BLK.	MINT SHEET	PLATE BLOCK	UNUSED F/NH	USED
3123	32¢ Swans, self-adhesive	2.25	....	....	....	1.10	.35
3123a	same, bklt pane of 20	14.50	....	....	....	19.50	....
3124	55¢ Swans, self-adhesive	2.50	....	....	....	2.00	.60
3124a	same, bklt pane of 20	19.75	....	....	....	33.50	....

SCOTT NO.	DESCRIPTION	FIRST DAY COVERS SING	FIRST DAY COVERS PL. BLK.	MINT SHEET	PLATE BLOCK	UNUSED F/NH	USED

3125

| 3125 | 32¢ Helping Children Learn | 2.25 | 4.75 | 19.50(20) | 5.00 | 1.10 | .25 |

3126, 3128

3127, 3129

3126	32¢ Citron, Moth, Larvae, Pupa, Beetle, self-adhesive (Die Cut 10.9 x 10.2) ..	2.25	....	....	....	1.10	.35
3127	32¢ Flowering Pineapple, Cockroaches, self-adhesive (Die Cut 10.9 x 10.2) ..	2.25	....	....	....	1.10	.35
3127a	same, bklt pane of 20 (10–#3126, 10–#3127)	14.50	....	....	....	19.50	....
3128	32¢ Citron, Moth, Larvae, Pupa, Beetle, self-adhesive (Die Cut 11.2 x 10.8) ..	2.25	....	....	....	1.75	.60
3128a	same, stamp sideways	2.25	....	....	....	5.00	1.00
3128b	same, bklt pane of 5 (2–#3128 & #3129, 1–#3128a)	5.50	....	....	....	10.00	....
3129	32¢ Flowering Pineapple, Cockroaches, self-adhesive (Die Cut 11.2 x 10.8) ..	2.25	....	....	....	1.75	.60
3129a	same, stamp sideways	2.25	....	....	....	10.00	2.00
3129b	same, bklt pane of 5 (2–#3128 & #3129, 1–#3129a)	5.50	....	....	....	15.00	....

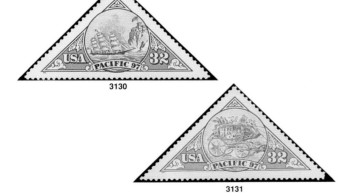

3130

3131

3130-31	32¢ Stagecoach & Ship, (Pacific '97) 2 varieties, attached...........	3.00	4.75	16.50(16)	5.00	2.25	2.00
3130	32¢ Ship	2.25	....	....	....	1.20	.35
3131	32¢ Stagecoach......	2.25	....	....	....	1.20	.35
3130-31v	same, as above, uncut sheet of 96 (6 panes)	....	....	110.00(96)	....	110.00	....
....	block of 32 with vertical or horizontal gutter between (2 panes)............	....	....	37.50(32)	....	37.50	....
....	cross gutter block of 16	....	....	....	....	30.00	....
....	vertical pairs with horizontal gutter...............	....	....	....	....	10.00	....
....	horizontal pairs with vertical gutter...............	....	....	....	....	8.00	....

3132

| 3132 | (25¢) Juke Box, self-adhesive linerless coil......... | 2.25 | .... | .... | 10.00 | 2.00 | 1.00 |
| 3133 | 32¢ Flag Over Porch, self-adhesive, linerless coil | 2.25 | .... | .... | 10.00 | 1.30 | 1.00 |

3134

3135

| 3134 | 32¢ Thornton Wilder .. | 2.25 | 4.75 | 17.50(20) | 4.50 | 1.10 | .25 |
| 3135 | 32¢ Raoul Wallenberg . | 3.00 | 4.75 | 17.50(20) | 4.50 | 1.10 | .25 |

THE WORLD OF DINOSAURS

3136

DINOSAURS

3136a	Ceratosaurus	3136f	Stegosaurus	3136k	Daspletosaurus
3136b	Camptosaurus	3136g	Allosaurus	3136l	Palaeosaniwa
3136c	Camarasaurus	3136h	Opisthias	3136m	Corythosaurus
3136d	Brachiosaurus	3136i	Edmontonia	3136n	Ornithominus
3136e	Goniopholis	3136j	Einiosaurus	3136o	Parasaurolophus

3136	32¢ Dinosaurs, 15 varieties, attached	11.50	....	....	....	20.00	18.00
....	set of singles	26.50	....	....	....	....	10.00
....	singles of above, each	....	....	....	....	....	.75

3137, 3138

3137	32¢ Bugs Bunny, self-adhesive, pane of 10	9.50	....	....	....	12.50	....
3137a	same, single from pane	2.50	....	....	....	1.25	.35
3137b	same, pane of 9 (#3137a)	....	....	....	....	7.00	....
3137c	same, pane of 1 (#3137a)	....	....	....	....	2.50	....
3137v	same, top press sheet (6 panes) ...	....	....	525.00	....	525.00	....
3137v	same, bottom press w/ plate# (6 panes)	....	....	800.00	....	800.00	....
....	pane of 10 from press sheet	....	....	95.00	....	95.00	....
....	pane of 10 from press sheet w/ plate#	....	....	500.00	....	500.00	....

SCOTT NO.	DESCRIPTION	FIRST DAY COVERS SING	FIRST DAY COVERS PL. BLK.	MINT SHEET	PLATE BLOCK	UNUSED F/NH	USED

1997 COMMEMORATIVES (continued)

3138	32¢ Bug Bunny, self-adhesive, Die Cut, pane of 10 . . .	....	....	....	....	250.00	....
3138a	same, single from pane	....	....	....	....	....	....
3138b	same, pane of 9 (#3138a)	....	....	....	....	....	....
3138c	same, pane of 1 (#3138a)	....	....	....	....	190.00	....

3139

3140

3139	50¢ Benjamin Franklin, Souvenir Sheet of 12 (Pacific '97)	25.00	....	....	....	20.00	....
3139a	same, single from sheet	5.00	....	....	....	1.60	1.50
3140	60¢ George Washington, Souvenir Sheet of 12 (Pacific '97)	25.00	....	....	....	22.00	....
3140a	same, single from sheet	5.00	....	....	....	1.85	1.50

3141

| 3141 | 32¢ Marshall Plan . . . . | 1.95 | 4.75 | 17.50(20) | 4.25 | 1.00 | .25 |

3142

CLASSIC AMERICAN AIRCRAFT

3142a	Mustang	3142k	Flying Fortress
3142b	Model B	3142l	Stearman
3142c	Cub	3142m	Constellation
3142d	Vega	3142n	Lightning
3142e	Alpha	3142o	Peashooter
3142f	B-10	3142p	Tri-Motor
3142g	Corsair	3142q	DC-3
3142h	Stratojet	3142r	314 Clipper
3142i	GeeBee	3142s	Jenny
3142j	Staggerwing	3142t	Wildcat

3142	32¢ Classic American Aircraft, 20 varieties, attached .	....	....	18.50(20)	....	20.00	15.00
....	set of singles	35.00	....	....	....	....	12.00
....	singles of above, each.	....	....	....	....	....	.75
3142v	same as above, uncut sheet of 120 (6 panes)	....	....	125.00(120)	....	125.00	....
....	cross gutter block of 20	....	....	....	....	28.00	....
....	cross gutter block of 4 .	....	....	....	....	18.50	....
....	vertical pair with horizontal gutter	....	....	....	....	3.50	....
....	horizontal pair with vertical gutter	....	....	....	....	3.50	....

3143, 3148   3144, 3149

3145, 3147   3146, 3150

3143-46	Legendary Football Coaches, 4 varieties, attached	4.00	4.75	25.00(20)	7.00	5.00	4.00
3143	32¢ Paul "Bear" Bryant	2.25	....	....	....	1.30	.80
3144	32¢ Glenn "Pop" Warner	2.25	....	....	....	1.30	.80
3145	32¢ Vince Lombardi. . .	2.25	....	....	....	1.30	.80
3146	32¢ George Halas	2.25	....	....	....	1.30	.80
3147	32¢ Vince Lombardi. . .	2.25	4.75	19.50(20)	7.00	1.30	.80
3148	32¢ Paul "Bear" Bryant	2.25	4.75	19.50(20)	7.00	1.30	.80
3149	32¢ Glenn "Pop" Warner	2.25	4.75	19.50(20)	7.00	1.30	.80
3150	32¢ George Halas	2.25	4.75	19.50(20)	7.00	1.30	.80

SCOTT NO.	DESCRIPTION	FIRST DAY COVERS SING	PL. BLK.	MINT SHEET	PLATE BLOCK	UNUSED F/NH	USED

CLASSIC AMERICAN DOLLS

3151

CLASSIC AMERICAN DOLLS

3151a	*"Alabama Baby," and doll by Martha Chase*	**3151i**	*"Babyland Rag"*
3151b	*"Columbian Doll"*	**3151j**	*"Scootles"*
3151c	*Johnny Gruelle's "Raggedy Ann"*	**3151k**	*Doll by Ludwig Greiner*
3151d	*Doll by Martha Chase*	**3151l**	*"Betsy McCall"*
3151e	*"American Child"*	**3151m**	*Percy Crosby's "Skippy"*
3151f	*"Baby Coos"*	**3151n**	*"Maggie Mix-up"*
3151g	*Plains Indian*	**3151o**	*Dolls by Albert Schoenhut*
3151h	*Doll by Izannah Walker*		

3151	32¢ Classic American Dolls, 15 varieties, attached .	....	....	20.00(15)	....	22.00	18.00
....	set of singles	30.00	....	....	....	....	12.00
....	singles of above. each.	....	....	....	....	....	.80

3152

3152	32¢ Humphrey Bogart .	3.00	....	25.00(20)	5.00	1.10	.25
3152v	same, as above, uncut sheet of 120 (6 panes)	....	....	125.00(120)	....	125.00	....
....	block of 8 with vertical gutter.	....	....	....	....	18.00	....
....	cross gutter block of 8 .	....	....	....	....	21.00	....
....	vertical pair with horizontal gutter	....	....	....	....	3.50	....
....	horizontal pair with vertical gutter	....	....	....	....	5.00	....

3153

| 3153 | 32¢ "The Stars & Stripes Forever" . . . . | 2.25 | 4.75 | 45.00(50) | 5.50 | 1.00 | .25 |

3154

3155

3156

3157

3154-57	Opera Singers, 4 varieties, attached . .	4.00	4.75	21.50(20)	5.25	4.75	4.00
3154	32¢ Lily Pons	2.25	....	....	....	1.25	1.00
3155	32¢ Richard Tucker . . .	2.25	....	....	....	1.25	1.00
3156	32¢ Lawrence Tibbett .	2.25	....	....	....	1.25	1.00
3157	32¢ Rosa Ponselle . . .	2.25	....	....	....	1.25	1.00

3158

3159

3160

3161

3162

3163

3164

3165

3158-65	Composers and Conductors, 8 varieties, attached . .	7.00	....	25.00(20)	12.00(8)	10.00	9.00
3158	32¢ Leopold Stokowski	2.25	....	....	....	1.50	1.00
3159	32¢ Arthur Fiedler	2.25	....	....	....	1.50	1.00
3160	32¢ George Szell.	2.25	....	....	....	1.50	1.00
3161	32¢ Eugene Ormandy .	2.25	....	....	....	1.50	1.00
3162	32¢ Samuel Barber . . .	2.25	....	....	....	1.50	1.00
3163	32¢ Ferde Grofé	2.25	....	....	....	1.50	1.00
3164	32¢ Charles Ives	2.25	....	....	....	1.50	1.00
3165	32¢ Louis Moreau Gottschalk	2.25	....	....	....	1.50	1.00

3166

3167

| 3166 | 32¢ Padre Félix Varela | 2.25 | 4.75 | 17.00(20) | 4.00 | 1.00 | .50 |
| 3167 | 32¢ U.S. Air Force 50th Anniversary . . . . . . | 4.00 | 6.00 | 17.00(20) | 4.00 | 1.25 | .30 |

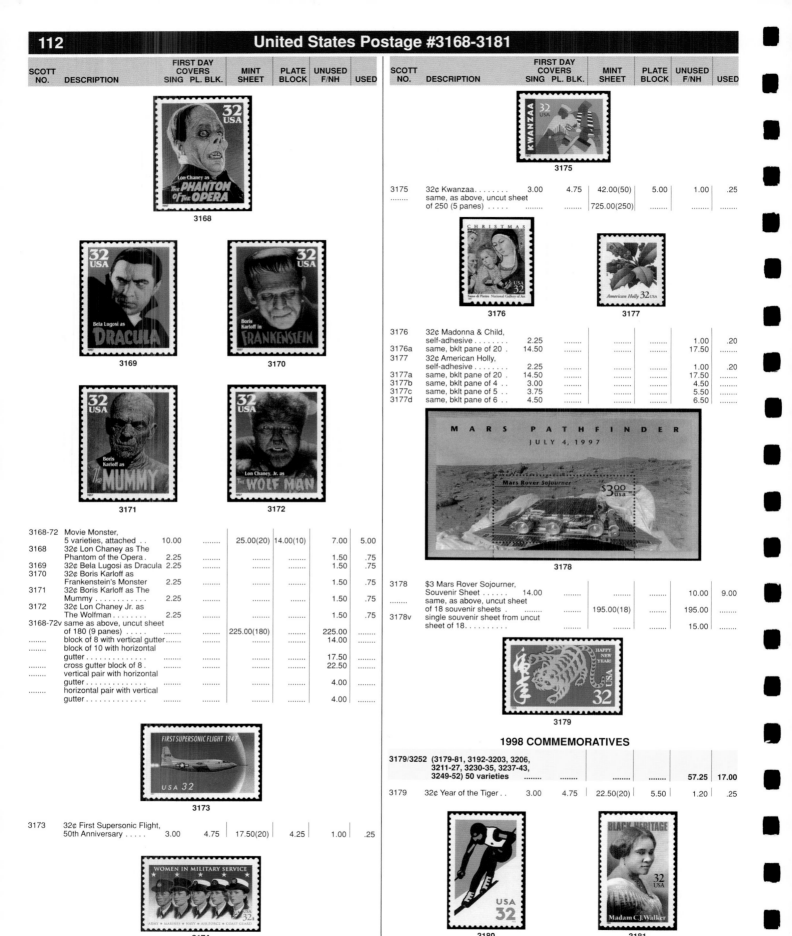

SCOTT NO.	DESCRIPTION	FIRST DAY COVERS SING	FIRST DAY COVERS PL. BLK.	MINT SHEET	PLATE BLOCK	UNUSED F/NH	USED
3168-72	Movie Monster, 5 varieties, attached . .	10.00	....	25.00(20)	14.00(10)	7.00	5.00
3168	32¢ Lon Chaney as The Phantom of the Opera .	2.25	....	....	....	1.50	.75
3169	32¢ Bela Lugosi as Dracula	2.25	....	....	....	1.50	.75
3170	32¢ Boris Karloff as Frankenstein's Monster	2.25	....	....	....	1.50	.75
3171	32¢ Boris Karloff as The Mummy	2.25	....	....	....	1.50	.75
3172	32¢ Lon Chaney Jr. as The Wolfman	2.25	....	....	....	1.50	.75
3168-72v	same as above, uncut sheet of 180 (9 panes)			225.00(180)		225.00	....
....	block of 8 with vertical gutter	....				14.00	....
....	block of 10 with horizontal gutter					17.50	....
....	cross gutter block of 8 .	....				22.50	....
....	vertical pair with horizontal gutter					4.00	....
....	horizontal pair with vertical gutter					4.00	....
3173	32¢ First Supersonic Flight, 50th Anniversary	3.00	4.75	17.50(20)	4.25	1.00	.25
3174	32¢ Women in Military Service	3.00	4.75	17.50(20)	4.25	1.00	.25

SCOTT NO.	DESCRIPTION	FIRST DAY COVERS SING	FIRST DAY COVERS PL. BLK.	MINT SHEET	PLATE BLOCK	UNUSED F/NH	USED
3175	32¢ Kwanzaa	3.00	4.75	42.00(50)	5.00	1.00	.25
....	same, as above, uncut sheet of 250 (5 panes)		....	725.00(250)	....	....	....
3176	32¢ Madonna & Child, self-adhesive	2.25	....	....	....	1.00	.20
3176a	same, bklt pane of 20 .	14.50	....	....	....	17.50	....
3177	32¢ American Holly, self-adhesive	2.25	....	....	....	1.00	.20
3177a	same, bklt pane of 20 .	14.50	....	....	....	17.50	....
3177b	same, bklt pane of 4 . .	3.00	....	....	....	4.50	....
3177c	same, bklt pane of 5 . .	3.75	....	....	....	5.50	....
3177d	same, bklt pane of 6 . .	4.50	....	....	....	6.50	....
3178	$3 Mars Rover Sojourner, Souvenir Sheet	14.00	....	....	....	10.00	9.00
....	same, as above, uncut sheet of 18 souvenir sheets .	....	....	195.00(18)	....	195.00	....
3178v	single souvenir sheet from uncut sheet of 18	....	....	....	....	15.00	....

1998 COMMEMORATIVES

SCOTT NO.	DESCRIPTION	FIRST DAY COVERS SING	FIRST DAY COVERS PL. BLK.	MINT SHEET	PLATE BLOCK	UNUSED F/NH	USED
3179/3252	(3179-81, 3192-3203, 3206, 3211-27, 3230-35, 3237-43, 3249-52) 50 varieties	....	....	....	....	57.25	17.00
3179	32¢ Year of the Tiger . .	3.00	4.75	22.50(20)	5.50	1.20	.25
3180	32¢ Alpine Skiing	2.25	4.75	30.00(20)	6.00	1.50	.25
3181	32¢ Madam C.J. Walker	3.00	4.75	30.00(20)	6.00	1.50	.25

SCOTT NO.	DESCRIPTION	FIRST DAY COVERS		MINT SHEET	PLATE BLOCK	UNUSED F/NH	USED
		SING	PL. BLK.				

3182

CELEBRATE THE CENTURY 1900's

3182a	Model T Ford	3182i	Immigrants arrive.
3182b	Theodore Roosevelt	3182j	John Muir, preservationist
3182c	"The Great Train Robbery" 1903	3182k	"Teddy" bear created
3182d	Crayola Crayons, introduced, 1903	3182l	W.E.B. DuBois, social activist
3182e	St. Louis World's Fair, 1904	3182m	Gibson Girl
3182f	Pure Food & Drug Act, 1906	3182n	First baseball World Series, 1903
3182g	Wright Brothers first flight, 1903	3182o	Robie House, Chicago
3182h	Boxing match in painting		

Scott	Description	Sing	Pl. Blk.	Mint Sheet	Plate Block	Unused	Used
3182	32¢ Celebrate the Century 1900's, 15 varieties, attached.	17.50	....	20.00(15)	....	20.00	15.00
....	set of singles	32.00	....	....	....	....	9.00
....	singles of above, each.	....	....	....	....	....	.75
3182v	same as above, uncut sheet of 60 (4 panes)	....	....	70.00(4)	....	70.00	....

3183

CELEBRATE THE CENTURY 1910's

3183a	Charlie Chaplin as the Little Tramp	3183i	United States enters WWI
3183b	Federal Reserve system created, 1913	3183j	Boy Scouts, 1910
3183c	George Washington Carver	3183k	Woodrow Wilson
3183d	Avant-garde art, 1913	3183l	First crossword puzzle, pub., 1913
3183e	First-Transcontinental telephone line, 1914	3183m	Jack Dempsey wins title, 1919
3183f	Panama Canal opens, 1914	3183n	Construction toys
3183g	Jim Thorpe wins decathlon, 1912	3183o	Child labor reform
3183h	Grand Canyon National Park, 1913		

Scott	Description	Sing	Pl. Blk.	Mint Sheet	Plate Block	Unused	Used
3183	32¢ Celebrate the Century 1910's, 15 varieties, attached.	17.50	....	20.00(15)	....	20.00	15.00
....	set of singles	32.00	....	....	....	....	9.00
....	singles of above, each.	....	....	....	....	....	.75
3183v	same as above, uncut sheet of 60 (4 panes)	....	....	70.00(4)	....	70.00	....

SCOTT NO.	DESCRIPTION	FIRST DAY COVERS		MINT SHEET	PLATE BLOCK	UNUSED F/NH	USED
		SING	PL. BLK.				

3184

CELEBRATE THE CENTURY 1920's

3184a	Babe Ruth	3184i	Radio entertains America
3184b	The Gatsby style	3184j	Art Deco style (Chrysler Building)
3184c	Prohibition enforced	3184k	Jazz flourishes
3184d	Electric toy trains	3184l	Four Horsemen of Notre Dame
3184e	19th Ammendment	3184m	Lindbergh flies the Atlantic
3184f	Emily Post's Etiquette	3184n	American realism
3184g	Margaret Mead, anthropologist	3184o	Stock Market crash, 1929
3184h	Flappers do the Charleston		

Scott	Description	Sing	Pl. Blk.	Mint Sheet	Plate Block	Unused	Used
3184	32¢ Celebrate the Century 1920's, 15 varieties, attached.	17.50	....	20.00(15)	....	20.00	15.00
....	set of singles	32.00	....	....	....	....	9.00
....	singles of above, each.	....	....	....	....	....	.75
3184v	same, as above, uncut sheet of 60 (4 panes)	....	....	70.00(4)	....	70.00	....

3185

CELEBRATE THE CENTURY 1930's

3185a	Franklin D. Roosevelt	3185i	"Gone with the Wind"
3185b	Empire State Building	3185j	Jesse Owens
3185c	1st Issue of Life Magazine	3185k	Streamline design
3185d	Eleanor Roosevelt	3185l	Golden Gate Bridge
3185e	FDR's New Deal	3185m	America survives the Depression
3185f	Superman arrives	3185n	Bobby Jones wins Grand Slam
3185g	Household conveniences	3185o	The Monopoly Game
3185h	"Snow White and the Seven Dwarfs"		

Scott	Description	Sing	Pl. Blk.	Mint Sheet	Plate Block	Unused	Used
3185	32¢ Celebrate the Century 1930's, 15 varieties, attached.	17.50	....	20.00(15)	....	20.00	15.00
....	set of singles	32.00	....	....	....	....	9.00
....	singles of above, each.	....	....	....	....	....	.75
3185v	same as above, uncut sheet of 60 (4 panes)	....	....	70.00(4)	....	70.00	....

SCOTT NO.	DESCRIPTION	FIRST DAY COVERS SING	PL. BLK.	MINT SHEET	PLATE BLOCK	UNUSED F/NH	USED

3186

CELEBRATE THE CENTURY 1940's

3186a	*World War II*	3186i	*GI Bill, 1944*
3186b	*Antibiotics save lives*	3186j	*Big Band Sounds*
3186c	*Jackie Robinson*	3186k	*Intl. Style of Architecture*
3186d	*Harry S. Truman*	3186l	*Postwar Baby Boom*
3186e	*Women support war effort*	3186m	*Slinky, 1945*
3186f	*TV entertains America*	3186n	*"A Streetcar Named Desire" 1947*
3186g	*Jitterbug sweeps nation*	3186o	*Orson Welles' "Citizen Kane"*
3186h	*Jackson Pollock, Abstract Expressionism*		

SCOTT NO.	DESCRIPTION	FIRST DAY COVERS SING	PL. BLK.	MINT SHEET	PLATE BLOCK	UNUSED F/NH	USED
3186	33¢ Celebrate the Century 1940's, 15 varieties, attached........	17.50	....	20.00(15)	....	20.00	15.00
....	set of singles........	32.00	....	....	....	....	10.00
....	singles of above, each.	....	....	....	....	....	.85
3186v	same as above, uncut sheet of 60 (4 panes)......	....	....	70.00(4)	....	70.00	....

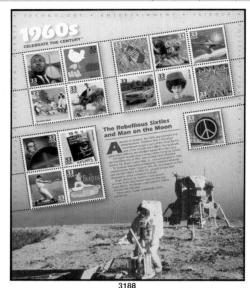

3188

CELEBRATE THE CENTURY 1960's

3188a	*"I Have a Dream" Martin Luther King*	3188i	*Barbie Doll*
3188b	*Woodstock*	3188j	*The Integrated Circuit*
3188c	*Man Walks on the Moon*	3188k	*Lasers*
3188d	*Green Bay Packers*	3188l	*Super Bowl I*
3188e	*Star Trek*	3188m	*Peace Symbol*
3188f	*The Peace Corps*	3188n	*Roger Maris, 61 in '61*
3188g	*The Vietnam War*	3188o	*The Beatles "Yellow Submarine"*
3188h	*Ford Mustang*		

SCOTT NO.	DESCRIPTION	FIRST DAY COVERS SING	PL. BLK.	MINT SHEET	PLATE BLOCK	UNUSED F/NH	USED
3188	33¢ Celebrate the Century 1960's, 15 varieties, attached........	17.50	....	20.00(15)	....	20.00	15.00
....	set of singles........	32.00	....	....	....	....	10.00
....	singles of above, each.	....	....	....	....	....	.85
3188v	same as above, uncut sheet of 60 (4 panes)......	....	....	70.00(4)	....	70.00	....

3187

CELEBRATE THE CENTURY 1950's

3187a	*Polio vaccine developed*	3187i	*Drive-in movies*
3187b	*teen fashions*	3187j	*World series rivals*
3187c	*The "Shot Heard Round the World"*	3187k	*Rocky Marciano, undefeated*
3187d	*US launches satellites*	3187l	*"I Love Lucy"*
3187e	*Korean War*	3187m	*Rock 'n Roll*
3187f	*Desegregation public schools*	3187n	*Stock car racing*
3187g	*Tail fins, chrome*	3187o	*Movies go 3-D*
3187h	*Dr. Seuss "The Cat in the Hat"*		

SCOTT NO.	DESCRIPTION	FIRST DAY COVERS SING	PL. BLK.	MINT SHEET	PLATE BLOCK	UNUSED F/NH	USED
3187	33¢ Celebrate the Century 1950's, 15 varieties, attached........	17.50	....	20.00(15)	....	20.00	15.00
....	set of singles........	32.00	....	....	....	....	10.00
....	singles of above, each.	....	....	....	....	....	.85
3187v	same as above, uncut sheet of 60 (4 panes)......	....	....	70.00(4)	....	70.00	....

3189

CELEBRATE THE CENTURY 1970's

3189a	*Earth Day Celebrated*	3189i	*Pioneer 10*
3189b	*"All in the Family", TV Series*	3189j	*Women's Rights Movement*
3189c	*Sesame Street*	3189k	*1970's Fashion*
3189d	*Disco Music*	3189l	*Monday Night Football*
3189e	*Steelers Win Four Super Bowls*	3189m	*America Smiles*
3189f	*U.S. Celebrates 200th Birthday*	3189n	*Jumbo Jets*
3189g	*Secretariat Wins Triple Crown*	3189o	*Medical Imaging*
3189h	*VCR's Transform Entertainment*		

SCOTT NO.	DESCRIPTION	FIRST DAY COVERS SING	PL. BLK.	MINT SHEET	PLATE BLOCK	UNUSED F/NH	USED
3189	33¢ Celebrate the Century 1970's, 15 varieties, attached........	17.50	....	20.00(15)	....	20.00	15.00
....	set of singles........	32.00	....	....	....	....	10.00
....	singles of above, each.	....	....	....	....	....	.85
3189v	same as above, uncut sheet of 60 (4 panes)......	....	....	70.00(4)	....	70.00	....

SCOTT NO.	DESCRIPTION	FIRST DAY COVERS SING	PL. BLK.	MINT SHEET	PLATE BLOCK	UNUSED F/NH	USED

3190

CELEBRATE THE CENTURY 1980's

3190a	Space Shuttle program						
3190b	Cats, Musucal Smash						
3190c	San Francisco 49ers						
3190d	Hostages Come Home						
3190e	Figure Skating						
3190f	Cable TV						
3190g	Vietnam Veterans Memorial						
3190h	Compact Discs						
3190i	Cabbage Patch Kids						
3190j	"The Cosby Show", Hit Comedy						
3190k	Fall of the Berlin Wall						
3190l	Video Games						
3190m	"E.T. The Extra-Terrestrial"						
3190n	Personal Computers						
3190o	Hip-hop Culture						

3190	33¢ Celebrate the Century 1980's, 15 varieties, attached	17.50	....	20.00(15)	....	20.00	15.00
....	set of singles	32.00	....	....	....	....	10.00
....	singles of above, each	....	....	....	....	....	.85
3190v	same as above, uncut sheet of 60 (4 panes)	....	....	70.00(4)	....	70.00	....

3191

CELEBRATE THE CENTURY 1990's

3191a	New Baseball Records						
3191b	Gulf War						
3191c	"Seinfield" Sitcom Sensation						
3191d	Extreme Sports						
3191e	Improving Education						
3191f	Computer Art and Graphics						
3191g	Recovering Species						
3191h	Return to Space						
3191i	Special Olympics						
3191j	Virtual Reality						
3191k	"Jurassic Park"						
3191l	"Titanic" Blockbuster Film						
3191m	Sport Utility Vehicles						
3191n	World Wide Web						
3191o	Cellular Phones						

3191	33¢ Celebrate the Century 1990's, 15 varieties, attached	17.50	....	20.00(15)	....	20.00	15.00
....	set of singles	32.00	....	....	....	....	10.00
....	singles of above, each	....	....	....	....	....	.85
3191v	same as above, uncut sheet of 60 (4 panes)	....	....	70.00(4)	....	70.00	....

3192

| 3192 | 32¢ "Remember the Maine" | 3.00 | 4.75 | 19.50(20) | 5.00 | 1.10 | .25 |

3193   **3194**   **3195**

3196   **3197**

3193-97	Flowering Trees, self-adhesive, 5 varieties, attached	5.75	....	19.50(20)	12.00(10)	5.00	4.50
3193	32¢ Southern Magnolia	2.25	....	....	....	1.10	.35
3194	32¢ Blue Paloverde	2.25	....	....	....	1.10	.35
3195	32¢ Yellow Poplar	2.25	....	....	....	1.10	.35
3196	32¢ Prairie Crab Apple	2.25	....	....	....	1.10	.35
3197	32¢ Pacific Dogwood	2.25	....	....	....	1.10	.35

3198   **3199**

3200   **3201**   **3202**

3198-3202	Alexander Calder, 5 varieties, attached	5.75	....	19.50(20)	10.50(10)	6.50	5.50
3198	32¢ Black Cascade, 13 Verticals, 1959	1.95	....	....	....	1.50	.75
3199	32¢ Untitled, 1965	1.95	....	....	....	1.50	.75
3200	32¢ Rearing Stallion, 1928	1.95	....	....	....	1.50	.75
3201	32¢ Potrait of a Young Man, c. 1945	1.95	....	....	....	1.50	.75
3202	32¢ Un Effet du Japonais, 1945	1.95	....	....	....	1.50	.75
3198-3202v	same, as above, uncut sheet of 120 (6 panes)	....	....	140.00(120)	....	....	....

SCOTT NO.	DESCRIPTION	FIRST DAY COVERS SING	FIRST DAY COVERS PL. BLK.	MINT SHEET	PLATE BLOCK	UNUSED F/NH	USED

3203

3203	32¢ Cinco De Mayo, self-adhesive	2.25	4.75	19.50(20)	5.00	1.10	.25
3203v	same as above, uncut sheet of 180 (9 panes)	....	....	180.00(180)	....	180.00	....
....	cross gutter block of 4	....	....	....	....	16.00	....
....	vertical pair with horizontal gutter	....	....	....	....	3.00	....
....	horizontal pair with vertical gutter	....	....	....	....	3.00	....

3204, 3205

3204	32¢ Sylvester & Tweety, self-adhesive, pane of 10	12.00	....	....	....	9.00	....
3204a	same, single from pane	2.25	....	....	....	1.00	.35
3204b	same, pane of 9 (#3204a)	....	....	....	....	8.00	....
3204c	same, pane of 1 (#3204a)	7.00	....	....	....	2.75	....
....	same, top press sheet of 60 (6 panes)	....	....	100.00(60)	....	100.00	....
....	same, bottom press sheet of 60 (6 panes)	....	....	175.00(60)	....	175.00	....
....	same, pane of 10 from press sheet	....	....	....	....	17.50	....
....	same, pane of 10 from press sheet w/ plate #	....	....	....	....	80.00	....
....	vert. pair with horiz. gutter	....	....	....	....	10.00	....
....	horiz pair with vert. gutter	....	....	....	....	20.00	....
3205	32¢ Sylvester & Tweety, self-adhesive, Die-Cut, pane of 10	20.00	....	....	....	18.00	....
3205a	same, single from pane	....	....	....	....	1.75	....
3205b	same, pane of 9 (#3205a)	....	....	....	....	14.00	....
3205c	same, pane of 1, imperf.	12.00	....	....	....	6.00	....

3206

| 3206 | 32¢ Wisconsin, self-adhesive | 1.95 | 4.75 | 17.50(20) | 4.25 | 1.20 | .25 |

3207, 3207a

3208, 3208a

		PLATE# STRIP 3			PLATE# STRIP 3		
3207	(5¢) Wetlands, Nonprofit, coil	2.25	10.00	....	2.00	.20	.20

SCOTT NO.	DESCRIPTION	FIRST DAY COVERS SING	FIRST DAY COVERS PL. BLK.	MINT SHEET	PLATE BLOCK	UNUSED F/NH	USED
		PLATE# STRIP 3			PLATE# STRIP 3		
3207A	same, self-adhesive coil	2.25	....	....	2.00	.20	.20
....	same, plate strip of 5	....	....	....	....	2.50	....
3208	(25¢) Diner, Presorted First-Class, coil	1.95	10.00	....	6.00	1.00	.50
3208a	same, self-adhesive coil, die cut 9.7	1.95	....	....	6.00	1.00	.50
....	same, plate strip of 5	....	....	....	....	5.75	....

3209

3209	1¢-$2 Trans-Mississippi, Souvenir Sheet of 9	12.00	....	....	12.00	10.00
....	same, set of 9 singles	18.00	....	....	9.25	7.25
3209v	block of 9 with horiz. gutter	....	....	....	60.00	....
3209v	vert. pair with horiz. gutter	....	....	....	12.50	....

3210

3210	$1 Cattle in Storm, Souvenir Sheet of 9	17.50	....	....	25.00	23.00
....	same, single stamp	....	....	....	3.00	2.25
3209-10	same, press sheet of 54 (6 panes, 3-#3209 & 3-#3210)	....	....	175.00(54)	175.00	....
3210v	cross gutter block of 12	....	....	....	85.00	....
3210v	vert. pair with horiz. gutter	....	....	....	12.50	....
3210v	horiz. pair with vert. gutter	....	....	....	12.50	....

3211

| 3211 | 32¢ Berlin Airlift, 50th Anniversary | 1.95 | 4.75 | 17.50(20) | 4.25 | 1.00 | .25 |

SCOTT NO.	DESCRIPTION	FIRST DAY COVERS SING	PL. BLK.	MINT SHEET	PLATE BLOCK	UNUSED F/NH	USED

3212   3213

3214   3215

3212-15	Folk Musicains, 4 varieties, attached ..	12.00	14.00	24.00(20)	6.00	5.00	4.00
3212	32¢ Huddie "Leadbelly" Ledbetter............	3.00	....	....	....	1.25	.50
3213	32¢ Woody Guthrie ...	3.00	....	....	....	1.25	.50
3214	32¢ Sonny Terry	3.00	....	....	....	1.25	.50
3215	32¢ Josh White	3.00	....	....	....	1.25	.50

3217   3216

3218   3219

3216-19	Gospel Singers, 4 varieties, attached ..	12.00	14.00	24.00(20)	6.00	5.00	4.00
3216	32¢ Mahalia Jackson..	3.00	....	....	....	1.25	.50
3217	32¢ Roberta Martin ...	3.00	....	....	....	1.25	.50
3218	32¢ Clara Ward	3.00	....	....	....	1.25	.50
3219	32¢ Sister Rosetta Tharpe	3.00	....	....	....	1.25	.50

3220

3221

| 3220 | 32¢ Spanish Settlement of the Southwest ...... | 2.25 | 4.75 | 18.50(20) | 4.50 | 1.00 | .25 |
| 3221 | 32¢ Stephen Vincent Benet | 2.25 | 4.75 | 18.50(20) | 4.50 | 1.00 | .25 |

SCOTT NO.	DESCRIPTION	FIRST DAY COVERS SING	PL. BLK.	MINT SHEET	PLATE BLOCK	UNUSED F/NH	USED

3222   3223

3224   3225

3222-25	Tropical Birds, 4 varieties, attached ..	5.00	6.00	22.00(20)	7.00	6.00	5.00
3222	32¢ Antillean Euphonia	2.25	....	....	....	1.25	.75
3223	32¢ Green-throated Carib	2.25	....	....	....	1.25	.75
3224	32¢ Crested Honeycreeper	2.25	....	....	....	1.25	.75
3225	32¢ Cardinal Honeyeater	2.25	....	....	....	1.25	.75

3226

3226	32¢ Alfred Hitchcock .	2.25	....	30.00(20)	6.00	1.50	.25
3226v	same as above, uncut sheet of 120 (6 panes)	....	....	120.00(120)	....	120.00	....
....	block of 8 with vertical gutter.....	....	....	....	....	18.00	....
....	cross gutter block of 8	....	....	....	....	25.00	....
....	vertical pair with horizontal gutter.............	....	....	....	....	4.50	....
....	horizontal pair with vertical gutter	....	....	....	....	6.00	....

3227

3228, 3229

3227	32¢ Organ & Tissue Donation, self-adhesive	2.25	....	19.50(20)	4.00	1.20	.25
3228	(10¢) Modern Bicycle, self-adhesive coil, die cut 9.8	2.25	....	....	3.75	.40	.20
....	same, plate strip of 5 .	....	....	....	....	4.50	....
3229	(10¢) Modern Bicycle, coil	2.25	10.00	....	3.75	.40	.20
....	same, plate strip of 5 .	....	....	....	....	4.50	....

3230

3231

3232

3233

SCOTT NO.	DESCRIPTION	FIRST DAY COVERS SING	FIRST DAY COVERS PL. BLK.	MINT SHEET	PLATE BLOCK	UNUSED F/NH	USED

1998 COMMEMORATIVES (continued)

3234

3230-34	Bright Eyes, self-adhesive, 5 varieties, attached	12.00	....	37.00(20)	19.00(10)	8.00	7.00
3230	32¢ Bright Eyes Dog	3.00	....	....	....	1.50	.40
3231	32¢ Bright Eyes Fish	3.00	....	....	....	1.50	.40
3232	32¢ Bright Eyes Cat	3.00	....	....	....	1.50	.40
3233	32¢ Bright Eyes Parakeet	3.00	....	....	....	1.50	.40
3234	32¢ Bright Eyes Hamster	3.00	....	....	....	1.50	.40

3235

| 3235 | 32¢ Klondike Gold Rush | 2.25 | .... | 18.50(20) | 4.50 | 1.20 | .25 |

3236

AMERICAN ART

3236a "Portrait of Richard Mather," by John Foster
3236b "Mrs. Elizabeth Freake and Baby Mary," by The Freake Limner
3236c "Girl in Red Dress with Cat and Dog," by Ammi Phillips
3236d "Rubens Peale with Geranium," by Rembrandt Peale
3236e "Long-billed Curlew, Numenius Longrostris," by John James Audubon
3236f "Boatmen on the Missouri," by George Caleb Bingham
3236g "Kindred Spirits," by Asher B. Durand
3236h "The Westwood Children," by Joshua Johnson
3236i "Music and Literature," by William Harnett
3236j "The Fog Warning," by Winslow Homer
3236k "The White Cloud, Head Chief of the Iowas," by George Catlin
3236l "Cliffs of Green River," by Thomas Moran
3236m "The Last of the Buffalo," by Alfred Bierstadt
3236n "Niagara," by Frederic Edwin Church
3236o "Breakfast in Bed," by Mary Cassatt
3236p "Nighthawks," by Edward Hopper
3236q "American Gothic," by Grany Wood
3236r "Two Against the White," by Charles Sheeler
3236s "Mahoning," by Franz Kline
3236t "No. 12," by Mark Rothko

3236	32¢ American Art, 20 varieties, attached	....	....	30.00(20)	....	30.00	25.00
....	set of singles	35.00	....	....	....	....	15.00
....	same as above, uncut sheet of 120 (6 panes)	....	....	175.00(120)	....	175.00	....
....	block of 24 with vert. gutter	....	....	....	....	27.50	....
....	block of 25 with horiz. gutter	....	....	....	....	32.50	....
....	cross gutter block of 20	....	....	....	....	40.00	....
....	vert. pair with horiz. gutter	....	....	....	....	7.00	....

AMERICAN ART (continued)

....	horiz. pair with vert. gutter	....	....	....	....	9.00	....
....	horiz. blk of 8 with vert. gutter	....	....	....	....	....	....
....	vert. blk of 10 with horiz. gutter	....	....	....	....	....	....

3237

3237	32¢ Ballet	1.95	....	25.00(20)	6.00	1.50	.25
....	same, uncut sheet of 120 (6 panes)	....	....	115.00(120)	....	115.00	....
....	cross gutter blk of 4	....	....	....	....	13.00	....
....	vert. pair with horiz. gutter	....	....	....	....	3.00	....
....	horiz. pair with vert. gutter	....	....	....	....	3.00	....

3238   **3239**   **3240**

3241   **3242**

3238-42	Space Discovery, 5 varieties, attached	5.75	11.00	22.00(20)	12.00(10)	7.50	6.50
3238	32¢ Space City	2.25	....	....	....	1.50	1.00
3239	32¢ Space ship landing	2.25	....	....	....	1.50	1.00
3240	32¢ Person in space suit	2.25	....	....	....	1.50	1.00
3241	32¢ Space Ship taking off	2.25	....	....	....	1.50	1.00
3242	32¢ Large domed structure	2.25	....	....	....	1.50	1.00
3238-42v	same, uncut sheet of 180 (9 panes)	....	....	185.00(180)	....	185.00	....
....	cross gutter blk of 10	....	....	....	....	27.50	....
....	vert. blk of 10 with horiz. gutter	....	....	....	....	20.00	....
....	horiz. pair with vert. gutter	....	....	....	....	3.50	....
....	vert. pair with horiz. gutter	....	....	....	....	3.50	....

3243   **3244**

3243	32¢ Giving and Sharing, self-adhesive	2.25	4.75	20.00(20)	5.00	1.20	.30
3244	32¢ Madonna & Child, self-adhesive	2.25	....	....	....	1.50	.20
3244a	same, booklet pane of 20	14.50	....	....	....	25.00	....

3245, 3249 — 3246, 3250 — 3247, 3251 — 3248, 3252

SCOTT NO.	DESCRIPTION	FIRST DAY COVERS SING	PL. BLK.	MINT SHEET	PLATE BLOCK	UNUSED F/NH	USED
3245	32¢ Evergreen Wreath, self-adhesive	2.25	....	....	....	2.00	1.00
3246	32¢ Victorian Wreath, self-adhesive	2.25	....	....	....	2.00	1.00
3247	32¢ Chili Pepper Wreath, self-adhesive	2.25	....	....	....	2.00	1.00
3248	32¢ Tropical Wreath, self-adhesive	2.25	....	....	....	2.00	1.00
3248a	32¢ Christmas Wreaths, self-adhesive, bklt pane of 4	4.00	....	....	....	30.00	....
3248b	same, bklt pane of 5	5.00	....	....	....	37.50	....
3248c	same, bklt pane of 6	5.50	....	....	....	45.00	....
3249-52	32¢ Christmas Wreaths, self-adhesive, 4 varieties, attached	4.00	4.75	40.00(20)	7.50	7.50	5.00
3249	32¢ Evergreen Wreath, self-adhesive	2.25	....	....	....	1.50	.25
3249a	32¢ Evergreen Wreath, self-adhesive, die-cut 11.7x11.6	2.25	....	....	....	2.25	.25
3250	32¢ Victorian Wreath, self-adhesive	2.25	....	....	....	1.50	.25
3250a	32¢ Victorian Wreath, self-adhesive, die-cut 11.7x11.6	2.25	....	....	....	2.25	.25
3251	32¢ Chili Pepper Wreath, self-adhesive	2.25	....	....	....	1.50	.25
3251a	32¢ Chili Pepper Wreath, self-adhesive, die-cut 11.7x11.6	2.25	....	....	....	2.25	.25
3252	32¢ Tropical Wreath, self-adhesive	2.25	....	....	....	1.50	.25
3252a	32¢ Tropical Wreath, self-adhesive, die-cut 11.7x11.6	2.25	....	....	....	2.25	.25
3252c	same, bklt pane of 20	14.50	....	....	....	37.50	....
3252e	bklt pane of 20, 5 each of 3249a-52a + label	14.50	....	....	....	37.50	....

3257, 3258 — 3259, 3263 — 3260, 3264, 3265, 3266, 3267, 3268, 3269,

3261 — 3262

SCOTT NO.	DESCRIPTION	FIRST DAY COVERS SING	PL. BLK.	MINT SHEET	PLATE BLOCK	UNUSED F/NH	USED
3257	(1¢) Weather Vane (white USA)	2.25	3.50	7.50(50)	1.10	.20	.20
3258	(1¢) Weather Vane (pale blue USA)	2.25	3.50	7.50(50)	1.10	.20	.20
3259	22¢ Uncle Sam, self-adhesive	2.25	4.75	12.00(20)	2.50	.55	.20
3260	(33¢) Uncle Sam's Hat	2.25	4.75	50.00(50)	6.00	1.00	.20
3261	$3.20 Space Shuttle Landing, self-adhesive	7.50	26.50	200.00(20)	45.00	10.00	5.00
3262	$11.75 Piggyback Space Shuttle, self-adhesive	28.50	95.00	600.00(20)	125.00	30.00	22.00
3263	22¢ Uncle Sam, self adhesive coil	2.25	....	....	....	.75	.25
....	same, plate strip of 5	....	....	....	....	6.50	....
3264	(33¢) Uncle Sam's Hat, coil	2.25	10.00	....	8.00	1.00	.50
....	same, plate strip of 5	....	....	....	....	9.50	....
3265	(33¢) Uncle Sam's Hat, self-adhesive coil, die cut 9.9	2.25	....	....	10.00	1.00	.30
....	same, plate strip of 5	....	....	....	....	11.00	....
3266	(33¢) Uncle Sam's Hat, self-adhesive coil, die cut 9.7	2.25	....	....	8.00	2.00	1.00
....	same, plate strip of 5	....	....	....	....	10.00	....
3267	(33¢) Uncle Sam's Hat, self-adhesive, die cut 9.9	2.25	....	....	....	1.10	.30
3267a	same, bklt pane of 10	7.25	....	....	....	11.00	....
3268	(33¢) Uncle Sam's Hat, self-adhesive die cut 11.2 x 11.1	2.25	....	....	....	1.10	.30
3268a	same, bklt pane of 10	7.25	....	....	....	11.00	....
3268b	same, bklt pane of 20	14.50	....	....	....	21.50	....
3269	(33¢) Uncle Sam's Hat, self-adhesive, die cut 8	2.25	....	....	....	1.10	.30
3269a	same, bklt pane of 18	13.50	....	....	....	19.50	....

3270, 3271

SCOTT NO.	DESCRIPTION	FIRST DAY COVERS SING	PL. BLK.	MINT SHEET	PLATE BLOCK	UNUSED F/NH	USED
3270	(10¢) Eagle, Presorted Std. coil	2.25	....	....	4.00	.35	.25
....	same, plate strip of 5	....	....	....	....	4.50	....
3271	(10¢) Eagle, Presorted Std., self-adhesive coil	2.25	....	....	4.00	.40	.25
....	same, plate strip of 5	....	....	....	....	4.50	....

3272 — 3273

1999 COMMEMORATIVES

SCOTT NO.	DESCRIPTION	FIRST DAY COVERS SING	PL. BLK.	MINT SHEET	PLATE BLOCK	UNUSED F/NH	USED
3272/3369	(3272-73, 3276, 3286-92, 3308-09, 3314-3350, 3352, 3354, 3356-59, 2368-69) 56 varieties	....	....	....	....	59.50	19.25
3272	33¢ Year of the Rabbit	2.25	4.75	25.00(20)	5.00	1.25	.25
3273	33¢ Malcolm X, Civil Rights, self-adhesive	2.25	4.75	30.00(20)	6.00	1.50	.25

3274 — 3275

SCOTT NO.	DESCRIPTION	FIRST DAY COVERS SING	PL. BLK.	MINT SHEET	PLATE BLOCK	UNUSED F/NH	USED
3274	33¢ Love, self-adhesive	2.25	....	....	....	1.10	.25
3274a	same, bklt pane of 20	14.50	....	....	....	20.00	....
3275	55¢ Love, self-adhesive	2.50	....	28.50(20)	6.50	1.50	.50

3276 — 3277, 3278, 3279, 3280, 3281, 3282 — 3283

SCOTT NO.	DESCRIPTION	FIRST DAY COVERS SING	PL. BLK.	MINT SHEET	PLATE BLOCK	UNUSED F/NH	USED
3276	33¢ Hospice Care, self-adhesive	2.25	4.75	20.00(20)	5.00	1.00	.25
3277	33¢ Flag and City	2.25	4.75	325.00(100)	65.00	3.00	.75
3278	33¢ Flag and City, self-adhesive, die cut 11.1	1.95	4.75	25.00(20)	8.00	1.00	.20
3278a	same, bklt pane of 4	4.00	....	....	....	4.50	....
3278b	same, bklt pane of 5	5.00	....	....	....	5.25	....
3278c	same, bklt pane of 6	5.50	....	....	....	6.75	....
3278d	same, bklt pane of 10	7.50	....	....	....	9.00	....
3278e	same, bklt pane of 20	14.50	....	....	....	17.50	....
3278F	33¢ Flag and City, self-adhesive, die cut 11.5x11.75	2.25	....	....	....	1.10	.50
3278Fg	same, bklt pane of 20	14.50	....	....	....	20.00	....
3278i	Flag and City, die cut 11.25	2.25	....	....	....	.90	.20
3278j	same, bklt pane of 10	7.25	....	....	....	8.50	....
3279	33¢ Flag and City, self-adhesive, die cut 9.8	2.25	....	....	....	1.25	.30
3279a	same, bklt pane of 10	7.25	....	....	....	10.50	....
3280	33¢ Flag and City, coil	2.25	....	....	4.50	1.00	.25
....	same, plate strip of 5	....	....	....	....	6.50	....
3281	33¢ Flag and City, self-adhesive coil (square corners) large date	2.25	....	....	7.50	1.00	.25
....	same, plate strip of 5	....	....	....	....	9.00	....
3281c	same, small date	2.25	....	....	9.00	2.00	.25
....	same, plate strip of 5	....	....	....	....	12.50	....

SCOTT NO.	DESCRIPTION	FIRST DAY COVERS SING	FIRST DAY COVERS PL. BLK.	MINT SHEET	PLATE BLOCK	UNUSED F/NH	USED
3282	33¢ Flag and City, self-adhesive coil (round corners)	2.25	....	....	8.00	1.10	.50
....	same, plate strip of 5 .	....	....	....	....	10.00	
3283	33¢ Flag and Chalkboard, self-adhesive,	2.25	....	....	....	1.20	.50
3283a	same, bklt pane of 18	13.50	....	....	....	17.00	

3286

3287

| 3286 | 33¢ Irish Immigration . | 2.25 | 4.75 | 20.00(20) | 4.00 | 1.20 | .25 |
| 3287 | 33¢ Alfred Lunt & Lynn Fontanne, Actors . . . . | 2.25 | 4.75 | 20.00(20) | 4.00 | 1.20 | .25 |

3288   **3289**   **3290**

3291   **3292**

3288-92	Arctic Animals, 5 varieties, attached .	12.00	....	20.00(15)	12.50(10)	6.00	5.00
3288	33¢ Arctic Hare	2.25	....	....	....	1.30	.40
3289	33¢ Arctic Fox	2.25	....	....	....	1.30	.40
3290	33¢ Snowy Owl	2.25	....	....	....	1.30	.40
3291	33¢ Polar Bear.	2.25	....	....	....	1.30	.40
3292	33¢ Gray Wolf	2.25	....	....	....	1.30	.40

3293

SONORAN DESERT

3293a	*Cactus wren, brittlebush, teddy bear cholla*	**3293g**	*Desert cottontail, hedgehog cactus*
3293b	*Desert tortoise*	**3293h**	*Gila monster*
3293c	*White-winged dove, prickly pear*	**3293i**	*Western diamondback rattlesnake, cactus mouse*
3293d	*Gambel quail*		
3293e	*Saquaro cactus*	**3293j**	*Gila woodpecker*
3293f	*Desert mule deer*		

3293	33¢ Sonoran Desert, 10 varieties, attached, self-adhesive . .	....	....	12.00(10)	....	12.00	9.00
....	set of singles	18.50	....	....	....	....	6.00
3293v	same, uncut sheet of 60 (6 panes)	....	....	60.00(60)	....	60.00	....

3294, 3298, 3302   **3295, 3299, 3303**   **3296, 3300, 3304**   **3297, 3301, 3305**

3294	33¢ Blueberries, self-adhesive, die cut 11.2 x 11.7	2.25	....	....	....	1.10	.30
3294a	same, dated "2000" . .	2.25	....	....	....	1.10	.30
3295	33¢ Raspberries, self-adhesive, die cut 11.2 x 11.7	2.25	....	....	....	1.10	.30
3295a	same, dated "2000" . .	2.25	....	....	....	1.10	.30
3296	33¢ Strawberries, self-adhesive, die cut 11.2x 11.7.	2.25	....	....	....	1.10	.30
3296a	same, dated "2000" . .	2.25	....	....	....	1.10	.30
3297	33¢ Blackberries, self-adhesive, die cut 11.2 x 11.7	2.25	....	....	....	1.10	.30
3297a	same, bklt pane of 20 (3294-97 x 5 of each)	14.50	....	....	....	20.00	....
3297c	same, dated "2000" . .	2.25	....	....	....	1.10	.20
3297d	same, bklt pane of 20	14.50	....	....	....	20.00	
3297e	same, block of 4, (#3294a-96a, 3297c) .	4.00	....	....	....	4.25	
3298	33¢ Blueberries, self-adhesive, die cut 9.5 x 10	2.25	....	....	....	1.20	.35
3299	33¢ Strawberries, self-adhesive, die cut 9.5 x 10	2.25	....	....	....	1.20	.35
3300	33¢ Raspberries, self-adhesive, die cut 9.5 x 10	2.25	....	....	....	1.20	.35
3301	33¢ Blackberries, self-adhesive, die cut 9.5 x 10	2.25	....	....	....	1.20	.35
3301a	same, bklt pane of 4 (3298-3301 x 1)	4.00	....	....	....	7.00	
3301b	same, bklt pane of 5, (3298, 3299, 3301, 3300 x 2)	5.00	....	....	....	8.00	
3301c	same, bklt pane of 6, (3300, 3301, 3298 x 2, 3299)	6.00	....	....	....	10.00	
3302-05	33¢ Berries, self-adhesive coil, strip of 4, attached	4.00	....	....	....	10.00	....
3302	33¢ Blueberries, self-adhesive coil. . . .	2.25	....	....	....	1.50	.40
3303	33¢ Raspberries, self-adhesive coil. . . .	2.25	....	....	....	1.50	.40
3304	33¢ Blackberries, self-adhesive coil. . . .	2.25	....	....	....	1.50	.40
3305	33¢ Strawberries, self-adhesive coil. . . .	2.25	....	....	....	1.50	.40
3302-05	33¢ Berries, self-adhesive coil, pl# strip of 5 (3302 x 2, 3303-05 x 1)	10.00	....	....	....	12.00	....

3306, 3307   **3308**

3306	33¢ Daffy Duck, self-adhesive, pane of 10	12.00	....	....	....	12.00	....
3306a	same, single from pane	2.25	....	....	....	1.10	.35
3306b	same, pane of 9 (3306a)	....	....	....	....	7.50	....
3306c	same, pane of 1 (3306a)	7.00	....	....	....	2.25	....
3306v	same, top press sheet of 60 (6 panes)	....	....	80.00(60)	....	80.00	....
....	same, bottom press sheet of 60 w/ plate # (6 panes)	....	....	110.00(60)	....	110.00	....
....	same, pane of 10 from press sheet	....	....	....	....	15.00	....
....	same, pane of 10 from press sheet w/ plate #. .	....	....	....	....	85.00	....
....	vert. pair with horiz. gutter	....	....	....	....	5.00	....
....	horiz. pair with vert. gutter	....	....	....	....	10.00	....
3307	33¢ Daffy Duck, self-adhesive, die cut, pane of 10	15.00	....	....	....	14.00	....
3307a	same, single from pane	....	....	....	....	1.10	....
3307b	same, pane of 9 (3307a)	....	....	....	....	10.00	....
3307c	same, pane of 1, imperf.	12.00	....	....	....	5.00	....
3308	33¢ Ayn Rand	2.25	4.75	20.00(20)	5.00	.90	.25

SCOTT NO.	DESCRIPTION	FIRST DAY COVERS SING	FIRST DAY COVERS PL. BLK.	MINT SHEET	PLATE BLOCK	UNUSED F/NH	USED

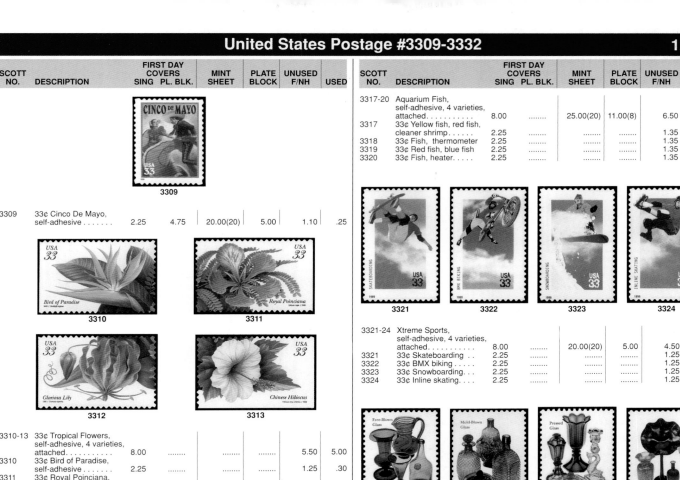

3309

| 3309 | 33¢ Cinco De Mayo, self-adhesive . . . . | 2.25 | 4.75 | 20.00(20) | 5.00 | 1.10 | .25 |

3310 Bird of Paradise **3311** Royal Poinciana **3312** Gloriosa Lily **3313** Chinese Hibiscus

3310-13	33¢ Tropical Flowers, self-adhesive, 4 varieties, attached.	8.00	. . . .	. . . .	. . . .	5.50	5.00
3310	33¢ Bird of Paradise, self-adhesive	2.25	. . . .			1.25	.30
3311	33¢ Royal Poinciana, self-adhesive	2.25	. . . .			1.25	.30
3312	33¢ Gloriosa Lily, self-adhesive	2.25	. . . .			1.25	.30
3313	33¢ Chinese Hibiscus, self-adhesive	2.25	. . . .			1.25	.30
3313a	same, bklt pane of 20 (3310-13 x 5)	. . . .	. . . .			22.00	. . . .

3314

3315

3316

3314	33¢ John & William Bartram, Botanists	2.25	4.75	20.00(20)	5.00	1.10	.25
3315	33¢ Prostate Cancer Awareness.	2.25	4.75	20.00(20)	5.00	1.10	.25
3316	33¢ California Gold Rush	2.25	4.75	20.00(20)	5.00	1.10	.25

3317

3318

3319

3320

3317-20	Aquarium Fish, self-adhesive, 4 varieties, attached.	8.00	. . . .	25.00(20)	11.00(8)	6.50	6.00
3317	33¢ Yellow fish, red fish, cleaner shrimp	2.25	. . . .	. . . .	. . . .	1.35	.30
3318	33¢ Fish, thermometer	2.25	. . . .	. . . .	. . . .	1.35	.30
3319	33¢ Red fish, blue fish	2.25	. . . .	. . . .	. . . .	1.35	.30
3320	33¢ Fish, heater.	2.25	. . . .	. . . .	. . . .	1.35	.30

3321 **3322** **3323** **3324**

3321-24	Xtreme Sports, self-adhesive, 4 varieties, attached.	8.00	. . . .	20.00(20)	5.00	4.50	4.00
3321	33¢ Skateboarding . .	2.25	. . . .	. . . .	. . . .	1.25	.35
3322	33¢ BMX biking	2.25	. . . .	. . . .	. . . .	1.25	.35
3323	33¢ Snowboarding. . .	2.25	. . . .	. . . .	. . . .	1.25	.35
3324	33¢ Inline skating. . . .	2.25	. . . .	. . . .	. . . .	1.25	.35

3325 **3326** **3327** **3328**

3325-28	American Glass, 4 varieties, attached .	10.00	. . . .	18.00(15)	. . . .	6.00	5.00
3325	33¢ Freeblown glass .	3.00	. . . .	. . . .	. . . .	1.30	.40
3326	33¢ Mold-blown glass	3.00	. . . .	. . . .	. . . .	1.30	.40
3327	33¢ Pressed glass. . .	3.00	. . . .	. . . .	. . . .	1.30	.40
3328	33¢ Art glass	3.00	. . . .	. . . .	. . . .	1.30	.40

3329

| 3329 | 33¢ James Cagney . . | 1.95 | 4.75 | 25.00(20) | 6.00 | 1.20 | .25 |

3330

3331

3332

3330	55¢ General William "Billy" Mitchell, self-adhesive	2.50	. . . .	32.00(20)	7.00	1.75	.75
3331	33¢ Honoring Those Who Served, self-adhesive	2.25	. . . .	25.00(20)	5.00	1.50	.25
3332	45¢ Universal Postal Union	2.25	5.00	25.00(20)	6.00	1.50	.75

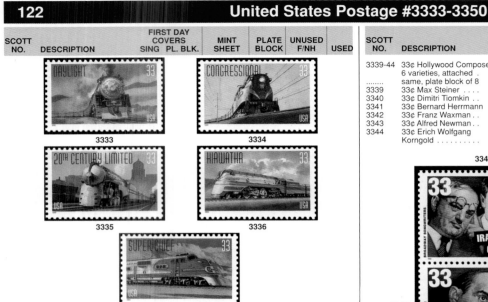

3333   3334

3335   3336

3337

SCOTT NO.	DESCRIPTION	FIRST DAY COVERS SING	PL. BLK.	MINT SHEET	PLATE BLOCK	UNUSED F/NH	USED
3333-37	33¢ Famous Trains, 5 varieties, attached .	10.00	15.00	22.00(20)	12.00(8)	6.00	5.00
3333	33¢ Daylight.	3.00	....	....	....	1.20	.40
3334	33¢ Congressional. . .	3.00	....	....	....	1.20	.40
3335	33¢ 20th Century Limited	3.00	....	....	....	1.20	.40
3336	33¢ Hiawatha.	3.00	....	....	....	1.20	.40
3337	33¢ Super Chief.	3.00	....	....	....	1.20	.40
3333-37v	same, uncut sheet of 120 (6 panes)	....	....	175.00(120)	....	175.00	....
....	block of 8 with horiz. gutter	....	....	....	....	22.50	....
....	block of 10 with vert. gutter	....	....	....	....	23.50	....
....	cross gutter block of 8	....	....	....	....	25.00	....
....	horiz. pair with vert. gutter	....	....	....	....	4.00	....
....	vert. pair with horiz. gutter	....	....	....	....	4.00	....

3338

3338	33¢ Frederick Law Olmstead, Landscape Architect . .	1.95	4.75	19.00(20)	5.00	1.10	.25

3339   3340

3341   3342

3343   3344

SCOTT NO.	DESCRIPTION	FIRST DAY COVERS SING	PL. BLK.	MINT SHEET	PLATE BLOCK	UNUSED F/NH	USED
3339-44	33¢ Hollywood Composers, 6 varieties, attached .	12.00	17.00	25.00(20)	9.50(6)	7.50	6.50
....	same, plate block of 8	....	....	....	8.00	....	....
3339	33¢ Max Steiner	3.00	....	....	....	1.25	.60
3340	33¢ Dimitri Tiomkin . .	3.00	....	....	....	1.25	.60
3341	33¢ Bernard Herrmann	3.00	....	....	....	1.25	.60
3342	33¢ Franz Waxman . .	3.00	....	....	....	1.25	.60
3343	33¢ Alfred Newman . .	3.00	....	....	....	1.25	.60
3344	33¢ Erich Wolfgang Korngold	3.00	....	....	....	1.25	.60

3345   3346

3347   3348

3349   3350

SCOTT NO.	DESCRIPTION	FIRST DAY COVERS SING	PL. BLK.	MINT SHEET	PLATE BLOCK	UNUSED F/NH	USED
3345-50	33¢ Broadway Songwriters, 6 varieties, attached .	12.00	17.00	25.00(20)	9.50(6)	7.50	6.50
....	same, plate block of 8	....	....	....	8.00	....	....
3345	33¢ Lra & George Gershwin	3.00	....	....	....	1.25	.60
3346	33¢ Lerner & Loewe .	3.00	....	....	....	1.25	.60
3347	33¢ Lorenz Hart.	3.00	....	....	....	1.25	.60
3348	33¢ Rodgers & Hammerstein.	3.00	....	....	....	1.25	.60
3349	33¢ Meredith Willson .	3.00	....	....	....	1.25	.60
3350	33¢ Frank Loesser. . .	3.00	....	....	....	1.25	.60

3351

INSECTS & SPIDERS

3351a	Black Widow	3351k	Monarch butterfly
3351b	Elderberry longhorn	3351l	Eastern hercules beetle
3351c	Lady beetle	3351m	Bombardier beetle
3351d	Yellow garden spider	3351n	Dung beetle
3351e	Dogbane beetle	3351o	Spotted water beetle
3351f	Flower fly	3351p	True Katydid
3351g	Assassin bug	3351q	Spinybacked spider
3351h	Ebony jewelwing	3351r	Periodical cicada
3351i	Velvet ant	3351s	Scorpionfly
3351j	Monarch caterpillar	3351t	Jumping spider

SCOTT NO.	DESCRIPTION	FIRST DAY COVERS SING	PL. BLK.	MINT SHEET	PLATE BLOCK	UNUSED F/NH	USED
	INSECTS & SPIDERS (continued)						
3351	33¢ Insects & Spiders, 20 varieties, attached	....	....	20.00(20)	....	20.00	19.00
....	set of singles	37.50	....	....	....	....	12.50
....	same, uncut sheet of 80 (4 panes)	....	....	80.00(80)	....	80.00	....
....	same, block of 10 with vert. gutter	....	....	....	....	20.00	....
....	same, block of 8 with horiz. gutter	....	....	....	....	20.00	....
....	same, cross gutter block of 20	....	....	....	....	35.00	....
....	same, vert. pair with horiz. gutter	....	....	....	....	3.00	....
....	same, horiz. pair with vert. gutter	....	....	....	....	3.00	....

3352

3352	33¢ Hanukkah, self-adhesive	2.25	4.75	16.50(20)	4.00	1.10	.25

3353

3353	22¢ Uncle Sam, coil	1.95	....	....	5.00	.70	.50
....	same, plate strip of 5	....	....	....	....	6.00	....

3354   **3355**

3354	33¢ NATO, 50th Anniv.	2.25	4.75	20.00(20)	5.00	1.10	.25
3355	33¢ Madonna & Child, self-adhesive	2.25	....	....	....	1.20	.20
3355a	same, bklt pane of 20	14.50	....	....	....	20.00	....

3356, 3360, 3364   **3357, 3361, 3365**   **3358, 3362, 3366**   **3359, 3363, 3367**

3356-59	33¢ Christmas Deer, self-adhesive	4.00	....	32.00(20)	7.00	6.00	....
3356	33¢ Christmas Deer, gold & red, self-adhesive	2.25	....	....	....	1.50	.50
3357	33¢ Christmas Deer, gold & blue, self-adhesive	2.25	....	....	....	1.50	.50
3358	33¢ Christmas Deer, gold & purple, self-adhesive	2.25	....	....	....	1.50	.50
3359	33¢ Christmas Deer, gold & green, self-adhesive	2.25	....	....	....	1.50	.50
3360	33¢ Christmas Deer, gold & red, bklt single, self-adhesive	2.25	....	....	....	1.50	.30
3361	33¢ Christmas Deer, gold & blue, bklt single, self-adhesive	2.25	....	....	....	1.50	.30
3362	33¢ Christmas Deer, gold & purple, bklt single, self-adhesive	2.25	....	....	....	1.50	.30
3363	33¢ Christmas Deer, gold & green, bklt single, self-adhesive	2.25	....	....	....	1.50	.30
3363a	same, bklt pane of 20	14.50	....	....	....	50.00	....
3364	33¢ Christmas Deer, gold & red, bklt single, (21x19mm), self-adhesive	2.25	....	....	....	2.50	.40
3365	33¢ Christmas Deer, gold & blue, bklt single, (21x19mm), self-adhesive	2.25	....	....	....	2.50	.40

SCOTT NO.	DESCRIPTION	FIRST DAY COVERS SING	PL. BLK.	MINT SHEET	PLATE BLOCK	UNUSED F/NH	USED
3366	33¢ Christmas Deer, gold & purple, bklt single, (21x19mm), self-adhesive	2.25	....	....	....	2.50	.40
3367	33¢ Christmas Deer, gold & green, bklt single, (21x19mm), self-adhesive	2.25	....	....	....	2.50	.40
3367a	same, bklt pane of 4 (3364-67 x 1)	4.00	....	....	....	15.00	....
3367b	same, bklt pane of 5 (3364, 3366, 3367, 3365 x 2)	5.00	....	....	....	13.00	....
3367c	same, bklt pane of 6 (3365, 3367, 3364 x 2, 3366)	6.00	....	....	....	16.00	....

3368   **3369**

3368	33¢ Kwanzaa, self-adhesive	2.25	....	18.00(20)	5.00	1.10	.25
3369	33¢ Baby New Year, self-adhesive	2.25	....	20.00(20)	5.00	1.10	.25

3370   **3371**   **3372**

2000 COMMEMORATIVES

3370/3446	(3370-72, 3379-90, 3393-3402 3414-17, 3438-46) 38 varieties	....	....	....	....	38.00	11.00
3370	33¢ Year of the Dragon	2.25	4.75	25.00(20)	6.00	1.20	.25
3371	33¢ Patricia Roberts Harris, self-adhesive	2.25	....	30.00(20)	7.00	1.50	.25
3372	33¢ Los Angeles Class Submarine (microprint USPS)	2.25	4.75	25.00(20)	6.00	1.00	.25

3373   **3374**

3375   **3376**

3377

3373	22¢ S Class Submarine	2.25	....	....	....	2.00	1.50
3374	33¢ Los Angeles Class Submarine (no microprint)	2.25	....	....	....	3.00	1.50
3375	55¢ Ohio Class Submarine	2.50	....	....	....	5.00	2.00
3376	60¢ USS Holland Submarine	2.50	....	....	....	5.00	3.00
3377	$3.20 Gato Class Submarine	7.50	....	....	....	30.00	9.50
3377a	same, bklt pane of 5, (#3373-77)	12.00	....	....	....	42.50	....
....	same, complete booklet of 2 panes	....	....	....	....	50.00	....

SCOTT NO.	DESCRIPTION	FIRST DAY COVERS SING	PL. BLK.	MINT SHEET	PLATE BLOCK	UNUSED F/NH	USED

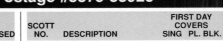

PACIFIC COAST RAIN FOREST

SECOND IN A SERIES

NATURE OF AMERICA

3378

PACIFIC COAST RAIN FOREST

3378a	Harlequin duck	**3378f**	Winter wren
3378b	Dwarf oregongrape, snail-eating ground beetle	**3378g**	Pacific giant salamander, Rough-skinned newt
3378c	American dipper	**3378h**	Western tiger swallowtail
3378d	Cutthroat trout	**3378i**	Douglas squirrel, foliose lichen
3378e	Roosevelt elk	**3378j**	Foliose lichen, banana slug

SCOTT NO.	DESCRIPTION	SING	PL. BLK.	MINT SHEET	PLATE BLOCK	UNUSED F/NH	USED
3378	33¢ Pacific Coast Rain Forest, 10 varieties, attached, self-adhesive	....	....	14.00(10)	....	14.00	10.00
....	set of singles	25.00	....			....	6.00
3378v	same, uncut sheet of 60 (6 panes)	....	....	60.00(60)	....	60.00	....

3379

3380

3381

3382

3383

SCOTT NO.	DESCRIPTION	SING	PL. BLK.	MINT SHEET	PLATE BLOCK	UNUSED F/NH	USED
3379-83	33¢ Louise Nevelson, (1899-1988), Sculptor, 5 varieties, attached	10.00	15.00	22.50(20)	11.00(10)	5.00	4.00
3379	33¢ Silent Music I	2.25	....	....	....	1.20	.40
3380	33¢ Royal Tide I	2.25	....	....	....	1.20	.40
3381	33¢ Black Chord	2.25	....	....	....	1.20	.40
3382	33¢ Nightsphere-Light	2.25	....	....	....	1.20	.40
3383	33¢ Dawn's Wedding Chapel I	2.25	....	....	....	1.20	.40

EAGLE NEBULA

3384

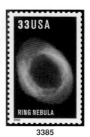

RING NEBULA

3385

LAGOON NEBULA

3386

EGG NEBULA

3387

GALAXY NGC 1316

3388

SCOTT NO.	DESCRIPTION	SING	PL. BLK.	MINT SHEET	PLATE BLOCK	UNUSED F/NH	USED
3384-88	33¢ Hubble Space Telescope Images, 5 varieties, attached	10.00	15.00	22.50(20)	11.00(10)	5.00	4.00
3384	33¢ Eagle Nebula	3.00	....	....	....	1.20	.40
3385	33¢ Ring Nebula	3.00	....	....	....	1.20	.40
3386	33¢ Lagoon Nebula	3.00	....	....	....	1.20	.40
3387	33¢ Egg Nebula	3.00	....	....	....	1.20	.40
3388	33¢ Galaxy NGC1316	3.00	....	....	....	1.20	.40

AMERICAN SAMOA 33 USA

3389

Library of Congress 33

1800 USA

3390

SCOTT NO.	DESCRIPTION	SING	PL. BLK.	MINT SHEET	PLATE BLOCK	UNUSED F/NH	USED
3389	33¢ American Samoa	2.25	4.75	17.50(20)	4.50	1.00	.25
3390	33¢ Library of Congress	2.25	4.75	17.50(20)	4.50	1.00	.25

33 USA

3391, 3392

SCOTT NO.	DESCRIPTION	SING	PL. BLK.	MINT SHEET	PLATE BLOCK	UNUSED F/NH	USED
3391	33¢ Road Runner & Wile E. Coyote, self-adhesive, pane of 10	12.00	....	....	....	9.50	....
3391a	same, single from pane	2.25	....	....	....	1.10	.35
3391b	same, pane of 9 (3391a)	....	....	....	....	7.00	....
3391c	same, pane of 1 (3391a)	7.00	....	....	....	2.75	....
....	same, top press sheet of 60 (6 panes) w/ plate #	....	....	80.00(60)	....	80.00	....
....	same, bottom press sheet of 60 (6 panes) w/ plate #	....	....	95.00(60)	....	95.00	....
....	same, pane of 10 from press sheet	....	....	....	....	15.00	....
....	same, pane of 10 with plate # on front	....	....	....	....	65.00	....
....	vert. pair with horiz. gutter	....	....	....	....	4.00	....
....	horiz. pair with vert. gutter	....	....	....	....	8.00	....
3392	33¢ Road Runner & Wile E. Coyote, self-adhesive, die cut, pane of 10	15.00	....	....	....	40.00	....
3392a	same, single from pane	....	....	....	....	3.00	....
3392b	same, pane of 9 (3392a)	....	....	....	....	30.00	....
3392c	same, pane of 1, imperf.	12.00	....	....	....	10.00	....

SCOTT NO.	DESCRIPTION	FIRST DAY COVERS SING PL. BLK.		MINT SHEET	PLATE BLOCK	UNUSED F/NH	USED

3393
3394
3395
3396

SCOTT NO.	DESCRIPTION	FIRST DAY COVERS SING	PL. BLK.	MINT SHEET	PLATE BLOCK	UNUSED F/NH	USED
3393-96	33¢ Distinguished Soldiers, 4 varieties, attached .	8.00	12.00	20.00(20)	5.00	4.50	4.00
3393	33¢ Major General John L. Hines (1868-1968). . .	2.25	....	....	....	1.25	.35
3394	33¢ General Omar N. Bradley (1893-1981) .	2.25	....	....	....	1.25	.35
3395	33¢ Sergeant Alvin C. York (1887-1964). . . .	2.25	....	....	....	1.25	.35
3396	33¢ Second Lieutenant Audie L. Murphy (1924-71)	2.25	....	....	....	1.25	.35

3397

3398

3397	33¢ Summer Sports. .	2.25	4.75	17.50(20)	4.50	1.00	.25
3398	33¢ Adoption, self-adhesive	2.25	....	17.50(20)	4.50	1.00	.25

3399
3400

3401
3402

3399-3402	33¢ Youth Team Sports, 4 varieites, attached .	8.00	12.00	20.00(20)	5.00	4.50	3.50
3399	33¢ Basketball.	3.00	....	....	....	1.25	.40
3400	33¢ Football.	3.00	....	....	....	1.25	.40
3401	33¢ Soccer	3.00	....	....	....	1.25	.40
3402	33¢ Baseball	3.00	....	....	....	1.25	.40

SCOTT NO.	DESCRIPTION	FIRST DAY COVERS SING	PL. BLK.	MINT SHEET	PLATE BLOCK	UNUSED F/NH	USED

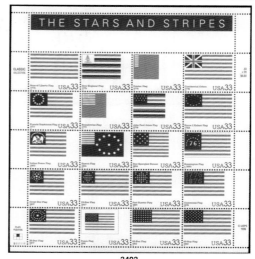

3403

THE STARS AND STRIPES

3403a Sons of Liberty Flag, 1775		**3403k** Star-Spangled Banner, 1814	
3403b New England, 1775		**3403l** Bennington Flag, c.1820	
3403c Forster Flag, 1775		**3403m** Great Star Flag, 1837	
3403d Continental Colors, 1776		**3403n** 29-Star Flag, 1847	
3403e Francis Hopkinson Flag, 1777		**3403o** Fort Sumter Flag, 1861	
3403f Brandywine Flag, 1777		**3403p** Centennial Flag, 1876	
3403g John Paul Jones Flag, 1779		**3403q** 38-Star Flag	
3403h Pierre L'Enfant Flag, 1783		**3403r** Peace Flag, 1891	
3403i Indian Peace Flag, 1803		**3403s** 48-Star Flag, 1912	
3403 j Easton Flag, 1814		**3403t** 50-Star Flag, 1960	

3403	33¢ The Stars & Stripes, 20 varieties, attached, self-adhesive	....	....	19.50(20)	....	19.50	15.00
....	set of singles	37.50	....	....	....	....	10.00
3403v	same, uncut sheet of 120 (6 panes)	....	....	120.00(120)	....	120.00	....
....	same, block of 8 with horiz. gutter	....	....	....	....	18.00	....
....	same, block of 10 with vert. gutter	....	....	....	....	20.00	....
....	same, cross gutter block of 20	....	....	....	....	40.00	....
....	vert. pair with horiz. gutter	....	....	....	....	4.50	....
....	horiz. pair with vert. gutter	....	....	....	....	4.50	....

3404
3405
3406
3407

3404	33¢ Blueberries, self-adhesive linerless coil	2.25	....	....	....	2.00	.50
3405	33¢ Strawberries, self-adhesive linerless coil	2.25	....	....	....	2.00	.50
3406	33¢ Blackberries, self-adhesive linerless coil	2.25	....	....	....	2.00	.50
3407	33¢ Raspberries, self-adhesive linerless coil	2.25	....	....	....	2.00	.50
3404-07	33¢ Berries, self-adhesive linerless coil, strip of 4	5.00	....	....	....	9.00	....
....	same, pl# strip of 5 . .	....	....	....	....	15.00	....

Tradewinds

Discount Stamp & Coin Supplies

Stamp Collecting Supplies
- Scott/Prinz Black Stamp Mounts
- Showgard Black/Clear Stamp Mounts
- Hagner Stock Sheets Black
- Vario/SafeT Pages

Also offering other products by Scott, Minkus & WhiteAce including Binders, Slipcases, Blank & Quad Pages, Glassine Interleaving, International Parts and much more!

Coin Collecting Supplies
- Dansco Albums
- Whitman Classic Albums
- Whitman Coin Folders
- 2x2 Cardboard Mylars
- SafeT Vinyl Pages - 3, 4, 12 and 20 Pockets
- Cowen Vinyl Pages - 3, 4, 12 and 20 Pockets
- Whitman Round Coin Tubes *(cent to dollar)*
- Square Coin Tubes *(cent to dollar)*
- SafeT Coin Flips, Twin Pocket Plus Inserts

MANY MORE GREAT PRODUCTS – ALWAYS GREAT PRICES

Order Online at www.TradeWindsSupplies.com

SCOTT NO.	DESCRIPTION	FIRST DAY COVERS SING	FIRST DAY COVERS PL. BLK.	MINT SHEET	PLATE BLOCK	UNUSED F/NH	USED

3408

LEGENDS OF BASEBALL

3408a	Jackie Robinson	**3408k**	Lefty Grove
3408b	Eddie Collins	**3408l**	Tris Speaker
3408c	Christy Mathewson	**3408m**	Cy Young
3408d	Ty Cobb	**3408n**	Jimmie Foxx
3408e	George Sisler	**3408o**	Pie Traynor
3408f	Rogers Hornsby	**3408p**	Satchel Paige
3408g	Mickey Cochrane	**3408q**	Honus Wagner
3408h	Babe Ruth	**3408r**	Josh Gibson
3408i	Walter Johnson	**3408s**	Dizzy Dean
3408 j	Roberto Clemente	**3408t**	Lou Gehrig

SCOTT NO.	DESCRIPTION	SING	PL. BLK.	MINT SHEET	PLATE BLOCK	UNUSED F/NH	USED
3408	33¢ Legends of Baseball, 20 varieties, attached, self-adhesive	....	....	30.00(20)	....	30.00	20.00
....	set of singles	37.50	....	....	....	....	12.00
3408v	same, uncut sheet of 120 (6 panes)	....	....	135.00(120)	....	135.00	....
....	cross gutter block of 20	....	....	....	....	40.00	....
....	block of 8 with vert. gutter	....	....	....	....	22.50	....
....	block of 10 with horiz. gutter	....	....	....	....	22.50	....
....	vert. pair with horiz. gutter	....	....	....	....	3.50	....
....	horiz. pair with vert. gutter	....	....	....	....	4.50	....

3409

SCOTT NO.	DESCRIPTION	SING	PL. BLK.	MINT SHEET	PLATE BLOCK	UNUSED F/NH	USED
3409	60¢ Probing the Vastness of Space, souvenir sheet of 6	15.00	....	....	....	25.00	20.00
3409a	60¢ Hubble Space Telescope	3.00	....	....	....	4.00	2.00
3409b	60¢ National Radio Astronomy Observatory	3.00	....	....	....	4.00	2.00
3409c	60¢ Keck Observatory	3.00	....	....	....	4.00	2.00
3409d	60¢ Cerro Tololo Inter-American Observatory	3.00	....	....	....	4.00	2.00
3409e	60¢ Mt. Wilson Observatory	3.00	....	....	....	4.00	2.00
3409f	60¢ Arecibo Observatory	3.00	....	....	....	4.00	2.00

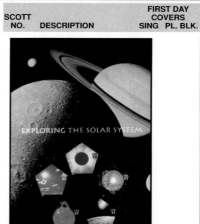

3410

3411

SCOTT NO.	DESCRIPTION	SING	PL. BLK.	MINT SHEET	PLATE BLOCK	UNUSED F/NH	USED
3410	$1 Exploring the Solar System, souvenir sheet of 5	13.50	....	....	....	22.50	20.00
3410a	$1 Solar eclipse	3.50	....	....	....	4.50	4.00
3410b	$1 Cross-section of sun	3.50	....	....	....	4.50	4.00
3410c	$1 Sun and Earth	3.50	....	....	....	4.50	4.00
3410d	$1 Sun & solar flare	3.50	....	....	....	4.50	4.00
3410e	$1 Sun with clouds	3.50	....	....	....	4.50	4.00
3411	$3.20 Escaping the Gravity of Earth hologram, souvenir sheet of 2	16.50	....	....	....	30.00	25.00
3411a	$3.20 International Space Station hologram, from souvenir sheet	7.50	....	....	....	15.00	10.00
3411b	$3.20 Astronauts Working hologram, from souvenir sheet	7.50	....	....	....	15.00	10.00

3412

SCOTT NO.	DESCRIPTION	SING	PL. BLK.	MINT SHEET	PLATE BLOCK	UNUSED F/NH	USED
3412	$11.75 Space Achievement and Exploration hologram, souvenir sheet of 1	27.50	....	....	....	60.00	40.00

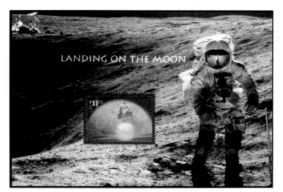

3413

SCOTT NO.	DESCRIPTION	SING	PL. BLK.	MINT SHEET	PLATE BLOCK	UNUSED F/NH	USED
3413	$11.75 Landing on the Moon hologram, souvenir sheet of 1	27.50	....	....	....	60.00	40.00

SCOTT NO.	DESCRIPTION	FIRST DAY COVERS SING	PL. BLK.	MINT SHEET	PLATE BLOCK	UNUSED F/NH	USED

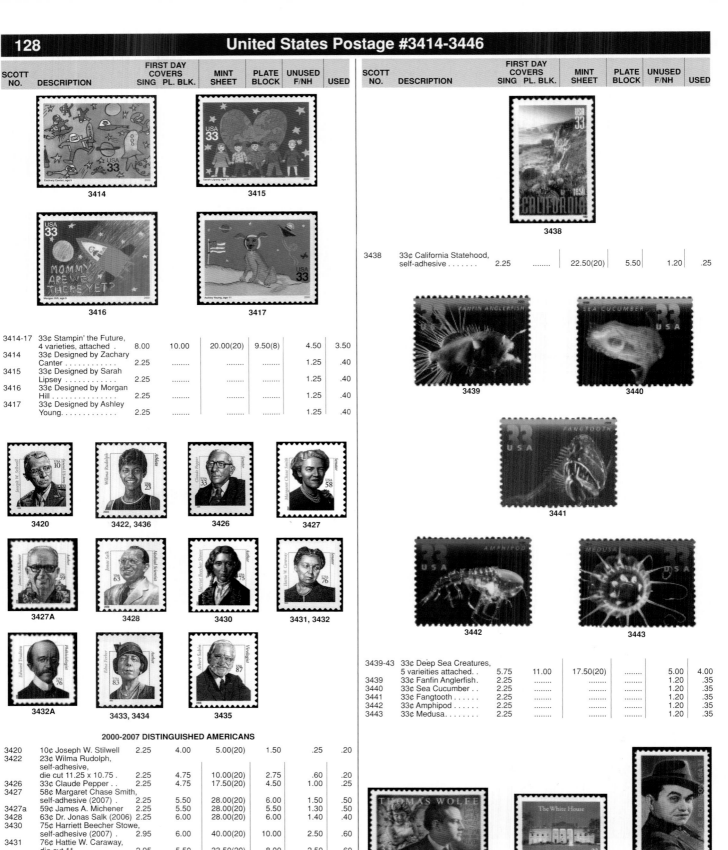

3414 · 3415

3416 · 3417

3414-17	33¢ Stampin' the Future, 4 varieties, attached .	8.00	10.00	20.00(20)	9.50(8)	4.50	3.50
3414	33¢ Designed by Zachary Canter	2.25	....	....		1.25	.40
3415	33¢ Designed by Sarah Lipsey	2.25	....	....		1.25	.40
3416	33¢ Designed by Morgan Hill	2.25	....	....		1.25	.40
3417	33¢ Designed by Ashley Young.	2.25	....	....		1.25	.40

3420 · 3422, 3436 · 3426 · 3427

3427A · 3428 · 3430 · 3431, 3432

3432A · 3433, 3434 · 3435

2000-2007 DISTINGUISHED AMERICANS

3420	10¢ Joseph W. Stilwell	2.25	4.00	5.00(20)	1.50	.25	.20
3422	23¢ Wilma Rudolph, self-adhesive, die cut 11.25 x 10.75 .	2.25	4.75	10.00(20)	2.75	.60	.20
3426	33¢ Claude Pepper . .	2.25	4.75	17.50(20)	4.50	1.00	.25
3427	58¢ Margaret Chase Smith, self-adhesive (2007) .	2.25	5.50	28.00(20)	6.00	1.50	.50
3427a	59¢ James A. Michener	2.25	5.50	28.00(20)	5.50	1.30	.50
3428	63¢ Dr. Jonas Salk (2006)	2.25	6.00	28.00(20)	6.00	1.40	.40
3430	75¢ Harriett Beecher Stowe, self-adhesive (2007) .	2.95	6.00	40.00(20)	10.00	2.50	.60
3431	76¢ Hattie W. Caraway, die cut 11	2.95	5.50	33.50(20)	8.00	2.50	.60
3432	76¢ Hattie W. Caraway, die cut 11.5 x 11.	....	....	75.00(20)	18.50	4.00	4.00
3432a	76¢ Edward Trudeau .	2.95	5.75	33.50(20)	8.00	2.50	.60
3433	83¢ Edna Ferber, die cut 11 x 11.5.	2.95	5.50	50.00(20)	12.00	3.00	.75
3434	83¢ Edna Ferber, die cut 11.25 (2003). .	2.95	5.50	38.00(20)	9.00	2.50	.75
3435	87¢ Dr. Albert Sabin (2006)	2.95	5.50	38.00(20)	9.00	1.95	.75
3436	23¢ Wilma Rudolph, self-adhesive, die cut 11.25 x 10.75 .	2.25	....	....		.60	.20
3436a	same, bklt pane of 4 .	3.00	....	....		2.75	......
3436b	same, bklt pane of 6 .	4.00	....	....		3.75	......
3436c	same, bklt pane of 10	6.75	....	....		6.50	......

3438

| 3438 | 33¢ California Statehood, self-adhesive . . . . | 2.25 | .... | 22.50(20) | 5.50 | 1.20 | .25 |

3439 · 3440

3441

3442 · 3443

3439-43	33¢ Deep Sea Creatures, 5 varieities attached. .	5.75	11.00	17.50(20)	....	5.00	4.00
3439	33¢ Fanfin Anglerfish.	2.25	....	....	....	1.20	.35
3440	33¢ Sea Cucumber . .	2.25	....	....	....	1.20	.35
3441	33¢ Fangtooth	2.25	....	....	....	1.20	.35
3442	33¢ Amphipod	2.25	....	....	....	1.20	.35
3443	33¢ Medusa.	2.25	....	....	....	1.20	.35

3444 · 3445 · 3446

3444	33¢ Thomas Wolfe. . .	2.25	4.75	17.50(20)	4.50	1.00	.25
3445	33¢ White House. . . .	2.25	4.75	30.00(20)	7.00	1.50	.25
3446	33¢ Edward G. Robinson	2.25	4.75	30.00(20)	7.00	1.50	.50
....	same, uncut sheet of 120 (6 panes)	....	....	175.00(120)	....	175.00	....
....	cross gutter block of 8	....	....	....	....	35.00	....
....	block of 8 with vert. gutter	....	....	....	....	24.00	....
....	horiz. pair with vert. gutter	....	....	....	....	6.00	....
....	vert. pair with horiz. gutter	....	....	....	....	4.50	....

SCOTT NO.	DESCRIPTION	FIRST DAY COVERS SING	FIRST DAY COVERS PL. BLK.	MINT SHEET	PLATE BLOCK	UNUSED F/NH	USED

3447   **3448, 3449, 3450,**   **3451, 3452, 3453**

SCOTT NO.	DESCRIPTION	FIRST DAY COVERS SING	FIRST DAY COVERS PL. BLK.	MINT SHEET	PLATE BLOCK	UNUSED F/NH	USED

3466, 3476, 3477,   **3467, 3468, 3475,**   **3468A, 3475A**   **3469, 3470**
3485   **3484, 3484A**

3471   **3471A**

Scott No.	Description	Sing	Pl. Blk.	Mint Sheet	Plate Block	Unused F/NH	Used
3447	10¢ New York Public Library Lion, coil	2.25	....	....	4.00	.50	.20
....	same, pl# strip of 5	....	....	....	....	5.00	....
3447a	10¢ New York Public Library, self-adhesive, coil, die cut 11.5	2.25	....	....	....	.50	.35
....	same, pl# strip of 5	....	....	....	....	4.00	....
3448	(34¢) Flag over Farm	2.25	4.75	25.00(20)	6.00	1.30	.60
3449	(34¢) Flag over Farm, self-adhesive	2.25	4.75	25.00(20)	6.00	1.30	.30
3450	(34¢) Flag over Farm, self-adhesive	2.25	....	....	....	1.25	.25
3450a	same, bklt pane of 18	14.00	....	....	....	21.50	....
3451	(34¢) Statue of Liberty, self-adhesive	2.25	....	....	....	1.20	.30
3451a	same, bklt pane of 20	14.50	....	....	....	24.00	....
3451b	same, bklt pane of 4	4.00	....	....	....	5.00	....
3451c	same, bklt pane of 6	5.50	....	....	....	7.00	....
3452	(34¢) Statue of Liberty, coil	2.25	....	....	7.00	1.00	.20
....	same, pl# strip of 5	....	....	....	....	9.00	....
3453	(34¢) Statue of Liberty, self-adhesive coil	1.95	....	....	10.00	1.00	.20
....	same, pl# strip of 5	....	....	....	....	12.00	....

3454, 3458, 3465   **3455, 3459, 3464**   **3456, 3460, 3463**   **3457, 3461, 3462**

Scott No.	Description	Sing	Pl. Blk.	Mint Sheet	Plate Block	Unused F/NH	Used
3454-57	(34¢) Flowers, self-adhesive, 4 varieties attached	4.25	....	....	....	6.00	....
3454	(34¢) Fressia, self-adhesive, die cut 10.25 x 10.75	2.25	....	....	....	1.50	.30
3455	(34¢) Symbidium Orchid, self-adhesive, die cut 10.25 x 10.75	2.25	....	....	....	1.50	.30
3456	(34¢) Longiflorum Lily, self-adhesive, die cut 10.25 x 10.75	2.25	....	....	....	1.50	.30
3457	(34¢) Asian Hybrid, self-adhesive, die cut 10.25 x 10.75	2.25	....	....	....	1.50	.30
3457b	same, bklt pane of 4 (3454-57)	4.00	....	....	....	6.00	....
3457c	same, bklt pane of 6 (3456, 3457, 3454 x 2 3455 x 2)	5.50	....	....	....	9.00	....
3457d	same, bklt pane of 6 (3454, 3455, 3456 x 2 3457 x 2)	5.50	....	....	....	9.00	....
3457e	(34¢) Flowers, bklt pane of 20, self-adhesive (5 each 3457 + label)	14.50	....	....	....	20.00	....
3458-61	(34¢) Flowers, self-adhesive, 4 varieties attached	4.25	....	....	....	15.00	....
3458	(34¢) Fressia, bklt single, self-adhesive, die cut 11.5 x 11.75	2.25	....	....	....	3.25	.50
3459	(34¢) Symbidium Orchid, bklt single, self-adhesive, die cut 11.5 x 11.75	2.25	....	....	....	3.25	.50
3460	(34¢) Longiflorum Lily, bklt single, self-adhesive, die cut 11.5 x 11.75	2.25	....	....	....	3.25	.50
3461	(34¢) Asian Hybrid Lily, bklt single, self-adhesive, die cut 11.5 x 11.75	2.25	....	....	....	3.25	.50
3461b	same, bklt pane of 20, self-adhesive (2 each 3461a, 3 each 3457a)	14.50	....	....	....	38.00	....
3461c	same, bklt pane of 20, self-adhesive (2 each 3457a, 3 each 3461a)	14.50	....	....	....	50.00	....
3462	(34¢) Longiflorum Lily, self-adhesive coil	2.25	....	....	....	4.00	.50
3463	(34¢) Asian Hybrid Lily, self-adhesive coil	2.25	....	....	....	4.00	.50
3464	(34¢) Symbidium Orchid, self-adhesive coil	2.25	....	....	....	4.00	.50
3465	(34¢) Fressia, self-adhesive coil	2.25	....	....	....	4.00	.50
3462-65	(34¢) Flowers, self-adhesive coil, strip of 4	4.25	....	....	....	16.50	....
....	same, pl# strip of 5	....	....	....	....	21.50	....

2001 REGULAR ISSUES

Scott No.	Description	Sing	Pl. Blk.	Mint Sheet	Plate Block	Unused F/NH	Used
3466	34¢ Statue of Liberty, self-adhesive coil, die cut 9.75 (round corners)	2.25	....	....	7.00	1.30	.50
....	same, pl# strip of 5	....	....	....	....	9.00	....
3467	21¢ Buffalo	2.25	4.75	130.00(100)	20.00	1.50	.75
3468	21¢ Buffalo, self-adhesive	2.25	4.75	12.00(20)	3.00	.65	.75
3468A	23¢ George Washington, self-adhesive	2.25	4.75	12.00(20)	2.75	.65	.75
3469	34¢ Flag over Farm	2.25	4.75	150.00(100)	32.00	1.50	.50
3470	34¢ Flag over Farm, self-adhesive	2.25	4.75	38.00(20)	8.00	2.00	.50
3471	55¢ Eagle, self-adhesive	2.50	5.00	35.00(20)	7.00	1.50	.50
3471A	57¢ Eagle, self-adhesive	2.50	5.00	30.00(20)	7.00	1.50	.50

3472   **3473**

Scott No.	Description	Sing	Pl. Blk.	Mint Sheet	Plate Block	Unused F/NH	Used
3472	$3.50 Capitol Dome, self-adhesive	8.00	30.00	200.00(20)	45.00	10.00	5.00
3473	$12.25 Washington Monument, self-adhesive	30.00	98.50	700.00(20)	150.00	40.00	11.00
3475	21¢ Buffalo, self-adhesive coil	2.25	....	....	5.00	.65	.30
....	same, pl# strip of 5	....	....	....	....	6.00	....
3475A	23¢ George Washington, self-adhesive coil	2.25	....	....	....	1.00	.30
....	same, pl# strip of 5	....	....	....	....	6.00	....
3476	34¢ Statue of Liberty, coil	2.25	....	....	6.00	1.00	.40
....	same, pl# strip of 5	....	....	....	....	7.50	....
3477	34¢ Statue of Liberty, self-adhesive coil die cut 9.75 (square corners)	2.25	....	....	6.00	1.00	.20
....	same, pl# strip of 5	....	....	....	....	7.50	....

3478, 3489   **3479, 3490**   **3480, 3488**   **3481, 3487**

Scott No.	Description	Sing	Pl. Blk.	Mint Sheet	Plate Block	Unused F/NH	Used
3478	34¢ Longiflorum, self-adhesive coil	2.25	....	....	....	1.50	.40
3479	34¢ Asain Hybrid Lily, self-adhesive coil	2.25	....	....	....	1.50	.40
3480	34¢ Symbidium Orchid, self-adhesive coil	2.25	....	....	....	1.50	.40
3481	34¢ Fressia, self-adhesive coil	2.25	....	....	....	1.50	.40
3478-81	34¢ Flowers, self-adhesive, coil, strip of 4	4.25	....	....	....	6.00	....
....	same, pl# strip of 5	....	....	....	....	10.00	....

SCOTT NO.	DESCRIPTION	FIRST DAY COVERS SING	PL. BLK.	MINT SHEET	PLATE BLOCK	UNUSED F/NH	USED
3482	20¢ George Washington, self-adhesive, die cut 11.25	2.25	....	....	....	1.00	.30
3482a	same, bklt pane of 10	5.50	....	....	....	8.00	....
3482b	same, bklt pane of 4, die cut 11.25 x 11....	3.00	....	....	....	3.00	....
3482c	same, bklt pane of 6, die cut 11.25 x 11....	4.00	....	....	....	5.00	....
3483	20¢ George Washington, self-adhesive, die cut 10.5 x 11.25........	2.25	....	....	....	5.00	1.00
3483a	same, bklt pane of 4 (2 each 3482-3483)..	3.00	....	....	....	15.00	....
3483b	same, bklt pane of 6 (3 each 3482-3483)..	4.00	....	....	....	22.00	....
3483c	same, bklt pane of 10, die cut 10.5 x 11 (3482 x 5 at L, 3483 x 5 at R) ..	5.50	....	....	....	25.00	....
3483d	same, bklt pane of 4 (2 each 3482-3483), die cut 11.25 x 11....	....	....	....	....	17.00	....
3483e	same, bklt pane of 6 (2 each 3482-3483), die cut 11.25 x 11....	....	....	....	....	22.00	....
3483f	same, bklt pane of 10 (5 each 3482-3483), die cut 11.25 x 11....	....	....	....	....	25.00	....
3483g	pair, 3482 at left, 3483 at right........	....	....	....	....	6.00	....
3483h	pair 3483 at left, 3482 at right........	....	....	....	....	6.00	....
3484	21¢ Buffalo, self-adhesive, die cut 11.25	2.25	....	....	....	1.00	.50
3484b	same, bklt pane of 4 .	3.00	....	....	....	3.25	....
3484c	same, bklt pane of 6 .	4.00	....	....	....	4.75	....
3484d	same, bklt pane of 10	5.50	....	....	....	8.00	....
3484A	21¢ Buffalo, self-adhesive, die cut 10.5 X 11.25..	2.25	....	....	....	4.00	.50
3484Ae	same, bklt pane of 4 (3484 x 2 at L, 3484A x 2 at R)	....	....	....	....	18.00	....
3484Af	same, bklt pane of 6 (3484 x 3 at L, 3484A x 3 at R)	....	....	....	....	20.00	....
3484Ag	same, bklt pane of 10 (3484 x 5 at L, 3484A x 5 at R)	....	....	....	....	20.00	....
3484Ah	same, bklt pane of 4 (3484A x 2 at L, 3484 x 2 at R)	....	....	....	....	16.00	....
3484Ai	same, bklt pane of 6 (3484A x 3 at L, 3484 x 3 at R)	....	....	....	....	25.00	....
3484Aj	same, bklt pane of 10 (3484A x 5 at L, 3484 x 5 at R)	....	....	....	....	25.00	....
3484Ak	same, pair (3484 at L, 3484A at R)	....	....	....	....	6.00	....
3484Al	same, pair (3484A at L, 3484 at R).......	....	....	....	....	6.00	....
3485	34¢ Statue of Liberty, self-adhesive	2.25	....	....	....	1.40	.20
3485a	same, bklt pane of 10	7.25	....	....	....	13.50	....
3485b	same, bklt pane of 20	14.50	....	....	....	27.00	....
3485c	same, bklt pane of 4 .	4.00	....	....	....	4.50	....
3485d	same, bklt pane of 6 .	5.50	....	....	....	6.50	....
3487-90	34¢ Flowers, self-adhesive 4 varieties attached ..	4.25	....	....	....	5.00	3.50
3487	34¢ Fressia, self-adhesive, die cut 10.25 x 10.75 .	2.25	....	....	....	1.20	.25
3488	34¢ Symbidium Orchid, self-adhesive, die cut 10.25 x 10.75.......	2.25	....	....	....	1.20	.25
3489	34¢ Longiflorum Lily, self-adhesive, die cut 10.25 x 10.75.......	2.25	....	....	....	1.20	.25
3490	34¢ Asian Hybrid Lily, self-adhesive, die cut 10.25 x 10.75.......	2.25	....	....	....	1.20	.25
3490b	same, bklt pane of 4 (3487-90 x 1).......	4.00	....	....	....	5.00	....
3490c	same, bklt pane of 6 (3489-3490, 3487 x 2, 3488 x 2)	5.50	....	....	....	7.50	....
3490d	same, bklt pane of 6 (3487-3488, 3498 x 2 3490 x 2)	5.50	....	....	....	7.50	....
3490e	same, bklt pane of 20 (3487-90 x 5 + label) .	14.50	....	....	....	22.50	....
3491	34¢ Apple, self-adhesive	2.25	....	....	....	1.75	.25
3492	34¢ Orange, self-adhesive	2.25	....	....	....	1.75	.25
3491-92	34¢ Apple & Orange, Pair	2.50	....	....	....	3.50	....
3492b	34¢ Apple & Orange, bklt pane of 20, self-adhesive	14.50	....	....	....	19.50	....
3493	34¢ Apple, self-adhesive, die cut 11.5 x 10.75 ..	2.25	....	....	....	1.50	.50
3494	34¢ Orange, self-adhesive, die cut 11.5 x 10.75 ..	2.25	....	....	....	1.50	.50
3493-94	34¢ Apple & Orange, Pair	2.50	....	....	....	3.50	....
3494b	same, bklt pane of 4 (3493 x 2, 3494 x 2)..	4.00	....	....	....	2.00	....

3482, 3483

3491, 3493

3492, 3494

3495

SCOTT NO.	DESCRIPTION	FIRST DAY COVERS SING	PL. BLK.	MINT SHEET	PLATE BLOCK	UNUSED F/NH	USED
3494c	same, bklt pane of 6 (3493 x 3, 3494 x 3) (3493 at UL)........	5.50	....	....	....	12.00	....
3494d	same, bklt pane of 6 (3493 x 3, 3494 x 3) (3494 at UL)........	5.50	....	....	....	12.00	....
3495	34¢ Flag over Farm, self-adhesive	1.95	....	....	....	1.50	.50
3495a	same, ATM bklt pane of 18	14.00	....	....	....	28.00	....
3496	(34¢) LOVE, self-adhesive, die cut 11.75	2.25	....	....	....	1.10	.25
3496a	same, bklt pane of 20	14.50	....	....	....	24.00	....
3497	34¢ LOVE, self-adhesive, die cut 11.25	2.25	....	....	....	1.10	.25
3497a	same, bklt pane of 20	14.50	....	....	....	24.00	....
3498	34¢ LOVE, self-adhesive, die cut 11.5 x 10.75 ..	2.25	....	....	....	1.10	.25
3498a	same, bklt pane of 4 .	4.00	....	....	....	6.00	....
3498b	same, bklt pane of 6 .	5.50	....	....	....	10.00	....
3499	55¢ LOVE, self-adhesive	2.50	5.00	32.00(20)	7.50	1.50	.50

3496

3497, 3498

3499

3500

3501

2001 COMMEMORATIVES

SCOTT NO.	DESCRIPTION	FIRST DAY COVERS SING	PL. BLK.	MINT SHEET	PLATE BLOCK	UNUSED F/NH	USED
3500/3548	(3500-01, 3503-04, 3507-19, 3521, 3523-33, 3536-40, 3545-48) 38 varieties.......	....	....	....	....	38.40	13.50
3500	34¢ Year of the Snake	2.25	4.75	26.00(20)	6.00	1.35	.30
3501	34¢ Roy Wilkins, self-adhesive.......	2.25	4.75	24.00(20)	5.50	1.25	.25

3502

AMERICAN ILLUSTRATORS

3502a	Marine Corps poster	3502k	"Galahad's Departure"
3502b	"Interlude (The Lute Players)"	3502l	"The First Lesson"
3502c	Advertisement for Arrow Collars and Shirts	3502m	Illustration for cover of McCall's
3502d	Advertisement for Carrier Corp. Refrigeration	3502n	"Back Home for Keeps"
3502e	Advertisement for Luxite Hosiery	3502o	"Something for Supper"
3502f	Illustration for correspondence school lesson	3502p	"A Dash for the Timber"
3502g	"Br'er Rabbit"	3502q	Illustration for "Moby Dick"
3502h	"An Attack on a Galleon"	3502r	"Captain Bill Bones"
3502i	Kewpie and Kewpie Doodle Dog	3502s	Illustration for The Saturday Evening Post
3502 j	Illustration for cover of True Magazine	3502t	"The Girl He Left Behind"

SCOTT NO.	DESCRIPTION	FIRST DAY COVERS SING	PL. BLK.	MINT SHEET	PLATE BLOCK	UNUSED F/NH	USED

AMERICAN ILLUSTRATORS (Continued)

3502	34¢ American Illustrators, 20 varieties, attached, self-adhesive	....	....	27.50(20)	....	27.50	25.00
....	set of singles	37.50	....	....	....	....	15.00
3502v	same, uncut sheet of 80 (4 panes)	....	....	120.00(80)	....	120.00	....
....	cross gutter block of 20	....	....	....	....	60.00	....
....	block of 8 with horiz. gutter	....	....	....	....	40.00	....
....	block of 10 with vert. gutter	....	....	....	....	40.00	....
....	vert. pair with horiz. gutter	....	....	....	....	7.00	....
....	horiz. pair with vert. gutter	....	....	....	....	7.00	....

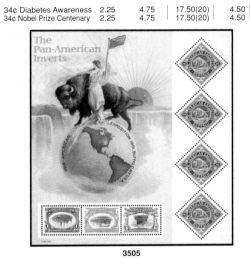

3503　　　**3504**

| 3503 | 34¢ Diabetes Awareness | 2.25 | 4.75 | 17.50(20) | 4.50 | 1.00 | .25 |
| 3504 | 34¢ Nobel Prize Centenary | 2.25 | 4.75 | 17.50(20) | 4.50 | 1.00 | .25 |

3505

| 3505 | 1¢-80¢ Pan-American Expo. Invert Souvenir Sheet of 7 | 10.00 | .... | .... | .... | 15.00 | 12.00 |
| .... | same, uncut sheet of 28 (4 panes) | .... | .... | .... | .... | 75.00 | .... |

3506

GREAT PLAINS PRAIRIE

3506a	*Pronghorns, Canada geese*	3506f	*Western Meadowlark, camel cricket, prairie coneflowers, prairie wild flowers*
3506b	*Burrowing owls, American buffalos*		
3506c	*American buffalo, Black-tailed prairie dogs, wild alfalfa*	3506g	*Badger, Harvester ants*
		3506h	*Eastern short-horned lizard, plains gopher*
3506d	*Black-tailed prairie dogs, American Buffalo*	3506i	*Plains spadefoot, dung beetle, prairie roses*
3506e	*Painted lady butterfly, American buffalo, prairie coneflowers, prairie wild roses*	3506j	*Two-striped grasshopper, Ord's kangaroo rat*

3506	34¢ Great Plains Prairie, 10 varieties, attached, self-adhesive	....	....	15.00(10)	....	15.00	12.00
....	set of singles	19.50	....	....	....	....	6.00
3506v	same, uncut sheet of 60 (6 panes)	....	....	60.00(60)	....	60.00	....

3507　　　**3509**　　　**3508**

3507	34¢ Peanuts, self-adhesive	2.25	4.75	25.00(20)	6.00	1.25	.25
3508	34¢ US Veterans, self-adhesive	2.25	4.75	25.00(20)	6.00	1.25	.25
3509	34¢ Frida Kahlo	2.25	4.75	20.00(20)	4.50	1.00	.25

3510　　　**3511**

3512　　　**3513**

3514　　　**3515**

3516　　　**3517**

3518　　　**3519**

BASEBALL'S LEGENDARY PLAYING FIELDS

3510	*Ebbets Field*	3515	*Forbes Field*
3511	*Tiger Stadium*	3516	*Fenway Field*
3512	*Crosley Field*	3517	*Comiskey Park*
3513	*Yankee Stadium*	3518	*Shibe Park*
3514	*Polo Grounds*	3519	*Wrigley Field*

3510-19	34¢ Baseball's Legendary Playing Fields, 10 varieties, self-adhesive	7.25	....	25.00(20)	15.00(10)	12.00	10.00
....	set of singles	25.00	....	....	....	....	6.00
3510-19v	same, uncut sheet of 160 (8 panes)	....	....	160.00(160)	....	160.00	....
....	cross gutter block of 12	....	....	....	....	25.00	....
....	block of 10 with vert. gutter	....	....	....	....	15.00	....
....	block of 4 with horiz. gutter	....	....	....	....	7.50	....
....	vert. pair with horiz. gutter	....	....	....	....	3.50	....
....	horiz. pair with vert. gutter	....	....	....	....	3.50	....

SCOTT NO.	DESCRIPTION	FIRST DAY COVERS SING	PL. BLK.	MINT SHEET	PLATE BLOCK	UNUSED F/NH	USED

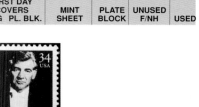

3521

3520

3522

3520	(10¢) Atlas Statue, coil	2.25	....	....	4.00	.30	.25
	self-adhesive, die cut 8.5						
....	same, pl# strip of 5 ..	....	....	....	....	4.50	....
3521	34¢ Leonard Bernstein	2.25	4.75	17.50(20)	4.50	1.00	.25
3522	(15¢) Woody Wagon,						
	self-adhesive coil	2.25	....	....	4.00	.50	.30
....	same, pl# strip of 5 ..	....	....	....	....	5.00	....

3523

3523	34¢ Lucille Ball,						
	self-adhesive	2.25	4.75	30.00(20)	7.00	1.50	.25
3523v	same, uncut sheet of						
	180 (9 panes)	....	....	185.00(180)	....	185.00	....
....	cross gutter block of 8	....	....	....	....	30.00	....
....	block of 8 with vert. gutter	....	....	....	....	22.50	....
....	vert. pair with horiz. gutter	....	....	....	....	3.00	....
....	horiz. pair with vert. gutter	....	....	....	....	4.00	....

3524   3525

3526   3527

3524-27	34¢ Amish Quilts,						
	4 varieties attached ..	4.25	5.25	20.00(20)	5.00	4.50	4.00
3524	34¢ Diamond in the Square	2.25				1.20	.40
3525	34¢ Lone Star	2.25				1.20	.40
3526	34¢ Sunshine and Shadow	2.25				1.20	.40
3527	34¢ Double Ninepatch Variation	2.25				1.20	.40

| 3528 | 3529 | 3530 | 3531 |

3528-31	34¢ Carnivorous Plants,						
	4 varieties attached ..	4.25	5.25	20.00(20)	5.00	4.50	4.00
3528	34¢ Venus Flytrap ...	2.25	....	....	....	1.20	.40
3529	34¢ Yellow Trumpet ..	2.25	....	....	....	1.20	.40
3530	34¢ Cobra	2.25	....	....	....	1.20	.40
3531	34¢ English Sundew .	2.25	....	....	....	1.20	.40

| 3532 | 3533 | 3534, 3535 |

3532	34¢ "Eid Mubarak",						
	self-adhesive	2.25	4.75	17.50(20)	4.50	1.00	.25
3533	34¢ Enrico Fermi,						
	self-adhesive	2.25	4.75	17.50(20)	4.50	1.00	.25
3534	34¢ That's All Folks,						
	self-adhesive, pane of 10	12.50	....	....	....	9.50	....
3534a	same, single from pane	2.50	....	....	....	1.10	.25
3534b	same, pane of 9 (3534a)	....	....	....	....	9.00	....
3534c	same, pane of 1 (3534a)	7.25	....	....	....	2.75	....
....	same, top press sheet of						
	60 (6 panes) w/ pl# ..	....	....	80.00(60)	....	80.00	....
....	same, bottom press sheet						
	of 60 (6 panes) w/ pl#	....	....	95.00(60)	....	95.00	....
....	same, pane of 10 from						
	press sheet	....	....	....	....	15.00	....
....	same, pane of 10 w/						
	pl# on front.........	....	....	....	....	70.00	....
....	vert. pair with horiz. gutter	....	....	....	....	4.00	....
....	horiz. pair with vert. gutter	....	....	....	....	7.50	....
3535	34¢ That's All Folks, die cut,						
	self-adhesive, pane of 10	15.00	....	....	....	75.00	....
3535a	same, single form pane	....	....	....	....	6.00	....
3535b	same, pane of 9 (3435a)	....	....	....	....	50.00	....
3535c	same, pane of 1, imperf.	12.50	....	....	....	20.00	....

3536

3536	34¢ Madonna and Child,						
	self-adhesive	2.25	....	....	....	1.00	.20
3536a	same, bklt pane of 20	14.50	....	....	....	18.50	....

| 3537, 3537a, 3541 | 3538, 3538a, 3542 | 3539, 3539a, 3543 | 3540, 3540a, 3544 |

3537-40	34¢ Santas, self-adhesive,						
	4 varieties attach, large date	4.25	5.25	20.00(20)	5.00	4.50	4.00
3537	34¢ Santa w/ horse, large date	2.25	....	....	....	1.20	.40
3538	34¢ Santa w/ horn, large date	2.25	....	....	....	1.20	.40
3539	34¢ Santa w/ drum, large date	2.25	....	....	....	1.20	.40
3540	34¢ Santa w/ dog, large date	2.25	....	....	....	1.20	.40

SCOTT NO.	DESCRIPTION	FIRST DAY COVERS SING	FIRST DAY COVERS PL. BLK.	MINT SHEET	PLATE BLOCK	UNUSED F/NH	USED
3537a-40a	34¢ Santas, self-adhesive, 4 varieties attach, small date	4.25	5.25	....	....	4.50	4.00
3537a	34¢ Santa w/ horse, small date	2.25	....	....	....	1.20	.40
3538a	34¢ Santa w/ horn, small date	2.25	....	....	....	1.20	.40
3539a	34¢ Santa w/ drum, small date	2.25	....	....	....	1.20	.40
3540a	34¢ Santa w/ dog, small date	2.25	....	....	....	1.20	.40
3540d	same, bklt pane of 20, 3537a-40a x 5 + label	14.50				20.00	....
3537b-40e	34¢ Santas, self-adhesive, 4 varieties attach, large date	4.25	5.25			12.00	9.00
3537b	34¢ Santa w/ horse, large date	2.25	....	....	....	1.20	.40
3538b	34¢ Santa w/ horn, large date	2.25	....	....	....	1.20	.40
3539b	34¢ Santa w/ drum, large date	2.25	....	....	....	1.20	.40
3540e	34¢ Santa w/ dog, large date	2.25	....	....	....	1.20	.40
3540g	same, bklt pane of 20, 3537b-40e x 5 + label	14.50				50.00	....
3541-44	34¢ Santas, self-adhesive, 4 varieties attach, green denom.	4.25				4.50	
3541	34¢ Santa w/ horse, green denom	2.25				1.20	.30
3542	34¢ Santa w/ horn, green denom	2.25				1.20	.30
3543	34¢ Santa w/ drum, green denom	2.25				1.20	.30
3544	34¢ Santa w/ dog, green denom	2.25				1.20	.30
3544b	same, bklt pane of 4 (3541-3544)	4.00				4.50	
3544c	same, bklt pane of 6 (3543-44, 3541-42 x 2)	5.50				6.00	
3544d	same, bklt pane of 6 (3541-42, 3543-44 x 2)	5.50				6.00	

3545

SCOTT NO.	DESCRIPTION	FIRST DAY COVERS SING	FIRST DAY COVERS PL. BLK.	MINT SHEET	PLATE BLOCK	UNUSED F/NH	USED
3545	34¢ James Madison	2.25	4.75	20.00(20)	4.50	1.00	.30
3545v	same, uncut sheet of 120 (6 panes)	....	....	110.00(120)	....	110.00	....
....	cross gutter block of 4	....	....	....	....	11.00	....
....	horiz. pair with vert. gutter	....	....	....	....	4.50	....
....	vert. pair with horiz. gutter	....	....	....	....	3.50	....

3546

3547

3548

SCOTT NO.	DESCRIPTION	FIRST DAY COVERS SING	FIRST DAY COVERS PL. BLK.	MINT SHEET	PLATE BLOCK	UNUSED F/NH	USED
3546	34¢ We Give Thanks, self-adhesive	2.25	4.75	20.00(20)	4.50	1.00	.25
3547	34¢ Hanukkah, self-adhesive	2.25	4.75	20.00(20)	4.50	1.00	.25
3548	34¢ Kwanzaa, self-adhesive	2.25	4.75	20.00(20)	4.50	1.00	.25

3549, 3549B, 3550, 3550A

3551

SCOTT NO.	DESCRIPTION	FIRST DAY COVERS SING	FIRST DAY COVERS PL. BLK.	MINT SHEET	PLATE BLOCK	UNUSED F/NH	USED
3549	34¢ United We Stand, self-adhesive	2.25	....	....	....	1.20	.25
3549a	same, bklt pane of 20	14.50	....	....	....	22.50	....
3549B	34¢ United We Stand, die cut 10.5 x 10.75 on 2 or 3 sides	2.25	....	....	....	1.30	.25
3549Bc	same, bklt pane of 4	4.00	....	....	....	4.50	....
3549Bd	same, bklt pane of 6	5.50	....	....	....	6.50	....
3549Be	same, bklt pane of 20 (double-sided)	....	....	....	....	24.00	....
3550	34¢ United We Stand, self-adhesive coil (square corners)	2.25	....	....	....	1.00	.20
....	same, pl# strip of 5	....	....	....	....	8.00	....
3550A	34¢ United We Stand, self-adhesive coil, (round corners)	2.25	....	....	....	1.00	.40
....	same, pl# strip of 5	....	....	....	....	9.00	....
3551	57¢ Love, self-adhesive	2.50	5.00	27.50(20)	7.00	1.50	.50

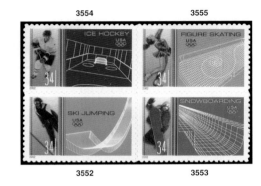

3554   3555

3552   3553

2002 COMMEMORATIVES

SCOTT NO.	DESCRIPTION	FIRST DAY COVERS SING	FIRST DAY COVERS PL. BLK.	MINT SHEET	PLATE BLOCK	UNUSED F/NH	USED
3552/3695	(3552-60, 3650-56, 3658-74, 3676-79, 3692, 3695) 39 varieties	....	....	....	....	43.75	12.25
3552-55	34¢ Winter Olympics, self-adhesive, 4 varieties attached	4.25	5.25	30.00(20)	7.00	6.00	4.00
3552	34¢ Ski Jumping	2.25	....	....	....	1.20	.40
3553	34¢ Snowboarding	2.25	....	....	....	1.20	.40
3554	34¢ Ice Hockey	2.25	....	....	....	1.20	.40
3555	34¢ Figure Skating	2.25	....	....	....	1.20	.40
3552-55v	same, uncut sheet of 180 (9 panes)	....	....	185.00(180)	....	185.00	....
....	cross gutter block of 8	....	....	....	....	25.00	....
....	block of 4 with vert. gutter	....	....	....	....	8.00	....
....	block of 8 with horiz. gutter	....	....	....	....	11.50	....
....	vert. pair with horiz. gutter	....	....	....	....	3.00	....
....	horiz. pair with vert. gutter	....	....	....	....	2.00	....

3556   3557   3558

SCOTT NO.	DESCRIPTION	FIRST DAY COVERS SING	FIRST DAY COVERS PL. BLK.	MINT SHEET	PLATE BLOCK	UNUSED F/NH	USED
3556	34¢ Mentoring a Child, self-adhesive	2.25	4.75	17.50(20)	4.50	1.00	.25
3557	34¢ Langston Hughes, self-adhesive	2.25	4.75	25.00(20)	6.00	1.50	.25
3558	34¢ Happy Birthday, self-adhesive	2.25	4.75	17.50(20)	4.50	1.20	.25

3559

3560

SCOTT NO.	DESCRIPTION	FIRST DAY COVERS SING	FIRST DAY COVERS PL. BLK.	MINT SHEET	PLATE BLOCK	UNUSED F/NH	USED
3559	34¢ Year of the Horse, self-adhesive	2.25	4.75	30.00(20)	7.00	1.50	.25
3560	34¢ Military Academy Bicentennial, self-adhesive	2.25	4.75	20.00(20)	5.00	1.00	.25

SCOTT NO.	DESCRIPTION	FIRST DAY COVERS SING	PL. BLK.	MINT SHEET	PLATE BLOCK	UNUSED F/NH	USED

| 3561 | | | 3610 |

GREETINGS FROM AMERICA

3561	Alabama	3578	Louisiana	3595	Ohio
3562	Alaska	3579	Maine	3596	Oklahoma
3563	Arizona	3580	Maryland	3597	Oregon
3564	Arkansas	3581	Massachusetts	3598	Pennsylvania
3565	California	3582	Michigan	3599	Rhode Island
3566	Colorado	3583	Minnesota	3600	South Carolina
3567	Connecticut	3584	Mississippi	3601	South Dakota
3568	Delaware	3585	Missouri	3602	Tennessee
3569	Florida	3586	Montana	3603	Texas
3570	Georgia	3587	Nebraska	3604	Utah
3571	Hawaii	3588	Nevada	3605	Vermont
3572	Idaho	3589	New Hampshire	3606	Virginia
3573	Illinois	3590	New Jersey	3607	Washington
3574	Indiana	3591	New Mexico	3608	West Virginia
3575	Iowa	3592	New York	3609	Wisconsin
3576	Kansas	3593	North Carolina	3610	Wyoming
3577	Kentucky	3594	North Dakota		

| 3561-3610 | 34¢ Greetings from America, self-adhesive, 50 varieties attached.. | .... | .... | 55.00(50) | .... | 55.00 | .... |
| .... | set of singles........ | 120.00 | .... | .... | .... | .... | 33.00 |

LONGLEAF PINE FOREST

3611

LONGLEAF PINE FOREST

3611a	Bachman's sparrow	3611g	Gray Fox, gopher tortoise
3611b	Northern bobwhite, yellow pitcher plants	3611h	Blind click beetle, sweetbay, pine woods freefrog
3611c	Fox squirrel, red-bellied woodpecker		
3611d	Brown-headed nuthatch	3611i	Rosebuds orchid, pipeworts, southern toad, yellow pitcher plants
3611e	Broadhead skink, yellow pitcher plants, pipeworts		
3611f	Eastern towhee, yellow pitcher plants, meadow beauties, toothache grass	3611j	Grass-pink orchid, yellow-sided skimmer, pipeworts

3611	34¢ Longleaf Pine Forest, 10 varieties, attached, self-adhesive.......	....	....	19.95(10)	....	19.95	10.00
....	set of singles........	25.00	....	....	....	....	7.00
3611v	same, uncut sheet of 90 (9 panes).......	....	....	100.00(90)	....	100.00	....

| 3612 | | 3613, 3614, 3615 | 3616, 3617, 3618, 3619 | 3620, 3621, 3622, 3623, 3624, 3625 |

3612	5¢ Toleware coffee pot, coil............	2.25	....	....	....	.25	.20
....	same, pl# strip of 5..	....	....	....	....	2.25	....
3613	3¢ Lithographed Star (year at LL).......	2.25	4.75	4.50(50)	.75	.20	.20
3614	3¢ Photogravure Star (year of LR).......	2.25	4.75	4.50(50)	.75	.20	.20
3615	3¢ Star, coil........	2.25	....	....	....	.20	.20
....	same, pl# strip of 5..	....	....	....	....	2.00	....
3616	23¢ George Washington	2.25	4.75	80.00(100)	12.00	.75	.35

3617	23¢ George Washington, self-adhesive coil....	2.25	....	....	....	.75	.20
....	same pl# strip of 5...	....	....	....	....	5.00	....
3618	23¢ George Washington, self-adhesive die cut 11.25	2.25	....	....	....	.75	.20
3618a	same, bklt pane of 4 .	3.00	....	....	....	3.00	....
3618b	same, bklt pane of 6 .	4.00	....	....	....	4.50	....
3618c	same, bklt pane of 10	6.75	....	....	....	7.25	....
3619	23¢ George Washington, self-adhesive, die cut 10.5 x 11.25	1.95	....	....	....	3.00	.50
3619a	same, bklt pane of 4 (3619 x 2 at L, 3618 x 2 at R).......	....	....	....	....	8.50	....
3619b	same, bklt pane of 6 (3619 x 3 at L, 3618 x 3 at R).......	....	....	....	....	13.00	....
3619c	same, bklt pane of 4 (3618 x 2 at L, 3619 x 2 at R).......	....	....	....	....	8.50	....
3619d	same, bklt pane of 6 (3618 x 3 at L, 3619 x 3 at R).......	....	....	....	....	13.00	....
3619g	same, pair (3619 at L, 3618 at R)	....	....	....	....	4.00	....
3619h	same, pair (3618 at L, 3619 at R)	....	....	....	....	3.00	....
3620	(37¢) Flag.........	2.25	4.75	110.00(100)	20.00	1.00	.20
3621	(37¢) Flag, self-adhesive	2.25	4.75	22.00(20)	6.00	1.00	.20
3622	(37¢) Flag, self-adhesive coil	2.25	....	....	....	1.00	.20
....	same, pl# strip of 5..	....	....	....	....	6.75	....
3623	(37¢) Flag, self-adhesive, die cut 11.25	2.25	....	....	....	1.00	.20
3623a	same, bklt pane of 20	....	....	....	....	19.50	....
3624	(37¢) Flag, self-adhesive, die cut 10.5 x 10.75..	2.25	....	....	....	1.00	.20
3624a	same, bklt pane of 4 .	4.00	....	....	....	4.25	....
3624b	same, bklt pane of 6 .	5.50	....	....	....	6.00	....
3624c	same, bklt pane of 20	15.00	....	....	....	22.00	....
3625	(37¢) Flag, self-adhesive, die cut 8...........	2.25	....	....	....	1.20	.35
3625a	same, ATM bklt pane of 18	15.00	....	....	....	22.00	....

| 3626 | 3627 | 3628 | 3629 |

3626	(37¢) Toy mail wagon, self-adhesive........	2.25	....	....	....	1.20	.35
3627	(37¢) Toy locomotive, self-adhesive.......	2.25	....	....	....	1.20	.35
3628	(37¢) Toy taxicab, self-adhesive.......	2.25	....	....	....	1.20	.35
3629	(37¢) Toy fire pumper, self-adhesive.......	2.25	....	....	....	1.20	.35
3626-29	(37¢) Antique Toys, self-adhesive, 4 varieties attached..	4.25	....	....	....	4.50	3.50
3629b	same, bklt pane of 4 (3626-29 x 1).......	4.25	....	....	....	4.50	....
3629c	same, bklt pane of 6 (3627, 3629, 3626 x 2, 3628 x 2)...........	5.50	....	....	....	6.50	....
3629d	same, bklt pane of 6 (3626, 3628, 3627 x 2, 3629 x 2)...........	5.50	....	....	....	6.25	....
3629e	same, bklt pane of 20	15.00	....	....	....	24.00	....
3629F	37¢ Flag...........	2.25	4.75	120.00(100)	20.00	1.50	.75

| 3638, 3643 | | 3639, 3642 |
| 3640, 3645 | 3629F, 3630, 3631, 3632, 3632A, 3632C, 3633, 3633A, 3635, 3636, 3636D, 3637 | 3641, 3644 |

3630	37¢ Flag, self-adhesive	2.25	4.75	24.00(20)	7.00	1.20	.30
3631	37¢ Flag, coil........	2.25	....	....	....	1.20	.30
....	same, pl# strip of 5..	....	....	....	....	8.00	....
3632	37¢ Flag, self-adhesive coil, die cut 10 vert......	2.25	....	....	....	1.20	.30
....	same, pl# strip of 5..	....	....	....	....	10.00	....
3632A	37¢ Flag coil, die cut 10, flag lacking star point.	2.25	....	....	....	1.20	.40
....	same, pl# strip of 5..	....	....	....	....	10.00	....
3632C	37¢ Flag, self-adhesive coil, die cut 11.75 (2004)..	2.25	....	....	....	1.20	.40
....	same, pl# strip of 5..	....	....	....	....	10.00	....
3633	37¢ Flag, self-adhesive coil, die cut 8.5 vert.....	2.25	....	....	....	1.20	.40
....	same, pl# strip of 5..	....	....	....	....	10.00	....

SCOTT NO.	DESCRIPTION	FIRST DAY COVERS SING	FIRST DAY COVERS PL. BLK.	MINT SHEET	PLATE BLOCK	UNUSED F/NH	USED
3633A	37¢ Flag coil. die cut 8.5, right angle corners...	1.95	....	....	....	2.00	.50
....	same, pl# strip of 5 ..	....	....	....	....	15.00	....
3633B	37¢ Flag coil, die cut 9.5 (dated 2005)	2.25	....	....	....	1.00	.30
....	same, plt. strip of 5 ..	....	....	....	....	30.00	....
3634	37¢ Flag, self-adhesive, die cut 11	2.25	....	....	....	1.20	.40
3634a	same, bklt pane of 10	....	....	....	....	9.50	....
3634b	same, self-adhesive, bklt single, dated 2003...	2.25	....	....	....	1.00	.50
3634c	same, bklt pane of 4 (3634b)	4.25	....	....	....	4.25	....
3634d	same, bklt pane of 6 (3634b)	5.50	....	....	....	5.75	....
3635	37¢ Flag, self-adhesive, die cut 11.25	2.25	....	....	....	1.20	.50
3635a	same, bklt pane of 20	....	....	....	....	19.50	....
3636	37¢ Flag, self-adhesive, die cut 10.5 x 10.75 ..	2.25	....	....	....	1.20	.50
3636c	same, bklt pane of 20	....	....	....	....	24.00	....
3636D	37¢ Flag, die cut 11.25 x 11, self-adhesive	2.25	....	....	....	.85	.50
3636De	same, bklt pane of 20	....	....	....	....	30.00	....
3637	37¢ Flag, self-adhesive, die cut 8	2.25	....	....	....	1.00	.50
3637a	same, ATM bklt pane of 18	15.00	....	....	....	24.00	....
3638	37¢ Toy locomotive, self-adhesive coil, die cut 8.5 horiz.	2.25	....	....	....	1.50	.50
3639	37¢ Toy mail wagon, self-adhesive coil, die cut 8.5 horiz.	2.25	....	....	....	1.50	.50
3640	37¢ Toy fire pumper, self-adhesive coil, die cut 8.5 horiz.	2.25	....	....	....	1.50	.50
3641	37¢ Toy taxicab, self-adhesive coil, die cut 8.5 horiz.	2.25	....	....	....	1.50	.50
3638-41	37¢ Antique Toys, self-adhesive coil, strip of 4.	4.25	....	....	....	6.00	5.00
....	same, pl# strip of 5 ..	....	....	....	....	12.50	....
3642	37¢ Toy mail wagon, self-adhesive, die cut 11	2.25	....	....	....	1.20	.30
3642a	same, die cut 11x11.25, 2003	2.25	....	....	....	1.20	.30
3643	37¢ Toy locomotive, self-adhesive, die cut 11	2.25	....	....	....	1.20	.30
3643a	same, die cut 11x11.25, 2003	2.25	....	....	....	1.20	.30
3644	37¢ Toy taxicab, self-adhesive, die cut 11	2.25	....	....	....	1.20	.30
3644a	same, die cut 11x11.25, 2003	2.25	....	....	....	1.20	.30
3645	37¢ Toy fire pumper, self-adhesive, die cut 11	2.25	....	....	....	1.20	.30
3645f	same, die cut 11x11.25, 2003	2.25	....	....	....	1.20	.30
3642-45	37¢ Antique Toys, self-adhesive, 4 varieties attach.	4.25	....	....	....	4.50	3.50
3645b	same, bklt pane of 4 (3642-45 x 1)	4.25	....	....	....	7.00	....
3645c	same, bklt pane of 6 (3643, 3645, 3642 x 2, 3644 x 2)	5.50	....	....	....	7.00	....
3645d	same, bklt pane of 6 (3642, 3644, 3642 x 2, 3645 x 2)	5.50	....	....	....	7.00	....
3645e	same, bklt pane of 20	15.00	....	....	....	19.50	....
3645g	37¢ Antique Toys, self-adhesive, blk of 4 (3642a, 3643a, 3644a, 3645f)	4.25	....	....	....	4.25	....
3645h	same, bklt pane of 20	15.00	....	....	....	24.00	....

3646

3648

3647

3646	60¢ Coverlet Eagle, self-adhesive	2.75	5.50	30.00(20)	7.00	1.35	.50
3647	$3.85 Jefferson Memorial, self-adhesive	8.75	35.00	200.00(20)	45.00	10.00	3.00
3647A	same, die cut 11x10.75, dated 2003.	8.75	35.00	200.00(20)	45.00	12.00	4.50
3648	$13.65 Capitol Dome, self-adhesive	35.00	105.00	600.00(20)	140.00	29.00	12.00

MASTERS OF AMERICAN PHOTOGRAPHY

3649a	Albert Sands Southworth & Josiah Johnson Hawes	3649k	James VanDerZee
3649b	Timothy H. O'Sullivan	3649l	Dorothea Lange
3649c	Carleton E. Watkins	3649m	Walker Evans
3649d	Getrude Kasebier	3649n	Eugene Smith
3649e	Lewis W. Hine	3649o	Paul Strand
3649f	Alvin Langdon Coburn	3649p	Ansel Adams
3649g	Edward Steichen	3649q	Imogen Cunningham
3649h	Alfred Steiglitz	3649r	Andre Kertesz
3649i	Man Ray	3649s	Garry Winogrand
3649j	Edward Weston	3649t	Minor White

3649

3649	37¢ Masters of American Photography, self-adhesive, 20 varieties attached .	....	....	19.50(20)	....	19.50	15.00
....	same, set of singles..	50.00	....	....	....	....	12.00

3650

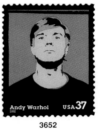
3652

3651

3650	37¢ John James Audubon, self-adhesive	2.25	4.75	30.00(20)	7.00	1.25	.30
3651	37¢ Harry Houdini, self-adhesive	2.25	4.75	20.00(20)	5.00	1.25	.30
3652	37¢ Andy Warhol, self-adhesive	2.25	4.75	20.00(20)	5.00	1.25	.30

3653   **3654**

3655   **3656**

3653-56	37¢ Teddy Bears, self-adhesive, 4 varieties attached.	5.00	6.00	27.00(20)	6.00	6.00	5.00
3653	37¢ Bruin Teddy Bear	2.25	....	....	....	1.50	.40
3654	37¢ Stick Teddy Bear.	2.25	....	....	....	1.50	.40
3655	37¢ Gund Teddy Bear	2.25	....	....	....	1.50	.40
3656	37¢ Ideal Teddy Bear.	2.25	....	....	....	1.50	.40

3657

3658

3659

3657	37¢ Love, self-adhesive	2.25	....	....	....	1.20	.25
....	same, bklt pane of 20	15.00	....	....	....	19.50	....
3658	60¢ Love, self-adhesive	2.75	5.50	40.00(20)	10.00	2.20	.75
3659	37¢ Ogden Nash, self-adhesive	2.25	4.75	17.50(20)	4.50	1.00	.25

3661   3660   3662   3663   3664

SCOTT NO.	DESCRIPTION	FIRST DAY COVERS SING	FIRST DAY COVERS PL. BLK.	MINT SHEET	PLATE BLOCK	UNUSED F/NH	USED
3660	37¢ Duke Kahanamoku, self-adhesive	2.25	4.75	20.00(20)	5.00	1.00	.30
3661-64	37¢ American Bats, self-adhesive, 4 varieties attached.	4.25	4.75	20.00(20)	6.00	4.50	3.50
3661	37¢ Red Bat.	2.25	. . . .	. . . .	. . . .	1.20	.35
3662	37¢ Leaf-nosed Bat . .	2.25	. . . .	. . . .	. . . .	1.20	.35
3663	37¢ Pallid Bat.	2.25	. . . .	. . . .	. . . .	1.20	.35
3664	37¢ Spotted Bat.	2.25	. . . .	. . . .	. . . .	1.20	.35

3665   3666   3667   3668

SCOTT NO.	DESCRIPTION	FIRST DAY COVERS SING	FIRST DAY COVERS PL. BLK.	MINT SHEET	PLATE BLOCK	UNUSED F/NH	USED
3665-68	37¢ Women In Journalism, self-adhesive, 4 varieties attached.	6.00	7.00	30.00(20)	7.00	5.00	4.00
3665	37¢Nellie Bly	2.25	. . . .	. . . .	. . . .	1.50	.40
3666	37¢ Ida M. Tarbel. . . .	2.25	. . . .	. . . .	. . . .	1.50	.40
3667	37¢ Ethel L. Payne . .	2.25	. . . .	. . . .	. . . .	1.50	.40
3668	37¢ Marguerite Higgins	2.25	. . . .	. . . .	. . . .	1.50	.40

3669

SCOTT NO.	DESCRIPTION	FIRST DAY COVERS SING	FIRST DAY COVERS PL. BLK.	MINT SHEET	PLATE BLOCK	UNUSED F/NH	USED
3669	37¢ Irving Berlin, self-adhesive	2.25	4.75	25.00(20)	5.50	1.25	.25

3670   3671

SCOTT NO.	DESCRIPTION	FIRST DAY COVERS SING	FIRST DAY COVERS PL. BLK.	MINT SHEET	PLATE BLOCK	UNUSED F/NH	USED
3670-71	37¢ Neuter and Spay, self-adhesive, 2 varieties attached.	4.00	4.75	30.00(20)	7.00	2.50	2.00
3670	37¢ Kitten	2.25	. . . .	. . . .	. . . .	1.20	.30
3671	37¢ Puppy	2.25	. . . .	. . . .	. . . .	1.20	.30

3672   3673   3674

SCOTT NO.	DESCRIPTION	FIRST DAY COVERS SING	FIRST DAY COVERS PL. BLK.	MINT SHEET	PLATE BLOCK	UNUSED F/NH	USED
3672	37¢ Hanukkah, self-adhesive	2.25	4.75	20.00(20)	5.00	1.20	.30
3673	37¢ Kwanzaa, self-adhesive	2.25	4.75	20.00(20)	5.00	1.20	.30
3674	37¢ EID, self-adhesive	2.25	4.75	20.00(20)	5.00	1.20	.30

3675

SCOTT NO.	DESCRIPTION	FIRST DAY COVERS SING	FIRST DAY COVERS PL. BLK.	MINT SHEET	PLATE BLOCK	UNUSED F/NH	USED
3675	37¢ Madonna & Child, self-adhesive	2.25	4.75	17.50(20)	4.50	1.20	.30
	same, bklt pane of 20	15.00	. . . .	. . . .	. . . .	16.00	. . . .

3676, 3683, 3684, 3688   3677, 3680, 3685, 3689   3678, 3681, 3686, 3690   3679, 3682, 3687, 3691

SCOTT NO.	DESCRIPTION	FIRST DAY COVERS SING	FIRST DAY COVERS PL. BLK.	MINT SHEET	PLATE BLOCK	UNUSED F/NH	USED
3676-79	37¢ Snowmen, self-adhesive, 4 varieties attached . .	6.00	7.00	20.00(20)	5.00	4.50	3.50
3676	37¢ Snowman with red and green scarf	2.25	. . . .	. . . .	. . . .	1.20	.40
3677	37¢ Snowman with blue scarf.	2.25	. . . .	. . . .	. . . .	1.20	.40
3578	37¢ Snowman with pipe	2.25	. . . .	. . . .	. . . .	1.20	.40
3679	37¢ Snowman with top hat	2.25	. . . .	. . . .	. . . .	1.20	.40
3680	37¢ Snowman with blue scarf, self-adhesive coil	2.25	. . . .	. . . .	. . . .	1.20	.50
3681	37¢ Snowman with pipe, self-adhesive coil. . . .	2.25	. . . .	. . . .	. . . .	1.20	.50
3682	37¢ Snowman with top hat, self-adhesive coil. . . .	2.25	. . . .	. . . .	. . . .	1.20	.50
3683	37¢ Snowman with red and green scarf, self-adhesive coil	2.25	. . . .	. . . .	. . . .	1.20	.50
3680-83	37¢ Snowmen, self-adhesive coil, strip of 4	4.25	. . . .	. . . .	. . . .	6.00	. . . .
	same, pl# strip of 5 . .	. . . .	. . . .	. . . .	. . . .	9.00	. . . .
3684	37¢ Snowman with red and green scarf, large design	2.25	. . . .	. . . .	. . . .	1.20	.40
3685	37¢ Snowman with blue scarf, large design. . .	2.25	. . . .	. . . .	. . . .	1.20	.40
3686	37¢ Snowman with pipe, large design.	2.25	. . . .	. . . .	. . . .	1.20	.40
3687	37¢ Snowman with top hat, large design.	2.25	. . . .	. . . .	. . . .	1.20	.40
3684-87	37¢ Snowman, self-adhesive, 4 varieties attached . .	4.25	. . . .	. . . .	. . . .	4.50	3.50
3687b	same, bklt pane of 20 (3684-87 x 5 + label) .	15.00	. . . .	. . . .	. . . .	21.50	. . . .
3688	37¢ Snowman with red and green scarf, small design	2.25	. . . .	. . . .	. . . .	1.20	.50
3689	37¢ Snowman with blue scarf, small design. . .	2.25	. . . .	. . . .	. . . .	1.20	.50
3690	37¢ Snowman with pipe, small design.	2.25	. . . .	. . . .	. . . .	1.20	.50
3691	37¢ Snowman with top hat, small design.	2.25	. . . .	. . . .	. . . .	1.20	.50
3688-91	37¢ Snowmen , self-adhesive, 4 varieties attached . .	4.25	. . . .	. . . .	. . . .	4.50	3.50
3691b	same, bklt pane of 4, (3688-91).	4.25	. . . .	. . . .	. . . .	4.50	. . . .
3691c	same, bklt pane of 6 (3690-91, 3688-89 x 2)	5.50	. . . .	. . . .	. . . .	6.00	. . . .
3691d	same, bklt pane of 6 (3688-89, 3690-91 x 2)	5.50	. . . .	. . . .	. . . .	6.00	. . . .

SCOTT NO.	DESCRIPTION	FIRST DAY COVERS SING	FIRST DAY COVERS PL. BLK.	MINT SHEET	PLATE BLOCK	UNUSED F/NH	USED

3693, 3775, 3785   **3692**   **3695**

3692	37¢ Cary Grant, self-adhesive	2.25	4.75	25.00(20)	5.00	1.20	.30
3693	(5¢) Sea Coast coil, self-adhesive	2.25	....	....	....	.25	.20
....	same, pl# strip of 5 . .	....	....	....	....	2.50	....

3694

3694	37¢ Hawaiian Missionary, self-adhesive, souvenir sheet of 4	5.00	....	....	....	5.25	4.00
3694a	37¢ Hawaii 2¢ of 1851	2.25	....	....	....	1.20	.75
3694b	37¢ Hawaii 5¢ of 1851	2.25	....	....	....	1.20	.75
3694c	37¢ Hawaii 13¢ of 1851	2.25	....	....	....	1.20	.75
3694d	37¢ Hawaii 13¢ of 1852	2.25	....	....	....	1.20	.75
3695	37¢ Happy Birthday, self-adhesive	2.25	4.75	17.50(20)	4.50	1.00	.25

3696   **3745**

GREETINGS FROM AMERICA

3696	*Alabama*	**3713**	*Louisiana*	**3730**	*Ohio*
3697	*Alaska*	**3714**	*Maine*	**3731**	*Oklahoma*
3698	*Arizona*	**3715**	*Maryland*	**3732**	*Oregon*
3699	*Arkansas*	**3716**	*Massachusetts*	**3733**	*Pennsylvania*
3700	*California*	**3717**	*Michigan*	**3734**	*Rhode Island*
3701	*Colorado*	**3718**	*Minnesota*	**3735**	*South Carolina*
3702	*Connecticut*	**3719**	*Mississippi*	**3736**	*South Dakota*
3703	*Delaware*	**3720**	*Missouri*	**3737**	*Tennessee*
3704	*Florida*	**3721**	*Montana*	**3738**	*Texas*
3705	*Georgia*	**3722**	*Nebraska*	**3739**	*Utah*
3706	*Hawaii*	**3723**	*Nevada*	**3740**	*Vermont*
3707	*Idaho*	**3724**	*New Hampshire*	**3741**	*Virginia*
3708	*Illinois*	**3725**	*New Jersey*	**3742**	*Washington*
3709	*Indiana*	**3726**	*New Mexico*	**3743**	*West Virginia*
3710	*Iowa*	**3727**	*New York*	**3744**	*Wisconsin*
3711	*Kansas*	**3728**	*North Carolina*	**3745**	*Wyoming*
3712	*Kentucky*	**3729**	*North Dakota*		

| 3696-3745 | 37¢ Greetings from America, self-adhesive, 50 varieties attached. . | .... | .... | 55.00(50) | .... | 55.00 | .... |
| .... | set of singles. . . . . . . | 120.00 | .... | .... | .... | .... | 30.00 |

3746   **3747**   **3748**

2003 COMMEMORATIVES

3746/3824	(3746-48, 3771, 3773-74, 3781-82, 3786-91, 3803, 3808-18, 3821-24) 30 varieties	....	....		....	33.00	10.50
3746	37¢ Thurgood Marshall, self-adhesive	2.25	4.75	25.00(20)	5.00	1.20	.30
3747	37¢ Year of the Ram, self-adhesive	2.25	4.75	25.00(20)	5.00	1.20	.30
3748	37¢ Zora Neale Hurston, self-adhesive	2.25	4.75	25.00(20)	5.00	1.20	.30

3749, 3749a, 3758   **3750, 3751, 3752, 3753**   **3754, 3759**

3755, 3761   **3756**   **3757, 3762**

AMERICAN DESIGN SERIES

3749	1¢ Tiffany Lamp, self-adhesive (2007)	2.25	4.75	3.00(20)	.50	.20	.20
3749a	1¢ Tiffany Lamp	2.95	5.75	33.50(20)	....	.25	.20
3750	2¢ Navajo Necklace, self-adhesive	2.25	4.75	3.00(20)	.75	.20	.15
3751	same, self-adhesvie, die cut 11.25 X 11.5 . .	2.25	4.75	3.00(20)	.75	.20	.20
3752	same, w/ USPS microprinting, self-adhesive, die cut 11.25 X 11 . . .	2.25	4.75	3.00(20)	.75	.20	.20
3753	same, die cut 11.5 X 11, (2007 date)	2.25	4.75	3.00(20)	.75	.20	.20
3754	3¢ Silver Coffeepot, self-adhesive (2007)	2.25	4.75	3.00(20)	.75	.20	.20
3755	4¢ Chippendale Chair, self-adhesive (2004) .	2.25	4.75	4.50(20)	.75	.20	.15
3756	5¢ Toleware, self-adhesive	2.25	4.75	4.50(20)	.85	.25	.15
3757	10¢ American Clock, self-adhesive	2.25	4.75	4.75(20)	1.35	.30	.15
3758	1¢ Tiffany Lamp, coil	2.25	....	....	....	.25	.15
....	same, pl# strip of 5 . .	....	....	....	....	2.25	....
3759	3¢ Silver Coffeepot, coil	2.25	....	....	....	.20	.20
....	same, pl# strip of 5 . .	....	....	....	....	8.00	....
3761	4¢ Chippendale Chair, coil (2007)	2.25	....	....	....	.25	.20
....	same, pl# strip of 5 . .	....	....	....	....	3.00	.20
3762	10¢ American Clock, coil	2.25	....	....	....	.30	.20
....	same, pl# strip of 5 . .	....	....	....	....	3.00	....

3766   **3769**   **3770**

3766	$1 Wisdom, self-adhesive	3.50	7.50	50.00(20)	12.00	2.25	.60
3769	(10¢) New York Library Lion, perf. 10 vert.	2.25	....	....	....	2.00	.30	.20
....	same, pl# strip of 5 . .	....	....	....	....	2.75	....
3770	(10¢) Atlas Statue, self-adhesive coil, die cut 11 dated 2003	2.25	....	....	....	.30	.25
....	same, pl# strip of 5 . .	....	....	....	....	3.00	....

3771

| 3771 | 80¢ Special Olympics, self-adhesive | 3.00 | 7.00 | 37.50(20) | 8.50 | 1.95 | 1.00 |

SCOTT NO.	DESCRIPTION	FIRST DAY COVERS SING	PL. BLK.	MINT SHEET	PLATE BLOCK	UNUSED F/NH	USED

3772

AMERICAN FILM MAKING

3772a Screenwriting	**3772d** Music	**3772g** Cinematography	
3772b Directing	**3772e** Make-up	**3772h** Film editing	
3772c Costume design	**3772f** Art Direction	**3772i** Special effects	
		3772j Sound	

Scott	Description	Sing	Pl.Blk	Mint Sheet	Plate Block	Unused	Used
3772	37¢ American Film Making, self-adhesive, 10 varieties attached			16.00(10)		16.00	12.50
	set of singles	25.00					6.00

3773   **3774**   **3781**   **3782**

Scott	Description	Sing	Pl.Blk	Mint Sheet	Plate Block	Unused	Used
3773	37¢ Ohio Statehood, self-adhesive	2.25	4.75	25.00(20)	5.00	1.20	.30
3774	37¢ Pelican Island National Wildlife Refuge, self-adhesive	2.25	4.75	25.00(20)	5.00	1.20	.30
3775	(5¢) Sea Coast coil, perf. 9.75 vert.	2.25				.20	.15
	same, pl# strip of 5					2.00	

3776   **3777**   **3778**   **3779**

3780   **3783**   **3784, 3784A**   **3786**

Scott	Description	Sing	Pl.Blk	Mint Sheet	Plate Block	Unused	Used
3776	37¢ Uncle Sam on Bicycle	2.25				1.50	.50
3777	37¢ 1888 Pres. Campaign badge	2.25				1.50	.50
3778	37¢ 1893 Silk bookmark	2.25				1.50	.50
3779	37¢ Modern hand fan	2.25				1.50	.50
3780	37¢ Carving of woman with flag & sword	2.25				1.50	.50
3776-80	37¢ Old Glory, self-adhesive, 5 varieties attached	5.00				7.00	
3780b	same, complete booklet of 2 panes					25.00	
3781	37¢ Cesar E. Chavez, self-adhesive	2.25	4.75	25.00(20)	6.00	1.20	.30
3782	37¢ Louisiana Purchase, self-adhesive	2.25	4.75	25.00(20)	6.00	1.20	.30

SCOTT NO.	DESCRIPTION	FIRST DAY COVERS SING	PL. BLK.	MINT SHEET	PLATE BLOCK	UNUSED F/NH	USED
3783	37¢ First Flight of the Wright Brothers, self-adhesive	2.25		12.00(10)		1.20	.30
3783a	same, bklt pane of 9					9.00	
3783b	same, bklt pane of 1	7.00				2.00	
3784	37¢ Purple Heart, self-adhesive	2.25	4.75	25.00(20)	5.00	1.20	.30
3784A	37¢ Purple Heart, self-adhesive, die cut 10.75 x 10.25	2.25	4.75	25.00(20)	5.00	1.20	.50
3785	(5¢) Sea Coast coil, four-side die cuts	2.25				.25	.20
	same, pl# strip of 5					2.25	
3785A	(5¢) Sea Coast coil, die cut 9.25 x 10	2.25				.25	.20
	same, pl# strip of 5					2.25	
3786	37¢ Audrey Hepburn, self-adhesive	2.25`	4.75	25.00(20)	6.00	1.20	.30

3787   **3788**   **3789**

3790   **3792-3801, 3792a-3801a**   **3791**

Scott	Description	Sing	Pl.Blk	Mint Sheet	Plate Block	Unused	Used
3787-91	37¢ Southern Lighthouses, self-adhesive, 5 varieties attached	5.00		39.50(20)		10.00	9.00
3787	37¢ Old Cape Henry, Virginia	2.25				2.00	.50
3788	37¢ Cape Lookout, North Carolina	2.25				2.00	.50
3788a	same, dropped denomination						
3789	37¢ Morris Island, South Carolina	2.25				2.00	.50
3790	37¢ Tybee Island, Georgia	2.25				2.00	.50
3791	37¢ Hillsboro Inlet, Florida	2.25				2.00	.50
3791b	same, strip of 5 (3787, 3788a, 3789-91)						
3792	(25¢) Eagle, gray with gold eagle, coil	2.25				.75	.40
3792a	same, serpentine die cut 11.5(2005)	2.25				.75	.40
3793	(25¢) Eagle, gold with red eagle, coil	2.25				.75	.40
3793a	same, serpentine die cut 11.5(2005)	2.25				.75	.40
3794	(25¢) Eagle, dull blue with gold eagle, coil	2.25				.75	.40
3794a	same, serpentine die cut 11.5(2005)	2.25				.75	.40
3795	(25¢) Eagle, gold with Prussian blue eagle, coil	2.25				.75	.40
3795a	same, serpentine die cut 11.5(2005)	2.25				.75	.40
3796	(25¢) Eagle, green with gold eagle, coil	2.25				.75	.40
3796a	same, die cut 11.5(2005)	2.25				.75	.40
3797	(25¢) Eagle, gold with gray eagle, coil	2.25				.75	.40
3797a	same, die cut 11.5(2005)	2.25				.75	.40
3798	(25¢) Eagle, Prussian blue with gold eagle, coil	2.25				.75	.40
3798a	same, die cut 11.5(2005)	2.25				.75	.40
3799	(25¢) Eagle, gold with dull blue eagle, coil	2.25				.75	.40
3799a	same, die cut 11.5(2005)	2.25				.75	.40
3800	(25¢) Eagle, red with gold eagle, coil	2.25				.75	.40
3800a	same, die cut 11.5(2005)	2.25				.75	.40
3801	(25¢) Eagle, gold with green eagle, coil	2.25				.75	.40
3801a	same, die cut 11.5(2005)	2.25				.75	.40
3792-3801	(25¢) Eagle, self-adhesive coil, strip of 10	6.00				6.00	
	same, pl# strip of 11					8.50	
3792a-3801a	same, self-adhesive, coil strip of 10, serpentine die cut 11.5(dated 2005)	6.00				8.00	
	same, plt. strip of 11					10.00	

SCOTT NO.	DESCRIPTION	FIRST DAY COVERS SING	FIRST DAY COVERS PL. BLK.	MINT SHEET	PLATE BLOCK	UNUSED F/NH	USED

3802

ARCTIC TUNDRA

3802a	Gyrfalcon	3802f	Caribou & willow ptarmigans
3802b	Gray wolf	3802g	Arctic ground squirrel
3802c	Common raven	3802h	Willow ptarmigan & bearberry
3802d	Musk oxen & caribou	3802i	Arctic grayling
3802e	Grizzly bears & caribou	3802j	Singing vole, thin-legged spider, lingonberry, Labrador tea

| 3802 | 37¢ Arctic Tundra, 10 varieties, attached, self-adhesive | .... | .... | 12.00(10) | .... | 12.00 | 10.00 |
| .... | set of singles | 25.00 | .... | .... | .... | .... | 6.00 |

3803

| 3803 | 37¢ Korean War Veterans, Memorial, self-adhesive | 2.25 | 4.75 | 20.00(20) | 5.00 | 1.20 | .30 |

| **3804** | | **3805** | | **3806** | | **3807** | |

3804	37¢ Young Mother . . .	2.25	....	....	,	1.20	.35
3805	37¢ Children Playing .	2.25	....	....		1.20	.35
3806	37¢ On a Balcony . . .	2.25	....	....		1.20	.35
3807	37¢ Child in Straw Hat	2.25	....	....		1.20	.35
3804-07	37¢ Mary Cassatt Paintings, self-adhesive, 4 varieties attached	4.25	....	....		5.00	4.00
3807b	same, bklt pane of 20 (3804-07 x 5)	15.00	....	....		20.00	....

3808   **3809**

3810   **3811**

3808-11	37¢ Early Football Heroes, self-adhesive, 4 varieties attached	4.25	4.75	25.00(20)	6.00	6.00	5.00
3808	37¢ Bronko Nagurski.	2.25	....	....	....	1.50	.40
3809	37¢ Ernie Nevers. . . .	2.25	....	....	....	1.50	.40
3810	37¢ Walter Camp. . . .	2.25	....	....	....	1.50	.40
3811	37¢ Red Grange	2.25	....	....	....	1.50	.40

3812   **3813**

| 3812 | 37¢ Roy Acuff, self-adhesive | 2.25 | 4.75 | 20.00(20) | 5.00 | 1.20 | .30 |
| 3813 | 37¢ District of Columbia, self-adhesive | 2.25 | 4.75 | 20.00(16) | 5.00 | 1.50 | .40 |

3814   **3815**

3816   **3817**

3819

3818   **3820**

3814-18	37¢ Reptiles & Amphibians, self-adhesive, 5 varieties attached	5.00	10.50	20.00(20)	11.50	6.00	5.00
3814	37¢ Scarlet Kingsnake	2.25	....	....	....	1.25	.50
3815	37¢ Blue-Spotted Salamander	2.25	....	....	....	1.25	.50
3816	37¢ Reticulate Lizard.	2.25	....	....	....	1.25	.50
3817	37¢ Ornate Chorus Frog	2.25	....	....	....	1.25	.50
3818	37¢ Ornate Box Turtle	2.25	....	....	....	1.25	.50
3819	23¢ George Washington, self-adhesive, die cut 11	2.25	4.75	18.00(20)	3.50	1.00	.50
3820	37¢ Madonna & Child, self-adhesive (2003) .	2.25	....	....	....	1.20	.50
3820a	same, bklt pane of 20	....	....	....	....	20.00	....

SCOTT NO.	DESCRIPTION	FIRST DAY COVERS SING	PL. BLK.	MINT SHEET	PLATE BLOCK	UNUSED F/NH	USED

3821, 3825   **3822, 3826**   **3823, 3827**   **3824, 3828**

SCOTT NO.	DESCRIPTION	FIRST DAY COVERS SING	PL. BLK.	MINT SHEET	PLATE BLOCK	UNUSED F/NH	USED
3821-24	37¢ Christmas Music Makers, self-adhesive, 4 varieties attached..........	4.25	4.75	20.00(20)	6.00	5.00	4.00
3821	37¢ Reindeer with Pipes	2.25	....	....	....	1.20	.50
3822	37¢ Santa Claus with Drum	2.25	....	....	....	1.20	.50
3823	37¢ Santa Claus with Trumpet	2.25	....	....	....	1.20	.50
3824	37¢ Reindeer with Horn	2.25	....	....	....	1.20	.50
3842b	same, bklt pane of 20, (3821-24 x 5 + label) .	15.00	....	....	....	20.00	....
3825	37¢ Reindeer with Pipes, die cut 10.5 x 10.75 ..	2.25	....	....	....	1.20	.50
3826	37¢ Santa Claus with Drum, die cut 10.5 x 10.75 ..	2.25	....	....	....	1.20	.50
3827	37¢ Santa Claus with Trumpet die cut 10.5 x 10.75 ..	2.25	....	....	....	1.20	.50
3828	37¢ Reindeer with Horn, die cut 10.5 x 10.75 ..	2.25	....	....	....	1.20	.50
3825-28	37¢ Christmas Music Makers, self-adhesive, 4 varieties attached, die cut 10.5 x 10.75	4.25	....	....	....	5.00	4.00
3828b	same, bklt pane of 4 (3825-28)	4.25	....	....	....	5.00	....
3828c	same, bklt pane of 6 (3827-28, 3825-26 x 2)	5.50	....	....	....	6.00	....
3828d	same, bklt pane of 6 (3825-26, 3827-28 x 2)	5.50	....	....	....	6.00	....

3829, 3829A, 3830, 3830D

3829	37¢ Snowy Egret, self-adhesive coil, die cut 8.5	1.95	....	....	....	1.20	.40
....	same, pl# strip of 5 ..	....	....	....	....	10.00	....
3829A	37¢ Snowy Egret, self-adhesive coil, die cut 9.5	1.95	....	....	....	1.20	.25
....	same, pl# strip of 5 ..	....	....	....	....	10.00	....

2004 COMMEMORATIVES AND REGULAR ISSUES

3830	37¢ Snowy Egret, self adhesive	2.25	....	....	....	.85	.20
3830a	same, bklt pane of 20	....	....	....	....	16.00	....
3830D	37¢ Snowy Egret, w/ USPS microprinting ..	2.25	....	....	....	7.00	.75
....	same, plt strip of 11 ..	....	....	....	....	16.00	....

3831

PACIFIC CORAL REEF

3831a	*Emperor angelfish, blue & mound coral*	**3831f**	*Pink anemonefish, sea anemone*
3831b	*Humphead wrasse, Moorish idol*	**3831g**	*Snowflake moray eel, Spanish dancer*
3831c	*Bumphead parrotfish*	**3831h**	*Lionfish*
3831d	*Black-spotted puffer, threadfin butterflyfish*	**3831i**	*Triton's trumpet*
3831e	*Hawksbill turtle, palette surgeonfish*	**3831j**	*Oriental sweetlips, bluestreak cleaner wrasse, mushroom coral*

3831	37¢ Pacific Coral Reef, 10 varieties, attached, self-adhesive ..	....	....	12.00(10)	....	12.00	8.00
....	set of singles	25.00	....	....	....	....	5.75

3832   **3834**   **3835**

3832	37¢ Year of the Monkey, self-adhesive	2.25	4.75	20.00(20)	5.00	1.20	.30
3833	37¢ Candy Hearts, self-adhesive	2.25	....	....	....	1.20	.25
3833a	same, bklt pane of 20	....	....	....	....	20.00	....
3834	37¢ Paul Robeson, self-adhesive	2.25	4.75	20.00(20)	5.00	1.20	.30
3835	37¢ Theodore Seuss Geisel (Dr. Seuss) self-adhesive	2.25	4.75	20.00(20)	5.00	1.20	.25

3836   **3833**   **3837**

3836	37¢ White Lilacs and Pink Roses, self-adhesive	2.25	....	....	....	1.20	.25
3836a	same, bklt pane of 20	....	....	....	....	20.00	....
3837	60¢ Five varieties of Pink Roses, self-adhesive .	2.75	5.50	30.00(20)	7.50	2.00	1.00

3838   **3839**

3838	37¢ United States Air Force Academy, self-adhesive	2.25	4.75	20.00(20)	5.00	1.20	.30
3839	37¢ Henry Mancini, self-adhesive	2.25	4.75	20.00(20)	5.00	1.20	.30

3841   **3840**

3842   **3843**

3840-43	37¢ American Choreographers, self-adhesive, 4 varieties attached..........	4.25	4.75	20.00(20)	10.00	4.50	4.00
3840	37¢ Martha Graham .	2.25	....	....	....	.85	.50
3841	37¢ Alvin Ailey	2.25	....	....	....	.85	.50
3842	37¢ Agnes de Mille ..	2.25	....	....	....	.85	.50
3843	37¢ George Balanchine	2.25	....	....	....	.85	.50

3844, 3845, 3846,
3847, 3848, 3849,
3850, 3851, 3852,
3853

SCOTT NO.	DESCRIPTION	FIRST DAY COVERS SING	FIRST DAY COVERS PL. BLK.	MINT SHEET	PLATE BLOCK	UNUSED F/NH	USED
3844-3853	(25¢) Eagle, water activated coil, strip of 10, perf. 9.75	6.00	....	....	....	8.00	....
....	same, pl# strip of 11 .	....	....	....	....	12.00	....
3844	(25¢) Eagle, gray with gold eagle, coil, perf. 9.75	2.25	....	....	....	1.00	.50
3845	(25¢) Eagle, gold with green eagle, coil, perf. 9.75 .	2.25	....	....	....	1.00	.50
3846	(25¢) Eagle, red with gold eagle, coil, perf. 9.75.	2.25	....	....	....	1.00	.50
3847	(25¢) Eagle, gold with dull blue eagle, coil, perf. 9.75 .	2.25	....	....	....	1.00	.50
3848	(25¢) Eagle, Prussian blue with gold eagle, coil, perf. 9.75 .	2.25	....	....	....	1.00	.50
3849	(25¢) Eagle, gold with gray eagle, coil, perf. 9.75	2.25	....	....	....	1.00	.50
3850	(25¢) Eagle, Prussian green with gold eagle, coil, perf. 9.75 .	2.25	....	....	....	1.00	.50
3851	(25¢) Eagle, gold with Prussian blue eagle, coil, perf. 9.75 .	2.25	....	....	....	1.00	.50
3852	(25¢) Eagle, dull blue with gold eagle, coil, perf. 9.75	2.25	....	....	....	1.00	.50
3853	(25¢) Eagle, gold with red eagle, coil, perf. 9.75	2.25	....	....	....	1.00	.50

3855

3854

3856

SCOTT NO.	DESCRIPTION	FIRST DAY COVERS SING	FIRST DAY COVERS PL. BLK.	MINT SHEET	PLATE BLOCK	UNUSED F/NH	USED
3854	37¢ Lewis & Clark Bicentennial, self-adhesive	2.25	4.75	30.00(20)	7.00	2.00	.40
3855	37¢ Lewis & Clark Bicentennial, Lewis booklet single .	2.25	....	....	....	1.50	.40
3856	37¢ Lewis & Clark Bicentennial, Clark booklet single . .	2.25	....	....	....	1.50	.40
3855-56	37¢ Lewis & Clark, pair	5.00	....	....	....	3.50	....
3856b	37¢ Lewis & Clark: The Corps of Discovery, 1804-06, self-adhesive, bklt pane of 10	....	....	....	....	25.00	....

3857

3858

3859

3860

3861

SCOTT NO.	DESCRIPTION	FIRST DAY COVERS SING	FIRST DAY COVERS PL. BLK.	MINT SHEET	PLATE BLOCK	UNUSED F/NH	USED
3857-61	37¢ Isamu Noguchi, self-adhesive, 5 varieties attached.	5.00	9.50	20.00(20)	10.00(10)	5.00	4.00
3857	37¢ Akari 25N	2.25	....	....	....	1.20	.35
3858	37¢ Margaret La Farge Osborn	2.25	....	....	....	1.20	.35
3859	37¢ Black Sun	2.25	....	....	....	1.20	.35
3860	37¢ Mother and Child	2.25	....	....	....	1.20	.35
3861	37¢ Figure (detail) . . .	2.25	....	....	....	1.20	.35

3862

3864, 3874,
3874a, 3875

3863

SCOTT NO.	DESCRIPTION	FIRST DAY COVERS SING	FIRST DAY COVERS PL. BLK.	MINT SHEET	PLATE BLOCK	UNUSED F/NH	USED
3862	37¢ National WWII Memorial, self-adhesive	2.25	4.75	20.00(20)	5.00	1.20	.30
3863	37¢ 2004 Olympic Games, Athens, Greece, self-adhesive	2.25	4.75	20.00(20)	5.00	1.20	.30
3864	(5¢) Sea Coast, coil, perf. 9.75 vert.	2.25	....	....	....	.25	.20
....	same, pl # strip of 5 . .	....	....	....	....	2.50	....

3865   3866

3867   3868

SCOTT NO.	DESCRIPTION	FIRST DAY COVERS SING	FIRST DAY COVERS PL. BLK.	MINT SHEET	PLATE BLOCK	UNUSED F/NH	USED
3865-68	37¢ Art of Disney: Friendship, self-adhesive, 4 varieties attached.	4.25	4.75	30.00(20)	7.00	6.00	3.50
3865	37¢ Goofy, Mickey Mouse, Donald Duck .	2.25	....	....	....	1.20	.35
3866	37¢ Bambi, Thumper .	2.25	....	....	....	1.20	.35
3867	37¢ Mufasa, Simba . .	2.25	....	....	....	1.20	.35
3868	37¢ Jiminy Cricket, Pinocchio	2.25	....	....	....	1.20	.35

3869

3870

SCOTT NO.	DESCRIPTION	FIRST DAY COVERS SING	FIRST DAY COVERS PL. BLK.	MINT SHEET	PLATE BLOCK	UNUSED F/NH	USED
3869	37¢ U.S.S. Constellation, self-adhesive	2.25	4.75	20.00(20)	5.00	1.20	.30
3870	37¢ R. Buckminster Fuller, self-adhesive	2.25	4.75	20.00(20)	5.00	1.20	.30

3871

3872

SCOTT NO.	DESCRIPTION	FIRST DAY COVERS SING	FIRST DAY COVERS PL. BLK.	MINT SHEET	PLATE BLOCK	UNUSED F/NH	USED
3871	37¢ James Baldwin, self-adhesive	2.25	4.75	20.00(20)	5.00	1.20	.30
3872	37¢ Giant Magnolias, self-adhesive	2.25	....	....	....	1.20	.30
3872a	same, bklt pane of 20	....	....	....	....	22.00	....

SCOTT NO.	DESCRIPTION	FIRST DAY COVERS SING	PL. BLK.	MINT SHEET	PLATE BLOCK	UNUSED F/NH	USED

ART OF THE AMERICAN INDIAN

3873

ART OF THE AMERICAN INDIAN

3873a	Mimbres bowl	3873f	Mississippian dffigy
3873b	Kutenai parfleche	3873g	Acoma pot
3873c	Tlingit sculptures	3873h	Navajo weaving
3873d	Ho-Chunk bag	3873i	Seneca carving
3873e	Seminole doll	3873j	Luiseno basket

3873	37¢ Art of the American Indian, 10 varieties attached.	....	....	35.00(10)	....	35.00	10.00
....	set of singles	25.00	....	....	....	....	6.00
3874	(5¢) Sea Coast, coil, perf. 10 vert., self-adhesive	2.25	....	....	....	.25	.20
....	same, pl# strip of 5 . .	....	....	....	....	2.25	....
3874a	(5¢) Sea Coast with small date, coil, die cut 10 vert., self-adhesive	2.25	....	....	....	.25	.20
....	same, pl# strip of 5 . .	....	....	....	....	2.25	....
3875	(5¢) Sea Coast, coil, perf. 11.5 vert., self-adhesive	2.25	....	....	....	.25	.20
....	same, pl# strip of 5 . .	....	....	....	....	2.25	....

3876   JOHN WAYNE

3877   TEST EARLY FOR SICKLE CELL

3876	37¢ John Wayne	2.25	4.75	20.00(20)	5.00	1.20	.30
....	same, uncut sheet of 120	....	....	120.00(20)	....	120.00	....
....	cross gutter block of 8	....	....	....	....	21.00	....
....	block of 8 with vert. gutter	....	....	....	....	13.50	....
....	horizontal pair with vertical gutter	....	....	....	....	4.00	....
....	vertical pair with horizontal gutter	....	....	....	....	3.00	....
3877	37¢ Sickle Cell Disease Awareness	2.25	4.75	20.00(20)	5.00	1.20	.30

CLOUDSCAPES

3878

CLOUDSCAPES

3878a	Cirrus radiatus	3878i	Altocumulus castellanus
3878b	Cirrostratus fibratus	3878j	Alotcumulus lenticularis
3878c	Cirrocumulus undulatus	3878k	Stratocumulus undulatus
3878d	Cumulonimbus mammatus	3878l	Stratus opacus
3878e	Cumulonimbus incus	3878m	Cumulus humilis
3878f	Alocumulus stratiformis	3878n	Cumulus congestus
3878g	Altostratus translucidus	3878o	Cumulonimbus with tornado
3878h	Altocumulus undulatus		

| 3878 | 37¢ Cloudscapes, 15 varieties attached . | 35.00 | .... | 20.00(15) | .... | 20.00 | 18.00 |
| .... | set of singles . . . . | 35.00 | .... | .... | .... | .... | 12.00 |

3879   CHRISTMAS

3880   HANUKAH

3879	37¢ Madonna & Child, self-adhesive, die cut 10.75 x 11	2.25	....	....	....	1.20	.30
3879a	same, bklt pane of 20	....	....	....	....	22.00	....
3880	37¢ Hanukkah-Dreidel, self-adhesive	2.25	4.75	16.00(20)	4.00	1.20	.30

3881   KWANZAA

3882   MOSS HART

| 3881 | 37¢ Kwanzaa-People in Robes, self-adhesive | 2.25 | 4.75 | 20.00(20) | 5.00 | 1.20 | .30 |
| 3882 | 37¢ Moss Hart, self-adhesive | 2.25 | 4.75 | 20.00(20) | 5.00 | 1.20 | .30 |

3883, 3887, 3892   3884, 3888, 3891   3885, 3889, 3894   3886, 3890, 3893

3883-86	37¢ Santa Christmas Ornaments, self-adhesive, 4 attached	4.25	4.75	20.00(20)	5.00	4.50	3.50
3883	37¢ Purple Santa Ornament	2.25	....	....	....	1.20	.40
3884	37¢ Green Santa Ornament	2.25	....	....	....	1.20	.40
3885	37¢ Blue Santa Ornament	2.25	....	....	....	1.20	.40
3886	37¢ Red Santa Ornament	2.25	....	....	....	1.20	.40
3886b	same, bklt pane of 20	....	....	....	....	20.00	....
3887	37¢ Purple Santa Ornament, die cut 10.25 x 10.75 .	2.25	....	....	....	1.20	.40
3888	37¢ Green Santa Ornament, die cut 10.25 x 10.75 .	2.25	....	....	....	1.20	.40
3889	37¢ Blue Santa Ornament, die cut 10.25 x 10.75 .	2.25	....	....	....	1.20	.40
3890	37¢ Red Santa Ornament, die cut 10.25 x 10.75 .	2.25	....	....	....	1.20	.40
3887-90	37¢ Santa Christmas Ornaments, self-adhesive, 4 attached die cut 10.25 x 10.75	4.25	....	....	....	3.75	2.75
3890b	same, bklt pane of 4	4.25	....	....	....	4.25	....
3890c	same, bklt pane of 6 (3889-90, 3887-88 x 2)	5.50	....	....	....	5.75	....
3890d	same, bklt pane of 6 (3887-88, 3889-90 x 2)	5.50	....	....	....	5.75	....
3891	37¢ Green Santa Ornament, die cut 8 . .	2.25	....	....	....	1.20	.50
3892	37¢ Purple Santa Ornament, die cut 8 . .	2.25	....	....	....	1.20	.50
3893	37¢ Red Santa Ornament, die cut 8 . .	2.25	....	....	....	1.20	.50
3894	37¢ Blue Santa Ornament, die cut 8 . .	2.25	....	....	....	1.20	.50
3891-94	37¢ Christmas Ornaments, self-adhesive, 4 attached, die cut 8	4.25	....	....	....	4.50	3.50
3894b	same, bklt pane of 18	15.00	....	....	....	30.00	....

SCOTT NO.	DESCRIPTION	FIRST DAY COVERS SING	FIRST DAY COVERS PL. BLK.	MINT SHEET	PLATE BLOCK	UNUSED F/NH	USED

2005 COMMEMORATIVES AND REGULAR ISSUES

3895

CHINESE NEW YEAR TYPES OF 1992-2004

3895a	Rat	3895g	Horse
3895b	Ox	3895h	Ram
3895c	Tiger	3895i	Rooster
3895d	Rabbit	3895j	Dog
3895e	Dragon	3895k	Boar
3895f	Snake	3895l	Monkey

SCOTT NO.	DESCRIPTION	SING	PL. BLK.	MINT SHEET	PLATE BLOCK	UNUSED F/NH	USED
3895	37¢ Chinese New Year, self-adhesive, 24 varieties attached .	....	....	....	....	25.00	....
....	set of singles	23.50	....	....	....	....	7.50

3896   **3897**   **3898**

SCOTT NO.	DESCRIPTION	SING	PL. BLK.	MINT SHEET	PLATE BLOCK	UNUSED F/NH	USED
3896	37¢ Marian Anderson, self-adhesive	3.00	4.75	20.00(20)	5.00	1.20	.30
3897	37¢ Ronald Reagan, self-adhesive	3.00	4.75	20.00(20)	5.00	1.20	.30
....	same, uncut sheet of 120	....	....	120.00(120)	....	120.00	....
....	cross gutter block of 4	....	....	....	....	9.50	....
....	horiz. pair with vert. gutter	....	....	....	....	4.00	....
....	vert. pair with horiz. gutter	....	....	....	....	3.00	....
3898	37¢ Love-Hand and Flower Bouquet, self-adhesive	3.00	....	....	....	1.20	.30
3898a	same, bklt pane of 20	....	....	....	....	19.50	....

3899

NORTHEAST DECIDUOUS FOREST

3899a	Eastern buckmouth	3899f	Long-tailed weasel
3899b	Red-shouldered hawk	3899g	Wild turkey
3899c	Eastern red bat	3899h	Ovenbird
3899d	White-tailed deer	3899i	Red eft
3899e	Black bear	3899j	Eastern chipmunk

SCOTT NO.	DESCRIPTION	SING	PL. BLK.	MINT SHEET	PLATE BLOCK	UNUSED F/NH	USED
3899	37¢ Northeast Deciduous Forest, self-adhesive, 10 varieties attached .	....	....	12.00(10)	....	12.00	....
....	set of singles	25.00	....	....	....	....	6.00

3900   **3901**   **3902**   **3903**

SCOTT NO.	DESCRIPTION	SING	PL. BLK.	MINT SHEET	PLATE BLOCK	UNUSED F/NH	USED
3900	37¢ Hyacinth	3.00	....	....	....	1.20	.30
3901	37¢ Daffodil	3.00	....	....	....	1.20	.30
3902	37¢ Tulip	3.00	....	....	....	1.20	.30
3903	37¢ Iris.	3.00	....	....	....	1.20	.30
3900-03	37¢ Spring Flowers, self-adhesive, 4 varieties attached . .	4.25	....	....	....	19.50	....
3903b	same, bklt pane of 20	....	....	....	....	19.50	....

3904   **3905**

SCOTT NO.	DESCRIPTION	SING	PL. BLK.	MINT SHEET	PLATE BLOCK	UNUSED F/NH	USED
3904	37¢ Robert Penn Warren, self-adhesive	3.00	4.75	20.00(20)	5.00	1.20	.30
3905	37¢ Yip Harburg, self-adhesive	3.00	4.75	20.00(20)	5.00	1.20	.30

3906   **3907**

3908   **3909**

SCOTT NO.	DESCRIPTION	SING	PL. BLK.	MINT SHEET	PLATE BLOCK	UNUSED F/NH	USED
3906-09	37¢ American Scientists, self-adhesive, 4 attached	4.25	4.75	20.00(20)	5.00	4.50	3.50
3906	37¢ Barbara McClintock	3.00	....	....	....	1.20	.40
3907	37¢ Josiah Willard Gibbs	3.00	....	....	....	1.20	.40
3908	37¢ John von Neuman	3.00	....	....	....	1.20	.40
3909	37¢ Richard Feynman	3.00	....	....	....	1.20	.40
....	same, plate blk of 8 with Top Label	....	....	....	8.00(8)	....	....

3910

MODERN AMERICAN ARCHITECTURE

3910a	Guggenheim Museum	3910g	National Gallery of Art
3910b	Chrysler Building	3910h	Glass House
3910c	Vanna Venturi House	3910i	Yale Art and Architecture Bldg.
3910d	TWA Terminal	3910j	High Museum of Atlanta
3910e	Walt Disney Concert Hall	3910k	Exeter Academy Library
3910f	860-880 Lake Shore Drive	3910l	Hancock Center

SCOTT NO.	DESCRIPTION	SING	PL. BLK.	MINT SHEET	PLATE BLOCK	UNUSED F/NH	USED
3910	37¢ Modern American Architecture, self-adhesive, 12 varieties attached . .	....	....	15.00(12)	....	15.00	....
....	set of singles	....	....	....	....	....	7.50

SCOTT NO.	DESCRIPTION	FIRST DAY COVERS SING	FIRST DAY COVERS PL. BLK.	MINT SHEET	PLATE BLOCK	UNUSED F/NH	USED

3911

SCOTT NO.	DESCRIPTION	SING	PL. BLK.	MINT SHEET	PLATE BLOCK	UNUSED F/NH	USED
3911	37¢ Henry Fonda, self-adhesive	3.00	4.75	20.00(20)	5.00	1.20	.30
....	same, uncut sheet of 180	....	....	180.00(180)		180.00	....
....	cross gutterblk of 8 . .	....	....	....		19.00	....
....	blk of 8 w/ vert. gutter	....	....	....		12.00	....
....	horiz. pair w/ vert. gutter	....	....	....		4.00	....
....	vert. pair w/ horiz. gutter	....	....	....		3.00	....

3912 **3913**

3914 **3915**

SCOTT NO.	DESCRIPTION	SING	PL. BLK.	MINT SHEET	PLATE BLOCK	UNUSED F/NH	USED
3912-15	37¢ Disney Characters, self-adhesive, 4 attached	4.25	4.75	20.00(20)	5.00	4.50	3.50
3912	37¢ Pluto, Mickey Mouse	3.00	....	....	....	.85	.20
3913	37¢ Mad Hatter, Alice	3.00	....	....	....	.85	.20
3914	37¢ Flounder, Ariel. . .	3.00	....	....	....	.85	.20
3915	37¢ Snow White, Dopey	3.00	....	....	....	.85	.20

3916

3917

3918

3919

3920

3921

3922

3923

3924

3925

ADVANCES IN AVIATION

3916	*Boeing 247*	3921	*Lockheed P80 Shooting Star*
3917	*Consolidated PBY Catalina*	3922	*Consolidated B24 Liberator*
3918	*Grumman F6F*	3923	*Boeing B29 Superfortress*
3919	*Republic P47 Thunderbolt*	3924	*Beechcraft 35 Bonanza*
3920	*E & R Corp. Ercoupe 415*	3925	*Northrop YB-49 Flying Wing*

SCOTT NO.	DESCRIPTION	SING	PL. BLK.	MINT SHEET	PLATE BLOCK	UNUSED F/NH	USED
3916-25	37¢ Advances in Aviation, self-adhesive, 10 attached	25.00	....	20.00(20)	10.00(10)	9.00	8.00
....	set of singles	....	....	....	....	....	6.00

3926

3927

3928

3929

SCOTT NO.	DESCRIPTION	SING	PL. BLK.	MINT SHEET	PLATE BLOCK	UNUSED F/NH	USED
3926	37¢ Blanket w/ yellow, orange, and red stripes	3.00	....	....	....	1.20	.40
3927	37¢ Blanket w/ black, orange red, and yellow	3.00	....	....	....	1.20	.40
3928	37¢ Blanket w/ yellow and black diamonds. .	3.00	....	....	....	1.20	.40
3929	37¢ Blanket w/ zigzag diamonds.	3.00	....	....	....	1.20	.40
3926-29	37¢ Rio Grande Blankets, self-adhesive, 4 attached	4.25	....	....	....	4.00	3.50
3929b	same, bklt pane of 20	15.00	....	....	....	20.00	....

3930

1953 Studebaker Starliner

3931

Arthur Ashe

3936

1954 Kaiser Darrin

3932

1953 Chevrolet Corvette

3933

1952 Nash Healey

3934

1955 Ford Thunderbird

3935

SCOTT NO.	DESCRIPTION	FIRST DAY COVERS SING	FIRST DAY COVERS PL. BLK.	MINT SHEET	PLATE BLOCK	UNUSED F/NH	USED
3930	37¢ Presidential Libraries Act, 50th Anniv., self-adhesive	3.00	4.75	20.00(20)	5.00	1.20	.30
3931	37¢ 1953 Studebaker Starliner.	3.00	....	....	....	1.50	.30
3932	37¢ 1954 Kaiser Darren	3.00	....	....	....	1.50	.30
3933	37¢ 1953 Chevrolet Corvette	3.00	....	....	....	1.50	.30
3934	37¢ 1952 Nash Healey	3.00	....	....	....	1.50	.30
3935	37¢ 1955 Ford Thunderbird	3.00	....	....	....	1.50	.30
3931-35	37¢ Sporty Cars of the 1950's, self-adhesive, 5 attached	5.00	....	....	....	8.50	....
3935b	same, bklt pane of 20	15.00	....	....	....	20.00	....
3936	37¢ Arthur Ashe, self-adhesive	3.00	4.75	16.00(20)	4.00	1.20	.30

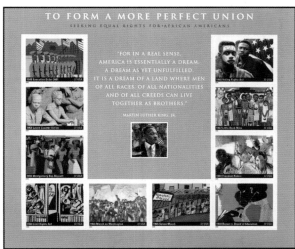

3937

TO FORM A MORE PERFECT UNION

3937a	*1948 Executive Order 9981*	**3937f**	*1961 Freedom Riders*
3937b	*1965 Voting Rights Act*	**3937g**	*1964 Civil Rights Act*
3937c	*1960 Lunch Counter Sit-Ins*	**3937h**	*1963 March on Washington*
3937d	*1957 Litte Rock Nine*	**3937i**	*1965 Selma March*
3937e	*1955 Montgomery Bus Boycott*	**3937j**	*1954 Brown vs. Board of Education*

SCOTT NO.	DESCRIPTION	SING	PL. BLK.	MINT SHEET	PLATE BLOCK	UNUSED F/NH	USED
3937	37¢ To Form A More Perfect Union, self-adhesive, 10 attached. .	15.00	....	12.00(10)	....	12.00	7.50
....	set of singles	....	....	....	....	....	6.00

3938

3939

3943

3940

3941

3942

SCOTT NO.	DESCRIPTION	SING	PL. BLK.	MINT SHEET	PLATE BLOCK	UNUSED F/NH	USED
3938	37¢ Child Health, self-adhesive	3.00	4.75	20.00(20)	5.00	1.20	.30
3939-42	37¢ Let's Dance, self-adhesive, 4 attached .	4.25	4.75	20.00(20)	5.00	4.00	3.50
3939	37¢ Merengue	3.00	....	....	....	1.20	.30
3940	37¢ Salsa.	3.00	....	....	....	1.20	.30
3941	37¢ Cha Cha Cha . . .	3.00	....	....	....	1.20	.30
3942	37¢ Mambo	3.00	....	....	....	1.20	.30
3943	37¢ Greta Garbo, self-adhesive	3.00	4.75	20.00(20)	5.00	1.20	.30

SCOTT NO.	DESCRIPTION	FIRST DAY COVERS SING	FIRST DAY COVERS PL. BLK.	MINT SHEET	PLATE BLOCK	UNUSED F/NH	USED

3944

JIM HENSON AND THE MUPPETS

3944a	*Kermit the Frog*	**3944g**	*Animal*
3944b	*Fozzie Bear*	**3944h**	*Dr. Brunsen Honeydew and Beaker*
3944c	*Sam the Eagle and flag*	**3944i**	*Rowlf the Dog*
3944d	*Miss Piggy*	**3944j**	*The Great Gonzo and Camilia*
3944e	*Statler and Waldorf*	**3944k**	*Jim Henson*
3944f	*The Swedish Chef and fruit*		

SCOTT NO.	DESCRIPTION	SING	PL. BLK.	MINT SHEET	PLATE BLOCK	UNUSED F/NH	USED
3944	37¢ Jim Henson and the Muppets, self-adhesive, 11 varieties attached. .	12.00	....	15.00(11)	....	9.35	6.50
....	set of singles	30.00	....	....	....	....	7.00

3945 **3946** **3947** **3948**

SCOTT NO.	DESCRIPTION	SING	PL. BLK.	MINT SHEET	PLATE BLOCK	UNUSED F/NH	USED
3945-48	37¢ Constellations, self-adhesive, 4 attached	4.25	4.75	20.00(20)	5.00	4.50	4.00
3945	37¢ Leo	3.00	....	....	....	1.20	.30
3946	37¢ Orion.	3.00	....	....	....	1.20	.30
3947	37¢ Lyra.	3.00	....	....	....	1.20	.30
3948	37¢ Pegasus	3.00	....	....	....	1.20	.30

3949, 3953, 3957 **3950, 3954, 3958** **3951, 3955, 3959** **3952, 3956, 3960**

SCOTT NO.	DESCRIPTION	SING	PL. BLK.	MINT SHEET	PLATE BLOCK	UNUSED F/NH	USED
3949-52	37¢ Christmas Cookies, self-adhesive, 4 attached	4.25	4.75	20.00(20)	5.00	4.50	4.00
3949	37¢ Santa Claus cookie	3.00	....	....	....	1.20	.30
3950	37¢ Snowmen cookie	3.00	....	....	....	1.20	.30
3951	37¢ Angel cookie	3.00	....	....	....	1.20	.30
3952	37¢ Elves cookie	3.00	....	....	....	1.20	.30
3953	37¢ Santa Claus cookie, die cut 10.75 X 11 . . .	3.00	....	....	....	1.20	.30
3954	37¢ Snowmen cookie, die cut 10.75 X 11 . . .	3.00	....	....	....	1.20	.30
3955	37¢ Angel cookie, die cut 10.75 X 11 . . .	3.00	....	....	....	1.20	.30
3956	37¢ Elves cookie, die cut 10.75 X 11 . . .	3.00	....	....	....	1.20	.30
3953-56	37¢ Christmas cookies, self-adhesive, 4 attached, die cut 10.75 X 11 . . .	4.25	....	....	....	4.50	4.00
3956b	same, bklt pane of 20	....	....	....	....	19.50	....

SCOTT NO.	DESCRIPTION	FIRST DAY COVERS SING	PL. BLK.	MINT SHEET	PLATE BLOCK	UNUSED F/NH	USED
3957	37¢ Santa Claus cookie, die cut 10.5 X 10.75..	3.00	....	....	....	1.20	.40
3958	37¢ Snowmen cookie, die cut 10.5 X 10.75..	3.00	....	....	....	1.20	.40
3959	37¢ Angel cookie, die cut 10.5 X 10.75..	3.00	....	....	....	1.20	.40
3960	37¢ Elves cookie, die cut 10.5 X 10.75..	3.00	....	....	....	1.20	.40
3957-60	37¢ Christmas Cookies, self-adhesvie, 4 attached die cut 10.5 X 10.75..	4.25	....	....	....	4.50	4.00
3960b	same, booklet pane of 4	4.25	....	....	....	5.00	....
3960c	same, bklt pane of 6 (3959-60, 3957-58 X 2)	5.50	....	....	....	10.00	....
3960d	same, bklt pane of 6 (3957-58, 3959-60 X 2)	5.50	....	....	....	10.00	....

3961 3962
3963 3964

SCOTT NO.	DESCRIPTION	FIRST DAY COVERS SING	PL. BLK.	MINT SHEET	PLATE BLOCK	UNUSED F/NH	USED
3961-64	37¢ Distinguished Marines, self-adhesive, 4 attached	4.25	4.75	20.00(20)	5.00	4.50	4.00
....	same, plate block of 8				10.00(8)	....	....
3961	37¢ Lt. General John A. Lejeune.....	3.00	....	....	....	.85	.20
3962	37¢ Lt. General Lewis B. Puller......	3.00	....	....	....	.85	.20
3963	37¢ Sgt. John Basilone	3.00	....	....	....	.85	.20
3964	37¢ Sgt. Major Daniel J. Daly	3.00	....	....	....	.85	.20

3965-3975 3976 3978, 3979, 3980

SCOTT NO.	DESCRIPTION	FIRST DAY COVERS SING	PL. BLK.	MINT SHEET	PLATE BLOCK	UNUSED F/NH	USED
3965	(39¢) Flag and Statue of Liberty	3.00	4.75	85.00(100)	10.00	1.30	.25
3966	(39¢) Flag and Statue of Liberty, self-adhesive	3.00	4.75	16.75(20)	4.50	1.30	.25
3966a	same, bklt pane of 20	16.00	....	....	....	18.00	....
3967	(39¢) Flag and Statue of Liberty, coil	3.00	....	....	....	1.20	.25
....	same, pl# strip of 5 ..		....	....	....	6.75	....
3968	(39¢) Flag and Statue of Liberty, self-adhesive coil, die cut 8.5......	3.00	....	....	....	1.20	.25
....	same, pl# strip of 5 ..		....	....	....	6.75	....
3969	(39¢) Flag and Statue of Liberty, coil, die cut 10.25	3.00	....	....	....	1.20	.25
....	same, pl# strip of 5........		....	....	....	6.75	....
3970	(39¢) Flag and Statue of Liberty, self-adhesive coil, die cut 9.5......	3.00	....	....	....	1.20	.25
....	same, pl# strip of 5 ..		....	....	....	6.75	....
3971	(39¢) Flag and Statue of Liberty, self-adhesive die cut 11.25 X 11 ...	3.00	....	....	....	1.20	.25
3971a	same, bklt pane of 20	16.00	....	....	....	18.00	....
3972	(39¢) Flag and Statue of Liberty, self-adhesive die cut 11.25 X 10.75.	3.00	....	....	....	1.20	.25
3972a	same, bklt pane of 20	16.00	....	....	....	18.00	....
3973	(39¢) Flag and Statue of Liberty, self-adhesive die cut 10.25 X 10.75.	3.00	....	....	....	1.20	.25
3973a	same, bklt pane of 20	16.00	....	....	....	18.00	....
3974	(39¢) Flag and Statue of Liberty, self-adhesive die cut 11.25 X 11 ...	3.00	....	....	....	1.20	.25
3974a	same, bklt pane of 4	4.50	....	....	....	3.75	....
3974b	same, bklt pane of 6 .	6.00	....	....	....	5.50	....

SCOTT NO.	DESCRIPTION	FIRST DAY COVERS SING	PL. BLK.	MINT SHEET	PLATE BLOCK	UNUSED F/NH	USED
3975	(39¢) Flag and Statue of Liberty, self-adhesive die cut 8	3.00	....	....	....	1.20	.25
....	same, bklt pane of 18	16.00	....	....	....	16.25	....

2006 COMMEMORATIVES AND REGULAR ISSUES

SCOTT NO.	DESCRIPTION	FIRST DAY COVERS SING	PL. BLK.	MINT SHEET	PLATE BLOCK	UNUSED F/NH	USED
3976	(39¢) Birds.........	3.00	....	....	....	1.20	.30
3976a	same, bklt pane of 20	16.00	....	....	....	18.00	....
3978	39¢ Flag and Statue of Liberty, self-adhesive die cut 11.25 X 10.75.	3.00	4.75	16.75(20)	4.50	1.20	.30
3978a	same, bklt pane of 10	....	....	....	....	9.00	....
3978b	same, bklt pane of 20	....	....	....	....	18.00	....
3979	39¢ Flag and Statue of Liberty, coil, perf 10	3.00	....	....	....	1.20	.30
....	same, pl# strip of 5 ..	....	....	....	....	6.75	....
3980	same, self-adhesive coil, die cut 11......	3.00	....	....	....	1.20	.30
....	same, pl# strip of 5 ..	....	....	....	....	7.50	....
3981	same, self-adhesive coil w/ USPS micro die cut 9.5	3.00	....	....	....	1.20	.30
....	same, pl# strip of 5 ..	....	....	....	....	7.50	....
3982	same, self-adhesive coil, die cut 10 vertical....	3.00	....	....	....	1.20	.30
....	same, pl# strip of 5 ..	....	....	....	....	7.50	....
3983	same, self-adhesive coil, die cut 8.5	3.00	....	....	....	1.20	.30
....	same, pl# strip of 5 ..	....	....	....	....	7.50	....
3985	39¢ Flag and Statue of Liberty, self-adhesive, die cut 11.25 X 10.75 on 2 or 3 sides .	3.00	....	....	....	1.20	.30
3985a	same, bklt pane of 20	....	....	....	....	18.00	....
3985b	same, die cut 11.1 on 2 or 3	3.00	....	....	....	1.20	.30
3985c	same, bklt pane of 4	....	....	....	....	3.75	....
3985d	same, bklt pane of 6 .	....	....	....	....	5.50	....

3987 3988 3989 3990

(Children's book animals stamps)

3991 3992 3993 3994

FAVORITE CHILDREN'S BOOK ANIMALS

3987	The Very Hungry Caterpillar	3991	Wild Thing
3988	Wilbur	3992	Curious George
3989	Fox in Socks	3993	Olivia
3990	Maisy	3994	Frederick

SCOTT NO.	DESCRIPTION	FIRST DAY COVERS SING	PL. BLK.	MINT SHEET	PLATE BLOCK	UNUSED F/NH	USED
3987-94	39¢ Children's Book Animals, self-adhesive 8 attached	10.00	....	14.50(16)	7.50(8)	7.25	6.00
....	set of singles						5.00
....	same, uncut sheet of 96	....	....	90.00(96)	....	90.00	....
....	cross gutter block of 8	....	....	....	....	17.50	....
....	blk of 8 w/ horiz. gutter	....	....	....	....	10.00	....
....	blk of 8 w/ vert. gutter	....	....	....	....	9.00	....
....	horz. pair w/ vert. gutter	....	....	....	....	2.50	....
....	vert. pair w/ horz. gutter	....	....	....	....	2.50	....

3995 3996

SCOTT NO.	DESCRIPTION	FIRST DAY COVERS SING	PL. BLK.	MINT SHEET	PLATE BLOCK	UNUSED F/NH	USED
3995	39¢ 2006 Winter Olympic games, Turin, Italy, self-adhesive	3.00	4.75	20.00(20)	5.00	1.20	.50
3996	39¢ Hattie McDaniel, self-adhesive	3.00	4.75	20.00(20)	5.00	1.20	.50

SCOTT NO.	DESCRIPTION	FIRST DAY COVERS SING	PL. BLK.	MINT SHEET	PLATE BLOCK	UNUSED F/NH	USED

CHINESE NEW YEAR TYPES OF 1992-2004

3997a	Rat	3997g	Horse
3997b	Ox	3997h	Ram
3997c	Tiger	3997i	Monkey
3997d	Rabbit	3997j	Rooster
3997e	Dragon	3997k	Dog
3997f	Snake	3997l	Boar

SCOTT NO.	DESCRIPTION	SING	PL. BLK.	MINT SHEET	PLATE BLOCK	UNUSED F/NH	USED
3997	39¢ Chinese New Year self-adhesive, 12 varieties attached . . .	....	....	10.75(12)	....	10.75	....
	set of singles	32.00	....	....	....	....	7.50

3998

Common Buckeye
USA 24
4000, 4001, 4002

63 USA
3999

3998	39¢ Wedding Doves, Dove Facing Left, self-adhesive	3.00	....	....	....	.90	.30
3998a	same, bklt pane of 20	16.00	....	....	....	18.00	....
3999	63¢ Wedding Doves, Dove Facing Right, self-adhesive	3.00	....	....	....	1.40	1.00
3999a	same, bklt pane of 40	....	....	....	....	46.00	....
4000	24¢ Common Buckeye butterfly	3.00	4.75	55.00(100)	6.75	.60	.30
4001	24¢ Common Buckeye butterfly self-adhesive, die cut 11	3.00	4.75	11.00(20)	2.75	.60	.30
4001a	same, single from bklt. pane, die cut 10.75 X11.25	3.00	....	....	....	.60	.30
4001b	same, bklt pane of 10 (4001a)	....	....	....	....	6.00	....
4001c	same, bklt pane of 4 (4001a)	....	....	....	....	2.40	....
4001d	same, bklt pane of 6 (4001a)	....	....	....	....	3.60	....
4002	24¢ Common Buckeye butterfly, self-adhesive, coil, die cut 8.5.	3.00	....	....	....	.60	.30
	same, pl# strip of 5 . .	....	....	....	....	4.25	....

USA 39
4003, 4008, 4013

39 USA
4004, 4009, 4014

USA 39
4005, 4010, 4015

USA 39
4006, 4011, 4016

USA 39
4007, 4012, 4017

4003	39¢ Chili Peppers, self-adhesive, coil . . .	3.00	....	....	....	.90	.30
4004	39¢ Beans, self-adhesive, coil	3.00	....	....	....	.90	.30
4005	39¢ Sunflower and Seeds self-adhesive, coil . . .	3.00	....	....	....	.90	.30
4006	39¢ Squashes, self-adhesive, coil	3.00	....	....	....	.90	.30
4007	39¢ Corn, self-adhesive, coil	3.00	....	....	....	.90	.30
4003-07	39¢ Crops of the Americas, coil, strip of 5	5.00	....	....	....	4.50	3.50
	same, pl# strip of 5 . .	....	....	....	....	6.75	....
	same, pl# strip of 11 . .	....	....	....	....	13.00	....
4008	39¢ Chili Peppers, self-adhesive, bklt single, die cut 10.75 X 11.25 . .	3.00	....	....	....	.90	.30
4009	39¢ Beans, self-adhesive bklt single, die cut 10.75 X 11.25	3.00	....	....	....	.90	.30
4010	39¢ Sunflower and Seeds self-adhesive, bklt single, die cut 10.75 X 11.25. .	3.00	....	....	....	.90	.30
4011	39¢ Squashes, self-adhesive, bklt single die cut 10.75 X 11.25. .	3.00	....	....	....	.90	.30
4012	39¢ Corn, self-adhesive bklt single, die cut 10.75 X 11.25 . .	3.00	....	....	....	.90	.30
4008-12	39¢ Crops of the Americas, strip of 5.	5.00	....	....	....	4.50	3.50
4012b	same, bklt pane of 20	....	....	....	....	18.00	....

4013	39¢ Chili Peppers, self-adhesive, bklt single, die cut 10.75 X 10.5. .	3.00	....	....	....	.90	.30
4014	39¢ Beans, self-adhesive bklt single, die cut 10.75 X10.5 . .	3.00	....	....	....	.90	.30
4015	39¢ Sunflower and Seeds self-adhesive, bklt single, die cut 10.75 X10.5 . .	3.00	....	....	....	.90	.30
4016	39¢ Squashes, self-adhesive, bklt single die cut 10.75 X 10.5. .	3.00	....	....	....	.90	.30
4016a	same, bklt pane of 4 .	....	....	....	....	3.60	....
4017	39¢ Corn, self-adhesive bklt single, die cut 10.75 X 10.5	3.00	....	....	....	.90	.30
4013-17	39¢ Crops of the Americas strip of 5.	5.00	....	....	....	4.50	3.50
4017b	same, bklt pane of 4 .	....	....	....	....	3.60	....
4017c	same, bklt pane of 6 (4013-16, 4017 X 2). .	....	....	....	....	5.40	....
4017d	same, bklt pane of 6 (4013-15, 4017, 4016 X2)	....	....	....	....	5.40	....

USA $4.05
4018

SUGAR RAY ROBINSON
USA 39
WORLD CHAMPION
4020

X
USA $14.40
4019

4018	$4.05 X-Plane, self-adhesive	9.00	25.00	175.00(20)	45.00	9.00	6.00
4019	$14.40 X-Plane, self-adhesive	30.00	75.00	575.00(20)	150.00	30.00	16.50
4020	39¢ Sugar Ray Robinson, self-adhesive	3.00	4.75	20.00(20)	4.50	1.00	.35

4021   4022

BENJAMIN FRANKLIN, STATESMAN
4023
BENJAMIN FRANKLIN, SCIENTIST
4024

4021-24	39¢ Benjamin Franklin (1706-90), self-adhesive 4 attached	4.25	4.75	20.00(20)	5.50	4.50	....
4021	39¢ Benjamin Franklin Statesman	3.00	....	....	....	1.00	.30
4022	39¢ Benjamin Franklin Scientist.	3.00	....	....	....	1.00	.30
4023	39¢ Benjamin Franklin Printer	3.00	....	....	....	1.00	.30
4024	39¢ Benjamin Franklin Postmaster	3.00	....	....	....	1.00	.30

4025   4026

39 USA
39 USA
39 USA
39 USA
4027   4028

4025-28	39¢ Disney Characters, self-adhesive, 4 attached	4.25	4.75	25.00(20)	6.00	5.00	....

SCOTT NO.	DESCRIPTION	FIRST DAY COVERS SING	FIRST DAY COVERS PL. BLK.	MINT SHEET	PLATE BLOCK	UNUSED F/NH	USED
4025	39¢ Mickey and Minnie Mouse	3.00	....	....	....	1.20	.40
4026	39¢ Cinderella and Prince Charming	3.00	....	....	....	1.20	.40
4027	39¢ Beauty and the Beast	3.00	....	....	....	1.20	.40
4028	39¢ Lady and the Tramp	3.00	....	....	....	1.20	.40

4029

4030

4029	39¢ Lovebirds, self-adhesive	3.00	....	....	....	.90	.30
....	same, bklt pane of 20	....	....	....	....	18.00	....
4030	39¢ Katherine Anne Porter self-adhesive	3.00	4.75	19.00(20)	4.50	.90	.30

4031

4032

| 4031 | 39¢ Amber Alert, self-adhesive | 3.00 | 4.75 | 19.00(20) | 4.50 | .90 | .30 |
| 4032 | 39¢ Purple Heart, self-adhesive | 3.00 | 4.75 | 19.00(20) | 4.50 | .90 | .30 |

4033-4072

WONDERS OF AMERICA

4033	American Alligator	4053	Mount Washington
4034	Moloka'i	4054	Grand Canyon
4035	Saguaro	4055	American Bullfrog
4036	Bering Glacier	4056	Oroville Dam
4037	Great Sand Dunes	4057	Peregrine Falcon
4038	Chesapeake Bay	4058	Mississippi River Delta
4039	Cliff Palace	4059	Steamboat Geyser
4040	Crater Lake	4060	Rainbow Bridge
4041	American Bison	4061	White Sturgeon
4042	Off the Florida Keys	4062	Rocky Mountains
4043	Pacific Crest Trail	4063	Coast Redwoods
4044	Gateway Arch	4064	American Beaver
4045	Appalachians	4065	Mississippi-Missouri
4046	American Lotus	4066	Mount Wai'ale'ale
4047	Lake Superior	4067	Kilauea
4048	Pronghorn	4068	Mammoth Cave
4049	Bristlecone Pines	4069	Blue Whale
4050	Yosemite Falls	4070	Death Valley
4051	Great Basin	4071	Cornish-Windsor Bridge
4052	Verrazano-Narrows Bridge	4072	Quaking Aspen

| 4033-72 | 39¢ Wonders of America, self-adhesive, 40 attached | .... | .... | 38.00(40) | .... | 38.00 | .... |
| .... | same, set of singles | .... | .... | .... | .... | .... | 30.00 |

4073, 4074a

4073	39¢ Samuel de Champlain, self-adhesive	3.00	4.75	25.00(20)	6.50	1.30	.50
4074	39¢ Samuel de Champlain, souvenir sheet of 4 (joint issue, 4074a x 2 and Canada 2156a x 2)	....	....	....	....	4.50	
4074a	same, single from s/s	....	....	....	....	....	.50

4075

4075	$1-$5 Washington 2006 World Exhibition, souvenir sheet of 3	....	....	....	....	16.00	....
4075a	$1 Lincoln Memorial	4.50	....	....	....	2.00	1.50
4075b	$2 U.S. Capitol	7.50	....	....	....	4.00	3.00
4075c	$5 "America"	15.00	....	....	....	10.00	8.00

Distinguished American Diplomats

4076

4076	39¢ Distinguished American Diplomats, self-adhesive, souvenir sheet of 6	15.00	....	....	....	5.50	....
4076a	39¢ Robert D. Murphy	3.00	....	....	....	.90	.30
4076b	39¢ Frances E. Willis	3.00	....	....	....	.90	.30
4076c	39¢ Hiram Bingham IV	3.00	....	....	....	.90	.30
4076d	39¢ Philip C. Habib	3.00	....	....	....	.90	.30
4076e	39¢ Charles E. Bohlen	3.00	....	....	....	.90	.30
4076f	39¢ Clifton R. Wharton Sr.	3.00	....	....	....	.90	.30

4077

4078

4077	39¢ Judy Garland, self-adhesive	3.00	4.75	19.00(20)	4.50	.90	.30
....	same, uncut sheet of 120	....	....	120.00(120)	....	120.00	....
....	block of 8 with vert. gutter	....	....	....	....	10.50	....
....	cross gutter block of 8	....	....	....	....	18.00	....
....	horiz. pair with vert. gutter	....	....	....	....	4.00	....
....	vert. pair with horiz. gutter	....	....	....	....	3.00	....
4078	39¢ Ronald Reagan, self-adhesive	3.00	4.75	19.00(20)	4.50	.90	.30

SCOTT NO.	DESCRIPTION	FIRST DAY COVERS SING	FIRST DAY COVERS PL. BLK.	MINT SHEET	PLATE BLOCK	UNUSED F/NH	USED

4079

| 4079 | 39¢ Happy Birthday, Self-adhesive....... | 3.00 | 4.75 | 16.75(20) | 4.50 | .90 | .30 |

4080 4081
4082 4083

4080-83	39¢ Baseball Sluggers, self-adhesive, 4 attached	4.25	4.75	16.75(20)	4.50	3.75	....
4080	39¢ Roy Campanella .	3.00	....	....	....	.90	.30
4081	39¢ Hank Greenberg .	3.00	....	....	....	.90	.30
4082	39¢ Mel Ott	3.00	....	....	....	.90	.30
4083	39¢ Mickey Mantle. . .	3.00	....	....	....	.90	.30
....	same, uncut sheet of 120	....	....	120.00(120)	....	120.00	....
....	cross gutter blk of 8 . .	....	....	....	....	18.00	....
....	blk of 8 with vert. gutter	....	....	....	....	10.50	....
....	horz. pair with vert. gutter	....	....	....	....	4.00	....
....	vert. pair with horz. gutter	....	....	....	....	4.00	....

SUPER HEROES

4084

D.C. COMICS SUPER HEROES

4084a	Superman	4084k	Superman Cover
4084b	Green Lantern	4084l	Green Lantern Cover
4084c	Wonder Woman	4084m	Wonder Woman Cover
4084d	Green Arrow	4084n	Green Arrow Cover
4084e	Batman	4084o	Batman Cover
4084f	The Flash	4084p	The Flash Cover
4084g	Plastic Man	4084q	Plastic Man Cover
4084h	Aquaman	4084r	Aquaman Cover
4084i	Supergirl	4084s	Supergirl Cover
4084j	Hawkman	4084t	Hawkman Cover

4084	39¢ D.C. Comics Super Heroes, self-adhesive, 20 varieties attached .	....	....	16.75(20)	....	16.75	....
....	same, uncut sheet of 80	....	....	75.00(80)	....	75.00	....
....	cross gutter block of 20	....	....	....	....	25.00	....
....	horz. pair w/ vert. gutter	....	....	....	....	4.00	....
....	vert. pair w/ horz. gutter	....	....	....	....	4.00	....
....	set of singles	....	....	....	....	....	16.00

4085 4086
4087 4088

4085-88	39¢ Motorcycles, self-adhesive, 4 attached .	4.25	4.75	16.75(20)	4.50	3.75	....
4085	39¢ 1940 Indian Four	3.00	....	....	....	.90	.30
4086	39¢ 1918 Cleveland. .	3.00	....	....	....	.90	.30
4087	39¢ 1970 Chopper. . .	3.00	....	....	....	.90	.30
4088	39¢ 1965 Harley Davidson Electa-Glide	3.00	....	....	....	.90	.30

4089 4096

4089-98	39¢ Quilts of Gee's Bend, Alabama, self-adhesive, 10 attached	....	....	....	....	9.00	....
4089	39¢ House Variation by Mary Lee Bendolph . .	3.00	....	....	....	.90	.30
4090	39¢ Pig in a Pen Medallion by Minnie Sue Coleman	3.00	....	....	....	.90	.30
4091	39¢ Nine Patch by Ruth P. Mosely.	3.00	....	....	....	.90	.30
4092	39¢ Housetop Four Block Half Log Cabin by Lottie Mooney	3.00	....	....	....	.90	.30
4093	39¢ Roman Stripes Variation by Loretta Pettway. . .	3.00	....	....	....	.90	.30
4094	39¢ Chinese Coins Variation by Arlonzia Pettway . .	3.00	....	....	....	.90	.30
4095	39¢ Blocks and Strips by Annie Mae Young . . .	3.00	....	....	....	.90	.30
4096	39¢ Medallion by Loretta Pettway	3.00	....	....	....	.90	.30
4097	39¢ Bars and String-pierced Columns by Jessie T. Pettway	3.00	....	....	....	.90	.30
4098	39¢ Medallion with Checkerboard Center by Patty Ann Williams	3.00	....	....	....	.90	.30
4098b	same, bklt pane of 20 (4089-4098 x 2)	....	....	....	....	18.00	....

4099

SOUTHERN FLORIDA WETLANDS

4099a	Snail Kite	4099f	Roseate Spoonbills
4099b	Wood Storks	4099g	Everglades Mink
4099c	Florida Panther	4099h	Cape Sable Seaside Sparrow
4099d	Bald Eagle	4099i	American Alligator
4099e	American Crocodile	4099j	White Ibis

| 4099 | 39¢ Southern Florida Wetlands, self-adhesive, 10 attached | .... | .... | 12.00(10) | .... | 12.00 | .... |
| .... | set of singles . . . . . . | 20.00 | .... | .... | .... | .... | 5.00 |

SCOTT NO.	DESCRIPTION	FIRST DAY COVERS SING	PL. BLK.	MINT SHEET	PLATE BLOCK	UNUSED F/NH	USED

4100

| 4100 | 39¢ Madonna and Child, self-adhesive | 3.00 | .... | .... | .... | .90 | .30 |
| 4100a | same, bklt pane of 20 | .... | .... | .... | .... | 18.00 | .... |

4101, 4105, 4109, 4113 **4102, 4106, 4110, 4115** **4103, 4107, 4111, 4114** **4104, 4108, 4112, 4116**

4101-04	39¢ Snowflakes, self-adhesive, die cut 11.25 x 11, 4 attached	4.25	4.75	16.75(20)	4.50	3.75	....
4101	39¢ Spindly Arms and Branches	3.00	....	....	....	.90	.30
4102	39¢ Leafy Arms	3.00	....	....	....	.90	.30
4103	39¢ Large Center	3.00	....	....	....	.90	.30
4104	39¢ Arms w/ Wide Centers	3.00	....	....	....	.90	.30
4105-08	39¢ Snowflakes, self-adhesive, die cut 11.25 x 11.5, 4 attached	4.25	....	....	....	3.75	....
4105	39¢ Spindly Arms and Branches	3.00	....	....	....	.90	.30
4106	39¢ Leafy Arms	3.00	....	....	....	.90	.30
4107	39¢ Large Center	3.00	....	....	....	.90	.30
4108	39¢ Arms w/ Wide Centers	3.00	....	....	....	.90	.30
4108b	same, bklt pane of 20 (4105-08 x 5)	....	....	....	....	18.00	....
4109-12	39¢ Snowflakes, self-adhesive, die cut 11.25 x 11, 4 attached	4.25	....	....	....	3.75	....
4109	39¢ Spindly Arms and Branches	3.00	....	....	....	.90	.30
4110	39¢ Leafy Arms	3.00	....	....	....	.90	.30
4111	39¢ Large Center	3.00	....	....	....	.90	.30
4112	39¢ Arms w/ Wide Centers	3.00	....	....	....	.90	.30
4112b	same, bklt pane of 4 (4109-12)	....	....	....	....	5.00	....
4112c	same, bklt pane of 6 (4111-4112, 4109-4110 x 2)	....	....	....	....	8.00	....
4112d	same, bklt pane of 6 (4109-4110, 4111-4112 x 2)	....	....	....	....	8.00	....
4113-16	39¢ Snowflakes, die cut 8, self-adhesive, 4 attached	4.25	....	....	....	8.00	....
4113	39¢ Spindly Arms and Branches	3.00	....	....	....	.90	.30
4114	39¢ Large Center	3.00	....	....	....	.90	.30
4115	39¢ Leafy Arms	3.00	....	....	....	.90	.30
4116	39¢ Arms w/ Wide Centers	3.00	....	....	....	.90	.30
4116b	same, bklt pane of 18 (4113 x 5, 4114 x 4, 4115 x 5, 4116 x 4)	....	....	....	....	25.00	....

4117

4118

4119

4117	39¢ EID, self-adhesive	3.00	4.75	16.75(20)	4.50	.90	.30
4118	39¢ Hanukkah-Dreidal, self-adhesive	3.00	4.75	16.75(20)	4.50	.90	.30
4119	39¢ Kwanzaa-People self-adhesive	3.00	4.75	16.75(20)	4.50	.90	.30

4120

4121

2007 COMMEMORATIVES AND REGULAR ISSUES

| 4120 | 39¢ Ella Fitzgerald, self-adhesive | 3.00 | 4.75 | 16.75(20) | 4.50 | .90 | .30 |
| 4121 | 39¢ Oklahoma Statehood self-adhesive | 3.00 | 4.75 | 16.75(20) | 4.50 | .90 | .30 |

4122

| 4122 | 39¢ Hershey's Kiss, self-adhesive | 3.00 | 4.75 | 16.75(20) | 4.50 | .90 | .30 |
| 4122a | same, bklt pane of 20 | .... | .... | .... | .... | 18.00 | .... |

International Polar Year 2007-2008
Continuing the tradition of international cooperation that began with the first IPY in 1882-1883, scientists from around the world will initiate a new era in polar research by participating in IPY 2007-2008. Working across many disciplines, they will conduct field observations, research, and analysis to build upon current knowledge and increase our understanding of the roles that both polar regions play in global processes.

USA 84 Aurora Borealis
USA 84 Aurora Australis

4123

4123	84¢ International Polar Year, self-adhesive, souvenir sheet of 2	....	....	....	....	3.50	....
4123a	84¢ Aurora Borealis	4.00	....	....	....	1.75	.75
4123b	84¢ Aurora Australis	4.00	....	....	....	1.75	.75

4124

4125, 4126, 4127, 4128

4124	39¢ Henry Wadsworth Longfellow, self-adhesive	3.00	4.75	16.75(20)	4.50	.90	.30
4125	(41¢) Forever Liberty Bell, self-adhesive, large micro print	3.50	....	....	....	.95	.35
4125a	same, bklt pane of 20	....	....	....	....	19.00	....
4126	(41¢) Forever, Liberty Bell, self-adhesive, small micro print	3.50	....	....	....	.95	.35
4126a	same, bklt pane of 20	....	....	....	....	.95	.35
4127	(41¢) Forever Liberty Bell, self-adhesive, medium micro print	3.50	....	....	....	.95	.35
4127a	same, bklt pane of 20	....	....	....	....	19.00	....
4127b	same, bklt pane of 4	....	....	....	....	3.80	....
4127c	same, bklt pane of 6	....	....	....	....	5.70	....
4127d	(42¢) Forever Liberty Bell, dated 2008	3.50	....	....	....	.95	.35
4127e	(42¢) Forever Liberty Bell, dbl-sided conv. bklt of 20	....	....	....	....	18.00	....
4128	(41¢) Forever Liberty Bell, self-adhesive, ATM	3.50	....	....	....	.95	.35
4128a	same, bklt pane of 18	....	....	....	....	17.00	....

4129, 4130, 4132, 4133, 4134, 4135

| 4129 | (41¢) American Flag, die cut 11.25 | 3.50 | 5.00 | 80.00(100) | 8.00 | .95 | .35 |
| 4130 | (41¢) American Flag, self-adhesive, 11.25 x 10.75 | 3.50 | 5.00 | 17.50(20) | 4.75 | .95 | .35 |

SCOTT NO.	DESCRIPTION	FIRST DAY COVERS SING	PL. BLK.	MINT SHEET	PLATE BLOCK	UNUSED F/NH	USED
4131	(41¢) American Flag, coil, die cut 9.75. . . .	3.50	....	....	....	.95	.35
....	same, pl# strip of 5 . .	....				7.00	....
4132	(41¢) American Flag, coil, self-adhesive, die cut 9.5	3.50	....	....	....	.95	.35
....	same, pl# strip of 5 . .	....				7.00	....
4133	(41¢) American Flag, coil, self-adhesive, die cut 11	3.50	....	....	....	.95	.35
....	same, pl# strip of 5 . .	....				7.00	....
4134	(41¢) American Flag, coil, self-adhesive, die cut 8.5	3.50	....	....	....	.95	.35
....	same, pl# strip of 5 . .	....				7.00	....
4135	(41¢) American Flag, coil, self-adhesive, rounded corners, die cut 11 . . .	3.50	....	....	....	.95	.35
....	same, pl# strip of 5 . .	....				7.00	....

4136

4136	41¢ Settlement of Jamestown, self-adhesive . .	3.50	5.00	22.00(20)	....	1.10	.35

4137, 4139, 4141, 4142

4138, 4140

4137	26¢ Florida Panther, water-activated, ...	3.00	4.75	10.00(20)	2.75	.60	.20
4138	17¢ Big Horn Sheep, self-adhesive	3.00	4.00	8.00(20)	1.75	.40	.15
4139	26¢ Florida Panther, self-adhesive	3.00	4.75	10.00(20)	2.75	.60	.20
4140	17¢ Big Horn Sheep, self-adhesive, coil . . .	3.00				.40	.15
....	same, pl# strip of 5 . .	....				3.00	....
4141	26¢ Florida Panther, self-adhesive, coil . . .	3.00				.60	.20
....	same, pl# strip of 5 . .	....				4.00	....
4142	26¢ Florida Panther, self-adhesive	3.00				.60	.20
4142a	same, bklt pane of 10	....				6.00	

4143

STAR WARS

4143a	Darth Vader	4143h	Queen Padme Amidala
4143b	Millennium Falcon	4143i	Obi-Wan Kenobi
4143c	Emperor Palpatine	4143j	Boba Fett
4143d	Anakin Skywalker and	4143k	Darth Maul
	Obi-Wan Kenobi	4143l	Chewbacca and Han Solo
4143e	Luke Skywalker	4143m	X-wing Starfighter
4143f	Princess Leia & R2-D2	4143n	Yoda
4143g	C-3PO	4143o	Stormtroopers

4143	41¢ Star Wars, self-adhesive, 15 attached	....	....	14.00(15)	....	14.00	....
....	same, set of singles. .	....	....	....	....		12.00

4144

4145

4144	$4.60 Air Force One, self-adhesive	10.00	30.00	195.00(20)	50.00	10.00	6.50
4145	$16.25 Marine One, self-adhesive	35.00	80.00	650.00(20)	160.00	35.00	18.00

4146	4147	4148	4149	4150

4146-50	41¢ Pacific Lighthouses, self-adhesive, 5 attached	5.50	8.00	17.50(20)	....	4.75	....
4146	41¢ Diamond Head . .	3.50	....	....	....	.95	.35
4147	41¢ Five Finger	3.50	....	....	....	.95	.35
4148	41¢ Grays Harbor . . .	3.50	....	....	....	.95	.35
4149	41¢ Umpqua River. . .	3.50	....	....	....	.95	.35
4150	41¢ St. George Reef .	3.50	....	....	....	.95	.35

4151

4152

4151	41¢ Wedding Hearts, self-adhesive	3.50	....	....	....	.95	.35
4151a	same, bklt pane of 20	....	....	....	....	19.00	....
4152	58¢ Wedding Hearts, self-adhesive	4.00	5.50	28.00(20)	6.00	1.50	.50

4153   **4154**

4155   **4156**

4153-56	41¢ Pollination, self-adhesive, 4 attached .	4.50	....	....	....	4.00	....
4153	41¢ Purple Nightshade and Morrison's Bumblebee, type I, straight edge at left . .	3.50	....	....	....	.95	.35
4153a	same, type II, straight edge at right.	3.50	....	....	....	.95	.35
4154	41¢ Hummingbird Trumpet and Calliope Hummingbird, type I, straight edge at right	3.50	....	....	....	.95	.35
4154a	same, type II, straight edge at left.	3.50	....	....	....	.95	.35
4155	41¢ Saguaro and Lesser Long-nosed Bat, type I, straight edge at left . .	3.50	....	....	....	.95	.35
4155a	same, type II, straight edge at right.	3.50	....	....	....	.95	.35
4156	41¢ Prairie Ironweed and Southern Dogface Butterfly, type I, straight edge at right	3.50	....	....	....	.95	.35
4156a	same, type II, straight edge at left.	3.50	....	....	....	.95	.35
4156b	same, blk of 4 (4153-4156)	4.50	....	....	....	4.00	....
4156c	same, blk of 4 (4153a-4156a)	4.50	....	....	....	4.00	....
4156d	same, bklt pane of 20 (4153-4156 x 3, 4153a-4156a x 2)	4.50	....	....	....	19.00	....

SCOTT NO.	DESCRIPTION	FIRST DAY COVERS SING	FIRST DAY COVERS PL. BLK.	MINT SHEET	PLATE BLOCK	UNUSED F/NH	USED

4157, 4158

4157	(10¢) Patriotic Banner, self-adhesive, round corners	....	....	....	....	.30	.20
....	same, pl# strip of 5 . .	....	....	....	....	3.00	....
4158	(10¢) Patriotic Banner, self-adhesive, straight corners	....	....	....	....	.30	.20
....	same, pl# strip of 5 . .	....	....	....	....	3.00	....

[Marvel Comics Super Heroes sheet]

4159

MARVEL COMICS SUPER HEROES

4159a	Spider-Man	4159k	Spider-Man Cover
4159b	The Incredible Hulk	4159l	The Incredible Hulk Cover
4159c	Sub-Mariner	4159m	Sub-Mariner Cover
4159d	The Thing	4159n	Fantastic Four Cover
4159e	Captain America	4159o	Captain America Cover
4159f	Silver Surfer	4159p	Silver Surfer Cover
4159g	Spider-Woman	4159q	Spider-Woman Cover
4159h	Iron Man	4159r	Iron Man Cover
4159i	Elektra	4159s	Elektra Cover
4159j	Wolverine	4159t	X-Men Cover

4159	41¢ Marvel Comics Super Heroes, self-adhesive, 20 varieties attached .	....	....	17.50(20)	....	17.50.	....
....	same, set of singles. .	....	....	....	....	....	16.75
4160-63	41¢ Vintage Mahogany Speedboats, self-adhesive, 4 attached .	4.50	6.50	17.50(20)	5.00	4.00	....
4164	41¢ Purple Heart, self-adhesive	3.50	5.00	17.50(20)	4.75	.95	.35
4165	41¢ Louis Comfort Tiffany, self-adhesive	3.50	....	....	....	.95	.35
4165a	same, bklt pane of 20	....	....	....	....	19.00	....

2008 COMMEMORATIVES AND REGULAR ISSUES

4166-75

4166-75	41¢ Flowers Strip of 10	....	....	....	....	10.00	....
....	same, plate strip of 11	....	....	....	....	14.50	....
4166	41¢ Iris S/A coil	$3.75	....	....	....	.95	.35
4167	41¢ Dahalia S/A coil .	$3.75	....	....	....	.95	.35
4168	41¢ Magnolia S/A coil	$3.75	....	....	....	.95	.35
4169	41¢ Red Gerbera Daisy, S/A coil.	$3.75	....	....	....	.95	.35
4170	41¢ Coneflower S/A coil	$3.75	....	....	....	.95	.35
4171	41¢ Tulip S/A coil. . . .	$3.75	....	....	....	.95	.35
4172	41¢ Water Lily S/A coil	$3.75	....	....	....	.95	.35
4173	41¢ Poppy S/A coil. . . .	$3.75	....	....	....	.95	.35
4174	41¢ Chrysanthemum, S/A coil.	$3.75	....	....	....	.95	.35
4175	41¢ Orange Gerbera Daisy, S/A coil	$3.75	....	....	....	.95	.35

4176	41¢ Chrysanthemum, booklet single	$3.75	....	....	....	.95	.35
4177	41¢ Orange Gerbera Daisy, booklet single	$3.75	....	....	....	.95	.35
4178	41¢ Iris, bklt single. . .	$3.75	....	....	....	.95	.35
4179	41¢ Dahalia, bklt single	$3.75	....	....	....	.95	.35
4180	41¢ Magnolia, bklt single	$3.75	....	....	....	.95	.35
4181	41¢ Red Gerbera Daisy, booklet single	$3.75	....	....	....	.95	.35
4182	41¢ Water Lily, bklt single	$3.75	....	....	....	.95	.35
4183	41¢ Poppy, bklt single	$3.75	....	....	....	.95	.35
4184	41¢ Coneflower, booklet single.	$3.75	....	....	....	.95	.35
4185	41¢ Tulip, bklt single. .	$3.75	....	....	....	.95	.35
4185a	41¢ Flowers dbl-sided, booklet pane	....	....	....	....	19.00	....

4186-91

4186	(41¢) Flag S/A coil, die cut 9.5, microprint, rt. side of flagpole . . .	3.75	....	....	....	.95	.35
....	same, plate strip of 5 .	....	....	....	....	7.00	....
4187	(41¢) Flag S/A coil, die cut 11, microprint, left side of flagpole. . .	3.75	....	....	....	.95	.35
....	same, plate strip of 5 .	....	....	....	....	7.00	....
4188	(41¢) Flag S/A coil, 8.5 perpendicular corners,	3.75	....	....	....	.95	.35
....	same, plate strip of 5 .	....	....	....	....	7.00	....
4189	(41¢) Flag S/A coil, die cut 11 w/round corners,	3.75	....	....	....	.95	.35
....	same, plate strip of 5 .	....	....	....	....	7.00	....
4190	(41¢) Flag bklt single, S/A die-cut 11.25x10.75, microprint rt. side of pole	3.75	....	....	....	.95	.35
4190a	same bklt pane of 10 .	....	....	....	....	9.50	....
4191	(41¢) Flag bklt single, S/A die-cut 11.25x10.75, microprint left side of pole	3.75	....	....	....	.95	.35
4191a	same bklt pane of 20 .	....	....	....	....	19.00	....

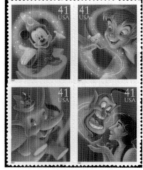

4192-95

4192-95	(41¢) Magic of Disney, 4 attached,.	4.25	4.75	17.50 (20)	4.75	4.00	....
4192	(41¢) Mickey Mouse .	3.75	....	....	....	.95	.40
4193	(41¢) Peter Pan & Tinkerbell	3.75	....	....	....	.95	.40
4194	(41¢) Dumbo & Timothy Mouse	3.75	....	....	....	.95	.40
4192	(41¢) Aladdin & Genie	3.75	....	....	....	.95	.40

4196

| 4196 | Celebrate . . . . | 3.75 | 4.50 | 17.50 (20) | 4.75 | .95 | .35 |

SCOTT NO.	DESCRIPTION	FIRST DAY COVERS SING	PL. BLK.	MINT SHEET	PLATE BLOCK	UNUSED F/NH	USED

4197

| 4197 | James Stewart...... | 3.75 | 4.50 | 17.50 (20) | 4.75 | .95 | .35 |

4198

ALPINE TUNDRA

4198a	Elk	4198f	Magdalena Alpine Butterfly
4198b	Golden Eagle	4198g	Big-White-Tailed Ptarmigan
4198c	Yellow-bellied marmot	4198h	Rocky Mountain Parnassian Butterfly
4198d	American Pike	4198i	Melissa Arctic Butterfly
4198e	Big Horn Sheep	4198j	Brown-Capped Rosy-Finch

| 4198 | 41¢ Alpine Tundra, sheet of 10 .... | .... | .... | 12.00 (10) | .... | 12.00 | .... |
| | set of singles .... | 20.00 | .... | .... | .... | .... | 5.75 |

4199

4200   **4201**

4199	41¢ Gerald R. Ford ..	3.75	4.50	17.50 (20)	4.75	.95	.35
4200	41¢ Jury Duty.......	3.75	4.50	17.50 (20)	4.75	.95	.35
4201	41¢ Mendez v. Westminster	3.75	4.50	17.50 (20)	4.75	.95	.35

4202

| 4202 | 41¢ EID .... | 3.75 | 4.50 | 17.50 (20) | 4.25 | .95 | .35 |

   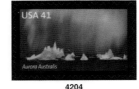

4203   **4204**

4203-04	41¢ Polar Lights	4.25	4.75	17.50 (20)	4.75	2.00	....
4203	41¢ Aurora Borealis...	3.75	....	....	....	.95	.35
4204	41¢ Aurora Australis ..	3.75	....	....	....	.95	.35

4205   **4206**

4205	41¢ Yoda	3.75	4.50	17.50 (20)	4.75	.95	.35
4206	41¢ Madonna of the Carnation, by Bernardino Luini ..	3.75	....	....	....	.95	.35
4206a	same, double-sided, booklet pane of 20 ...	....	....	....	....	17.50	....

4207, 4211, 4215   **4208, 4212, 4216**   **4209, 4213, 4217**   **4210, 4214, 4218**

4207-10	41¢ Christmas Knits, S/A, die-cut 10.75 ...	4.75	....	17.50 (20)	4.75	4.00	....
4207	41¢ Knit Reindeer, S/A, die-cut 10.75	3.75	....	....	....	.95	.35
4208	41¢ Knit Christmas Tree, S/A, die-cut 10.75	3.75	....	....	....	.95	.35
4209	41¢ Knit Snowman, S/A, die-cut 10.75	3.75	....	....	....	.95	.35
4210	41¢ Knit Bear, S/A, die-cut 10.75	3.75	....	....	....	.95	.35
4210b	41¢ Christmas Knits, booklet pane of 20 ...	....	....	....	....	17.50	....
4211-14	41¢ Christmas Knits, S/A, die-cut 11.25X11, block of 4 attached ..	4.75	....	....	....	4.00	....
4211	41¢ Knit Reindeer, S/A, die-cut 11.25x11 ..	3.75	....	....	....	.95	.35
4212	41¢ Knit Christmas Tree, S/A, die-cut 11.25x11 ..	3.75	....	....	....	.95	.35
4213	41¢ Knit Snowman, S/A, die-cut 11.25x11 ..	3.75	....	....	....	.95	.35
4214	41¢ Knit Bear, S/A, die-cut 11.25x11 .	3.75	....	....	....	.95	.35
4214b	booklet pane of 4, 4211-14	....	....	....	....	4.00	....
4214c	booklet pane of 6, 4213-14, 2 ea. 4211-12	....	....	....	....	5.25	....
4214d	booklet pane of 6, 4211-12, 2 ea. 4213-14	....	....	....	....	5.25	....
4215-18	41¢ Christmas Knits, S/A, die-cut 8.......	4.50	....	....	....	4.00	....
4215	41¢ Knit Reindeer, S/A, die-cut 8........	3.75	....	....	....	.95	.35
4216	41¢ Knit Christmas Tree, S/A, die-cut 8........	3.75	....	....	....	.95	.35
4217	41¢ Knit Snowman, S/A, die-cut 8........	3.75	....	....	....	.95	.35
4218	41¢ Knit Bear, S/A, die-cut 8	3.75	....	....	....	.95	.35
4218b	booklet pane of 18, 4 ea. of 4215, 4218, 5 ea. of 4216, 4217...	....	....	....	....	17.50	....

4219   **4220**

| 4219 | 41¢ Hanukkah S/A, die-cut 10.75x11 ..... | 3.75 | 4.50 | 17.50 (20) | 4.75 | .95 | .35 |
| 4220 | 41¢ Kwanza, S/A, die-cut, 11x10.75..... | 3.75 | 4.50 | 17.50 (20) | 4.75 | .95 | .35 |

SCOTT NO.	DESCRIPTION	FIRST DAY COVERS SING	FIRST DAY COVERS PL. BLK.	MINT SHEET	PLATE BLOCK	UNUSED F/NH	USED

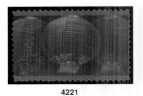

4222

4221

4223

4221	41¢ Year of the Rat, SA. .	3.75	....	12.00 (12)	....	.95	.35
4222	41¢ Charles W. Chestnutt	3.75	....	17.50 (20)	4.75	.95	.35
4223	41¢ Marjorie Kinnan Rawlings	3.75	4.50	17.50 (20)	4.75	.95	.35

4224-27

4224-27	41¢ American Scientists..	4.50	7.50	17.50 (20)	7.50	3.75	....
4224	41¢ Gerty Cori.	3.75	....	....	....	.95	.40
4225	41¢ Linus Pauling. . . .	3.75	....	....	....	.95	.40
4226	41¢ Edwin Hubble. . .	3.75	....	....	....	.95	.40
4227	41¢ John Bardeed. . .	3.75	....	....	....	.95	.40

4228-31, 4232-35, 4236-39, 4240-43, 4244-47

4228-31	42¢ Flag 24/7, W/A coil..	6.50	....	....	....	3.75	....
	same, plate # strip of 5	....	....	....	....	6.75	....
	same, plate # strip of 9	....	....	....	....	9.75	....
4228	42¢ Flag at Dusk, W/A coil..	3.50	....	....	....	.95	.45
4229	42¢ Flag at Night, W/A coil..	3.50	....	....	....	.95	.45
4230	42¢ Flag at Dawn, W/A coil..	3.50	....	....	....	.95	.45
4231	42¢ Flag at Midday, W/A coil..	3.50	....	....	....	.95	.45
4232-35	42¢ Flag 24/7, S/A coil 9.5 (AP).	6.50	....	....	....	3.75	.30
	same, plate # strip of 5	....	....	....	....	6.75	....
	same, plate # strip of 9	....	....	....	....	9.75	....
4232	42¢ Flag at Dusk, S/A coil 9.5 (AP). . . .	3.50	....	....	....	.95	.30
4233	42¢ Flag at Night, S/A coil 9.5 (AP). . . .	3.50	....	....	....	.95	.30
4234	42¢ Flag at Dawn, S/A coil 9.5 (AP) . . .	3.50	....	....	....	.95	.30
4235	42¢ Flag at Midday, S/A coil 9.5 (AP).	3.50	....	....	....	.95	.30
4236-39	42¢ Flag 24/7, S/A coil, 11 perpend. corners (SSP)	6.50	....	....	....	3.75	.30
	same, plate # strip of 5	....	....	....	....	6.75	....
	same, plate # strip of 9	....	....	....	....	9.75	....
4236	42¢ Flag at Dusk, S/A coil, 11 perpend. corners (SSP)	3.50	....	....	....	.95	.30
4237	42¢ Flag at Night, S/A coil, 11 perpend. corners (SSP)	3.50	....	....	....	.95	.30
4238	42¢ Flag at Dawn, S/A coil, 11 perpend. corners (SSP)	3.50	....	....	....	.95	.30
4239	42¢ Flag at Midday, S/A coil, 11 perpend. corners (SSP)	3.50	....	....	....	.95	.30
4240-43	42¢ Flag 24/7, S/A coil, 8.5 perpend. corners (AV)	6.50	....	....	....	3.75	.30
	same, plate # strip of 5	....	....	....	....	6.75	....
	same, plate # strip of 9	....	....	....	....	9.75	....
4240	42¢ Flag at Dusk, S/A coil, 8.5 perpend. corners (AV)	3.50	....	....	....	.95	.30
4241	42¢ Flag at Night, S/A coil, 8.5 perpend. corners (AV)	3.50	....	....	....	.95	.30
4242	42¢ Flag at Dawn, S/A coil, 8.5 perpend. corners (AV)	3.50	....	....	....	.95	.30
4243	42¢ Flag at Midday, S/A coil, 8.5 perpend. corners (AV)	3.50	....	....	....	.95	.30
4244-47	42¢ Flag 24/7, S/A coil, 11 rounded corners (AV)	6.50	....	....	....	3.75	.30
	same, plate # strip of 5	....	....	....	....	6.75	....
	same, plate # strip of 9	....	....	....	....	9.75	....
4244	42¢ Flag at Dusk, S/A coil, 11 rounded corners (AV)	3.50	....	....	....	.95	.35
4245	42¢ Flag at Night, S/A coil, 11 rounded corners (AV)	3.50	....	....	....	.95	.35
4246	42¢ Flag at Dawn, S/A coil, 11 rounded corners (AV)	3.50	....	....	....	.95	.35
4247	42¢ Flag at Midday, S/A coil, 11 rounded corners (AV)	3.50	....	....	....	.95	.35

4248

4249

4250

4251

4252

4248-52	42¢ American Journalists	4.50	5.25	17.50(20)	9.50(10)	5.25	....
	same	....	....	....	8.00(8)	....	....
4248	42¢ Martha Gellhorn..	3.75	....	....	....	.95	.35
4249	42¢ John Hersey.. . . .	3.75	....	....	....	.95	.35
4250	42¢ George Polk.. . . .	3.75	....	....	....	.95	.35
4251	42¢ Ruben Salazar.. . .	3.75	....	....	....	.95	.35
4252	42¢ Eric Sevareid. . . .	3.75	....	....	....	.95	.35

4253-57, 4258-62

4253-57	27¢ Tropical Fruit. . . .	4.75	....	12.00(20)	6.50(10)	3.25	....
4253	27¢ Pomegranate. . . .	2.50	....	....	....	.65	.30
4254	27¢ Star Fruit.	2.50	....	....	....	.65	.30
4255	27¢ Kiwi.	2.50	....	....	....	.65	.30
4256	27¢ Papaya	2.50	....	....	....	.65	.30
4257	27¢ Guava.	2.50	....	....	....	.65	.30
4258-62	27¢ Tropical Fruit. . . .	4.75	....	....	....	3.25	....
	same, plate strip of 5 .	....	....	....	....	5.25	....
	same, plate strip of 11	....	....	....	....	8.25	....
4258	27¢ Pomegranate Coil. .	2.50	....	....	....	.65	.30
4259	27¢ Star Fruit Coil. . .	2.50	....	....	....	.65	.30
4260	27¢ Kiwi Coil.	2.50	....	....	....	.65	.30
4261	27¢ Papaya Coil	2.50	....	....	....	.65	.30
4262	27¢ Guava Coil..	2.50	....	....	....	.65	.30

4263, 4264

| 4263 | 42¢ Purple Heart . . . . | 3.50 | 4.75 | 85.00 (100) | 4.50 | .95 | .35 |
| 4264 | 42¢ Purple Heart, S/A | 3.50 | 4.75 | 17.50 (20) | 4.50 | .95 | .35 |

4265

4266

| 4265 | 42¢ Frank Sinatra . . . | 3.75 | 4.75 | 17.50 (20) | 4.50 | .95 | .35 |
| 4266 | 42¢ Minnesota Statehood | 3.75 | 4.75 | 17.50 (20) | 4.50 | .95 | .35 |

SCOTT NO.	DESCRIPTION	FIRST DAY COVERS SING	PL. BLK.	MINT SHEET	PLATE BLOCK	UNUSED F/NH	USED

4267

4268

4267	69¢ Dragonfly	3.75	5.00	27.00 (20)	5.50	1.40	.35
4268	$4.50 Mount Rushmore	12.00	....	240.00 (20)	62.50	14.00	12.00
4269	$16.50 Hoover Dam	35.00	....	800.00 (20)	150.00	38.00	35.00

4270

4271

4272

4270	42¢ All Heart	3.75	....	....	....	.95	.30
4270a	42¢ All Heart, pane of 20	....	....	....	....	17.50	....
4271	42¢ Weddings	3.75	....	....	....	.95	.35
4271a	42¢ Weddings, pane of 20	12.00	....	....	....	17.50	....
4272	59¢ Silver Heart	3.75	....	34.00(20)	9.50	1.60	.50

4273

4274

4275

4276

4277

4278

4279

4280

4281

4282

4273-82	42¢ Flags of Our Nation, coil strip of 10	....	....	....	....	9.75	....
	same, plate # strip of 10	....	....	....	....	12.75	....
4273	42¢ American Flag	3.75	....	....	....	.95	.40
4274	42¢ Alabama Flag	3.75	....	....	....	.95	.40
4275	42¢ Alaska Flag	3.75	....	....	....	.95	.40
4276	42¢ American Samoa Flag	3.75	....	....	....	.95	.40

SCOTT NO.	DESCRIPTION	FIRST DAY COVERS SING	PL. BLK.	MINT SHEET	PLATE BLOCK	UNUSED F/NH	USED
4277	42¢ Arizona Flag	3.75	....	....	....	.95	.40
4278	42¢ Arkansas Flag	3.75	....	....	....	.95	.40
4279	42¢ California Flag	3.75	....	....	....	.95	.40
4280	42¢ ColoradoFlag	3.75	....	....	....	.95	.40
4281	42¢ Connecticut Flag	3.75	....	....	....	.95	.40
4282	42¢ Deleware Flag	3.75	....	....	....	.95	.40

4333

4333	42¢ Charles & Ray Eames	....	....	17.50 (16)	....	17.50	....
4333a	42¢ Charles & Ray Eames	3.75	....	....	....	.95	.35
4333b	42¢ Crosspatch Fabric Design	3.75	....	....	....	.95	.35
4333c	42¢ Stacking Chairs	3.75	....	....	....	.95	.35
4333d	42¢ Case Study House No.8	3.75	....	....	....	.95	.35
4333e	42¢ Wire Base Tables	3.75	....	....	....	.95	.35
4333f	42¢ Lounge Chair & Ottoman	3.75	....	....	....	.95	.35
4333g	42¢ Hang-It-All	3.75	....	....	....	.95	.35
4333h	42¢ La Chaise	3.75	....	....	....	.95	.35
4333i	42¢ "Tops"	3.75	....	....	....	.95	.35
4333j	42¢ Wire Mesh Chair	3.75	....	....	....	.95	.35
4333k	42¢ "Arts & Architecture" Cover	3.75	....	....	....	.95	.35
4333l	42¢ House of Cards	3.75	....	....	....	.95	.35
4333m	42¢ Molded Plastic Sculpture	3.75	....	....	....	.95	.35
4333n	42¢ Eames Storage Unit	3.75	....	....	....	.95	.35
4333o	42¢ Aluminum Group Chair	3.75	....	....	....	.95	.35
4333p	42¢ Lounge Chair Metal	3.75	....	....	....	.95	.35

CELEBRATE

BALLGAME

4334	Summer Olympics	3.75	4.50	17.50 (20)	4.75	.95	.30
....	42¢ Celebrate	3.75	4.50	17.50 (20)	4.75	.95	.30
....	42¢ Take Me Out To Ballgame	3.75	4.50	17.50 (20)	4.75	.95	.35

ART OF DISNEY: IMAGINATION

....	42¢ Art of Disney	4.25	4.75	17.50 (20)	4.75	4.50	....
....	42¢ Lucky & Pongo, from 101 Dalmations	3.75	....	....	....	.95	.40
....	42¢ Mickey Mouse	3.75	....	....	....	.95	.40
....	42¢ Sleeping Beauty	3.75	....	....	....	.95	.40
....	42¢ Mowgli & Baloo, from Jungle Book	3.75	....	....	....	.95	.40

SCOTT NO.	DESCRIPTION	FIRST DAY COVERS SING	PL. BLK.	MINT SHEET	PLATE BLOCK	UNUSED F/NH	USED

SEMI-POSTAL

B1   B2   B3

1998

| B1 | (32¢ + 8¢) Breast Cancer | 2.25 | 5.50 | 22.50(20) | 5.50 | 1.25 | .70 |

2002

| B2 | (34¢ + 11¢)Heroes of 2001 | 2.50 | 5.50 | 30.00(20) | 7.50 | 1.50 | .70 |

2003

| B3 | (37¢ + 8¢)Stop Family Violence | 2.50 | 5.50 | 22.50(20) | 5.50 | 1.25 | .50 |

PLATE NUMBER STRIPS OF 5

SCOTT NO.	UNUSED F/NH	SCOTT NO.	UNUSED F/NH
1891	7.50	2451	1.60
1895	6.00	2451b	1.60
1897	.95	2452	3.00
1897A	.85	2452a	3.00
1898	1.20	2452B	3.00
1898A	2.00	2452D	2.50
1899	1.60	2453	2.75
1900	15.00	2454	2.75
1901	19.00	2457	3.25
1902	13.25	2458	5.00
1903	20.00	2463	7.00
1904	50.00	2464	5.50
1905	5.50	2466	9.00
1906	4.00	2468	21.50
1907	5.25	2495Ab	20.00
1908	5.00	2518	5.50
1898Ab	10.00	2523	8.00
1900A	16.50	2523A	6.50
1901A	67.50	2525	8.00
1902A	7.00	2526	8.00
1903A	5.25	2529	5.00
1904A	42.00	2529a	5.00
1905A	5.25	2529c	11.50
1906A	7.00	2598b	10.00
2005	165.00	2599b	10.00
2112	10.00	2602	4.25
2115	5.50	2603	4.50
2115b	6.75	2604	4.50
2123	2.00	2605	5.25
2124	1.80	2606	6.25
2125	2.75	2607	7.50
2126	2.40	2608	8.00
2127	3.50	2609	6.75
2128	2.75	2802b	14.00
2129	5.00	2813b	12.00
2130	3.50	2886b	20.00
2131	3.00	2888	8.00
2132	4.50	2889	16.50
2133	4.75	2890	9.50
2134	3.50	2891	14.00
2135	6.00	2892	12.00
2136	6.50	2893	3.00
2123A	7.00	2902	2.00
2124A	2.50	2902B	2.75
2125A	3.50	2903	2.50
2126A	3.00	2904	2.95
2127A	4.50	2904A	2.75
2127Av	3.25	2904B	2.75
2128A	3.00	2905	3.50
2129A	4.50	2906	3.75
2130A	3.50	2907	6.00
2130Av	4.50	2908	4.00
2132A	4.50	2909	4.00
2132B	35.00	2910	4.00
2133A	4.50	2911	7.50
2149	5.50	2912	7.50
2149A	5.00	2912A	8.75
2150	5.50	2912B	8.75
2150A	5.25	2913	8.00
2225	1.20	2914	9.00
2225a	1.50	2915	20.00
2226	1.10	2915A	10.00
2226a	1.35	2915B	16.50
2228	2.00	2915C	23.00
2228a	16.00	2915D	23.00
2231	13.00	3017a	35.00
2252	1.40	3018	13.50
2252a	1.90	3044	1.00
2253	2.50	3045	1.25
2254	2.50	3053	8.50
2255	3.50	3054	10.00
2256	3.50	3055	8.00
2257	4.50	3132	15.00
2257a	18.00	3133	10.00
2258	7.50	3207	3.00
2259	5.00	3207A	2.50
2260	4.00	3208	6.00
2260a	6.25	3208A	5.75
2261	4.75	3228	4.50
2262	8.00	3229	4.50
2262a	8.00	3263	9.50
2263	5.00	3264	8.50
2263b	12.00	3265	11.00
2264	10.00	3266	10.00
2265	7.50	3270	4.50
2266	6.00	3271	4.50
2279	5.00	3280	9.00
2280	5.00	3281	12.00
2280a	6.00	3282	10.00
2281	6.00	3305A	11.00

SCOTT NO.	DESCRIPTION	UNUSED O.G. VF	F	AVG	USED VF	F	AVG

AIR POST

C1-C3	C4	C5	C6
Curtiss Jenny Biplane	Airplane Propeller	Badge of Air Service	Airplane

1918 (C1-6 NH + 75%)

SCOTT NO.	DESCRIPTION	VF	F	AVG	VF	F	AVG
C1-3	6¢-24¢, 3 varieties, complete.........	360.00	270.00	187.50	151.00	105.00	74.75
C1	6¢ orange	100.00	75.00	52.50	42.00	30.00	21.00
C2	16¢ green	140.00	105.00	72.50	52.00	38.50	25.75
C3	24¢ carmine rose & blue	140.00	105.00	72.50	65.00	42.00	32.00
C3a	same, center inverted	....	140000.00	....	....	....	....

SCOTT NO.	DESCRIPTION	CENTER LINE BLOCKS F/NH	F/OG	A/OG	ARROW BLOCKS F/NH	F/OG	A/OG
C1	6¢ orange	495.00	280.00	225.00	450.00	240.00	190.00
C2	16¢ green	795.00	400.00	325.00	695.00	360.00	285.00
C3	24¢ carmine rose & blue	795.00	400.00	325.00	650.00	350.00	275.00

1923

C4-6	8¢-24¢, 3 varieties, complete.........	320.00	237.00	160.00	98.50	69.50	47.50
C4	8¢ dark green	40.00	29.50	20.50	20.50	15.00	10.00
C5	16¢ dark blue......	142.00	105.00	71.50	42.00	28.00	19.50
C6	24¢ carmine.......	155.00	115.00	77.50	41.25	30.50	20.50

C7-C9
Map of U.S. and Airplanes

1926-30 (C7-12 NH + 50%)

C7-9	10¢-20¢, 3 varieties, complete.........	19.95	15.25	7.60	6.95	5.00	3.45
C7	10¢ dark blue......	4.00	3.05	2.20	.55	.40	.25
C8	15¢ olive brown....	4.75	3.60	2.75	3.50	2.50	1.75
C9	20¢ yellow green (1927)	14.00	9.75	6.50	3.25	2.25	1.65

C10
Lindbergh's Airplane "Spirit of St. Louis"

1927 LINDBERGH TRIBUTE ISSUE

C10	10¢ dark blue......	10.75	8.25	5.50	2.85	2.20	1.40
C10a	same, bklt pane of 3	125.00	95.00	67.50	....	....	....

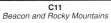

C11
Beacon and Rocky Mountains

C12, C16, C17, C19
Winged Globe

1928 BEACON

C11	5¢ carmine & blue ..	7.00	4.75	3.00	1.00	.65	.35

1930 Flat Plate Printing, Perf.11

C12	5¢ violet..........	15.00	12.00	8.50	.70	.55	.40

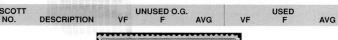

C13
Graf Zeppelin

C14	C15

1930 GRAF ZEPPELIN ISSUE (NH + 50%)

SCOTT NO.	DESCRIPTION	VF	F	AVG	VF	F	AVG
C13-15	65¢-$2.60, 3 varieties, complete.........	2350.00	1975.00	1480.00	1825.00	1450.00	1050.00
C13	65¢ green	400.00	300.00	260.00	325.00	240.00	175.00
C14	$1.30 brown......	850.00	725.00	500.00	650.00	500.00	340.00
C15	$2.60 blue	1300.00	1050.00	800.00	950.00	750.00	575.00

1931-32 Rotary Press Printing. Perf. 10½ x 11, Designs as #C12 (C16-C24 NH + 40%)

C16	5¢ violet..........	10.00	7.50	5.50	.80	.55	.35
C17	8¢ olive bistre	3.95	3.25	2.15	.55	.40	.30

C18
Graf Zeppelin

1933 CENTURY OF PROGRESS ISSUE

C18	50¢ green	125.00	100.00	75.00	100.00	80.00	60.00

1934 DESIGN OF 1930

C19	6¢ dull orange	4.50	3.25	2.00	.40	.30	.20

C20-22
China Clipper

1935 TRANS-PACIFIC ISSUE

C20	25¢ blue..........	1.80	1.40	1.05	1.40	1.00	.70

1937. Type of 1935 Issue, Date Omitted

C21	20¢ green	13.00	9.75	7.50	2.00	1.65	1.25
C22	50¢ carmine.......	12.00	10.25	7.75	5.40	4.50	3.50

C23
Eagle

1938

C23	6¢ dark blue & carmine	.65	.55	.45	.30	.25	.20

C24
Winged Globe

1939 TRANS-ATLANTIC ISSUE

C24	30¢ dull blue	14.00	12.00	10.50	1.70	1.40	1.10

AIR POST PLATE BLOCKS #C1-C24

SCOTT NO.		UNUSED NH			UNUSED O.G.		
		VF	F	AVG	VF	F	AVG
C1(6)	6¢ orange	1550.00	1150.00	925.00	1115.00	825.00	550.00
C2(6)	16¢ green	2665.00	1975.00	1575.00	2000.00	1485.00	1100.00
C3(12)	24¢ carmine rose & blue	3100.00	2300.00	1825.00	2450.00	1815.00	1250.00
C4(6)	8¢ dark green	610.00	450.00	360.00	445.00	330.00	260.00
C5(6)	16¢ dark blue	3845.00	2850.00	2250.00	2975.00	2200.00	1650.00
C6(6)	24¢ carmine	4790.00	3550.00	2825.00	3700.00	2750.00	2100.00
C7(6)	10¢ dark blue . . .	71.50	55.00	44.00	54.00	41.50	27.50
C8(6)	15¢ olive brown . . .	85.00	66.00	52.75	65.00	50.00	33.00
C9(6)	20¢ yellow green . .	200.00	155.00	125.00	145.00	110.00	85.00
C10(6)	10¢ dark blue	265.00	205.00	165.00	195.00	150.00	110.00
C11(6)	5¢ carmine & blue .	82.00	63.25	50.00	60.00	46.50	31.50
C12(6)	5¢ violet	285.00	220.00	175.00	215.00	165.00	120.00
C13(6)	65¢ green	4500.00	3500.00	2500.00	3100.00	2475.00	1950.00
C14(6)	$1.30 brown	12000.00	9500.00	5700.00	8000.00	6750.00	5000.00
C15(6)	$2.60 blue	18500.00	14000.00	11000.00	12000.00	10000.00	8000.00
C16(4)	5¢ violet	175.00	135.00	105.00	125.00	95.00	65.00
C17(4)	8¢ olive bistre . . .	58.50	45.00	36.00	40.00	30.00	24.00
C18(4)	50¢ green	1500.00	1150.00	800.00	1050.00	795.00	635.00
C19(4)	6¢ dull orange	39.50	33.00	26.00	30.00	25.00	20.00
C20(6)	25¢ blue	33.00	27.50	22.00	26.50	22.00	17.50
C21(6)	20¢ green	185.00	155.00	122.50	150.00	125.00	100.00
C22(6)	50¢ carmine	180.00	150.00	115.00	145.00	120.00	90.00
C23(4)	6¢ dark blue & carmine	14.00	10.50	8.00	9.50	8.00	6.00
C24(6)	30¢ dull blue	250.00	210.00	160.00	200.00	165.00	130.00

SCOTT NO.	DESCRIPTION	FIRST DAY COVERS		MINT SHEET	PLATE BLOCK	UNUSED F/NH	USED
		SING	PL. BLK.				

C25-C31

1941-44 TRANSPORT ISSUE

C25-31	6¢-50¢, 7 varieties, complete.	. . . .	. . . .	. . . .	127.50	23.95	5.60
C25	6¢ Transport Plane . . .	7.00	10.00	9.50(50)	1.05	.20	.20
C25a	same, bklt pane of 3 . .	30.00			4.25		
C26	8¢ Transport Plane . . .	6.00	11.25	11.50(50)	2.20	.25	.20
C27	10¢ Transport Plane . .	8.00	15.00	82.50(50)	10.50	1.65	.20
C28	15¢ Transport Plane . .	8.00	15.00	150.00(50)	13.95	3.50	.40
C29	20¢ Transport Plane . .	10.00	20.00	125.00(50)	12.65	2.60	.35
C30	30¢ Transport Plane . .	20.00	30.00	140.00(50)	14.00	3.00	.40
C31	50¢ Transport Plane . .	28.50	68.75	625.00(50)	80.00	14.00	4.25

C32

1946

C32	5¢ DC-4 Skymaster . . .	2.00	4.25	8.00(50)	.75	.20	.20

C33, C37, C39, C41

C34

C35

C36

SCOTT NO.	DESCRIPTION	FIRST DAY COVERS		MINT SHEET	PLATE BLOCK	UNUSED F/NH	USED
		SING	PL. BLK.				

1947

C33-36	5¢-25¢, 4 varieties, complete.	. . . .	. . . .		. . . .	2.10	.70
C33	5¢ DC-4 Skymaster . . .	2.00	4.25	17.00(100)	.75	.20	.20
C34	10¢ Pan American Bldg.	2.00	4.25	14.00(50)	1.50	.30	.20
C35	15¢ New York Skyline .	2.00	4.25	22.50(50)	1.85	.50	.20
C36	25¢ Plane over Bridge .	2.00	5.00	55.00(50)	6.00	1.25	.20

1948
Rotary Press Coil–Perf. 10 Horiz.

			LINE PR.		LINE PR.		
C37	5¢ DC-4 Skymaster . . .	2.00	4.25	. . . .	9.50	1.40	1.00

C38

C40

C38	5¢ New York Jubliee . .	2.00	4.25	20.00(100)	5.75	.25	.20

1949

C39	6¢ DC-4 Skymaster (as #C33).	2.00	4.25	20.00(100)	.75	.25	.20
C39a	same, bklt pane of 6 . .	10.00				11.50	
C40	6¢ Alexandria, Virginia.	2.00	4.25	11.00(50)	.95	.25	.20

Rotary Press Coil–Perf. 10 Horiz.

			LINE PR.		LINE PR.		
C41	6¢ DC-4 Skymaster (as#C37)	2.00	4.25	. . . .	15.00	3.50	.20

NOTE: Unused Air Mail coil pairs can be supplied at two times the single price.

C42

C43

C44

1949 U.P.U. ISSUES

C42-44	10¢-25¢, 3 varieties, complete.	. . . .	. . . .		. . . .	1.90	1.05
C42	10¢ Post Office	2.00	4.25	17.50(50)	1.70	.40	.30
C43	15¢ Globe & Doves . . .	3.00	5.00	25.00(50)	1.50	.60	.35
C44	25¢ Plane & Globe . . .	4.00	6.25	42.00(50)	7.25	1.00	.50

C45

C46

C47

1949-58

C45-51	7 varieties, complete .	. . . .	. . . .		. . . .	9.00	2.30
C45	6¢ Wright Brothers (1949)	2.00	4.25	25.00(50)	2.00	.50	.25
C46	80¢ Hawaii (1952)	15.00	35.00	350.00(50)	35.00	8.00	2.00
C47	6¢ Powered Flight (1953)	2.00	4.25	9.25(50)	.75	.25	.20

SCOTT NO.	DESCRIPTION	FIRST DAY COVERS SING	PL. BLK.	MINT SHEET	PLATE BLOCK	UNUSED F/NH	USED

C48, C50

1949-58 (continued)

| C48 | 4¢ Eagle (1954)..... | 2.00 | 4.25 | 16.50(100) | 1.95 | .25 | .20 |

C49

C51, C52, C60, C61

C49	6¢ Air Force (1957) ..	2.00	4.25	10.00(50)	.75	.25	.20
C50	5¢ Eagle (1958).....	2.00	4.25	19.50(100)	1.85	.25	.20
C51	7¢ Silhouette of Jet, blue (1958)	2.00	4.25	19.50(100)	1.00	.25	.20
C51a	same, bklt pane of 6 .	8.00	....	....	....	12.00	....

Rotary Press Coil–Perf. 10 Horiz.

			LINE PR.		LINE PR.		
C52	7¢ Silhouette of Jet, blue	2.00	3.25	....	20.00	2.50	.20

C53

C54

1959

C53-56	4 varieties, complete .	....	....	....	....	1.50	.85
C53	7¢ Alaska Statehood ..	2.00	4.25	14.00(50)	1.25	.30	.20
C54	7¢ Balloon Jupiter	2.00	4.25	20.00(50)	1.60	.45	.20

C55

C56

| C55 | 7¢ Hawaii Statehood . | 2.00 | 4.25 | 14.00(50) | 1.25 | .30 | .20 |
| C56 | 10¢ Pan-Am Games . | 2.00 | 4.25 | 25.00(50) | 2.75 | .55 | .30 |

C57

C58, C63

C59

C62

1959-66 REGULAR ISSUES

| C57/63 | (C57-60, C62-63) 6 varieties........ | .... | .... | .... | .... | 3.90 | 1.90 |

1959-66

C57	10¢ Liberty Bell (1960)	2.00	4.25	85.00(50)	8.00	1.75	1.00
C58	15¢ Statue of Liberty ..	2.00	4.25	22.50(50)	1.95	.45	.25
C59	25¢ Abraham Lincoln (1960)	2.00	4.25	40.00(50)	4.00	.90	.20

1960. Design of 1958

| C60 | 7¢ Jet Plane, carmine . | 2.00 | 4.25 | 22.50(100) | 1.25 | .30 | .20 |
| C60a | same, bklt pane of 6 .. | 9.00 | .... | .... | .... | 15.00 | .... |

Rotary Press Coil–Perf. 10 Horiz.

			LINE PR.		LINE PR.		
C61	7¢ Jet Plane, carmine	2.00	3.25	....	45.00	5.00	.35

1961-67

| C62 | 13¢ Liberty Bell ...... | 2.00 | 4.25 | 21.50(50) | 2.10 | .45 | .20 |
| C63 | 15¢ Statue re-drawn .. | 2.00 | 4.25 | 27.50(50) | 2.60 | .60 | .20 |

C64, C65

1962-64

| C64/69 | (C64, C66-69) 5 varieties | .... | .... | .... | .... | 2.00 | 1.25 |

1962

C64	8¢ Plane & Capitol....	2.00	4.25	23.00(100)	1.20	.25	.20
C64b	same, bklt pane of 5, Slogan I	1.95	....	....	....	6.25	....
C64b	bklt pane of 5, Slogan II, (1963)	....	....	....	....	75.00	....
C64b	bklt pane of 5, Slogan III (1964)	....	....	....	....	13.00	....
C64c	bklt pane of 5 tagged, Slogan III (1964)	....	....	....	....	1.85	....

SLOGAN I–Your Mailman Deserves Your Help...   **SLOGAN II**–Use Zone Numbers..

SLOGAN III–Always Use Zip Code....

Rotary Press Coil–Perf. 10 Horiz.

			LINE PR.		LINE PR.		
C65	8¢ Plane & Capitol....	2.00	3.25	....	5.75	.45	.20

C68

C66

C67

1963

C66	15¢ Montgomery Blair .	2.00	4.25	33.50(50)	4.00	.75	.60
C67	6¢ Bald Eagle	2.00	4.25	16.50(100)	2.25	.20	.20
C68	8¢ Amelia Earhart	2.00	4.25	18.50(50)	1.80	.40	.20

C69

1964

| C69 | 8¢ Dr. Robert H. Goddard | 2.00 | 5.00 | 23.75(50) | 2.25 | .50 | .20 |

SCOTT NO.	DESCRIPTION	FIRST DAY COVERS SING	FIRST DAY COVERS PL. BLK.	MINT SHEET	PLATE BLOCK	UNUSED F/NH	USED

C70, C71, C72, C73 (stamp images)

1967-69

| C70/76 | (C70-72, C74-76) 6 varieties........ | .... | .... | .... | .... | **2.95** | **1.00** |

1967-68

C70	8¢ Alaska Purchase...	2.00	4.25	16.50(50)	1.95	.35	.20
C71	20¢ "Columbia Jays" ..	2.00	4.25	48.00(50)	4.50	1.00	.20
C72	10¢ 50-Stars (1968)...	2.00	4.25	32.50(100)	1.75	.40	.20
C72b	same, bklt pane of 8 ..	3.00	....	....	....	2.50	....
C72c	same, bklt pane of 5, Slogan IV or V......	140.00	....	....	....	4.00	....

SLOGAN IV–Mail Early in the Day...   **SLOGAN V–Use Zip Code...**

1968 Rotary Press Coil–Perf. 10 Vert.

			LINE PR.		LINE PR.		
C73	10¢ 50-Star	2.00	3.25	....	2.25	.35	.20

C74, C75 (stamp images)

| C74 | 10¢ Air Mail Anniversary | 2.00 | 4.25 | 15.00(50) | 3.10 | .30 | .20 |
| C75 | 20¢ "USA" & Plane ... | 2.00 | 4.25 | 28.00(50) | 2.50 | .55 | .20 |

C76 (stamp image)

1969

| C76 | 10¢ Man on the Moon . | 6.00 | 14.50 | 15.00(32) | 2.25 | .50 | .20 |

C77, C78/C82, C79/C83 (stamp images)

1971-73

| C77-81 | 9¢-21¢, 5 varieties, complete.......... | .... | .... | .... | .... | **1.95** | **.80** |

C77	9¢ Delta Winged Plane	2.00	4.25	25.00(100)	1.30	.30	.25
C78	11¢ Silhouette of Plane	2.00	4.25	35.00(100)	1.60	.40	.20
C78b	same, precanceled ...	....	....	....	....	....	.50
C78a	11¢ bklt pane of 4	2.25	....	....	....	1.20	....
C79	13¢ Letter (1973).....	2.00	4.25	35.00(100)	1.60	.40	.20
C79b	same, precanceled ...	....	....	....	....	....	.90
C79a	13¢ bklt pane of 5	2.25	....	....	....	1.50	....

C80 (stamp image)

| C80 | 17¢ Liberty Head..... | 2.00 | 4.25 | 22.50(50) | 2.25 | .50 | .20 |
| C81 | 21¢ "USA" & Plane ... | 2.00 | 4.25 | 27.00(50) | 2.25 | .50 | .20 |

Rotary Press Coils–Perf. 10 Vert.

			LINE PR.		LINE PR.		
C82	11¢ Silhouette of Jet ..	2.00	3.25	....	.90	.30	.20
C83	13¢ Letter	2.00	3.25	....	1.15	.35	.20

C84, C85 (stamp images)

1972-76

| C84-90 | 11¢-31¢, 7 varieties, complete.......... | .... | .... | .... | .... | **4.40** | **1.50** |

1972

| C84 | 11¢ City of Refuge.... | 2.00 | 4.25 | 18.50(50) | 1.50 | .40 | .20 |
| C85 | 11¢ Olympics........ | 2.00 | 4.25 | 18.50(50) | 3.10(10) | .40 | .20 |

C86 (stamp image)

1973

| C86 | 11¢ Electronics ...... | 2.00 | 4.25 | 26.50(50) | 2.50 | .55 | .20 |

C87, C88 (stamp images)

1974

| C87 | 18¢ Statue of Liberty .. | 2.00 | 4.25 | 27.50(50) | 2.50 | .60 | .40 |
| C88 | 26¢ Mt. Rushmore..... | 2.00 | 4.25 | 55.00(50) | 5.00 | 1.25 | .20 |

C89, C90 (stamp images)

1976

| C89 | 25¢ Plane & Globes... | 2.00 | 4.25 | 35.0050) | 3.50 | .80 | .20 |
| C90 | 31¢ Plane, Flag & Globes | 2.00 | 4.25 | 45.00(50) | 4.25 | 1.00 | .20 |

ORDER BY MAIL, PHONE (800) 546-2995
OR FAX (256) 246-1116

SCOTT NO.	DESCRIPTION	FIRST DAY COVERS SING	FIRST DAY COVERS PL. BLK.	MINT SHEET	PLATE BLOCK	UNUSED F/NH	USED

C91

C92

1978-80

SCOTT NO.	DESCRIPTION	SING	PL. BLK.	MINT SHEET	PLATE BLOCK	UNUSED F/NH	USED
C91-100	21¢-40¢, 10 varieties, complete.........	....	....	....	....	11.50	4.85
C91-92	Wright Brothers, 2 varieties, attached ..	2.40	5.00	95.00(100)	5.00	2.10	1.75
C91	31¢ Wright Brothers & Plane	2.00	....	....	....	1.00	.50
C92	31¢ Wright Brothers & Shed	2.00	....	....	....	1.00	.50

C93

C94

1979

C93-94	Octave Chanute, 2 varieties, attached ..	2.40	5.00	95.00(100)	5.00	2.10	1.75
C93	21¢ Chanute & Plane .	2.00	....	....	....	1.00	.50
C94	21¢ Chanute & 2 Planes	2.00	....	....	....	1.00	.50

C95

C96

C95-96	Wiley Post, 2 varieties, attached ..	2.40	5.00	165.00(100)	13.50	3.50	2.75
C95	25¢ Post & Plane.....	2.00	....	....	....	1.80	1.00
C96	25¢ Plane & Post.....	2.00	....	....	....	1.80	1.00

C97

C97	31¢ High Jumper....	2.00	4.25	44.00(50)	12.00(12)	.95	.40

C98

C99

1980

C98	40¢ Philip Mazzei ...	2.00	4.25	65.00(50)	15.00(12)	1.40	.25
C98a	40¢ Philip Mazzei, perf. 10-1/2x11-1/4	2.00	4.25	....	....	8.50	2.00
C99	28¢ Blanche S. Scott.	2.00	4.25	42.50(50)	12.50(12)	.90	.25

C100

C100	35¢ Glenn Curtiss ...	2.00	4.25	45.00(50)	13.00(12)	1.10	.25

SCOTT NO.	DESCRIPTION	FIRST DAY COVERS SING	FIRST DAY COVERS PL. BLK.	MINT SHEET	PLATE BLOCK	UNUSED F/NH	USED

C101   C102

C103   C104

1983-85

C101-16	28¢-44¢, 16 varieties, complete..........	....	....	....	....	21.50	7.50

1983

C101-04	Summer Olympics, 4 varieties, attached ..	3.50	4.50	64.00(50)	6.50	5.75	4.00
C101	28¢ Women's Gymnastics	2.00	....	....	....	1.50	.50
C102	28¢ Hurdles.........	2.00	....	....	....	1.50	.50
C103	28¢ Women's Basketball	2.00	....	....	....	1.50	.50
C104	28¢ Soccer	2.00	....	....	....	1.50	.50

C105   C106

C107   C108

C105-08	Summer Olympics, 4 varieties, attached .	4.50	5.75	60.00(50)	6.75	6.00	4.00
C105	40¢ Shot Put.......	2.00	....	....	....	1.55	.50
C106	40¢ Men's Gymnastics	2.00	....	....	....	1.55	.50
C107	40¢ Women's Swimming	2.00	....	....	....	1.55	.50
C108	40¢ Weight Lifting ...	2.00	....	....	....	1.55	.50

C109   C110

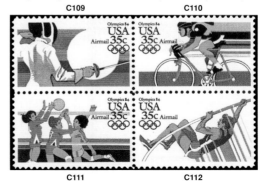

C111   C112

C109-12	Summer Olympics, 4 varieties, attached .	4.00	5.00	68.00(50)	9.50	6.00	4.00
C109	35¢ Fencing........	2.00	....	....	....	1.55	.60
C110	35¢ Cycling........	2.00	....	....	....	1.55	.60
C111	35¢ Volleyball	2.00	....	....	....	1.55	.60
C112	35¢ Pole Vault......	2.00	....	....	....	1.55	.60

SCOTT NO.	DESCRIPTION	FIRST DAY COVERS SING	FIRST DAY COVERS PL. BLK.	MINT SHEET	PLATE BLOCK	UNUSED F/NH	USED

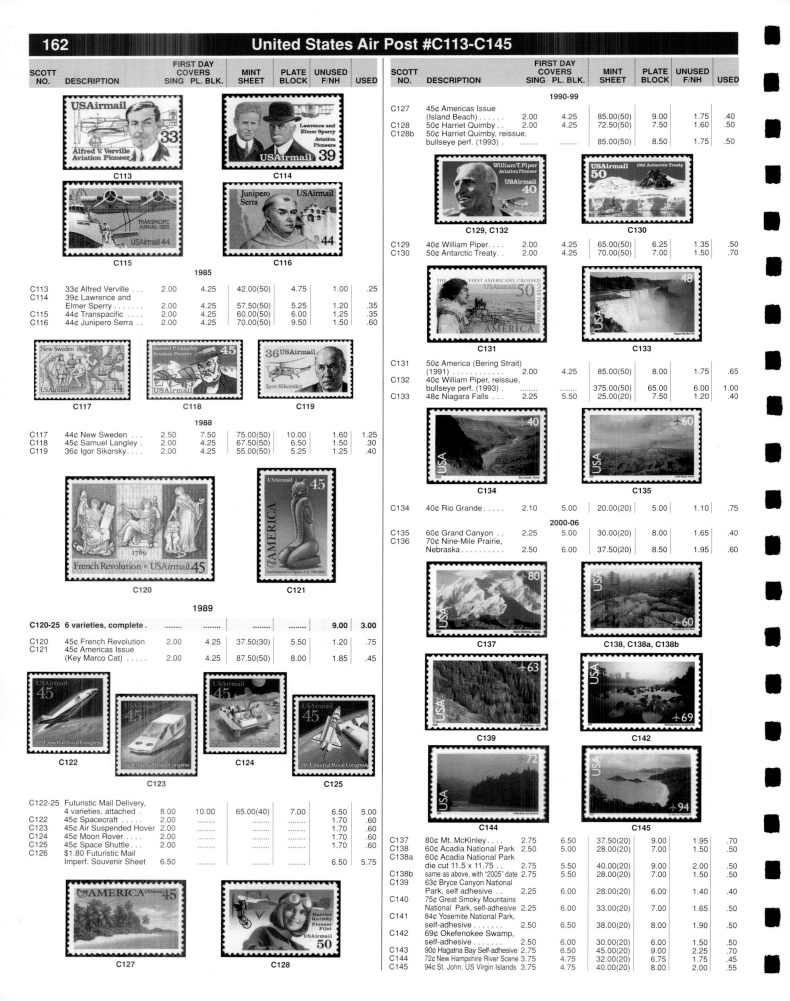

C113

C114

C115

C116

1985

C113	33¢ Alfred Verville . . .	2.00	4.25	42.00(50)	4.75	1.00	.25
C114	39¢ Lawrence and Elmer Sperry	2.00	4.25	57.50(50)	5.25	1.20	.35
C115	44¢ Transpacific	2.00	4.25	60.00(50)	6.00	1.25	.35
C116	44¢ Junipero Serra . .	2.00	4.25	70.00(50)	9.50	1.50	.60

C117

C118

C119

1988

C117	44¢ New Sweden . . .	2.50	7.50	75.00(50)	10.00	1.60	1.25
C118	45¢ Samuel Langley .	2.00	4.25	67.50(50)	6.50	1.50	.30
C119	36¢ Igor Sikorsky. . . .	2.00	4.25	55.00(50)	5.25	1.25	.40

C120

C121

1989

C120-25	**6 varieties, complete** .	....	....	....	....	**9.00**	**3.00**
C120	45¢ French Revolution	2.00	4.25	37.50(30)	5.50	1.20	.75
C121	45¢ Americas Issue (Key Marco Cat)	2.00	4.25	87.50(50)	8.00	1.85	.45

C122

C123

C124

C125

C122-25	Futuristic Mail Delivery, 4 varieties, attached .	8.00	10.00	65.00(40)	7.00	6.50	5.00
C122	45¢ Spacecraft	2.00	....			1.70	.60
C123	45¢ Air Suspended Hover	2.00	....			1.70	.60
C124	45¢ Moon Rover	2.00	....			1.70	.60
C125	45¢ Space Shuttle . . .	2.00	....			1.70	.60
C126	$1.80 Futuristic Mail Imperf. Souvenir Sheet	6.50	....			6.50	5.75

C127

C128

1990-99

C127	45¢ Americas Issue (Island Beach)	2.00	4.25	85.00(50)	9.00	1.75	.40
C128	50¢ Harriet Quimby . .	2.00	4.25	72.50(50)	7.50	1.60	.50
C128b	50¢ Harriet Quimby, reissue, bullseye perf. (1993) .	....	....	85.00(50)	8.50	1.75	.50

C129, C132

C130

| C129 | 40¢ William Piper. . . . | 2.00 | 4.25 | 65.00(50) | 6.25 | 1.35 | .50 |
| C130 | 50¢ Antarctic Treaty. . | 2.00 | 4.25 | 70.00(50) | 7.00 | 1.50 | .70 |

C131

C133

C131	50¢ America (Bering Strait) (1991)	2.00	4.25	85.00(50)	8.00	1.75	.65
C132	40¢ William Piper, reissue, bullseye perf. (1993) .	....	....	375.00(50)	65.00	6.00	1.00
C133	48¢ Niagara Falls . . .	2.25	5.50	25.00(20)	7.50	1.20	.40

C134

C135

| C134 | 40¢ Rio Grande . . . . . | 2.10 | 5.00 | 20.00(20) | 5.00 | 1.10 | .75 |

2000-06

| C135 | 60¢ Grand Canyon . . | 2.25 | 5.00 | 30.00(20) | 8.00 | 1.65 | .40 |
| C136 | 70¢ Nine-Mile Prairie, Nebraska. . . . . | 2.50 | 6.00 | 37.50(20) | 8.50 | 1.95 | .60 |

C137

C138, C138a, C138b

C139

C142

C144

C145

C137	80¢ Mt. McKinley. . . .	2.75	6.50	37.50(20)	9.00	1.95	.70
C138	60¢ Acadia National Park	2.50	5.00	28.00(20)	7.00	1.50	.50
C138a	60¢ Acadia National Park die cut 11.5 x 11.75 . .	2.75	5.50	40.00(20)	9.00	2.00	.50
C138b	same as above, with "2005" date	2.75	5.50	28.00(20)	7.00	1.50	.50
C139	63¢ Bryce Canyon National Park, self adhesive . .	2.25	6.00	28.00(20)	6.00	1.40	.40
C140	75¢ Great Smoky Mountains National Park, self-adhesive	2.25	6.00	33.00(20)	7.00	1.65	.50
C141	84¢ Yosemite National Park, self-adhesive	2.50	6.50	38.00(20)	8.00	1.90	.50
C142	69¢ Okefenokee Swamp, self-adhesive.	2.50	6.00	30.00(20)	6.00	1.50	.50
C143	90¢ Hagatna Bay Self-adhesive	2.75	6.50	45.00(20)	9.00	2.25	.70
C144	72¢ New Hampshire River Scene	3.75	4.75	32.00(20)	6.75	1.75	.45
C145	94¢ St. John, US Virgin Islands	3.75	4.75	40.00(20)	8.00	2.00	.55

AIR MAIL SPECIAL DELIVERY STAMPS

771, CE1, CE2

SCOTT NO.	DESCRIPTION	PLATE BLOCK F/NH	F	AVG	UNUSED F/NH	F	AVG	USED F	AVG
CE1	16¢ dark blue (1934)	30.00	18.00	14.50	.90	.70	.55	.70	.55
CE2	16¢ red & blue (1936)	8.00	6.00	4.50	.50	.40	.30	.25	.20
CE2	same, center line block	2.75	2.15	1.75	....	....	....		....
CE2	same, arrow block of 4	2.50	1.95	1.50	....	....	....		....

SPECIAL DELIVERY STAMPS

E1

E2, E3

E4, E5

(E1-E14 for VF Centering–Fine Price + 35%)

SCOTT NO.	DESCRIPTION	UNUSED NH F	AVG	UNUSED OG F	AVG	USED F	AVG

1885 Inscribed "Secures Immediate Delivery at Special Delivery Office" Perf. 12

| E1 | 10¢ blue . . . . | 1200.00 | 950.00 | 550.00 | 375.00 | 85.00 | 60.00 |

1888 Inscribed "Secures Immediate Delivery at any Post Office"

| E2 | 10¢ blue . . . . | 1300.00 | 1050.00 | 550.00 | 460.00 | 40.00 | 32.50 |

1893

| E3 | 10¢ orange . . . . | 675.00 | 525.00 | 300.00 | 225.00 | 45.00 | 38.00 |

1894 Same type as preceding issue, but with line under "Ten Cents" Unwatermarked

| E4 | 10¢ blue . . . . | 2300.00 | 1850.00 | 1700.00 | 1300.00 | 60.00 | 52.00 |

1895 Double Line Watermark

| E5 | 10¢ blue . . . . | 500.00 | 325.00 | 300.00 | 185.00 | 12.00 | 8.50 |

E6, E8-11

E7

1902

| E6 | 10¢ ultramarine . . . . | 550.00 | 425.00 | 350.00 | 225.00 | 12.00 | 8.00 |

1908

| E7 | 10¢ green . . . . | 170.00 | 120.00 | 80.00 | 55.00 | 50.00 | 38.00 |

1911 Single Line Watermark

| E8 | 10¢ ultramarine . . . . | 275.00 | 160.00 | 125.00 | 75.00 | 12.00 | 9.00 |

1914 Perf. 10

| E9 | 10¢ ultramarine . . . . | 500.00 | 300.00 | 200.00 | 130.00 | 14.00 | 11.00 |

1916 Unwatermarked Perf. 10

| E10 | 10¢ pale ultra . . . . . . | 775.00 | 500.00 | 350.00 | 220.00 | 50.00 | 35.00 |

1917 Perf. 11

| E11 | 10¢ ultramarine . . . . | 55.00 | 40.00 | 30.00 | 20.00 | .95 | .70 |
| E11 | same, plate block of 6 | 400.00 | 300.00 | 270.00 | 160.00 | .... | |

E12, E15

E14, E19

1922-25 Flat Plate Printing Perf. 11

SCOTT NO.	DESCRIPTION	PLATE BLOCK F/NH	F	AVG	UNUSED F/NH	F	AVG	USED F	AVG
E12	10¢ gray violet	(6) 700.00	500.00	400.00	75.00	50.00	30.00	1.50	1.35
E13	15¢ deep orange (1925)	(6) 550.00	420.00	300.00	60.00	40.00	35.00	2.00	1.25
E14	20¢ black (1925)	(6) 70.00	50.00	30.00	4.75	2.75	1.90	2.50	1.75

1927-51 Rotary Press Printing Perf. 11 x 10¹/²

SCOTT NO.	DESCRIPTION	FIRST DAY COVERS SING	PL. BLK.	MINT SHEET	PLATE BLOCK	UNUSED F/NH	USED
E15-19	10¢-20¢, 5 varieties .	....	....	....	50.00	9.00	3.25
E15	10¢ gray violet	....	....	45.00(50)	6.75	1.30	.30
E16	15¢ orange (1931) . . .	....	....	50.00(50)	6.50	1.30	.30
E17	13¢ blue (1944)	9.00	20.00	42.50(50)	5.00	1.20	.30
E18	17¢ orange yellow (1944)	12.00	28.00	175.00(50)	28.00	4.00	2.75
E19	20¢ black (1951)	5.00	12.50	97.50(50)	12.00	1.95	.20

E20

E22

1954-57

| E20 | 20¢ deep blue . . . . . . | 2.50 | 6.25 | 28.00(50) | 3.00 | .60 | .20 |
| E21 | 30¢ lake (1957) . . . . . | 2.50 | 6.25 | 37.50(50) | 4.00 | .80 | .20 |

1969-71

| E22 | 45¢ carmine & violet blue | 2.50 | 6.25 | 67.50(50) | 7.25 | 1.40 | .35 |
| E23 | 60¢ violet blue & carmine (1971) . . . . | 2.75 | 6.75 | 67.50(50) | 7.00 | 1.40 | .20 |

REGISTRATION STAMP

F1

1911 Registration

SCOTT NO.	DESCRIPTION	UNUSED NH F	AVG	UNUSED OG F	AVG	USED F	AVG
F1	10¢ ultramarine	175.00	125.00	75.00	55.00	12.00	8.00

U.S. CERTIFIED STAMP

FA1

1955 Certified Mail

SCOTT NO.	DESCRIPTION	FIRST DAY COVERS SING	PL. BLK.	MINT SHEET	PLATE BLOCK	UNUSED F/NH	USED
FA1	15¢ red	2.50	6.25	22.50(50)	5.00	.50	.40

SCOTT NO.	DESCRIPTION	UNUSED NH F	UNUSED NH AVG	UNUSED OG F	UNUSED OG AVG	USED F	USED AVG

J1-J28 / J29-J68

1879 Unwatermarked Perf. 12

J1	1¢ brown	275.00	165.00	95.00	70.00	17.00	11.00
J2	2¢ brown	1200.00	900.00	450.00	450.00	20.00	14.00
J3	3¢ brown	325.00	270.00	120.00	75.00	7.50	6.00
J4	5¢ brown	1900.00	1300.00	750.00	600.00	80.00	38.00
J5	10¢ brown	2700.00	1800.00	1100.00	800.00	80.00	60.00
J6	30¢ brown	1000.00	700.00	500.00	300.00	70.00	55.00
J7	50¢ brown	1900.00	1400.00	700.00	450.00	95.00	75.00

1884-89

J15	1¢ red brown	225.00	165.00	85.00	55.00	8.00	6.50
J16	2¢ red brown	275.00	200.00	100.00	70.00	7.00	5.00
J17	3¢ red brown	2900.00	2300.00	2000.00	875.00	350.00	275.00
J18	5¢ red brown	1600.00	1200.00	675.00	475.00	50.00	36.00
J19	10¢ red brown	1600.00	450.00	675.00	460.00	40.00	30.00
J20	30¢ red brown	325.00	400.00	275.00	185.00	70.00	60.00
J21	50¢ red brown	4400.00	3000.00	2000.00	1450.00	250.00	185.00

1891

J22	1¢ bright claret	100.00	75.00	40.00	28.00	2.25	1.25
J23	2¢ bright claret	110.00	85.00	45.00	30.00	2.25	1.25
J24	3¢ bright claret	225.00	150.00	85.00	65.00	18.00	12.00
J25	5¢ bright claret	350.00	200.00	125.00	80.00	18.00	12.00
J26	10¢ bright claret . . .	575.00	400.00	200.00	120.00	35.00	20.00
J27	30¢ bright claret . . .	2000.00	1550.00	700.00	525.00	350.00	175.00
J28	50¢ bright claret . . .	2100.00	1600.00	800.00	600.00	225.00	150.00

1894 Unwatermarked Perf. 12 (†)

J29	1¢ pale vermillion . . .	6500.00	4200.00	2850.00	2250.00	800.00	600.00
J30	2¢ dark vermillion . . .	2250.00	1375.00	900.00	700.00	400.00	255.00
J31	1¢ deep claret	325.00	260.00	90.00	70.00	14.00	12.00
J32	2¢ deep claret	300.00	250.00	75.00	50.00	12.00	9.00
J33	3¢ deep claret	625.00	400.00	225.00	175.00	55.00	40.00
J34	5¢ deep claret	1050.00	825.00	350.00	270.00	60.00	48.00
J35	10¢ deep claret	1200.00	900.00	450.00	300.00	45.00	35.00
J36	30¢ deep claret	1450.00	925.00	650.00	425.00	250.00	150.00
J36b	30¢ pale rose	1300.00	1000.00	600.00	400.00	225.00	125.00
J37	50¢ deep claret	5000.00	3800.00	2250.00	1750.00	850.00	600.00

1895 Double Line Watermark Perf. 12 (†)

J38	1¢ deep claret	48.00	40.00	18.00	13.50	1.50	1.00
J39	2¢ deep claret	48.00	40.00	18.00	13.50	1.50	1.00
J40	3¢ deep claret	300.00	250.00	120.00	90.00	4.50	3.00
J41	5¢ deep claret	325.00	275.00	130.00	100.00	4.50	3.00
J42	10¢ deep claret	325.00	275.00	130.00	100.00	7.00	5.50
J43	30¢ deep claret	1900.00	1300.00	800.00	650.00	75.00	60.00
J44	50¢ deep claret	1300.00	900.00	500.00	350.00	60.00	48.00

1910-12 Single Line Watermark Perf. 12

J45	1¢ deep claret	135.00	105.00	50.00	40.00	6.00	4.50
J46	2¢ deep claret	125.00	95.00	45.00	35.00	3.00	2.00
J47	3¢ deep claret	1800.00	1500.00	750.00	600.00	60.00	45.00
J48	5¢ deep claret	350.00	250.00	150.00	115.00	15.00	10.00
J49	10¢ deep claret	375.00	225.00	165.00	125.00	25.00	18.00
J50	50¢ deep claret (1912)	3200.00	2300.00	1200.00	900.00	185.00	150.00

1914 Single Line Watermark Perf. 10

J52	1¢ carmine lake	275.00	150.00	95.00	60.00	16.00	12.00
J53	2¢ carmine lake	225.00	130.00	75.00	50.00	1.25	.80
J54	3¢ carmine lake	3400.00	2500.00	1200.00	900.00	85.00	60.00
J55	5¢ carmine lake	175.00	135.00	60.00	45.00	7.00	5.00
J56	10¢ carmine lake	250.00	200.00	95.00	75.00	5.00	3.00
J57	30¢ carmine lake	650.00	400.00	300.00	185.00	60.00	40.00
J58	50¢ carmine lake . . .	....	....	18500.00	15500.00	1600.00	1300.00

1916 Unwatermarked Perf. 10

| J59 | 1¢ rose . . . . | 11000.00 | 7500.00 | 5000.00 | 3500.00 | 750.00 | 600.00 |
| J60 | 2¢ rose . . . . | 800.00 | 600.00 | 325.00 | 250.00 | 80.00 | 60.00 |

SCOTT NO.	DESCRIPTION	PLATE BLOCK (OG) F/NH	F	AVG	UNUSED (OG) F/NH	F	AVG	USED F	AVG

1917 Unwatermarked Perf. 11

J61	1¢ carmine rose . . (6)	85.00	53.00	35.00	11.00	5.00	3.00	.30	.20
J62	2¢ carmine rose . . (6)	85.00	53.00	35.00	11.00	5.00	3.00	.30	.20
J63	3¢ carmine rose . . (6)	160.00	95.00	70.00	45.00	17.00	10.00	.95	.45
J64	5¢ carmine . . . . . (6)	160.00	95.00	70.00	40.00	16.00	8.00	.95	.45
J65	10¢ carmine rose . (6)	225.00	140.00	125.00	75.00	30.00	18.00	1.25	.85
J66	30¢ carmine rose .	....	....	....	275.00	95.00	70.00	2.50	1.75
J67	50¢ carmine rose .	....	....	....	425.00	160.00	85.00	1.25	.85

1925

| J68 | 1/2¢ dull red . . . . (6) | 20.00 | 15.00 | 12.50 | 2.00 | 1.25 | 1.00 | .30 | .20 |

SCOTT NO.	DESCRIPTION	PLATE BLOCK (OG) F/NH	F	AVG	UNUSED (OG) F/NH	F	AVG	USED F	AVG

J69-J76, J79-J86 / J77, J78, J87 / J88-J104

1930 Perf. 11

J69	1/2¢ carmine . . . .(6)	70.00	50.00	40.00	11.00	6.00	5.00	2.00	1.50
J70	1¢ carmine . . . . . .(6)	40.00	32.00	27.00	7.50	3.50	2.50	.40	.30
J71	2¢ carmine . . . . . .(6)	55.00	42.00	35.00	10.00	4.50	3.00	.40	.25
J72	3¢ carmine . . . . . .(6)	300.00	240.00	190.00	55.00	28.00	20.00	3.00	2.50
J73	5¢ carmine . . . . . .(6)	300.00	200.00	145.00	50.00	22.00	17.00	6.00	4.00
J74	10¢ carmine . . . . .(6)	575.00	400.00	300.00	100.00	65.00	45.00	2.50	1.85
J75	30¢ carmine	....	....	....	350.00	160.00	125.00	4.50	3.75
J76	50¢ carmine	....	....	....	500.00	325.00	250.00	2.50	1.75
J77	$1 scarlet . . . . . .(6)	325.00	260.00	210.00	75.00	40.00	28.00	.40	.30
J78	$5 scarlet . . . . . .(6)	350.00	295.00	220.00	95.00	50.00	38.00	.40	.30

1931 Rotary Press Printing Perf. 11 x 10½

J79-86	1/2¢-50¢, 8 varieties, complete	....	....	....	30.00	24.00	15.00	1.90	1.50
J79	1/2¢ dull carmine .	28.00	20.00	14.00	1.75	1.00	.65	.25	.20
J80	1¢ dull carmine . . .	2.25	1.80	1.25	.30	.25	.20	.25	.20
J81	2¢ dull carmine . . .	2.25	1.80	1.25	.30	.25	.20	.25	.20
J82	3¢ dull carmine . . .	3.10	2.50	1.75	.30	.25	.20	.25	.20
J83	5¢ dull carmine . . .	4.75	3.75	3.00	.40	.35	.25	.25	.20
J84	10¢ dull carmine . .	9.75	7.50	5.50	1.90	1.25	.40	.25	.20
J85	30¢ dull carmine . .	60.00	45.00	33.00	12.00	8.00	5.25	.25	.20
J86	50¢ dull carmine . .	95.00	65.00	50.00	17.00	12.50	8.50	.25	.20

1956 Rotary Press Printing Perf. 10½ x 11

| J87 | $1 scarlet . . . . | 260.00 | 210.00 | .... | 50.00 | 40.00 | .... | .30 | |

SCOTT NO.	DESCRIPTION	MINT SHEET	PLATE BLOCK F/NH	F	UNUSED F/NH	F	USED F

1959

J88-101	1/2¢-$5, 14 varieties, complete	....	....	....	20.50	14.50	3.90
J88	1/2¢ carmine rose & black	400.00(100)	210.00	175.00	1.70	1.50	1.50
J89	1¢ carmine rose & black	9.50(100)	1.25	.75	.20	.15	.20
J90	2¢ carmine rose & black	1.25(100)	1.25	.75	.20	.15	.20
J91	3¢ carmine rose & black	14.00(100)	1.00	.70	.20	.15	.20
J92	4¢ carmine rose & black	20.00(100)	1.25	.85	.20	.15	.20
J93	5¢ carmine rose & black	20.00(100)	1.00	.70	.20	.15	.20
J94	6¢ carmine rose & black	20.00(100)	1.35	.90	.20	.15	.20
J95	7¢ carmine rose & black	32.00(100)	2.25	1.75	.20	.15	.20
J96	8¢ carmine rose & black	32.00(100)	2.25	1.75	.20	.15	.20
J97	10¢ carmine rose & black	26.00(100)	1.80	1.30	.30	.20	.20
J98	30¢ carmine rose & black	87.00(100)	5.25	4.25	1.00	.60	.20
J99	50¢ carmine rose & black	132.00(100)	7.00	5.75	1.25	1.00	.20
J100	$1 carmine rose & black	280.00(100)	12.50	9.00	2.75	1.95	.20
J101	$5 carmine rose & black	1500.00(100)	60.00	47.50	13.00	9.00	.40

1978-1985

J102	11¢ carmine rose & black	37.00(100)	4.00	....	.35	....	.50
J103	13¢ carmine rose & black	38.00(100)	2.95	....	.35	....	.50
J104	17¢ carmine rose & black	125.00(100)	40.00	....	.70	....	.55

OFFICES IN CHINA

SCOTT NO.	DESCRIPTION	UNUSED NH F	UNUSED NH AVG	UNUSED OG F	UNUSED OG AVG	USED F	USED AVG

SHANGHAI 2¢ CHINA

1919 K1-16: U.S. Postage 498-518 surcharged

SHANGHAI 2 Cts. CHINA

1922 K17-18: U.S. Postage 498-528B with local surcharge

1919

K1	2¢ on 1¢ green	75.00	45.00	35.00	25.00	50.00	40.00
K2	4¢ on 2¢ rose	75.00	50.00	35.00	25.00	50.00	40.00
K3	6¢ on 3¢ violet	160.00	125.00	70.00	40.00	115.00	85.00
K4	8¢ on 4¢ brown	160.00	135.00	70.00	40.00	115.00	85.00
K5	10¢ on 5¢ blue	180.00	145.00	70.00	40.00	115.00	85.00
K6	12¢ on 6¢ red orange	225.00	185.00	90.00	60.00	165.00	111.00
K7	14¢ on 7¢ black	230.00	190.00	90.00	60.00	180.00	120.00
K8	16¢ on 8¢ olive bister	185.00	130.00	75.00	50.00	125.00	90.00
K8a	16¢ on 8¢ olive green	165.00	125.00	75.00	50.00	110.00	95.00
K9	18¢ on 9¢ salmon red	175.00	135.00	70.00	50.00	150.00	100.00
K10	20¢ on 10¢ orange yellow	165.00	125.00	70.00	50.00	125.00	80.00
K11	24¢ on 12¢ brown carmine	225.00	175.00	70.00	50.00	130.00	70.00
K11a	24¢ on 12¢ claret brown	280.00	200.00	115.00	80.00	175.00	110.00
K12	30¢ on 15¢ gray	225.00	160.00	100.00	60.00	200.00	160.00
K13	40¢ on 20¢ deep ultra.	325.00	235.00	150.00	90.00	285.00	200.00
K14	60¢ on 30¢ orange red	300.00	200.00	150.00	90.00	240.00	180.00
K15	$1 on 50¢ light violet	1350.00	950.00	600.00	400.00	850.00	600.00
K16	$2 on $1 violet brown	1200.00	800.00	600.00	400.00	750.00	450.00

1922 LOCAL ISSUES

| K17 | 2¢ on 1¢ green . . . . . | 300.00 | 200.00 | 140.00 | 90.00 | 170.00 | 125.00 |
| K18 | 4¢ on 2¢ carmine . . . | 300.00 | 200.00 | 140.00 | 90.00 | 150.00 | 120.00 |

SCOTT NO.	DESCRIPTION	UNUSED F	UNUSED AVG	USED F	USED AVG

OFFICIAL STAMPS

O1-O9, O94, O95

O10-O14

O15-O24, O96-O103

O25-O34, O106, O107

Except for the Post Office Department, portraits for the various denominations are the same as on the regular issues of 1870-73

1873 Printed by the Continental Bank Note Co.
Thin hard paper
(OG + 40%)
(O1-O120 for VF Centering–Fine Price + 50%)

DEPARTMENT OF AGRICULTURE

O1	1¢ yellow	300.00	240.00	190.00	150.00
O2	2¢ yellow	250.00	200.00	90.00	70.00
O3	3¢ yellow	225.00	175.00	18.00	13.00
O4	6¢ yellow	270.00	225.00	65.00	50.00
O5	10¢ yellow	540.00	410.00	225.00	165.00
O6	12¢ yellow	475.00	325.00	270.00	225.00
O7	15¢ yellow	440.00	310.00	240.00	185.00
O8	24¢ yellow	440.00	310.00	240.00	185.00
O9	30¢ yellow	575.00	410.00	280.00	200.00

EXECUTIVE DEPARTMENT

O10	1¢ carmine	875.00	625.00	490.00	385.00
O11	2¢ carmine	565.00	410.00	250.00	195.00
O12	3¢ carmine	725.00	550.00	225.00	165.00
O13	6¢ carmine	925.00	750.00	560.00	400.00
O14	10¢ carmine	1150.00	990.00	650.00	530.00

DEPARTMENT OF THE INTERIOR

O15	1¢ vermillion	75.00	55.00	11.00	8.50
O16	2¢ vermillion	70.00	50.00	13.00	11.00
O17	3¢ vermillion	85.00	65.00	7.00	5.75
O18	6¢ vermillion	75.00	55.00	11.00	9.00
O19	10¢ vermillion	75.00	55.00	22.00	18.00
O20	12¢ vermillion	95.00	95.00	13.00	10.00
O21	15¢ vermillion	210.00	160.00	26.00	22.00
O22	24¢ vermillion	185.00	135.00	21.00	18.00
O23	30¢ vermillion	285.00	200.00	21.00	17.00
O24	90¢ vermillion	300.00	245.00	55.00	45.00

DEPARTMENT OF JUSTICE

O25	1¢ purple	250.00	210.00	110.00	85.00
O26	2¢ purple	310.00	240.00	115.00	95.00
O27	3¢ purple	325.00	220.00	38.00	24.00
O28	6¢ purple	310.00	240.00	50.00	36.00
O29	10¢ purple	315.00	240.00	110.00	70.00
O30	12¢ purple	265.00	195.00	80.00	65.00
O31	15¢ purple	450.00	350.00	210.00	160.00
O32	24¢ purple	1275.00	900.00	450.00	355.00
O33	30¢ purple	1275.00	900.00	360.00	240.00
O34	90¢ purple	1950.00	1400.00	950.00	750.00

O35-O45 O47-O56, O108 O57-O67 O68-O71

NAVY DEPARTMENT
(OG + 30%)

O35	1¢ ultramarine	150.00	120.00	55.00	46.00
O36	2¢ ultramarine	155.00	125.00	30.00	26.00
O37	3¢ ultramarine	160.00	130.00	30.00	26.00
O38	6¢ ultramarine	175.00	140.00	16.00	12.00
O39	7¢ ultramarine	650.00	500.00	240.00	185.00
O40	10¢ ultramarine	200.00	160.00	50.00	40.00
O41	12¢ ultramarine	215.00	170.00	50.00	40.00
O42	15¢ ultramarine	370.00	310.00	80.00	68.00
O43	24¢ ultramarine	400.00	350.00	90.00	75.00
O44	30¢ ultramarine	340.00	280.00	55.00	45.00
O45	90¢ ultramarine	1100.00	800.00	400.00	320.00

OFFICIAL STAMPS: From 1873 to 1879, Congress authorized the use of Official Stamps to prepay postage on government mail. Separate issues were produced for each department so that mailing costs could be assigned to that department's budget. Penalty envelopes replaced Official Stamps on May 1, 1879.

O72-O82, O109-O113

O83-O93, O1140-O120

POST OFFICE DEPARTMENT

O47	1¢ black	25.00	22.00	13.00	10.00
O48	2¢ black	30.00	24.00	11.00	9.00
O49	3¢ black	11.00	8.00	2.50	1.50
O50	6¢ black	31.00	25.00	9.00	7.00
O51	10¢ black	135.00	115.00	58.00	49.00
O52	12¢ black	125.00	105.00	13.00	11.00
O53	15¢ black	140.00	120.00	22.00	16.00
O54	24¢ black	200.00	175.00	27.00	23.00
O55	30¢ black	225.00	185.00	28.00	24.00
O56	90¢ black	230.00	190.00	28.00	24.00

DEPARTMENT OF STATE

O57	1¢ dark green	260.00	150.00	80.00	65.00
O58	2¢ dark green	310.00	250.00	110.00	93.00
O59	3¢ bright green	225.00	185.00	26.00	22.00
O60	6¢ bright green	225.00	185.00	32.00	25.00
O61	7¢ dark green	390.00	230.00	70.00	55.00
O62	10¢ dark green	230.00	135.00	60.00	50.00
O63	12¢ dark green	320.00	250.00	130.00	95.00
O64	15¢ dark green	325.00	250.00	95.00	78.00
O65	24¢ dark green	525.00	450.00	240.00	185.00
O66	30¢ dark green	525.00	400.00	190.00	145.00
O67	90¢ dark green	1000.00	700.00	350.00	265.00
O68	$2 green & black	1500.00	1200.00	1500.00	1200.00
O69	$5 green & black	6500.00	5000.00	12500.00	9000.00
O70	$10 green & black	4750.00	3800.00	7000.00	5500.00
O71	$20 green & black	5200.00	4500.00	4200.00	2900.00

TREASURY DEPARTMENT
(OG + 30%)

O72	1¢ brown	120.00	100.00	11.00	9.00
O73	2¢ brown	125.00	105.00	9.00	7.50
O74	3¢ brown	110.00	95.00	2.50	1.25
O75	6¢ brown	120.00	100.00	4.50	3.50
O76	7¢ brown	240.00	190.00	40.00	33.00
O77	10¢ brown	240.00	190.00	13.00	10.00
O78	12¢ brown	285.00	240.00	11.00	8.00
O79	15¢ brown	290.00	250.00	13.00	10.00
O80	24¢ brown	650.00	500.00	95.00	75.00
O81	30¢ brown	400.00	325.00	13.00	10.00
O82	90¢ brown	425.00	330.00	16.00	12.00

WAR DEPARTMENT

O83	1¢ rose	230.00	180.00	16.00	13.00
O84	2¢ rose	230.00	180.00	16.00	13.00
O85	3¢ rose	230.00	180.00	7.00	4.75
O86	6¢ rose	600.00	475.00	11.00	9.00
O87	7¢ rose	160.00	135.00	95.00	75.00
O88	10¢ rose	135.00	125.75	28.00	21.00
O89	12¢ rose	250.00	220.00	13.00	10.00
O90	15¢ rose	85.00	70.00	16.00	13.00
O91	24¢ rose	85.00	70.00	13.00	11.00
O92	30¢ rose	125.00	110.00	13.00	11.00
O93	90¢ rose	210.00	185.00	55.00	45.00

1879 Printed by American Bank Note Co.
Soft Porous Paper
DEPARTMENT OF AGRICULTURE

O94	1¢ yellow	6000.00	4900.00	....	....
O95	3¢ yellow	525.00	450.00	105.00	90.00

DEPARTMENT OF INTERIOR

O96	1¢ vermillion	300.00	230.00	285.00	225.00
O97	2¢ vermillion	10.00	8.00	3.50	2.50
O98	3¢ vermillion	9.00	7.00	3.25	2.25
O99	6¢ vermillion	11.00	8.00	13.00	10.00
O100	10¢ vermillion	110.00	85.00	80.00	70.00
O101	12¢ vermillion	225.00	185.00	120.00	100.00
O102	15¢ vermillion	400.00	210.00	270.00	215.00
O103	24¢ vermillion	4200.00	3500.00	....	....

DEPARTMENT OF JUSTICE

O106	3¢ bluish purple	175.00	140.00	110.00	85.00
O107	6¢ bluish purple	450.00	385.00	260.00	195.00

POST OFFICE DEPARTMENT

O108	3¢ black	32.00	27.00	9.00	6.00

TREASURY DEPARTMENT

O109	3¢ brown	80.00	60.00	11.00	8.75
O110	6¢ brown	200.00	130.00	55.00	48.00
O111	10¢ brown	275.00	215.00	45.00	28.00
O112	30¢ brown	2400.00	2000.00	440.00	350.00
O113	90¢ brown	4500.00	3400.00	550.00	450.00

SCOTT NO.	DESCRIPTION	UNUSED F	UNUSED AVG	USED F	USED AVG
	WAR DEPARTMENT				
O114	1¢ rose red	7.00	5.00	4.50	3.75
O115	2¢ rose red	13.00	10.00	4.50	3.75
O116	3¢ rose red	13.00	10.00	2.25	1.50
O117	6¢ rose red	12.00	9.00	3.25	2.50
O118	10¢ rose red	68.00	57.00	55.00	44.00
O119	12¢ rose red	65.00	55.00	15.00	8.00
O120	30¢ rose red	225.00	180.00	110.00	85.00

SCOTT NO.	DESCRIPTION	UNUSED NH F	UNUSED NH AVG	UNUSED OG F	UNUSED OG AVG	USED F	USED AVG

1910-11
Double Line Watermark

O121	2¢ black	40.00	25.00	20.00	11.00	2.50	1.75
O122	50¢ dark green	380.00	250.00	175.00	135.00	65.00	45.00
O123	$1 ultramarine	460.00	350.00	225.00	175.00	17.00	12.00

Single Line Watermark

O124	1¢ dark violet	25.00	15.00	10.00	7.00	2.25	1.75
O125	2¢ black	130.00	75.00	60.00	35.00	7.50	5.00
O126	10¢ carmine	50.00	30.00	20.00	15.00	2.25	1.75

SCOTT NO.	DESCRIPTION	FIRST DAY COVERS SING	FIRST DAY COVERS PL. BLK.	MINT SHEET	PLATE BLOCK	UNUSED	USED

O127-O136   O138-O143

1983-89

O127	1¢ Great Seal	2.00	4.25	11.00(100)	.85	.20	.20
O128	4¢ Great Seal	2.00	4.25	14.00(100)	1.00	.20	.25
O129	13¢ Great Seal	2.00	4.25	40.00(100)	2.50	.50	1.00
O129A	14¢ Great Seal (1985)	2.00	. . . .	40.00(100)	. . . .	.50	.55
O130	17¢ Great Seal	2.00	4.25	60.00(100)	3.50	.60	.50
O132	$1 Great Seal	5.75	14.25	260.00(100)	14.00	2.50	1.25
O133	$5 Great Seal	16.50	41.25	1100.00(100)	55.00	12.50	10.00

		PLATE# STRIP 3		PLATE# STRIP 3			
O135	20¢ Great Seal, coil . .	2.00	30.00		19.50	2.00	2.25
O136	22¢ Seal, coil (1985)	2.00	. . . .		. . . .	1.60	2.50

1985 Non-Denominated Issues

O138	(14¢) Great Seal, postcard D	2.00	30.00	525.00(100)	45.00	5.50	11.00
O138A	15¢ Great Seal, coil (1988)	2.00	. . . .	. . . .	. . . .	.65	.60
O138B	20¢ Great Seal, coil (1988)	2.00	. . . .	. . . .	. . . .	.80	.75

		PLATE# STRIP 3		PLATE# STRIP 3			
O139	(22¢) Great Seal "D" coil (1985)	2.00	80.00		60.00	5.50	11.00
O140	(25¢) Great Seal "E" coil (1988)	2.00	. . . .		. . . .	1.30	2.25
O141	25¢ Great Seal, coil (1988)	2.00	. . . .		. . . .	.95	.60
O143	1¢ Great Seal (1989) .	2.00	. . . .	10.00(100)	. . . .	.25	.25

O144   O145   O146

O146A   O147   O148

1991-94

O144	(29¢) Great Seal "F" coil	2.00	. . . .	. . . .	. . . .	1.75	.60
O145	29¢ Great Seal, coil . .	2.00	. . . .	. . . .	. . . .	1.10	.50
O146	4¢ Great Seal	2.00	. . . .	20.00(100)	. . . .	.25	.35
O146A	10¢ Great Seal	2.00	. . . .	35.00(100)	. . . .	.40	.50
O147	19¢ Great Seal	2.00	. . . .	65.00(100)	. . . .	.70	.95
O148	23¢ Great Seal	2.00	. . . .	80.00(100)	. . . .	1.10	1.10

SCOTT NO.	DESCRIPTION	FIRST DAY COVERS SING PL. BLK.	MINT SHEET	PLATE BLOCK	UNUSED	USED

O151   O152   O153   O154

O155   O156   O157, O158, O159, O160, O162   O161

1993-95

O151	$1 Great Seal	6.00	. . . .	600.00(100)	. . . .	6.00	4.00
O152	(32¢) Great Seal "G" coil	2.75	. . . .		. . . .	1.00	1.25
O153	32¢ Official Mail	1.95	. . . .		. . . .	2.00	1.00
O154	1¢ Official Mail	1.95	. . . .	10.00(100)	. . . .	.25	.25
O155	20¢ Official Mail	1.95	. . . .	70.00(100)	. . . .	.80	1.00
O156	23¢ Official Mail	1.95	. . . .	90.00(100)	. . . .	1.00	.85

1999-2007

O157	33¢ Great Seal, coil . .	1.95	. . . .		. . . .	1.50	1.35
O158	34¢ Great Seal, coil . .	1.95	. . . .		. . . .	1.35	1.00
O159	37¢ Great Seal, coil . .	1.95	. . . .		. . . .	1.40	1.10
. . . .	same, pl# strip of 5 . .					8.00	. . . .
O160	39¢ Great Seal, coil . .	1.95	. . . .		. . . .	.90	.50
. . . .	same, pl# strip of 5 . .					6.75	. . . .
O161	$1 Great Seal	2.75	. . . .	45.00(20)	9.00	2.25	1.25
O162	41¢ Great Seal, water-activated, coil	2.25	. . . .		. . . .	1.25	.50
. . . .	same, pl# strip of 5 . .					7.50	. . . .

PARCEL POST STAMPS

Q1-Q12 Various Designs

SPECIAL HANDLING STAMPS

QE1-QE4

PARCEL POST DUE STAMPS

JQ1-JQ5

SCOTT NO.	DESCRIPTION	UNUSED NH F	UNUSED NH AVG	UNUSED OG F	UNUSED OG AVG	USED F	USED AVG
	(Q1-QE4a for VF Centering–Fine Price + 50%)						
	1912-13 Parcel Post–All Printed in Carmine Rose						
Q1	1¢ Post Office Clerk .	15.00	10.00	7.00	5.00	2.00	1.50
Q2	2¢ City Carrier	20.00	12.00	10.00	7.00	1.50	1.20
Q3	3¢ Railway Clerk . . .	45.00	30.00	20.00	15.00	7.00	5.50
Q4	4¢ Rural Carrier	115.00	85.00	50.00	30.00	4.00	2.85
Q5	5¢ Mail Train	100.00	70.00	50.00	50.00	3.00	2.50
Q6	10¢ Steamship	170.00	120.00	80.00	50.00	4.00	3.00
Q7	15¢ Auto Service . . .	185.00	135.00	80.00	45.00	16.00	13.00
Q8	20¢ Airplane	400.00	200.00	200.00	120.00	32.00	28.00
Q9	25¢ Manufacturing . .	200.00	120.00	75.00	50.00	9.00	7.00
Q10	50¢ Dairying	800.00	500.00	350.00	220.00	52.00	39.00
Q11	75¢ Harvesting	270.00	160.00	120.00	70.00	42.00	36.00
Q12	$1 Fruit Growing . . .	1000.00	650.00	420.00	250.00	48.00	38.00
	1912 Parcel Post Due						
JQ1	1¢ dark green	30.00	20.00	12.00	8.00	5.00	3.50
JQ2	2¢ dark green	250.00	150.00	100.00	65.00	18.00	14.00
JQ3	5¢ dark green	45.00	30.00	20.00	12.00	6.00	4.50
JQ4	10¢ dark green	450.00	300.00	200.00	130.00	50.00	39.00
JQ5	25¢ dark green	300.00	200.00	120.00	80.00	6.00	4.75
	1925-29 Special Handling						
QE1	10¢ yellow green . . .	4.50	3.00	2.75	1.50	1.50	1.20
QE2	15¢ yellow green . . .	4.75	3.25	3.00	1.65	2.00	1.20
QE3	20¢ yellow green . . .	8.00	5.00	4.00	3.00	1.95	1.35
QE4	25¢ yellow green . . .	38.00	22.00	21.00	16.00	8.00	5.00
QE4a	25¢ deep green	50.00	40.00	30.00	19.00	13.00	8.50

POSTAL NOTE STAMPS
PN1-P18
All values printed in black

SCOTT NO.	DESCRIPTION	UNUSED F/NH	UNUSED F/OG	USED F
PN1-18	1¢-90¢, 18 varieties, complete	38.00	28.00	5.00

SCOTT NO.	DESCRIPTION	UNUSED ENTIRE	UNUSED CUT SQ.	USED CUT SQ.

ENVELOPES

U1-U10
Washington

U19-U24
Franklin

U26, U27
Washington

1853-55

SCOTT NO.	DESCRIPTION	UNUSED ENTIRE	UNUSED CUT SQ.	USED CUT SQ.
U1	3¢ red on white, die 1	2300.00	425.00	38.00
U2	3¢ red on buff, die 1	1050.00	110.00	27.00
U3	3¢ red on white, die 2	6100.00	1350.00	50.00
U4	3¢ red on buff, die 2	2600.00	375.00	45.00
U5	3¢ red on white, die 3	......	......	600.00
U6	3¢ red on buff, die 3	......	5000.00	85.00
U7	3¢ red on white, die 4	......	6000.00	160.00
U8	3¢ red on buff, die 4	......	9000.00	185.00
U9	3¢ red on white, die 5	175.00	45.00	5.00
U10	3¢ red on buff, die 5	75.00	24.00	5.00
U11	6¢ red on white	475.00	330.00	95.00
U12	6¢ red on buff	285.00	185.00	95.00
U13	6¢ green on white	800.00	425.00	135.00
U14	6¢ green on buff	475.00	240.00	110.00
U15	10¢ green on white, die 1	1000.00	575.00	110.00
U16	10¢ green on buff, die 1	525.00	195.00	77.00
U17	10¢ green on white, die 2	925.00	560.00	150.00
U18	10¢ green on buff, die 2	775.00	425.00	95.00

1860-61

SCOTT NO.	DESCRIPTION	UNUSED ENTIRE	UNUSED CUT SQ.	USED CUT SQ.
U19	1¢ blue on buff, die 1	95.00	45.00	16.50
W20	1¢ blue on buff, die 1	130.00	75.00	52.00
W21	1¢ blue on manila, die 1	130.00	65.00	47.00
W22	1¢ blue on orange, die 1	8250.00	4500.00	......
U23	1¢ blue on orange, die 2	1050.00	775.00	360.00
U24	1¢ blue on buff, die 3	750.00	400.00	135.00
U26	3¢ red on white	65.00	37.00	22.00
U27	3¢ red on buff	48.00	27.00	14.00
U28	3¢ & 1¢ red & blue on white	850.00	400.00	285.00
U29	3¢ & 1¢ red & blue on buff	840.00	400.00	285.00
U30	6¢ red on white	6600.00	3600.00	1600.00
U31	6¢ red on buff	7100.00	4100.00	1600.00
U32	10¢ green on white	......	1700.00	460.00
U33	10¢ green on buff	4600.00	1700.00	385.00

U34-U37
Washington

U40-U41

1861

SCOTT NO.	DESCRIPTION	UNUSED ENTIRE	UNUSED CUT SQ.	USED CUT SQ.
U34	3¢ pink on white	65.00	35.00	7.00
U35	3¢ pink on buff	65.00	35.00	7.00
U36	3¢ pink on blue (letter sheet)	300.00	85.00	65.00
U37	3¢ pink on orange	8200.00	5700.00	......
U38	6¢ pink on white	225.00	135.00	85.00
U39	6¢ pink on buff	240.00	85.00	65.00
U40	10¢ yellow green on white	85.00	50.00	33.00
U41	10¢ yellow green on buff	85.00	50.00	33.00
U42	12¢ brown & red on buff	575.00	290.00	185.00
U43	20¢ blue & red on buff	600.00	350.00	225.00
U44	24¢ green & red on buff	875.00	350.00	240.00
U45	40¢ red & black on buff	875.00	400.00	365.00

U46-U49
Jackson

U50-W57

1863-64

SCOTT NO.	DESCRIPTION	UNUSED ENTIRE	UNUSED CUT SQ.	USED CUT SQ.
U46	2¢ black on buff, die 1	90.00	58.00	23.00
W47	2¢ black on dark manila, die 1	110.00	90.00	52.00
U48	2¢ black on buff, die 2	6500.00	3500.00	......
U49	2¢ black on orange, die 2	5900.00	3000.00	......
U50	2¢ black on buff, die 3	45.00	20.00	10.00
W51	2¢ black on buff, die 3	675.00	450.00	210.00
U52	2¢ black on orange, die 3	39.00	20.00	10.00
W53	2¢ black on dark manila, die 3	185.00	55.00	42.00

SCOTT NO.	DESCRIPTION	UNUSED ENTIRE	UNUSED CUT SQ.	USED CUT SQ.
U54	2¢ black on buff, die 4	40.00	20.00	10.00
W55	2¢ black on buff, die 4	165.00	110.00	70.00
U56	2¢ black on orange, die 4	35.00	24.00	9.00
W57	2¢ black on light manila, die 4	40.00	26.00	15.00

U58-U61
Washington

U66-U67

1864-65

SCOTT NO.	DESCRIPTION	UNUSED ENTIRE	UNUSED CUT SQ.	USED CUT SQ.
U58	3¢ pink on white	22.00	14.00	1.80
U59	3¢ pink on buff	22.00	14.00	1.40
U60	3¢ brown on white	150.00	80.00	42.00
U61	3¢ brown on buff	140.00	65.00	35.00
U62	6¢ pink on white	200.00	115.00	30.00
U63	6¢ pink on buff	115.00	57.00	29.00
U64	6¢ purple on white	110.00	77.00	27.00
U65	6¢ purple on buff	85.00	65.00	24.00
U66	9¢ lemon on buff	650.00	490.00	260.00
U67	9¢ orange on buff	240.00	165.00	95.00
U68	12¢ brown on buff	650.00	350.00	280.00
U69	12¢ red brown on buff	210.00	160.00	60.00
U70	18¢ red on buff	210.00	105.00	98.00
U71	24c blue on buff	210.00	100.00	98.00
U72	30c green on buff	225.00	130.00	85.00
U73	40¢ rose on buff	360.00	130.00	260.00

U74-W77, U108-U121
Franklin

U78-W81, U122-W158
Jackson

U82-U84, U159-U169
Washington

U172-U180
Taylor

U85-U87, U181-U184
Lincoln

U88, U185, U186
Stanton

U89-U92, U187-U194
Jefferson

U93-U95, U195-U197
Clay

U96-U98, U198-U200
Webster

U99-U101, U201-U203
Scott

U102-U104, U204-U210, U336-U341
Hamilton

U105-U107, U211-U217, U342-U347
Perry

NOTE: For details on die or silmilar appearing varieties of envelopes, please refer to the Scott Specialized Catalogue.

1870-71 REAY ISSUE

SCOTT NO.	DESCRIPTION	UNUSED ENTIRE	UNUSED CUT SQ.	USED CUT SQ.
U74	1¢ blue on white	82.00	47.00	32.00
U74a	1¢ ultramarine on white	150.00	75.00	38.00
U75	1¢ blue on amber	62.00	39.00	30.00
U75a	1¢ ultramarine on amber	105.00	72.00	31.00
U76	1¢ blue on orange	35.00	22.00	15.00
W77	1¢ blue on manila	85.00	47.00	38.00
U78	2¢ brown on white	65.00	45.00	18.00
U79	2¢ brown on amber	42.00	25.00	11.00
U80	2¢ brown on orange	18.00	13.00	7.00
W81	2¢ brown on manila	66.00	30.00	23.00
U82	3¢ green on white	19.00	9.00	1.25
U83	3¢ green on amber	18.00	8.00	2.25
U84	3¢ green on cream	18.00	12.00	5.00
U85	6¢ dark red on white	62.00	34.00	22.00
U86	6¢ dark red on amber	80.00	45.00	22.00
U87	6¢ dark red on cream	82.00	45.00	22.00
U88	7¢ vermillon on amber	85.00	58.00	200.00
U89	10¢ olive black on white	1400.00	1000.00	925.00
U90	10¢ olive black on amber	1400.00	1000.00	925.00
U91	10¢ brown on white	150.00	95.00	74.00
U92	10¢ brown on amber	150.00	115.00	54.00
U93	12¢ plum on white	245.00	130.00	84.00
U94	12¢ plum on amber	250.00	145.00	120.00
U95	12¢ plum on cream	385.00	280.00	260.00
U96	15¢ red orange on white	180.00	92.00	90.00
U97	15¢ red orange on amber	410.00	230.00	310.00
U98	15¢ red orange on cream	440.00	340.00	350.00
U99	24¢ purple on white	225.00	155.00	155.00
U100	24¢ purple on amber	400.00	210.00	350.00
U101	24¢ purple on cream	500.00	295.00	575.00
U102	30¢ black on white	315.00	85.00	120.00
U103	30¢ black on amber	675.00	260.00	500.00
U104	30¢ black on cream	425.00	260.00	525.00
U105	90¢ carmine on white	275.00	185.00	375.00
U106	90¢ carmine on amber	815.00	340.00	425.00
U107	90¢ carmine on cream	925.00	350.00	2550.00

1874-86 PLIMPTON ISSUE

SCOTT NO.	DESCRIPTION	UNUSED ENTIRE	UNUSED CUT SQ.	USED CUT SQ.
U108	1¢ dark blue on white, die 1	280.00	220.00	72.00
U109	1¢ dark blue on amber, die 1	225.00	200.00	78.00
U110	1¢ dark blue on cream, die 1	......	1800.00	......
U111	1¢ dark blue on orange, die 1	36.00	26.00	18.00
U111a	1¢ light blue on orange, die 1	36.00	26.00	18.00
W112	1¢ dark blue on manila, die 1	120.00	75.00	45.00
U113	1¢ light blue on white, die 2	3.25	2.00	1.00
U113a	1¢ dark blue on white, die 2	30.00	10.00	8.00
U114	1¢ light blue on amber, die 2	9.00	4.50	4.00
U115	1¢ blue on cream, die 2	11.00	6.00	5.00
U116	1¢ light blue on orange, die 2	1.40	.85	.50
U116a	1¢ dark blue on orange, die 2	17.00	5.00	2.50
U117	1¢ light blue on blue, die 2	14.00	9.00	5.50
U118	1¢ light blue on fawn, die 2	16.00	9.00	5.50
U119	1¢ light blue on manila, die 2	17.00	10.00	3.60
W120	1¢ light blue on manila, die 2	3.00	1.75	1.20
W120a	1¢ dark blue on manila, die 2	17.00	9.50	8.00
U121	1¢ blue on amber manila, die 2	30.00	20.00	11.00
U122	2¢ brown on white, die 1	180.00	155.00	52.00
U123	2¢ brown on amber, die 1	130.00	75.00	48.00
U124	2¢ brown on cream, die 1	......	1275.00	......
W126	2¢ brown on manila, die 1	310.00	180.00	88.00
W127	2¢ vermillon on manila, die 1	4800.00	3200.00	260.00
U128	2¢ brown on white, die 2	120.00	65.00	40.00
U129	2¢ brown on amber, die 2	130.00	90.00	48.00
W131	2¢ brown on manila, die 2	30.00	21.00	17.50
U132	2¢ brown on white, die 3	130.00	90.00	30.00
U133	2¢ brown on amber, die 3	550.00	375.00	75.00
U134	2¢ brown on white, die 4	2275.00	1500.00	165.00
U135	2¢ brown on amber, die 4	725.00	550.00	130.00
U136	2¢ brown on orange, die 4	90.00	60.00	30.00
W137	2¢ brown on manila, die 4	135.00	90.00	40.00
U139	2¢ brown on white, die 5	85.00	65.00	38.00
U140	2¢ brown on amber, die 5	150.00	100.00	64.00
W141	2¢ brown on manila, die 5	47.00	40.00	28.00
U142	2¢ vermillon on white, die 5	15.00	11.00	5.50
U143	2¢ vermillon on amber, die 5	15.00	11.00	5.00
U144	2¢ vermillon on cream, die 5	28.00	22.00	8.00
U146	2¢ vermillon on blue, die 5	210.00	145.00	42.00
U147	2¢ vermillon on fawn, die 5	18.00	12.00	5.50
W148	2¢ vermillon on manila, die 5	10.00	5.00	4.50
U149	2¢ vermillon on white, die 6	100.00	65.00	35.00
U150	2¢ vermillon on amber, die 6	65.00	45.00	18.00
U151	2¢ vermillon on blue, die 6	22.00	15.00	9.50
U152	2¢ vermillon on fawn, die 6	21.00	16.00	5.00
U153	2¢ vermillon on white, die 7	120.00	80.00	30.00
U154	2¢ vermillon on amber, die 7	475.00	425.00	95.00
W155	2¢ vermillon on manila, die 7	50.00	25.00	12.00
U156	2¢ vermillon on white, die 8	3800.00	1800.00	175.00
W158	2¢ vermillon on manila,die 8	200.00	120.00	65.00
U159	3¢ green on white, die 1	65.00	38.00	7.00
U160	3¢ green on amber, die 1	68.00	42.00	12.00
U161	3¢ green on cream, die 1	72.00	45.00	16.00
U163	3¢ green on white, die 2	4.50	1.75	.40
U164	3¢ green on amber, die 2	4.50	1.75	.75
U165	3¢ green on cream, die 2	20.00	10.00	7.00
U166	3¢ green on blue,die 2	18.00	9.00	7.00
U167	3¢ green on fawn, die 2	10.00	6.00	4.00
U168	3¢ green on white, die 3	5100.00	1600.00	95.00
U169	3¢ green on amber, die 3	650.00	350.00	120.00
U172	5¢ blue on white, die 1	22.00	16.00	9.50
U173	5¢ blue on amber, die 1	22.00	16.00	10.00
U174	5¢ blue on cream, die 1	200.00	130.00	45.00
U175	5¢ blue on blue, die 1	60.00	42.00	16.50
U176	5¢ blue on fawn, die 1	310.00	165.00	72.00
U177	5¢ blue on white, die 2	22.00	15.00	8.50
U178	5¢ blue on amber, die 2	22.00	12.00	8.50
U179	5¢ blue on blue, die 2	50.00	35.00	12.00
U180	5¢ blue on fawn, die 2	250.00	150.00	60.00
U181	6¢ red on white	16.00	11.00	7.00
U182	6¢ red on amber	25.00	16.00	7.00
U183	6¢ red on cream	95.00	60.00	18.00
U184	6¢ red on fawn	37.50	25.00	14.00
U185	7¢ vermilion on white	......	2000.00	......
U186	7¢ vermilion on amber	225.00	175.00	75.00
U187	10¢ brown on white,die 1	70.00	50.00	25.00
U188	10¢ brown on amber, die 1	165.00	85.00	38.00
U189	10¢ chocolate on white, die 2	14.00	9.00	4.50
U190	10¢ chocolate on amber, die 2	15.00	10.00	7.75
U191	10¢ brown on buff, die 2	24.00	21.00	9.00
U192	10¢ brown on blue, die 2	24.00	21.00	9.00
U193	10¢ brown on manila, die 2	25.00	20.00	11.00
U194	10¢ brown/amber manila, die 2	28.00	22.00	10.00
U195	12¢ plum on white	750.00	500.00	110.00
U196	12¢ plum on amber	375.00	300.00	195.00
U197	12¢ plum on cream	975.00	240.00	185.00
U198	15¢ orange on white	95.00	56.00	42.00
U199	15¢ orange on amber	325.00	165.00	120.00
U200	15¢ orange on cream	1150.00	600.00	370.00
U201	24¢ purple on white	275.00	180.00	155.00
U202	24¢ purple on amber	275.00	200.00	130.00
U203	24¢ purple on cream	800.00	200.00	130.00
U204	30¢ black on white	95.00	68.00	29.00
U205	30¢ black on amber	140.00	75.00	65.00
U206	30¢ black on cream	825.00	410.00	380.00
U207	30¢ black on oriental buff	165.00	110.00	85.00
U208	30¢ black on blue	210.00	115.00	85.00
U209	30¢ black on manila	165.00	100.00	85.00
U210	30¢ black on amber manila	225.00	180.00	85.00
U211	90¢ carmine on white	160.00	130.00	85.00
U212	90¢ carmine on amber	275.00	230.00	310.00
U213	90¢ carmine on cream	3500.00	1800.00	......
U214	90¢ carmine on oriental buff	310.00	210.00	280.00
U215	90¢ carmine on blue	285.00	210.00	260.00
U216	90¢ carmine on manila	280.00	180.00	280.00
U217	90¢ carmine on amber manila	230.00	150.00	220.00

U218-U221, U582
Pony Express Rider and Train

U222-U226
Garfield

Die 1. Single thick line under "POSTAGE" Die 2. Two thin lines under "POSTAGE"

1876 CENTENNIAL ISSUE

SCOTT NO.	DESCRIPTION	UNUSED ENTIRE	UNUSED CUT SQ.	USED CUT SQ.
U218	3¢ red on white, die 1	80.00	55.00	30.00
U219	3¢ green on white, die 1	67.00	50.00	19.00
U221	3¢ green on white, die 2	87.00	55.00	24.00

1882-86

SCOTT NO.	DESCRIPTION	UNUSED ENTIRE	UNUSED CUT SQ.	USED CUT SQ.
U222	5¢ brown on white	11.00	6.00	3.00
U223	5¢ brown on amber	12.00	6.00	3.50
U224	5¢ brown on oriental buff	210.00	150.00	75.00
U225	5¢ brown on blue	130.00	85.00	40.00
U226	5¢ brown on fawn	550.00	385.00	......

U227-U230
Washington

1883 OCTOBER

SCOTT NO.	DESCRIPTION	UNUSED ENTIRE	UNUSED CUT SQ.	USED CUT SQ.
U227	2¢ red on white	11.00	5.00	2.50
U228	2¢ red on amber	11.00	6.00	3.00
U229	2¢ red on blue	14.00	9.00	5.00
U230	2¢ red on fawn	15.00	9.50	5.50

SCOTT NO.	DESCRIPTION	UNUSED ENTIRE	UNUSED CUT SQ.	USED CUT SQ.

U231-U249, U260-W292
Washington

U250-U259
Jackson

1883 NOVEMBER
Four Wavy Lines in Oval

U231	2¢ red on white	11.00	6.00	2.50
U232	2¢ red on amber	12.00	7.00	4.00
U233	2¢ red on blue	20.00	11.00	8.00
U234	2¢ red on fawn	13.00	9.00	5.00
W235	2¢ red on manila	33.00	24.00	6.50

1884 JUNE

U236	2¢ red on white	23.00	15.00	4.50
U237	2¢ red on amber	28.00	18.00	11.00
U238	2¢ red on blue	42.00	30.00	13.00
U239	2¢ red on fawn	25.00	25.00	12.00
U240	2¢ red on white ....(3-1/2links)	175.00	110.00	50.00
U241	2¢ red on amber ....(3-1/2links)	2800.00	1000.00	340.00
U243	2¢ red on white ....(2 links)	180.00	140.00	80.00
U244	2¢ red on amber ....(2links)	525.00	350.00	105.00
U245	2¢ red on blue ....(2links)	675.00	500.00	225.00
U246	2¢ red on fawn ....(2links)	725.00	475.00	175.00
U247	2¢ red on white ....(round O)	4600.00	3600.00	775.00
U249	2¢ red on fawn ....(round O)	2300.00	1450.00	525.00

1883-86

U250	4¢ green on white, die 1	7.00	4.00	3.50
U251	4¢ green on amber,die 1	8.00	5.50	4.00
U252	4¢ green on buff, die 1	18.00	14.00	10.00
U253	4¢ green on blue, die 1	18.00	14.00	7.00
U254	4¢ green on manila, die 1	22.00	16.00	8.00
U255	4¢ green/amber manila,die 1	33.00	25.00	11.00
U256	4¢ green on white, die 2	20.00	12.00	5.00
U257	4¢ green on amber, die 2	26.00	15.00	7.00
U258	4¢ green on manila, die 2	26.00	16.00	8.00
U259	4¢ green/amber manila,die 2	26.00	16.00	8.00

1884 MAY

U260	2¢ brown on white	22.00	20.00	6.00
U261	2¢ brown on amber	22.00	20.00	7.00
U262	2¢ brown on blue	30.00	24.00	11.00
U263	2¢ brown on fawn	21.00	19.00	9.50
W264	2¢ brown on manila	27.00	20.00	12.00

1884 JUNE

U265	2¢ brown on white	28.00	20.00	7.00
U266	2¢ brown on amber	77.00	68.00	45.00
U267	2¢ brown on blue	35.00	25.00	10.00
U268	2¢ brown on fawn	23.00	18.00	11.00
W269	2¢ brown on manila	36.00	30.00	14.50
U270	2¢ brown on white ....(2links)	180.00	150.00	50.00
U271	2¢ brown on amber ....(2links)	625.00	525.00	120.00
U273	2¢ brown on white ....(round O)	425.00	325.00	120.00
U274	2¢ brown on amber ....(round O)	425.00	325.00	115.00
U276	2¢ brown on fawn ....(round O)	1600.00	1100.00	725.00

1884-86
Two Wavy Lines in Oval

U277	2¢ brown on white, die 1	.85	.50	.25
U277a	2¢ brown lake on white, die 1	28.00	23.00	22.00
U278	2¢ green on amber, die 1	1.50	.75	.50
U279	2¢ brown on buff, die 1	8.00	5.00	2.25
U280	2¢ brown on blue, die 1	5.00	3.00	2.25
U281	2¢ brown on fawn, die 1	6.00	4.00	2.50
U282	2¢ brown on manila, die 1	18.00	14.00	4.00
W283	2¢ brown on manila, die 1	12.00	8.00	6.00
U284	2¢ brown/amber manila, die 1	16.00	10.00	6.00
U285	2¢ red on white, die 1	1700.00	800.00	......
U286	2¢ red on blue, die 1	400.00	325.00	......
W287	2¢ red on manila, die 1	225.00	150.00	......
U288	2¢ brown on white, die 2	900.00	400.00	50.00
U289	2¢ brown on amber, die 2	25.00	19.00	12.00
U290	2¢ brown on blue, die 2	2500.00	1950.00	325.00
U291	2¢ brown on fawn, die 2	47.50	35.00	23.00
W292	2¢ brown on manila, die 2	37.00	25.00	20.00

NOTE: For details on die or silmilar appearing varieties of envelopes, please refer to the Scott Specialized Catalogue.

SCOTT NO.	DESCRIPTION	UNUSED ENTIRE	UNUSED CUT SQ.	USED CUT SQ.

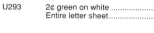

U293
Grant

1886

U293	2¢ green on white	....	....	....
	Entire letter sheet	31.00	....	21.00

U294-U304, U352-W357
Franklin

U305-U323, U358-U370
Washington

U324-U329
Jackson

U330-U335, U377-U378
Grant

1887-94

U294	1¢ blue on white	1.10	.60	.25
U295	1¢ dark blue on white	11.40	7.80	3.00
U296	1¢ blue on amber	6.50	4.00	1.50
U297	1¢ dark blue on amber	60.00	48.00	27.00
U300	1¢ blue on manila	1.15	.75	.40
W301	1¢ blue on manila	1.25	.50	.35
U302	1¢ dark blue on manila	38.00	31.00	13.00
W303	1¢ dark blue on manila	26.00	18.00	12.00
U304	1¢ blue on amber manila	18.00	13.00	5.00
U305	2¢ green on white, die 1	37.50	20.00	11.00
U306	2¢ green on amber, die 1	55.00	45.00	18.00
U307	2¢ green on buff, die 1	130.00	100.00	36.00
U308	2¢ green on blue, die 1	......	21000.00	1300.00
U309	2¢ green on manila, die 1	......	......	800.00
U311	2¢ green on white, die 2	.80	.40	.25
U312	2¢ green on amber, die 2	.80	.45	.25
U313	2¢ green on buff, die 2	1.25	.70	.30
U314	2¢ green on blue, die 2	1.25	.70	.30
U315	2¢ green on manila, die 2	3.00	2.00	.60
W316	2¢ green on manila, die 2	12.00	5.00	3.00
U317	2¢ green/amber manila, die 2	6.50	3.00	2.00
U318	2¢ green on white, die 3	210.00	160.00	15.00
U319	2¢ green on amber, die 3	300.00	200.00	25.00
U320	2¢ green on buff, die 3	250.00	180.00	50.00
U321	2¢ green on blue, die 3	325.00	200.00	71.50
U322	2¢ green on blue, die 3	325.00	280.00	70.00
U323	2¢ green/amber manila, die 3	700.00	600.00	150.00
U324	4¢ carmine on white	6.50	3.50	2.25
U325	4¢ carmine on amber	8.00	4.00	3.50
U326	4¢ carmine on oriental buff	17.00	8.00	4.00
U327	4¢ carmine on blue	14.00	7.00	4.25
U328	4¢ carmine on manila	14.00	10.00	7.00
U329	4¢ carmine on amber/manila	14.00	8.00	4.00
U330	5¢ blue on white, die 1	9.00	5.00	5.00
U331	5¢ blue on amber, die 1	11.00	6.00	3.00
U332	5¢ blue on oriental buff, die 1	17.00	7.00	5.00
U333	5¢ blue on blue, die 1	17.00	11.00	6.00
U334	5¢ blue on white, die 2	45.00	30.00	13.00
U335	5¢ blue on amber, die 2	25.00	15.00	8.00
U336	30¢ red brown on white	75.00	65.00	50.00
U337	30¢ red brown on amber	75.00	65.00	50.00
U338	30¢ red brown/oriental buff	75.00	65.00	50.00
U339	30¢ red brown on blue	75.00	65.00	50.00
U340	30¢ red brown on manila	75.00	65.00	50.00
U341	30¢ red brown/amber manila	75.00	65.00	50.00
U342	90¢ purple on white	120.00	80.00	90.00
U343	90¢ purple on amber	150.00	95.00	90.00
U344	90¢ purple on oriental buff	150.00	95.00	90.00
U345	90¢ purple on blue	150.00	95.00	95.00
U346	90¢ purple on manila	150.00	110.00	95.00
U347	90¢ purple on amber manila	150.00	110.00	95.00

SCOTT NO.	DESCRIPTION	UNUSED ENTIRE	UNUSED CUT SQ.	USED CUT SQ.

U348-U351
Columbus and Liberty, with Shield and Eagle

1893 COLUMBIAN ISSUE

SCOTT NO.	DESCRIPTION	UNUSED ENTIRE	UNUSED CUT SQ.	USED CUT SQ.
U348	1¢ deep blue on white	3.00	2.50	1.25
U349	2¢ violet on white	3.50	2.00	.75
U350	5¢ chocolate on white	15.00	9.60	9.00
U351	10¢ slate brown on white	72.00	35.00	32.00

U371-U373   **U374-W376**
Lincoln

1899

SCOTT NO.	DESCRIPTION	UNUSED ENTIRE	UNUSED CUT SQ.	USED CUT SQ.
U352	1¢ green on white	3.00	1.20	.25
U353	1¢ green on amber	9.00	6.00	1.80
U354	1¢ green on oriental buff	20.00	15.00	3.00
U355	1¢ green on blue	20.00	15.00	8.00
U356	1¢ green on manila	7.00	2.50	1.10
W357	1¢ green on manila	10.00	3.00	1.10
U358	2¢ carmine on white, die 1	8.00	3.00	2.00
U359	2¢ carmine on amber, die 1	35.00	25.00	15.00
U360	2¢ carmine on buff, die 1	35.00	25.00	13.00
U361	2¢ carmine on blue, die 1	80.00	67.00	38.00
U362	2¢ carmine on white, die 2	.70	.40	.25
U363	2¢ carmine on amber. die 2	3.25	1.50	.25
U364	2¢ carmine on buff, die 2	3.25	1.25	.25
U365	2¢ carmine on blue, die 2	4.00	2.00	.60
W366	2¢ carmine on manila, die 2	13.00	9.00	3.50
U367	2¢ carmine on white, die 3	12.00	7.00	3.00
U368	2¢ carmine on amber, die 3	16.00	10.00	7.00
U369	2¢ carmine on buff, die 3	35.00	25.00	14.00
U370	2¢ carmine on blue, die 3	26.00	13.00	11.00
U371	4¢ brown on white, die 1	32.00	22.00	13.25
U372	4¢ brown on amber, die 1	35.00	22.00	14.00
U373	4¢ brown on white, die 2	......	......	1300.00
U374	4¢ brown on white, die 3	28.00	16.00	9.00
U375	4¢ brown on amber, die 3	85.00	70.00	25.00
W376	4¢ brown on manila, die 3	28.00	18.00	10.00
U377	5¢ blue on white, die 3	18.00	14.00	10.25
U378	5¢ blue on amber, die 3	25.00	18.00	11.50

U379-W384
Franklin

U385-W389,
U395-W399
Washington

U390-W392
Grant

U393, U394
Lincoln

U400-W405,
U416, U417
Franklin

U406-W415,
U418, U419
Washington

1903

SCOTT NO.	DESCRIPTION	UNUSED ENTIRE	UNUSED CUT SQ.	USED CUT SQ.
U379	1¢ green on white	1.40	.85	.25
U380	1¢ green on amber	23.00	16.00	2.25
U381	1¢ green on oriental buff	27.00	19.00	3.00
U382	1¢ green on blue	35.00	24.00	5.00
U383	1¢ green on manila	6.25	4.75	1.00
W384	1¢ green on manila	5.25	3.00	.50
U385	2¢ carmine on white	1.10	.60	.25
U386	2¢ carmine on amber	4.25	2.75	.30
U387	2¢ carmine on oriental buff	4.00	2.50	.35
U388	2¢ carmine on blue	3.50	2.25	.60
W389	2¢ carmine on manila	28.00	22.00	11.00
U390	4¢ chocolate on white	34.00	25.00	13.00
U391	4¢ chocolate on amber	35.00	25.00	13.00
W392	4¢ chocolate on manila	52.00	26.00	13.00
U393	5¢ blue on white	36.00	25.00	13.00
U394	5¢ blue on amber	36.00	25.00	13.00

1904 RECUT DIE

SCOTT NO.	DESCRIPTION	UNUSED ENTIRE	UNUSED CUT SQ.	USED CUT SQ.
U395	2¢ carmine on white	2.00	1.00	.25
U396	2¢ carmine on amber	15.00	10.00	1.20
U397	2¢ carmine on oriental buff	9.00	7.00	1.50
U398	2¢ carmine on blue	7.00	5.00	1.10
W399	2¢ carmine on manila	36.00	17.00	11.00

1907-16

SCOTT NO.	DESCRIPTION	UNUSED ENTIRE	UNUSED CUT SQ.	USED CUT SQ.
U400	1¢ green on white	.65	.40	.25
U401	1¢ green on amber	3.00	2.25	.50
U402	1¢ green on oriental buff	14.00	11.00	1.50
U403	1¢ green on blue	14.00	11.00	2.00
U404	1¢ green on manila	6.50	3.75	2.10
W405	1¢ green on manila	2.50	1.25	.30
U406	2¢ brown red on white	3.00	1.25	.25
U407	2¢ brown red on amber	9.00	7.00	3.00
U408	2¢ brown red on oriental buff	12.00	9.00	2.00
U409	2¢ brown red on blue	8.00	6.00	2.10
W410	2¢ brown red on manila	60.00	48.00	36.00
U411	2¢ carmine on white	1.25	.35	.25
U412	2¢ carmine on amber	1.00	.65	.25
U413	2¢ carmine on oriental buff	1.50	.75	.25
U414	2¢ carmine on blue	1.50	.75	.25
W415	2¢ carmine on manila	9.00	6.00	2.50
U416	4¢ black on white	12.00	6.50	3.50
U417	4¢ black on amber	14.00	8.00	3.00
U418	5¢ blue on white	14.00	8.00	2.85
U419	5¢ blue on amber	23.00	17.00	13.00

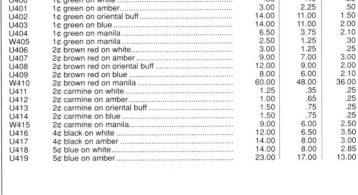

U420-U428, U440-U442
Franklin

U429-U439, U443-U445,
U481-U485, U529-U531
Washington

1916-32

SCOTT NO.	DESCRIPTION	UNUSED ENTIRE	UNUSED CUT SQ.	USED CUT SQ.
U420	1¢ green on white	.40	.35	.25
U421	1¢ green on amber	.80	.60	.35
U422	1¢ green on oriental buff	3.50	2.50	1.20
U423	1¢ green on blue	1.00	.60	.40
U424	1¢ green on manila	9.50	7.20	4.80
W425	1¢ green on manila	.95	.30	.25
U426	1¢ green on brown (glazed)	60.00	50.00	19.25
W427	1¢ green on brown (glazed)	76.00	66.50	35.00
U428	1¢ green on brown (unglazed)	25.00	17.00	9.00
U429	2¢ carmine on white	.45	.30	.25
U430	2¢ carmine on amber	.50	.30	.25
U431	2¢ carmine on oriental buff	5.00	2.50	.70
U432	2¢ carmine on blue	.65	.40	.25
W433	2¢ carmine on manila	.55	.30	.25
W434	2¢ carmine on brown (glazed)	126.00	100.00	55.00
W435	2¢ carmine/brown (unglazed)	126.00	100.00	55.00
U436	3¢ dark violet on white	.75	.60	.25
U436f	3¢ purple on white (1932)	.65	.40	.25
U436h	3¢ carmine on white (error)	62.00	38.00	33.00
U437	3¢ dark violet on amber	6.00	2.70	1.20
U437a	3¢ purple on amber (1932)	.70	.35	.25
U437g	3¢ carmine on amber (error)	525.00	500.00	360.00
U437h	3¢ black on amber (error)	300.00	200.00	......
U438	3¢ dark violet on buff	36.00	28.00	1.80
U439	3¢ dark violet on blue	10.80	7.20	1.70
U439a	3¢ purple on blue (1932)	.80	.35	.25
U439g	3¢ carmine on blue (error)	500.00	400.00	320.00
U440	4¢ black on white	3.50	1.75	.60
U441	4¢ black on amber	5.00	3.00	.90
U442	4¢ black on blue	6.00	3.50	1.00
U443	5¢ blue on white	6.00	3.20	3.00
U444	5¢ blue on amber	7.00	4.00	1.70
U445	5¢ blue on blue	8.75	4.50	3.50

SCOTT NO.	DESCRIPTION	UNUSED ENTIRE	UNUSED CUT SQ.	USED CUT SQ.

1920-21 SURCHARGED

Type 1   Type 2

| U446 | 2¢ on 3¢ dark violet on white ....(U436) | 26.00 | 17.00 | 11.75 |

Surcharge on Envelopes of 1916-21 Type 2

U447	2¢ on 3¢ dark violet on white, rose ....(U436)	18.00	11.00	7.70
U448	2¢ on 3¢ dark violet on white ....(U436)	14.00	3.00	2.10
U449	2¢ on 3¢ dark violet on amber ....(U437)	11.00	8.00	6.00
U450	2¢ on 3¢ dark violet on oriental buff.............(U438)	26.00	20.00	16.00
U451	2¢ on 3¢ dark violet on blue........................(U439)	23.00	17.00	11.00

Type 3

Surcharge on Envelopes of 1874-1921
Type 3 bars 2mm apart

U454	2¢ on 2¢ carmine on white ....(U429)	210.00	160.00	......
U455	2¢ on 2¢ carmine on amber ....(U430)	4300.00	2300.00	......
U456	2¢ on 2¢ carmine on oriental buff ....(U431)	350.00	295.00	......
U457	2¢ on 2¢ carmine on blue ....(U432)	450.00	400.00	......
U458	2¢ on 3¢ dark violet on white ....(U436)	.85	.60	.40
U459	2¢ on 3¢ dark violet on amber ....(U437)	5.50	3.50	1.20
U460	2¢ on 3¢ dark violet on oriental buff ....(U438)	5.00	4.00	2.00
U461	2¢ on 3¢ dark violet on blue ....(U439)	10.00	7.00	1.20
U462	2¢ on 4¢ chocolate on white ....(U390)	1100.00	650.00	275.00
U463	2¢ on 4¢ chocolate on amber ....(U391)	1750.00	1300.00	375.00
U464	2¢ on 5¢ blue on white ....(U443)	2050.00	1500.00	......

Type 4 like Type 3, but bars 1-1/2 mm apart

U465	2¢ on 1¢ green on white ....(U420)	3000.00	1800.00	......
U466A	2¢ on 2¢ carmine on white ....(U429)	1700.00	1000.00	......
U467	2¢ on 3¢ green on white ....(U163)	600.00	450.00	......
U468	2¢ on 3¢ dark violet on white ....(U436)	1.10	.75	.45
U469	2¢ on 3¢ dark violet on amber ....(U437)	5.50	4.00	2.50
U470	2¢ on 3¢ dark violet on oriental buff ....(U438)	10.00	6.00	3.00
U471	2¢ on 3¢ dark violet on blue ....(U439)	13.00	8.00	2.00
U472	2¢ on 4¢ chocolate on white ....(U390)	28.00	16.00	9.60
U473	2¢ on 4¢ chocolate on amber ....(U391)	28.00	17.00	11.00
U474	2¢ on 1¢ on 3¢ dark violet on white ....(U436)	400.00	300.00	......
U475	2¢ on 1¢ on 3¢ dark violet on amber ....(U437)	480.00	300.00	......

Type 5   Type 6   Type 7

Surcharge on Envelope of 1916-21 Type 5

| U476 | 2¢ on 3¢ dark violet on amber ....(U437) | 500.00 | 300.00 | ...... |

Surcharge on Envelope of 1916-21 Type 6

| U477 | 2¢ on 3¢ dark violet on white ....(U436) | 200.00 | 150.00 | ...... |
| U478 | 2¢ on 3¢ dark violet on amber ....(U437) | 500.00 | 375.00 | ...... |

Surcharge on Envelope of 1916-21 Type 7

| U479 | 2¢ on 3¢ dark violet on white (black) ....(U436) | 575.00 | 475.00 | ...... |

1925

U481	1-1/2¢ brown on white...................................	.65	.30	.25
U481b	1-1/2¢ purple on white (error)	130.00	105.00	......
U482	1-1/2¢ brown on amber.................................	1.75	1.10	.45
U483	1-1/2¢ brown on blue....................................	2.75	1.80	1.00
U484	1-1/2¢ brown on manila................................	13.25	7.25	3.75
W485	1-1/2¢ brown on manila................................	1.50	.90	.25

Type 8

Surcharge on Envelopes of 1887 Type 8

| U486 | 1-1/2¢ on 2¢ green on white ....(U311) | 1350.00 | 925.00 | ...... |
| U487 | 1-1/2¢ on 2¢ green on amber ....(U312) | 1900.00 | 1500.00 | ...... |

Surcharge on Envelopes of 1899 Type 8

| U488 | 1-1/2¢ on 1¢ green on white ....(U352) | 1050.00 | 700.00 | ...... |
| U489 | 1-1/2¢ on 1¢ green on amber ....(U353) | 210.00 | 130.00 | 70.00 |

Surcharge on Envelopes of 1907-10 Type 8

U490	1-1/2¢ on 1¢ green on white ....(U400)	12.00	7.00	4.20
U491	1-1/2¢ on 1¢ green on amber ....(U401)	13.00	9.00	3.00
U492	1-1/2¢ on 1¢ green on oriental buff ....(U402a)	750.00	625.00	145.00
U493	1-1/2¢ on 1¢ green on blue ....(U403c)	170.00	130.00	70.00
U494	1-1/2¢ on 1¢ green on manila ....(U404)	575.00	425.00	110.00

Surcharge on Envelopes of 1916-21 Type 8

U495	1-1/2¢ on 1¢ green on white ....(U420)	1.25	.85	.30
U496	1-1/2¢ on 1¢ green on amber ....(U421)	31.00	22.00	14.00
U497	1-1/2¢ on 1¢ green on oriental buff ....(U422)	7.50	5.00	2.50
U498	1-1/2¢ on 1¢ green on blue ....(U423)	2.50	1.65	.90
U499	1-1/2¢ on 1¢ green on manila ....(U424)	20.00	13.00	8.00
U500	1-1/2¢ on 1¢ green on brown (unglazed).....(U428)	105.00	86.00	40.00
U501	1-1/2¢ on 1¢ green on brown (glazed) ....(U426)	105.00	85.00	36.00
U502	1-1/2¢ on 2¢ carmine on white ....(U429)	525.00	300.00	......
U503	1-1/2¢ on 2¢ carmine on oriental buff ......(U431)	540.00	400.00	......
U504	1-1/2¢ on 2¢ carmine on blue ....(U432)	540.00	475.00	......

Surcharge on Envelopes of 1925 Type 8

| U505 | 1-1/2¢ on 1-1/2¢ brown on white ....(U481) | 675.00 | 525.00 | ...... |
| U506 | 1-1/2¢ on 1-1/2¢ brown on blue ....(U483) | 675.00 | 525.00 | ...... |

Type 9

Surcharge on Envelopes of 1899 Type 9

| U508 | 1-1/2¢ on 1¢ green on amber ....(U353) | 105.00 | 72.00 | ...... |

Surcharge on Envelopes of 1903 Type 9

U508A	1-1/2¢ on 1¢ green on white ....(U379)	7000.00	4800.00	......
U509	1-1/2¢ on 1¢ green on amber ....(U380)	32.00	17.00	12.00
U509B	1-1/2¢ on 1¢ green on oriental buff ....(U381)	75.00	60.00	50.00

Surcharge on Envelopes of 1907-10 Type 9

U510	1-1/2¢ on 1¢ green on white ....(U400)	5.00	3.00	1.50
U511	1-1/2¢ on 1¢ green on amber ....(U401)	400.00	275.00	105.00
U512	1-1/2¢ on 1¢ green on oriental buff ....(U402)	17.00	9.00	4.75
U513	1-1/2¢ on 1¢ green on blue ....(U403)	11.00	7.00	5.00
U514	1-1/2¢ on 1¢ green on manila ....(U404)	46.00	35.00	12.00
U515	1-1/2¢ on 1¢ green on white ....(U420)	.80	.45	.25
U516	1-1/2¢ on 1¢ green on amber ....(U421)	66.00	52.00	32.00
U517	1-1/2¢ on 1¢ green on oriental buff ....(U422)	9.50	6.50	1.50
U518	1-1/2¢ on 1¢ green on blue ....(U423)	8.00	6.00	1.50
U519	1-1/2¢ on 1¢ green on manila ....(U424)	46.00	33.00	12.00
U520	1-1/2¢ on 2¢ carmine on white ....(U429)	525.00	375.00	......
U521	1-1/2¢ on 1¢ green on white, magenta surcharged ....(U420)	7.50	5.00	4.00

U522   U523-U528

U522: Die 1, "E" of "POSTAGE" has center bar shorter than top bar.

U522a: Die 2, "E" of "POSTAGE" has center and top bars same length.

U525: Die 1 "S" of "POSTAGE" even with "T".

U525a: Die 2 "S" of "POSTAGE" higher than "T".

1926 SESQUICENTENNIAL EXPOSITION

| U522 | 2¢ carmine on white, die 1 .... | 2.00 | 1.50 | .60 |
| U522a | 2¢ carmine on white, die 2 .... | 12.50 | 9.00 | 5.50 |

1932 WASHINGTON BICENTENNIAL

U523	1¢ olive green on white...................................	2.00	1.25	1.00
U524	1-1/2¢ chocolate on white..............................	3.25	2.25	2.00
U525	2¢ carmine on white, die 1............................	.75	.50	.25
U525a	2¢ carmine on white, die 2............................	100.00	85.00	20.00
U526	3¢ violet on white.......................................	3.00	2.50	.50
U527	4¢ black on white.......................................	27.50	22.00	21.00
U528	5¢ dark blue on white..................................	6.00	5.00	4.00

1932 Designs of 1916-32

U529	6¢ orange on white.......................................	11.00	7.25	5.00
U530	6¢ orange on amber.....................................	19.00	13.00	10.00
U531	6¢ orange on blue.......................................	19.00	13.00	11.00

SCOTT NO.	DESCRIPTION	FIRST DAY COVER	UNUSED ENTIRE	USED CUT SQ.

U532
Franklin

U533
Washington

U535

1950

U532	1¢ green	2.00	9.50	2.00
U533	2¢ carmine	2.00	1.25	.30
U534	3¢ dark violet	2.00	.50	.25

1952

U535	1-1/2¢ brown	....	6.50	4.00

U537, U538, U552, U556

U539, U540, U545, U553

Surcharge on Envelopes of 1916-32, 1950, 1965, 1971

1958

U536	4¢ red violet	1.75	1.00	.30
U537	2¢ & 2¢ (4¢) carmine ....(U429)	......	4.00	2.00
U538	2¢ & 2¢ (4¢) carmine ....(U533)	......	1.00	1.50
U539	3¢ & 1¢ (4¢) purple, die1 ....(U436a)	......	18.50	12.00
U539a	3¢ & 1¢ (4¢) purple, die 7 ....(U436e)	......	15.00	10.00
U539b	3¢ & 1¢ (4¢) purple, die 9 ....(U436f)	......	36.00	16.00
U540	3¢ & 1¢ (4¢) dark violet ....(U534)	......	.70	1.25

U541
Franklin

U542
Washington

1960

U541	1-1/4¢ turquoise	1.75	1.00	.60
U542	2-1/2¢ dull blue	1.75	1.00	.60

U543

U543	4¢ Pony Express	2.00	.80	.40

U544
Lincoln

U546

1962

U544	5¢ dark blue	1.75	1.20	.25

Surcharge on Envelope of 1958

U545	4¢+1¢ red violet ....(U536)	......	1.80	1.35

1964

U546	5¢ New York World's Fair	1.75	.75	.45

U547, U548, U548A, U566

U549

U550

U551

1965-69

U547	1-1/4¢ brown	1.75	.95	.25
U548	1-4/10¢ brown (1968)	1.75	1.00	.25
U548A	1-6/10¢ orange (1969)	1.75	.90	.25
U549	4¢ bright blue	1.75	.95	.25
U550	5¢ bright purple	1.75	.90	.25
U551	6¢ light green (1968)	1.75	.85	.25

U554

1968
1958 Type Surcharges on Envelopes of 1965

U552	4¢ & 2¢ (6¢) blue ....(U549)	9.00	4.75	2.25
U553	5¢ & 1¢ (6¢) purple ....(U550)	9.00	4.00	2.50

1970

U554	6¢ Moby Dick	1.75	.65	.25

U555

U557

1971

U555	6¢ Conference on Youth	1.75	.90	.25
U556	1-7/10¢ deep lilac	1.75	.40	.25
U557	8¢ ultramarine	1.75	.50	.25

U561 & U562 Sur-charge

U561	6¢ & (2¢) (8¢) green ....(on U551)	4.00	1.25	1.35
U562	6¢ & (2¢) (8¢) blue ....(on U555)	4.00	3.00	2.75

U563

U564

U563	8¢ Bowling	1.75	.90	.25
U564	8¢ Conference on Aging	1.75	.75	.25

SCOTT NO.	DESCRIPTION	FIRST DAY COVER	UNUSED ENTIRE	USED CUT SQ.

U565

U576

1975

| U576 | 13¢ orange brown | 1.75 | .50 | .25 |

U567

1972

| U565 | 8¢ Transpo '72 | 1.75 | .80 | .25 |

1973

| U566 | 8¢ & 2¢ ultramarine ....(on U557) | 3.00 | .55 | 1.35 |
| U567 | 10¢ emerald | 1.75 | .55 | .25 |

U577

U578

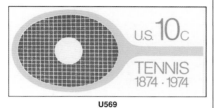

U568   **U569**

1974

| U568 | 1-8/10¢ blue green | 1.75 | .35 | .25 |
| U569 | 10¢ Tennis Centenary | 2.50 | .80 | .30 |

U579

U580

U571

U572

U581

1976-78

U577	2¢ red	1.75	.35	.25
U578	2.1¢ green (1977)	1.75	.35	.25
U579	2.7¢ green (1978)	1.75	.40	.25
U580	(15¢) "A" orange (1978)	1.75	.60	.25
U581	15¢ red & white (1978)	1.75	.60	.25

1976

| U582 | 13¢ Bicentennial (design of U218) | 1.75 | .55 | .25 |

U573

U574

U583

1977

| U583 | 13¢ Golf | 8.00 | .80 | .25 |

U575

1975-76 BICENTENNIAL ERA

U571	10¢ Seafaring	1.75	.55	.25
U572	13¢ Homemaker (1976)	1.75	.55	.25
U573	13¢ Farmer (1976)	1.75	.55	.25
U574	13¢ Doctor (1976)	1.75	.55	.25
U575	13¢ Craftsman (1976)	1.75	.55	.25

U584

U585

CUT SQUARES: From 1947 to date, Unused Envelope Cut Squares can be supplied at the Unused Entire Price.

| U584 | 13¢ Energy Conservation | 1.75 | .50 | .25 |
| U585 | 13¢ Energy Development | 1.75 | .50 | .25 |

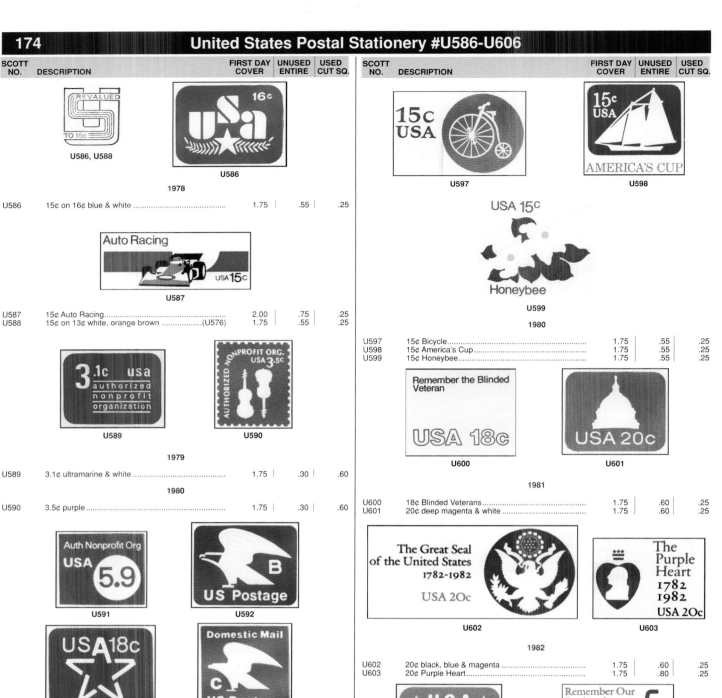

SCOTT NO.	DESCRIPTION	FIRST DAY COVER	UNUSED ENTIRE	USED CUT SQ.

U586, U588

U586

1978

| U586 | 15¢ on 16¢ blue & white | 1.75 | .55 | .25 |

U587

| U587 | 15¢ Auto Racing | 2.00 | .75 | .25 |
| U588 | 15¢ on 13¢ white, orange brown (U576) | 1.75 | .55 | .25 |

U589

U590

1979

| U589 | 3.1¢ ultramarine & white | 1.75 | .30 | .60 |

1980

| U590 | 3.5¢ purple | 1.75 | .30 | .60 |

U591

U592

U593

U594

1981-82

U591	5.9¢ brown (1982)	1.85	.30	.60
U592	(18¢) "B" violet & white	1.75	.60	.30
U593	18¢ white & dark blue	1.75	.60	.30
U594	(20¢) "C" brown & white	1.75	60	.30

U595

U596

1979

| U595 | 15¢ Veterinarians | 1.75 | .60 | .25 |
| U596 | 15¢ Moscow Olympics | 1.75 | .90 | .25 |

U597

U598

USA 15¢

Honeybee

U599

1980

U597	15¢ Bicycle	1.75	.55	.25
U598	15¢ America's Cup	1.75	.55	.25
U599	15¢ Honeybee	1.75	.55	.25

Remember the Blinded Veteran

USA 18c

U600

USA 20c

U601

1981

| U600 | 18¢ Blinded Veterans | 1.75 | .60 | .25 |
| U601 | 20¢ deep magenta & white | 1.75 | .60 | .25 |

The Great Seal of the United States 1782-1982 USA 20c

U602

The Purple Heart 1782 1982 USA 20c

U603

1982

| U602 | 20¢ black, blue & magenta | 1.75 | .60 | .25 |
| U603 | 20¢ Purple Heart | 1.75 | .80 | .25 |

U604

Remember Our Paralyzed Veterans USA 20c

U605

U606

1983

| U604 | 5.2¢ orange & white | 1.75 | .50 | .25 |
| U605 | 20¢ Paralyzed Veterans | 1.75 | .60 | .25 |

1984

| U606 | 20¢ Small Business | 2.00 | .60 | .25 |

SCOTT NO.	DESCRIPTION	FIRST DAY COVER	UNUSED ENTIRE	USED CUT SQ.

U607   **U608**   **U609**

1985

U607	(22¢) "D"	1.75	.75	.40
U608	22¢ Bison	1.75	.75	.25
U609	6¢ Old Ironsides	1.75	.30	.25

U610

1986

| U610 | 8.5¢ Mayflower | 1.75 | .30 | .25 |

U611   **U612**

U613

1988

U611	25¢ Stars	1.75	.80	.25
U612	8.4¢ Constellation	1.75	.30	.25
U613	25¢ Snowflake	1.75	1.50	25.00

U614   **U615**

U616   **U617, U639**

1989

U614	25¢ Stamped Return Envelope	1.75	.60	.30
U615	25¢ "USA" and Stars	1.75	.60	.30
U616	25¢ LOVE	1.75	.60	1.00
U617	25¢ Shuttle Docking Hologram	1.75	1.25	.80

U618   **U619**

1990-91

| U618 | 25¢ Football Hologram | 2.75 | 1.25 | .75 |
| U619 | 29¢ Star | 1.75 | .75 | .30 |

U620

| U620 | 11.1¢ Birds on Wire | 1.75 | .60 | .55 |

U621   **U622**

| U621 | 29¢ Love | 1.75 | .75 | .70 |
| U622 | 29¢ Magazine Industry | 1.75 | .75 | .60 |

U623   **U624**

| U623 | 29¢ Star | 1.75 | .75 | .30 |
| U624 | 26¢ Country Geese | 1.75 | .75 | .70 |

U625   **U626**

1992

| U625 | 29¢ Space Station | 1.75 | 1.25 | .60 |
| U626 | 29¢ Saddle & Blanket | 1.75 | .75 | .30 |

U627   **U628**

| U627 | 29¢ Protect the Environment | 1.75 | .75 | .30 |
| U628 | 19.8¢ Star | 1.75 | .60 | .45 |

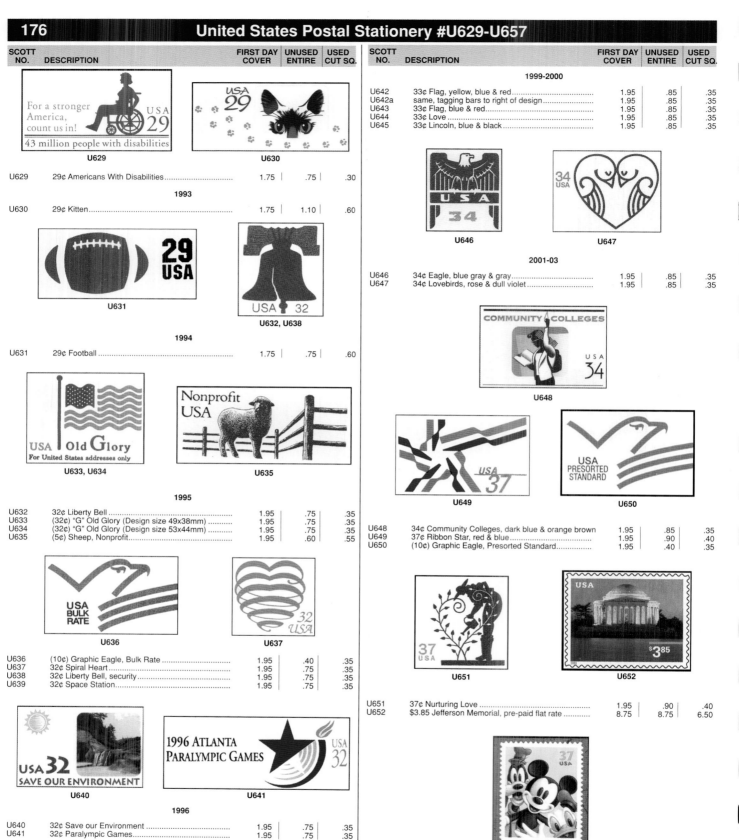

SCOTT NO.	DESCRIPTION	FIRST DAY COVER	UNUSED ENTIRE	USED CUT SQ.
	U629			
	U630			
U629	29¢ Americans With Disabilities	1.75	.75	.30
	1993			
U630	29¢ Kitten	1.75	1.10	.60
	U631			
	U632, U638			
	1994			
U631	29¢ Football	1.75	.75	.60
	U633, U634			
	U635			
	1995			
U632	32¢ Liberty Bell	1.95	.75	.35
U633	(32¢) "G" Old Glory (Design size 49x38mm)	1.95	.75	.35
U634	(32¢) "G" Old Glory (Design size 53x44mm)	1.95	.75	.35
U635	(5¢) Sheep, Nonprofit	1.95	.60	.55
	U636			
	U637			
U636	(10¢) Graphic Eagle, Bulk Rate	1.95	.40	.35
U637	32¢ Spiral Heart	1.95	.75	.35
U638	32¢ Liberty Bell, security	1.95	.75	.35
U639	32¢ Space Station	1.95	.75	.35
	U640			
	U641			
	1996			
U640	32¢ Save our Environment	1.95	.75	.35
U641	32¢ Paralympic Games	1.95	.75	.35
	U642, U643			
	U645			
	U644			

SCOTT NO.	DESCRIPTION	FIRST DAY COVER	UNUSED ENTIRE	USED CUT SQ.
	1999-2000			
U642	33¢ Flag, yellow, blue & red	1.95	.85	.35
U642a	same, tagging bars to right of design	1.95	.85	.35
U643	33¢ Flag, blue & red	1.95	.85	.35
U644	33¢ Love	1.95	.85	.35
U645	33¢ Lincoln, blue & black	1.95	.85	.35
	U646			
	U647			
	2001-03			
U646	34¢ Eagle, blue gray & gray	1.95	.85	.35
U647	34¢ Lovebirds, rose & dull violet	1.95	.85	.35
	U648			
	U649			
	U650			
U648	34¢ Community Colleges, dark blue & orange brown	1.95	.85	.35
U649	37¢ Ribbon Star, red & blue	1.95	.90	.40
U650	(10¢) Graphic Eagle, Presorted Standard	1.95	.40	.35
	U651			
	U652			
U651	37¢ Nurturing Love	1.95	.90	.40
U652	$3.85 Jefferson Memorial, pre-paid flat rate	8.75	8.75	6.50
	U653			
	2004			
U653	37¢ Goofy, Mickey Mouse, Donald Duck	3.00	3.00	2.50
U654	37¢ Bambi, Thumper	3.00	3.00	2.50
U655	37¢ Mufasa, Simba	3.00	3.00	2.50
U656	37¢ Jiminy Cricket, Pinocchio	3.00	3.00	2.50
	2005			
U657	37¢ Wedding Flowers, letter sheet	1.95	3.00	2.50

SCOTT NO.	DESCRIPTION	FIRST DAY COVER	UNUSED ENTIRE	USED CUT SQ.

U658

U659

2006

U658	$4.05 X-Planes, pre-paid flat rate	....	9.25	7.00
U659	39¢ Benjamin Franklin	1.95	.90	.40

U660

U661

2007

U660	$4.60 Air Force One, priority mail, pre-paid flat rate	....	10.00	7.50
U661	$16.25 Marine One, express mail, pre-paid flat rate	....	35.00	30.00

U662

U662	41¢ Horses..	2.00	1.00	.50

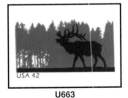
U663

U664

2008

U663	42¢ Elk Mint Entire..	3.75	1.00	.50
U664	$4.80 Mount Rushmore	11.00	11.00	9.00

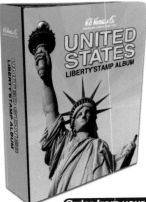
SCOTT NO.	DESCRIPTION	UNUSED ENTIRE	UNUSED CUT SQ.	USED CUT SQ.

UC1

UC2-UC7

Airplane in Circle

Die 1. Vertical rudder not semi-circular, but slopes to the left. Tail projects into "G".
Die 2. Vertical rudder is semi-circular. Tail only touches "G" Die 2a. "6" is 6-1/2mm. wide.
Die 2b. "6" is 6mm. wide.
Die 2c. "6" is 5-1/2mm. wide.
Die 3. Vertical rudder leans forward. "S" closer to "O" than to "T" of "POSTAGE" and "E" has short center bar.

1929-44

UC1	5¢ blue, die 1	5.25	4.00	2.00
UC2	5¢ blue, die 2	15.00	12.00	6.00
UC3	6¢ orange, die 2a	1.80	1.50	.50
UC3n	6¢, die 2a, no border	3.00	1.50	.50
UC4	6¢, die 2b, with border	62.00	3.00	2.50
UC4n	6¢, die 2b, no border	4.80	3.00	2.50
UC5	6¢, die 2c, no border	1.25	1.00	.50
UC6	6¢ orange on white, die 3........................	2.00	1.25	.45
UC6n	6¢, die 3, no border	3.00	1.50	.50
UC7	8¢ olive green	21.00	14.50	4.00

Envelopes of 1916-32 surcharged

1945

UC8	6¢ on 2¢ carmine on white ....(U429)	1.75	1.40	.75
UC9	6¢ on 2¢ carmine on white ....(U525)	120.00	90.00	45.00

REVALUED 5¢ P.O. DEPT.

1946

UC10	5¢ on 6¢, die 2a ....(UC3n)	4.00	3.00	1.75
UC11	5¢ on 6¢, die 2b ....(UC4n)	12.00	10.75	5.50
UC12	5¢ on 6¢, die 2c ....(UC5)	1.50	.90	.60
UC13	5¢ on 6¢, die 3 ....(UC6n)	1.15	.95	.75

UC14: Die 1. Small projection below rudder is rounded.
UC15: Die 2. Small projection below rudder is sharp pointed.

UC14, UC15, UC18, UC26
DC-4 Skymaster

SCOTT NO.	DESCRIPTION	FIRST DAY COVER	UNUSED ENTIRE	USED CUT SQ.
UC14	5¢ carmine, die 1	2.50	1.10	.25
UC15	5¢ carmine, die 2	......	1.10	.30

UC16
DC-4 Skymaster

UC17
Washington and Franklin, Mail-carrying Vehicles

1947

UC16	10¢ red on blue, Entire "Air Letter" on face, 2-line inscription on back	6.00	9.00	6.50
UC16a	Entire, "Air Letter" on face, 4-line inscription on back	......	18.00	15.00
UC16c	Entire "Air Letter" and "Aerogramme" on face, 4-line inscription on back	......	55.00	13.50
UC16d	Entire "Air Letter" and "Aerogramme" on face, 3-line inscription on back	......	9.50	9.00

SCOTT NO.	DESCRIPTION	FIRST DAY COVER	UNUSED ENTIRE	USED CUT SQ.

1947 CIPEX COMMEMORATIVE

| UC17 | 5¢ carmine | 3.00 | .60 | .35 |

1950 Design of 1946

| UC18 | 6¢ carmine | 1.75 | .60 | .35 |

REVALUED 6¢ P. O. DEPT.
ENVELOPE of 1946 Surcharged

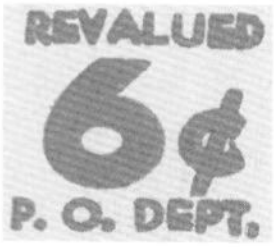

REVALUED 6¢ P. O. DEPT.
ENVELOPE of 1946-47 Surcharged

1951 (Shaded Numeral)

| UC19 | 6¢ on 5¢, die 1 | (UC14) | ...... | 1.35 | .60 |
| UC20 | 6¢ on 5¢, die 2 | (UC15) | ...... | 1.25 | .60 |

1952 (Solid Numeral)

UC21	6¢ on 5¢, die 1	(UC14)	......	37.50	19.00
UC22	6¢ on 5¢, die 2	(UC15)	......	5.75	2.75
UC23	6¢ on 5¢	(UC17)	......	2700.00	......

UC25

1956 FIPEX COMMEMORATIVE

| UC25 | 6¢ red | 1.75 | 1.10 | .60 |

1958 Design of 1946

| UC26 | 7¢ blue | 1.75 | 1.10 | .60 |

UC27-UC31

Surcharge on Envelopes of 1934 to 1956

1958

UC27	6¢ & 1¢ (7¢) orange, die 2a	(UC3n)	......	400.00	......
UC28	6¢ & 1¢ (7¢), die 2b	(UC4n)	......	125.00	82.50
UC29	6¢ & 1¢ (7¢) orange, die 2c	(UC5)	......	60.00	52.50
UC30	6¢ & 1¢ (7¢) carmine	(UC18)	......	1.35	.60
UC31	6¢ & 1¢ (7¢) red	(UC25)	......	1.40	.60

UC32    **UC33, UC34**    **UC35**

1958-59

| UC32 | 10¢ blue & red Entire letter sheet, 2-line inscription on back (1959) | ...... | 7.00 | 5.25 |
| UC32a | Entire letter sheet, 3 line inscription on back | 2.25 | 12.00 | 5.25 |

1958

| UC33 | 7¢ blue | 1.75 | .80 | .25 |

1960

| UC34 | 7¢ carmine | 1.75 | .75 | .25 |

1961

| UC35 | 11¢ red & blue | 3.25 | 3.00 | 2.50 |

UC36

1962

| UC36 | 8¢ red | 1.75 | .85 | .25 |

UC37    **UC38, UC39**

1965

| UC37 | 8¢ red | 1.75 | .60 | .25 |
| UC38 | 11¢ J.F. Kennedy | 1.75 | 4.00 | 3.00 |

UC40    **UC41 (surcharge on UC37)**

UC42

1967

| UC39 | 13¢ J.F. Kennedy | 1.75 | 3.50 | 3.00 |

1968

UC40	10¢ red	1.75	.85	.25
UC41	8¢ & 2¢ (10¢) red	12.00	.95	.25
UC42	13¢ Human Rights Year	1.75	8.00	4.50

UC43    **UC44**

1971

UC43	11¢ red & blue	1.75	.70	.25
UC44	15¢ gray, red, white and blue Birds in Flight	1.75	1.60	1.25
UC44a	Aerogramme added	1.75	1.60	1.25

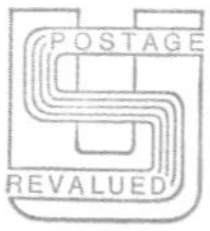

UC45 (surcharge on UC40)    **UC47**

1971 Revalued

| UC45 | 10 & (1¢) (11¢) red | 6.00 | 2.00 | .25 |

1973

| UC46 | 15¢ Ballooning | 1.75 | 1.25 | .50 |
| UC47 | 13¢ rose red | 1.75 | .75 | .25 |

UC48    **UC49**

1974

| UC48 | 18¢ red & blue | 1.75 | 1.00 | .35 |
| UC49 | 18¢ NATO 25th Anniversary | 1.75 | 1.00 | .50 |

SCOTT NO.	DESCRIPTION	FIRST DAY COVER	UNUSED ENTIRE	USED CUT SQ.

UC50

UC51

1976

| UC50 | 22¢ red, white & blue | 1.75 | 1.00 | .50 |

1978

| UC51 | 22¢ blue | 1.75 | .85 | .30 |

UC52   **UC53, UC54**   **UC55**

1979

| UC52 | 22¢ Moscow Olympics | 1.75 | 1.70 | .30 |

1980-81

| UC53 | 30¢ red, blue & brown | 1.75 | .85 | 1.25 |
| UC54 | 30¢ yellow, magenta, blue & black (1981) | 1.75 | .85 | 1.25 |

1982

| UC55 | 30¢ Made in U.S.A. | 1.75 | .85 | 1.25 |

UC56   **UC57**

1983

| UC56 | 30¢ Communications | 1.75 | 1.00 | 1.25 |
| UC57 | 30¢ Olympics | 1.75 | .95 | 2.00 |

UC58

1985

| UC58 | 36¢ Landsat Satellite | 1.75 | .85 | 1.25 |

UC59

| UC59 | 36¢ Travel | 1.75 | .85 | 1.25 |

UC60

| UC60 | 36¢ Mark Twain, Halley's Comet | 1.75 | 1.25 | 2.00 |

UC61   **UC62**

1986

| UC61 | 39¢ Letters | 1.75 | 1.00 | 1.25 |

1989

| UC62 | 39¢ Blair & Lincoln | 1.75 | 1.00 | 1.25 |

UC63   **UC64**

1991

| UC63 | 45¢ Eagle | 1.75 | 1.00 | 1.25 |

1995

| UC64 | 50¢ Thaddeus Lowe | 1.95 | 1.25 | 1.25 |

UC65

1999

| UC65 | 60¢ Voyagers National Park, Minnesota | 1.95 | 1.35 | 1.25 |

SCOTT NO.	DESCRIPTION	UNUSED ENTIRE	UNUSED CUT SQ.	USED CUT SQ.

UO1-UO13

UO14-UO17

UO18-UO69
Washington

OFFICIAL ENVELOPES

NOTE: For details on similar appearing varieties please refer to the Scott Specialized Catalogue

POST OFFICE DEPARTMENT

1873 SMALL NUMERALS

UO1	2¢ black on lemon	40.00	25.00	11.00
UO2	3¢ black on lemon	30.00	17.00	7.00
UO4	6¢ black on lemon	40.00	28.00	17.00

1874-79 LARGE NUMERALS

UO5	2¢ black on lemon	17.00	11.00	5.00
UO6	2¢ black on white	200.00	150.00	40.00
UO7	3¢ black on white	5.00	3.50	1.00
UO8	3¢ black on white	6000.00	3250.00	2400.00
UO9	3¢ black on amber	180.00	155.00	42.00
UO12	6¢ black on lemon	28.00	17.00	7.00
UO13	6¢ black on white	6000.00	3250.00	......

1877 POSTAL SERVICE

UO14	black on white	12.00	8.00	5.00
UO15	black on amber	950.00	250.00	45.00
UO16	blue on amber	950.00	225.00	38.00
UO17	blue on blue	14.00	10.00	7.00

Portraits for the various denominations are the same as on the regular issue of 1870-73

WAR DEPARTMENT

1873 REAY ISSUE

UO18	1¢ dark red on white	1250.00	750.00	325.00
UO19	2¢ dark red on white	3250.00	2500.00	475.00
UO20	3¢ dark red on white	110.00	75.00	48.00
UO22	3¢ dark red on cream	1250.00	1050.00	275.00
UO23	6¢ dark red on white	450.00	350.00	95.00
UO24	6¢ dark red on cream	......	8500.00	440.00
UO25	10¢ dark red on white	......	......	2500.00
UO26	12¢ dark red on white	275.00	190.00	65.00
UO27	15¢ dark red on white	225.00	175.00	65.00
UO28	24¢ dark red on white	250.00	200.00	55.00
UO29	30¢ dark red on white	750.00	600.00	165.00
UO30	1¢ vermillion on white	425.00	225.00	......
WO31	1¢ vermillion on manila	38.00	22.00	15.00
UO32	2¢ vermillion on white	......	550.00	......
WO33	2¢ vermillion on manila	400.00	250.00	......
UO34	3¢ vermillion on white	180.00	110.00	45.00
UO35	3¢ vermillion on amber	400.00	140.00	......
UO36	3¢ vermillion on cream	45.00	18.00	14.00
UO37	6¢ vermillion on white	180.00	110.00	......
UO38	6¢ vermillion on cream	......	600.00	......
UO39	10¢ vermillion on white	475.00	375.00	......
UO40	12¢ vermillion on white	240.00	185.00	......
UO41	15¢ vermillion on white	3250.00	275.00	......
UO42	24¢ vermillion on white	675.00	475.00	......
UO43	30¢ vermillion on white	650.00	550.00	......

1875 PLIMPTON ISSUE

UO44	1¢ red on white	275.00	210.00	95.00
UO45	1¢ red on amber	......	1200.00	......
WO46	1¢ red on manila	10.00	4.50	3.00
UO47	2¢ red on white	200.00	150.00	......
UO48	2¢ red on amber	50.00	40.00	18.00
UO49	2¢ red on orange	85.00	72.00	18.00
WO50	2¢ red on manila	250.00	110.00	60.00
UO51	3¢ red on white	25.00	18.00	11.00
UO52	3¢ red on amber	32.00	23.00	11.00
UO53	3¢ red on cream	10.00	8.00	4.00
UO54	3¢ red on blue	7.00	4.50	3.00
UO55	3¢ red on fawn	12.00	7.00	3.00
UO56	6¢ red on white	110.00	75.00	35.00
UO57	6¢ red on amber	140.00	100.00	50.00
UO58	6¢ red on cream	300.00	250.00	95.00
UO59	10¢ red on white	325.00	275.00	90.00
UO60	10¢ red on amber	1750.00	1320.00	......
UO61	12¢ red on white	200.00	75.00	42.00
UO62	12¢ red on amber	1000.00	850.00	......
UO63	12¢ red on cream	1000.00	800.00	......
UO64	15¢ red on white	325.00	275.00	150.00
UO65	15¢ red on amber	1300.00	1000.00	......
UO66	15¢ red on cream	1200.00	850.00	......
UO67	30¢ red on white	250.00	200.00	150.00
UO68	30¢ red on amber	2500.00	1150.00	......
UO69	30¢ red on cream	1400.00	1100.00	......

SCOTT NO.	DESCRIPTION	UNUSED ENTIRE	UNUSED CUT SQ.	USED CUT SQ.

UO70-UO72

1911 POSTAL SAVINGS

UO70	1¢ green on white	100.00	80.00	25.00
UO71	1¢ green on oriental buff	275.00	210.00	77.00
UO72	2¢ carmine on white	24.00	13.50	4.50

SCOTT NO.	DESCRIPTION	FIRST DAY COVER	UNUSED ENTIRE	USED CUT SQ.

UO73

UO74

UO75

1983

UO73	20¢ blue and white	2.50	1.40	40.00

1985

UO74	22¢ blue and white	2.00	1.00	35.00

1987 Design Similar to UO74

UO75	22¢ Savings Bond	3.25	1.40	35.00

UO76

UO77

UO78

UO81

UO83

UO84

1989

UO76	(25¢) "E" black and blue Savings Bonds	2.00	1.40	35.00
UO77	25¢ black and blue	2.00	1.00	25.00
UO78	25¢ black and blue Savings Bonds	2.00	1.00	35.00

1990

UO79	45¢ black & blue seal	2.25	1.40	......
UO80	65¢ black & blue seal	3.00	1.95	......
UO81	45¢ Self-sealing Envelope	2.25	1.40	......
UO82	65¢ Self-sealing Envelope	3.00	1.95	......

UO85

UO86, UO87

UO88, UO89, UO90,
UO91, UO92, UO93

1991-92

UO83	(29¢) "F" black and blue Savings Bond	2.00	1.40	33.00
UO84	29¢ black and blue	2.00	1.00	25.00
UO85	29¢ black and blue Savings Bond	2.00	.90	25.00
UO86	52¢ Consular Service	2.50	6.00	......
UO87	75¢ Consular Service	3.00	11.00	......

1995

UO88	32¢ Great Seal, red and blue	2.00	.90	25.00

1999

UO89	33¢ Great Seal, red and blue	2.00	.90	25.00

2001-07

UO90	34¢ Great Seal, red and blue	2.00	1.00	25.00
UO91	37¢ Great Seal, red and blue	2.00	1.00	....
UO92	39¢ Great Seal, red and blue	2.00	1.00	....
UO93	41¢ Great Seal, red and blue	2.00	1.25	....
UO94	42¢ Great Seal, official stamped envelope	2.50	1.25	....

SCOTT NO.	DESCRIPTION	MINT	UNUSED	USED

POSTAL CARDS

Prices Are For Entire Cards
MINT: As Issued, no printing or writing added.
UNUSED: Uncancelled, with printing or writing added.

UX1, UX3, U65

UX4, UX5, UX7
Liberty

UX6, UX13, UX16

1873

UX1	1¢ brown, large watermark	425.00	75.00	27.00
UX3	1¢ brown, small watermark	90.00	22.00	3.00

1875 Inscribed "Write the Address", etc.

UX4	1¢ black, watermarked	4100.00	800.00	450.00
UX5	1¢ black, unwatermarked	85.00	7.50	.50

1879

UX6	2¢ blue on buff	38.00	12.00	27.50

1881 Inscribed "Nothing but the Address", etc.

UX7	1¢ black on buff	75.00	7.00	.50

UX8
Jefferson

UX9

UX10, UX11
Grant

1885

UX8	1¢ brown on buff	60.00	12.00	1.50

1886

UX9	1¢ black on buff	28.00	2.00	.65

1891

UX10	1¢ black on buff	50.00	7.50	1.75
UX11	1¢ blue on grayish white	25.00	6.00	3.00

UX12

UX14
Jefferson

UX15
John Adams

1894

UX12	1¢ black on buff Small Wreath	47.50	2.50	.75

1897

UX13	2¢ blue on cream	230.00	95.00	95.00
UX14	1¢ black on buff Large Wreath	45.00	3.00	.50

1898

UX15	1¢ black on buff	50.00	14.00	16.00
UX16	2¢ black on buff	16.00	6.25	20.00

UX18

UX19, UX20
McKinley

UX21

1902 Profile Background

UX18	1¢ black on buff	18.00	1.85	.40

1907

UX19	1¢ black on buff	50.00	2.50	.60

1908 Correspondence Space at Left

UX20	1¢ black on buff	60.00	9.00	4.50

1910 Background Shaded

UX21	1¢ blue on bluish	120.00	18.00	14.00

UX22, UX24
McKinley

UX23, UX26
Lincoln

UX25
Grant

White Portrait Background

UX22	1¢ blue on bluish	22.00	2.25	.45

1911

UX23	1¢ red on cream	12.00	4.00	6.00
UX24	1¢ red on cream	12.00	1.50	.40
UX25	2¢ red on cream	1.75	.75	22.00

1913

UX26	1¢ green on cream	14.00	3.00	9.00

UX27
Jefferson

UX28, UX43
Lincoln

UX29, UX30
Jefferson

UX32, UX33
surcharge

1914

UX27	1¢ green on buff	.35	.25	.30

1917-18

UX28	1¢ green on cream	1.00	.40	.40
UX29	2¢ red on buff, die 1	44.00	7.00	2.50
UX30	2¢ red on cream, die 2 (1918)	35.00	5.00	1.80

NOTE: On UX29 end of queue slopes sharply down to right while on UX30 it extends nearly horizontally.

1920 UX29 & UX30 Revalued

UX32	1¢ on 2¢ red, die 1	55.00	16.50	13.00
UX33	1¢ on 2¢ red, die 2	14.00	2.75	2.25

UX37
McKinley

UX38
Franklin

UX39-42 surcharge

1926

UX37	3¢ red on buff	4.75	2.00	17.50

SCOTT NO.	DESCRIPTION	FIRST DAY COVER	MINT	USED
	1951			
UX38	2¢ carmine rose	1.75	.40	.35
	1952 UX27 & UX28 Surcharged by cancelling machine, light green			
UX39	2¢ on 1¢ green	......	.60	.35
UX40	2¢ on 1¢ green	......	.70	.50
	UX27 & UX28 Surcharge Typographed, dark green			
UX41	2¢ on 1¢ green	......	5.00	2.00
UX42	2¢ on 1¢ green	......	5.25	2.75
	1952 Design of 1917			
UX43	2¢ carmine	1.75	.35	1.00

UX44 **UX45, UY16** **UX46, UY17**

	1956 FIPEX COMMEMORATIVE			
UX44	2¢ deep carmine & dark violet	1.75	.35	1.00
	1956 INTERNATIONAL CARD			
UX45	4¢ deep red & ultramarine	1.75	1.75	100.00
	1958			
UX46	3¢ purple	1.75	.60	.25
	As above, but with printed precancel lines			
UX46d	3¢ purple	......	5.00	3.00

ONE CENT ADDITIONAL PAID
UX47 surcharge

UX48, UY18
Lincoln

UX49, UX54, UX59, UY19, UY20

	1958 UX38 Surcharged			
UX47	2¢ & 1¢ carmine rose	......	250.00	685.00

Mint *UX47 has advertising

	1962-66			
UX48	4¢ red violet	1.75	.60	.25
UX48a	4¢ luminescent (1966)	3.00	.65	.25
	1963			
UX49	7¢ Tourism	1.75	4.25	75.00

UX50 **UX51**

	1964			
UX50	4¢ Customs Service	1.75	.50	1.00
UX51	4¢ Social Security	1.75	.50	1.00

UX52 **UX53**

SCOTT NO.	DESCRIPTION	FIRST DAY COVER	MINT	USED
	1965			
UX52	4¢ Coast Guard...	1.75	.45	1.00
UX53	4¢ Census Bureau..	1.75	.45	1.00
	1967 Design of UX49			
UX54	8¢ Tourism	1.75	4.25	75.00

UX55, UY21
Lincoln

UX56

	1968			
UX55	5¢ emerald	1.75	.35	.75
UX56	5¢ Women Marines...	1.75	.40	1.00

UX57

	1970			
UX57	5¢ Weather Bureau...	1.75	.35	1.00

UX58, UY22

	1971			
UX58	6¢ Paul Revere	1.75	.30	1.00
	Design of UX49			
UX59	10¢ Tourism	1.75	4.75	65.00

UX60

	1971			
UX60	6¢ New York Hospital..	1.75	.35	1.00

UX61 **UX62**

UX63 **UX64, UY23**

	1972			
UX61	6¢ U.S.F. Constellation	1.75	1.00	12.00
UX62	6¢ Monument Valley	1.75	.45	12.00
UX63	6¢ Gloucester, Massachusetts...................................	1.75	.45	7.00
UX64	6¢ John Hanson...	1.75	.60	1.00

SCOTT NO.	DESCRIPTION	FIRST DAY COVER	MINT	USED

UX66, UY24

UX78

UX79

UX67

UX80

1973

UX65	6¢ Liberty, magenta, Design of 1873	1.75	.35	1.00
UX66	8¢ Samuel Adams	1.75	.65	1.00

1979

1974

UX67	12¢ Visit USA	1.75	.45	50.00

UX78	10¢ Fort Sackville	1.75	.35	2.00
UX79	10¢ Casimir Pulaski	1.75	.35	2.00
UX80	10¢ Moscow Olympics	1.75	.65	2.00
UX81	10¢ Iolani Palace	1.75	.35	2.00

UX68, UY25

UX69, UY26

UX81

UX82

UX83

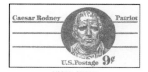

UX70, UY27

1975-76

UX68	7¢ Charles Thomson..	1.75	.35	12.00
UX69	9¢ J. Witherspoon	1.75	.35	1.00
UX70	9¢ Caesar Rodney	1.75	.35	1.00

UX84

UX85

UX86

1980

UX71

UX72, UY28

UX82	14¢ Winter Olympics..	1.75	.65	22.00
UX83	10¢ Salt Lake Temple	1.75	.35	2.00
UX84	10¢ Count Rochambeau	1.75	.35	2.00
UX85	10¢ Kings Mountain	1.75	.35	2.00
UX86	19¢ Sir Francis Drake	1.75	.75	40.00

1977

UX71	9¢ Federal Court House...	1.75	.50	1.00
UX72	9¢ Nathan Hale	1.75	.55	1.00

UX87

HISTORIC PRESERVATION USA

UX73

UX74, UX75, UY29, UY30

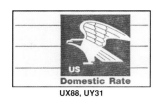

UX88, UY31

UX89, UY32

UX76

UX77

1981

1978

UX73	10¢ Music Hall	1.75	.35	1.00
UX74	(10¢) John Hancock...	1.75	.35	1.00
UX75	10¢ John Hancock	1.75	.35	1.00
UX76	14¢ "Eagle"	1.75	.50	35.00
UX77	10¢ multicolored...	1.75	.50	2.00

UX87	10¢ Cowpens	1.75	.35	18.50
UX88	"B" (12¢) violet & white...	1.75	.35	.75
UX89	12¢ Isaiah Thomas	1.75	.35	.75

SCOTT NO.	DESCRIPTION	FIRST DAY COVER	MINT	USED

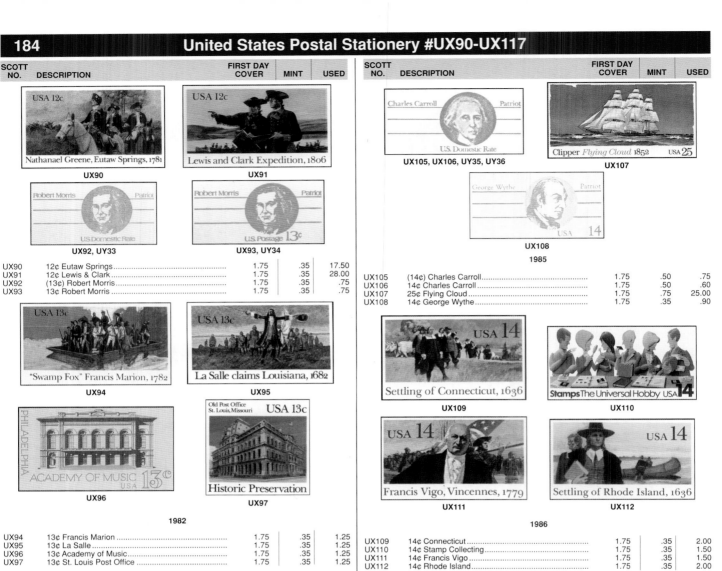

UX90 — USA 12c — Nathanael Greene, Eutaw Springs, 1781

UX91 — USA 12c — Lewis and Clark Expedition, 1806

UX92, UY33 — Robert Morris Patriot — U.S. Domestic Rate

UX93, UY34 — Robert Morris Patriot — U.S. Postage 13¢

UX90	12¢ Eutaw Springs	1.75	.35	17.50
UX91	12¢ Lewis & Clark	1.75	.35	28.00
UX92	(13¢) Robert Morris	1.75	.35	.75
UX93	13¢ Robert Morris	1.75	.35	.75

UX94 — USA 13c — "Swamp Fox" Francis Marion, 1782

UX95 — USA 13c — La Salle claims Louisiana, 1682

UX96 — PHILADELPHIA ACADEMY OF MUSIC USA 13¢

UX97 — Old Post Office St. Louis, Missouri — USA 13c — Historic Preservation

1982

UX94	13¢ Francis Marion	1.75	.35	1.25
UX95	13¢ La Salle	1.75	.35	1.25
UX96	13¢ Academy of Music	1.75	.35	1.25
UX97	13¢ St. Louis Post Office	1.75	.35	1.25

UX98 — USA 13c — Landing of Oglethorpe, Georgia, 1733

UX99 — USA 13c — Old Post Office, Washington, D.C.

UX100 — Olympics 84 — USA 13c

1983

UX98	13¢ General Oglethorpe	1.75	.35	1.25
UX99	13¢ Washington Post Office	1.75	.35	1.25
UX100	13¢ Olympics	1.75	.35	1.25

UX101 — USA 13c — Ark and Dove, Maryland, 1634

UX102 — Olympics 84 — USA 13c

UX103 — USA 13c — Frederic Baraga, Michigan, 1835

UX104 — Dominguez Adobe Rancho San Pedro — The California Ranchos 1784-1984 — Historic Preservation USA 13

1984

UX101	13¢ "Ark" & "Dove"	1.75	.35	1.25
UX102	13¢ Olympics	1.75	.35	1.50
UX103	13¢ Frederic Baraga	1.75	.35	1.25
UX104	13¢ Historic Preservation	1.75	.35	1.25

UX105, UX106, UY35, UY36 — Charles Carroll Patriot — U.S. Domestic Rate

UX107 — Clipper Flying Cloud 1852 — USA 25

UX108 — George Wythe Patriot — USA 14

1985

UX105	(14¢) Charles Carroll	1.75	.50	.75
UX106	14¢ Charles Carroll	1.75	.50	.60
UX107	25¢ Flying Cloud	1.75	.75	25.00
UX108	14¢ George Wythe	1.75	.35	.90

UX109 — USA 14 — Settling of Connecticut, 1636

UX110 — Stamps The Universal Hobby USA 14

UX111 — USA 14 — Francis Vigo, Vincennes, 1779

UX112 — USA 14 — Settling of Rhode Island, 1636

1986

UX109	14¢ Connecticut	1.75	.35	2.00
UX110	14¢ Stamp Collecting	1.75	.35	1.50
UX111	14¢ Francis Vigo	1.75	.35	1.50
UX112	14¢ Rhode Island	1.75	.35	2.00

UX113 — 14 USA — Wisconsin Territory, 1836

UX114 — 14 USA — National Guard Heritage, 1636-1986

| UX113 | 14¢ Wisconsin | 1.75 | .35 | 1.25 |
| UX114 | 14¢ National Guard | 1.75 | .35 | 1.50 |

UX115 — USA 14 — Self-scouring steel plow, 1837

UX116 — USA 14 — Constitutional Convention, 1787

UX117 — USA 14 (Flag)

1987

UX115	14¢ Steel Plow	1.75	.35	1.50
UX116	14¢ Constitution	1.75	.35	1.00
UX117	14¢ Flag	1.75	.35	.75

SCOTT NO.	DESCRIPTION	FIRST DAY COVER	MINT	USED

UX118 — Take Pride in America 14 USA

UX119 — Historic Preservation USA 14 (Timberline Lodge Mt. Hood, Oregon)

1987 (continued)

UX118	14¢ Take Pride in America	1.75	.35	1.50
UX119	14¢ Timberline Lodge	1.75	.35	1.50

UX120 — America the Beautiful USA 15

UX121 — Blair House USA 15

1988

UX120	15¢ America the Beautiful	1.75	.35	.75
UX121	15¢ Blair House	1.75	.35	.85

UX122 — 28 USA (Yorkshire)

UX123 — Iowa Territory, 1838 USA 15

UX122	28¢ Yorkshire	1.75	.65	22.50
UX123	15¢ Iowa Territory	1.75	.35	.85

UX124 — Settling of Ohio, Northwest Territory, 1788 USA 15

UX125 — Hearst Castle San Simeon California USA 15

UX124	15¢ Northwest Territory	1.75	.35	.85
UX125	15¢ Hearst Castle	1.75	.35	.85

UX126 — The Federalist Papers, 1787-88 USA 15

UX126	15¢ Federalist Papers	1.75	.35	.85

UX127 — America the Beautiful USA 15

UX128 — USA 15

1989

UX127	15¢ The Desert	1.75	.35	.85
UX128	15¢¡ Healy Hall	1.75	.35	.85

UX129 — America the Beautiful USA 15

UX130 — Settling of Oklahoma 15 USA

UX129	15¢ The Wet Lands	1.75	.35	.85
UX130	15¢ Oklahoma Territory	1.75	.35	.85

UX131 — America the Beautiful USA 21

UX132 — America the Beautiful USA 15

UX131	21¢ The Mountains	1.75	.65	20.00
UX132	15¢ The Seashore	1.75	.35	.85

UX133 — America the Beautiful USA 15

UX134 — USA 15

UX133	15¢ The Woodlands	1.75	.35	.85
UX134	15¢ Hull House	1.75	.35	.85

UX135 — America the Beautiful USA 15

UX136 — America the Beautiful USA 15

UX135	15¢ Philadelphia Cityscape	1.75	.35	.85
UX136	15¢ Baltimore Cityscape	1.75	.35	.85

UX137 — America the Beautiful USA 15

UX138 — America the Beautiful USA 15

UX137	15¢ New York Cityscape	1.75	.35	.85
UX138	15¢ Washington Cityscape	1.75	.35	.85
UX139-42	15¢ Cityscape sheet of 4 postcards	8.00	20.00	27.50

UX143 — 15 USA (White House)

UX144 — USA 15 (Jefferson Memorial)

UX143	15¢ White House	1.75	1.70	3.00
UX144	15¢ Jefferson Memorial	1.75	1.70	3.00

UX145 — USA 15

UX146 — 15 USA The world is an open book.

SCOTT NO.	DESCRIPTION	FIRST DAY COVER	MINT	USED

UX147

UX148

UX150

UX151

UX152

1990

SCOTT NO.	DESCRIPTION	FIRST DAY COVER	MINT	USED
UX145	15¢ Papermaking	1.75	.35	.50
UX146	15¢ Literacy	1.75	.35	.85
UX147	15¢ Bingham	1.75	1.60	3.00
UX148	15¢ Isaac Royall House	1.75	.50	.85
UX150	15¢ Stanford University	1.75	.50	.85
UX151	15¢ DAR Memorial Hall	1.75	1.60	2.50
UX152	15¢ Chicago Orchestra Hall	1.75	.50	.85

UX153

UX154

UX155

1991

SCOTT NO.	DESCRIPTION	FIRST DAY COVER	MINT	USED
UX153	19¢ Flag	1.75	.50	.85
UX154	19¢ Carnegie Hall	1.75	.50	.85
UX155	19¢ Old Red Administration Building	1.75	.50	.50

UX156

UX157

UX156	19¢ Bill of Rights	1.75	.50	.85
UX157	19¢ University of Notre Dame, Administration Building	1.75	.50	.85

UX158

UX159

SCOTT NO.	DESCRIPTION	FIRST DAY COVER	MINT	USED
UX158	30¢ Niagara Falls	1.75	.90	10.00
UX159	19¢ Old Mill University of Vermont	1.75	.45	1.00

UX160

UX161

UX162

UX163

UX164

UX165

1992

UX160	19¢ Wadsworth Atheneum	1.75	.50	.85
UX161	19¢ Cobb Hall University of Chicago	1.75	.50	.85
UX162	19¢ Waller Hall	1.75	.50	.85
UX163	19¢ America's Cup	1.75	1.85	4.00
UX164	19¢ Columbia River Gorge	1.75	.50	.85
UX165	19¢ Great Hall, Ellis Island	1.75	.50	.85

UX166

UX167

1993

UX166	19¢ National Cathedral	1.75	.50	.85
UX167	19¢ Wren Building	1.75	.50	.85

UX168

UX169

UX168	19¢ Holocaust Memorial	2.00	1.85	4.00
UX169	19¢ Fort Recovery	1.75	.50	.85

UX170

UX171

UX170	19¢ Playmakers Theatre	1.75	.50	.85
UX171	19¢ O'Kane Hall	1.75	.50	.85

SCOTT NO.	DESCRIPTION	FIRST DAY COVER	MINT	USED

UX172

UX173

1993 (continued)

UX172	19¢ Beecher Hall	1.75	.50	.85
UX173	19¢ Massachusetts Hall	1.75	.50	.85

UX174

UX175

UX176

UX177

1994

UX174	19¢ Abraham Lincoln Home	1.75	.50	.85
UX175	19¢ Myers Hall	1.75	.50	.85
UX176	19¢ Canyon de Chelly	1.75	.50	.85
UX177	19¢ St. Louis Union Station	1.75	.50	.85

Legends of the West

UX178

UX178	Home on the Range	UX188	Nellie Cashman
UX179	Buffalo Bill	UX189	Charles Goodnight
UX180	Jim Bridger	UX190	Geronimo
UX181	Annie Oakley	UX191	Kit Carson
UX182	Native American Culture	UX192	Wild Bill Hickok
UX183	Chief Joseph	UX193	Western Wildlife
UX184	Bill Pickett	UX194	Jim Beckwourth
UX185	Bat Masterson	UX195	Bill Tilghman
UX186	John Fremont	UX196	Sacagawea
UX187	Wyatt Earp	UX197	Overland Mail

UX178-97	19¢ Legends of the West, set of 20	35.00	35.00	65.00

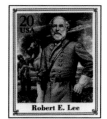
UX198

UX198

USA **Old Glory**
For United States addresses only
UX199

1995

UX198	20¢ Red Barn	1.75	.50	.75
UX199	(20¢) "G" Old Glory	1.75	3.50	3.00

Civil War

UX200	Monitor-Virginia	UX210	Tubman
UX201	Lee	UX211	Watie
UX202	Barton	UX212	Johnston
UX203	Grant	UX213	Hancock
UX204	Shiloh	UX214	Chestnut
UX205	Davis	UX215	Chancellorsville
UX206	Farragut	UX216	Sherman
UX207	Douglass	UX217	Pember
UX208	Semmes	UX218	Jackson
UX209	Lincoln	UX219	Gettysburg

UX201

UX200-19	20¢ Civil War, set of 20	35.00	42.50	65.00
UX219a	50¢ Eagle	1.75	1.75	10.00

SCOTT NO.	DESCRIPTION	FIRST DAY COVER	MINT	USED

UX220

UX241

UX220	20¢ American Clipper Ships	1.75	.50	.85

American Comic Strips

UX221

UX221	Yellow Kid	UX231	Popeye
UX222	Katzenjammer Kids	UX232	Blondie
UX223	Little Nemo	UX233	Dick Tracy
UX224	Bring Up Father	UX234	Alley Oop
UX225	Krazy Kat	UX235	Nancy
UX226	Rube Goldberg	UX236	Flash Gordon
UX227	Toonerville Folks	UX237	Li'l Abner
UX228	Gasoline Alley	UX238	Terry/Pirates
UX229	Barney Google	UX239	Prince Valiant
UX230	Little Orphan Annie	UX240	Brenda Starr

UX221-40	20¢ American Comic Strips, set of 20	35.00	60.00	65.00

1996

UX241	20¢ Winter Farm Scene	1.75	.50	.50

Centennial Olympic Games

UX242

UX242	Men's cycling	UX252	Women's softball
UX243	Women's diving	UX253	Women's swimming
UX244	Women's running	UX254	Men's sprints
UX245	Men's canoeing	UX255	Men's rowing
UX246	Decathlon	UX256	Beach volleyball
UX247	Women's soccer	UX257	Men's basketball
UX248	Men's shot put	UX258	Equestrian
UX249	Women's sailboarding	UX259	Men's gymnastics
UX250	Women's gymnastics	UX260	Men's swimming
UX251	Freestyle wrestling	UX261	Men's hurdles

UX242-61	20¢ Centennial Olympic Games, set of 20	35.00	60.00	65.00

UX262

UX263

UX262	20¢ McDowell Hall	1.75	.50	.85
UX263	20¢ Alexander Hall	1.75	.50	.85

Engandered Species

UX264

UX264	Florida panther	
UX265	Black-footed ferret	
UX266	American crocodile	
UX267	Piping plover	
UX268	Gila trout	
UX269	Florida manatee	
UX270	Schaus swallowtail butterfly	
UX271	Woodland caribou	
UX272	Thick-billed parrot	
UX273	San Francisco garter snake	
UX274	Ocelot	
UX275	Wyoming toad	
UX276	California condor	
UX277	Hawaiian monk seal	
UX278	Brown pelican	

UX264-78	20¢ Endangered Species, set of 15	26.50	70.00	65.00

UX279

UX280

1997

UX279	20¢ Swans	2.50	6.00	2.00
UX279a	20¢ Swans, set of 12	20.00(8)	60.00	
UX280	20¢ Shepard Hall	1.75	.60	1.00

SCOTT NO.	DESCRIPTION	FIRST DAY COVER	MINT	USED

UX281
UX282

UX281	20¢ Bugs Bunny		1.65	2.50
UX282	20¢ Golden Gate Bridge	1.75	.45	1.00

UX283
UX284

UX283	50¢ Golden Gate Bridge at Sunset	1.95	1.40	3.00
UX284	20¢ Fort McHenry	1.75	.50	.85

Classic Movie Monsters

UX285 *Lon Chaney as The Phantom of the Opera*
UX286 *Bela Lugosi as Dracula*
UX287 *Boris Karloff as Frankenstein's Monster*
UX288 *Boris Karloff as The Mummy*
UX289 *Lon Chaney Jr. as The Wolfman*

UX285
UX291

UX285	20¢ Classic Movie Monsters, set of 5	8.75	9.00	7.50
UX289a	same, bklt of 20 (4 of each)		35.00	

UX290
UX292

1998

UX290	20¢ University of Mississippi	1.75	.50	.85
UX291	20¢ Sylvester & Tweety	1.75	1.75	3.00
UX291a	same, bklt of 10		17.00	
UX292	20¢ Girard College, Philadelphia, PA	1.75	.50	.85

UX293
UX297
UX298

UX293-96	20¢ Tropical Birds, set of 4	7.00	5.00	7.50
UX296a	same, bklt of 20 (5 of each)		24.00	
UX297	20¢ Ballet	1.75	1.75	1.50
UX297a	same, bklt of 10		17.00	
UX298	20¢ Kerr Hall, Northeastern University	1.75	.50	.85

UX299
UX300
UX301

SCOTT NO.	DESCRIPTION	FIRST DAY COVER	MINT	USED
UX299	20¢ Usen Castle, Brandeis University	1.75	.60	.85

1999

UX300	20¢ Love, Victorian	1.75	1.40	2.00
UX301	20¢ University of Wisc.-Madison-Bascom Hill	1.75	.60	.60

UX302
UX303

UX302	20¢ Washington and Lee University	1.75	.60	.60
UX303	20¢ Redwood Library & Anthenaum, Newport, RI	1.75	.60	.60

UX304
UX305

UX304	20¢ Daffy Duck	1.75	1.75	1.50
UX304a	same, bklt of 10		17.00	
UX305	20¢ Mount Vernon	1.75	.60	.60

Famous Trains

UX307 *Super Chief*
UX308 *Hiawatha*
UX309 *Daylight*
UX310 *Congressional*
UX311 *20th Century Limited*

UX306
UX307

1999

UX306	20¢ Block Island Lighthouse	1.75	.50	.50
UX307-11	20¢ Famous Trains, set of 5	8.75	7.00	6.00
UX311a	same, bklt of 20 (4 of each)		27.50	

UX312
UX313

UX315

UX316

2000

UX312	20¢ University of Utah	1.75	.50	.60
UX313	20¢ Ryman Auditorium, Nashville, Tennessee	1.75	.50	.60
UX314	20¢ Road Runner & Wile E. Coyote	1.75	1.75	1.50
UX314a	same, bklt of 10		17.00	
UX315	20¢ Adoption	1.75	1.75	1.75
UX315a	same, bklt of 10		17.00	
UX316	20¢ Old Stone Row, Middlebury College, Vermont	1.75	.50	.60

SCOTT NO.	DESCRIPTION	FIRST DAY COVER	MINT	USED

UX336

The Stars and Stripes

UX317	Sons of Liberty Flag, 1775	UX327	Star-Spangled Banner, 1814
UX318	New England Flag, 1775	UX328	Bennington Flag, c. 1820
UX319	Forster Flag, 1775	UX329	Great Star Flag, 1837
UX320	Continental Colors, 1776	UX330	29-Star Flag, 1847
UX321	Francis Hopkinson Flag, 1777	UX331	Fort Sumter Flag, 1861
UX322	Brandywine Flag, 1777	UX332	Centennial Flag, 1876
UX323	John Paul Jones Flag, 1779	UX333	38-Star Flag
UX324	Pierre L'Enfant Flag, 1783	UX334	Peace Flag, 1891
UX325	Indian Peace Flag, 1803	UX335	48-Star Flag, 1912
UX326	Easton Flag, 1814	UX336	50-Star Flag, 1960

UX317-36	The Stars and Stripes, set of 20	35.00	45.00	45.00

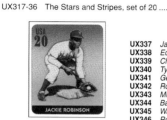

Legends of Baseball

UX337	Jackie Robinson	UX347	Lefty Grove
UX338	Eddie Collins	UX348	Tris Speaker
UX339	Christy Mathewson	UX349	Cy Young
UX340	Ty Cobb	UX350	Jimmie Foxx
UX341	George Sisler	UX351	Pie Traynor
UX342	Rogers Hornsby	UX352	Satchel Paige
UX343	Mickey Cochrane	UX353	Honus Wagner
UX344	Babe Ruth	UX354	Josh Gibson
UX345	Walter Johnson	UX355	Dizzy Dean
UX346	Roberto Clemente	UX356	Lou Gehrig

UX337

UX337-56	20¢ Legends of Baseball, set of 20	35.00	35.00	30.00

UX357-60

UX361

UX357-60	20¢ Christmas Deer, set of 4	7.00	6.00	5.00

2001

UX361	20¢ Connecticut Hall, Yale University	1.75	.50	.75

UX362   **UX363**   **UX364**

UX362	20¢ University of South Carolina	1.75	.50	.85
UX363	20¢ Northwestern University Sesquicentennial 1851-2001	1.75	.50	.85
UX364	20¢ Waldschmidt Hall, The University of Portland	1.75	.50	.75

Legendary Playing Fields

UX365	Ebbets Field	UX370	Forbes Field
UX366	Tiger Stadium	UX371	Fenway Park
UX367	Crosley Field	UX372	Comiskey Park
UX368	Yankee Stadium	UX373	Shibe Park
UX369	Polo Grounds	UX374	Wrigley Field

2001

UX365-74	21¢ Legendary Playing Fields, set of 10	35.00	24.00	20.00
UX374a	same, bklt of 10		24.00	

UX375   **UX376**   **UX377**

UX375	21¢ White Barn	1.75	.50	.60
UX376	21¢ That's All Folks	2.00	1.75	1.75
UX376a	same, bklt of 10		17.00	
UX377-80	21¢ Santas, set of 4	7.50	6.00	5.00
UX380a	same, complete bklt of 20		22.50	

UX381   **UX382**   **UX386**

2002

UX381	23¢ Carlsbad Caverns	1.75	.55	.60
UX382-85	23¢ Teddy Bears, set of 4	7.50	6.00	5.00
UX385a	same, complete bklt of 20		27.50	
UX386-89	23¢ Christmas Snowmen, set of 4	7.50	6.00	5.00
UX389a	same, complete bklt of 20		27.50	

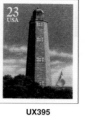

UX390   **UX395**   **UX400**

2003

UX390-94	23¢ Old Glory, set of 5	8.75	7.00	6.00
UX394a	same, complete booklet of 20 cards		27.50	
UX395-99	23¢ Southern Lighthouses, set of 5	8.75	7.00	6.00
UX399a	same, complete bklt of 20		27.50	
UX400	23¢ Ohio University, 200th Anniversary	1.75	.55	.60
UX401-04	23¢ Christmas Music Makers, set of 4	7.50	5.00	5.00
UX404a	same, complete bklt of 20		22.50	

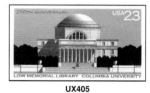

UX401   **UX405**

2004

UX405	23¢ Columbia University, 250th Anniversary	1.75	.55	.60

UX406   **UX407**

UX406	23¢ Harriton House, 300th Anniversary	1.75	.55	.60
UX407-10	23¢ Art of Disney, set of 4	7.00	5.75	5.00
UX410a	same, complete booklet of 20		26.00	

UX411   **UX421**

UX411-20	23¢ Art of the American Indian, set of 10	17.50	14.00	13.00
UX420a	same, complete booklet of 20		26.00	
UX421-35	23¢ Cloudscapes, set of 15	26.25	20.00	17.50
UX435a	same, complete booklet of 20		26.00	

SCOTT NO.	DESCRIPTION	FIRST DAY COVER	MINT	USED

1953 Chevrolet Corvette USA 23

UX440

USA 24

Pike Expedition, November 1806, Rocky Mountains

UX449

2005

SCOTT NO.	DESCRIPTION	FIRST DAY COVER	MINT	USED
UX436-39	Disney Characters, set of 4	7.00	5.75	5.00
UX439a	same, complete booklet of 20	....	27.50	....
UX440-44	23¢ Sporty Cars, set of 4	7.00	5.75	5.00
UX444a	same, complete booklet of 20	....	27.50	....
UX445-48	23¢ Let's Dance, set of 4	7.00	5.75	4.00
UX448a	same, complete booklet of 20	....	27.50	....

2006

UX449	24¢ Zebulon Pike Expedition, Bicentennial	1.75	.60	.65

24 USA

UX450

USA 24

MICKEY MANTLE

UX454

UX450-53	24¢ Disney Characters, set of 4	7.00	5.75	5.00
UX453a	same, complete booklet of 20	....	27.50	....
UX454-57	24¢ Baseball Sluggers, set of 4	7.00	5.75	5.00
UX457a	same, complete booklet of 20	....	27.50	....

SUPERMAN

USA 24

UX458

D.C. Comics Super Heroes

UX458	Superman Cover	UX468	The Flash Cover
UX459	Superman	UX469	The Flash
UX460	Batman Cover	UX470	Plastic Man Cover
UX461	Batman	UX471	Plastic Man
UX462	Wonder Woman Cover	UX472	Aquaman Cover
UX463	Wonder Woman	UX473	Aquaman
UX464	Green Lantern Cover	UX474	Supergirl Cover
UX465	Green Lantern	UX475	Supergirl
UX466	Green Arrow Cover	UX476	Hawkman Cover
UX467	Green Arrow	UX477	Hawkman

UX458-77	24¢ D.C. Comics Super Heroes, set of 20	40.00	35.00	30.00

USA 39

UX483

Southern Florida Wetlands

UX478	Snail Kite	UX483	White Ibis
UX479	Cape Sable Seaside Sparrow	UX484	American Crocodile
UX480	Wood Storks	UX485	Everglades Mink
UX481	Florida Panthers	UX486	Roseate Spoonbills
UX482	Bald Eagle	UX487	American Alligators

UX478-87	39¢ Southern Florida Wetlands, set of 10	....	50.00	....

26 USA

UX488

2007

UX488	26¢ Pineapple	1.95	.70	.75

USA 26

UX501

Star Wars

UX489	Darth Vader	UX496	Obi-Wan Kenobi
UX490	Luke Skywalker	UX497	Boba Fett
UX491	C-3PO	UX498	Darth Maul
UX492	Queen Padme Amidala	UX499	Yoda
UX493	Millennium Falcon	UX500	Princess Leia and R2-D2
UX494	Emperor Palpatine	UX501	Chewbacca and Han Solo
UX495	Anakin Skywalker and	UX502	X-wing Starfighter
	Obi-Wan Kenobi	UX503	Stormtroopers

UX489-503	26¢ Star Wars, set of 15	27.50	29.00	24.00

26 USA

UX505

UX504-08	26¢ Pacific Coast Lighthouses, set of 5	8.00	7.50	6.00
UX508a	same, complete booklet of 20	....	28.75	....
UX509-28	26¢ Marvel Comic Book Heroes, set of 20	40.00	35.00	30.00
UX529-32	26¢ Disney Characters, set of 4	7.50	6.00	2.50
	same, complete booklet of 20	....	28.75	....
UX533	27¢ Mount St. Mary's University postal card	2.75	.70	.70
UX534	27¢ Corinthian Column postal card	2.75	.70	.70

USA 27

The Terrace Mount St. Mary's University

UX533

USA 27 CORINTHIAN ORDER UNITED STATES CAPITOL

UX534

2008

UX533	27¢ Mount St. Mary's University postal card	2.75	.70	.70
UX534	27¢ Corinthian Column postal card	2.75	.70	.70

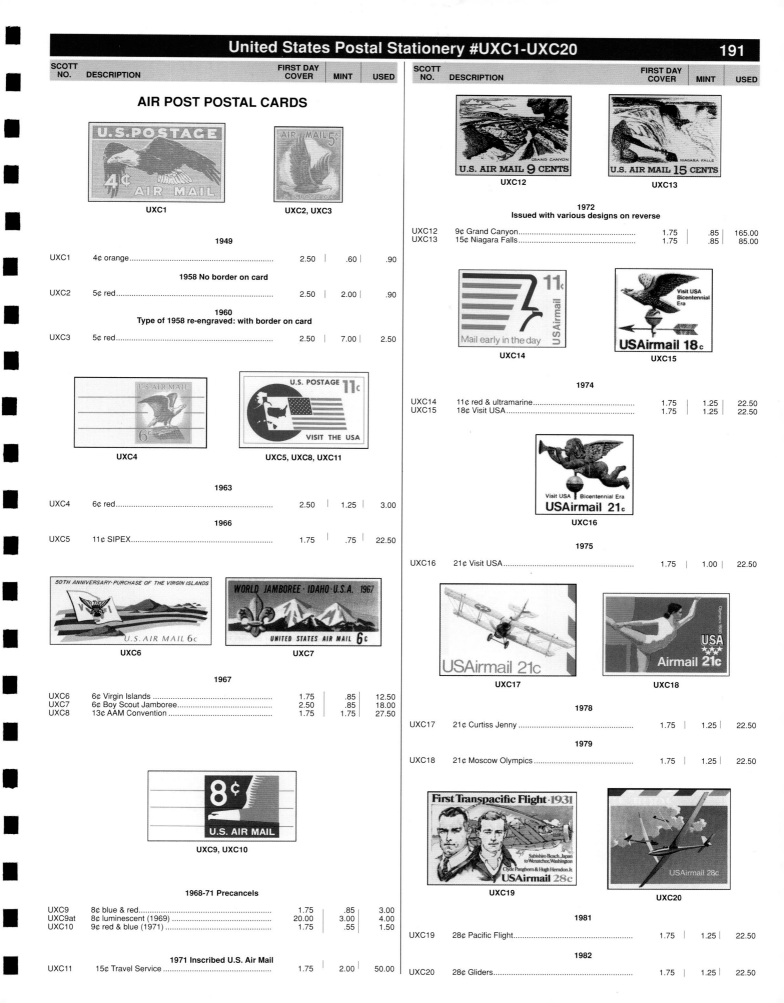

SCOTT NO.	DESCRIPTION	FIRST DAY COVER	MINT	USED

AIR POST POSTAL CARDS

UXC1

UXC2, UXC3

1949

| UXC1 | 4¢ orange | 2.50 | .60 | .90 |

1958 No border on card

| UXC2 | 5¢ red | 2.50 | 2.00 | .90 |

1960
Type of 1958 re-engraved: with border on card

| UXC3 | 5¢ red | 2.50 | 7.00 | 2.50 |

UXC4

UXC5, UXC8, UXC11

1963

| UXC4 | 6¢ red | 2.50 | 1.25 | 3.00 |

1966

| UXC5 | 11¢ SIPEX | 1.75 | .75 | 22.50 |

UXC6

UXC7

1967

UXC6	6¢ Virgin Islands	1.75	.85	12.50
UXC7	6¢ Boy Scout Jamboree	2.50	.85	18.00
UXC8	13¢ AAM Convention	1.75	1.75	27.50

UXC9, UXC10

1968-71 Precancels

UXC9	8¢ blue & red	1.75	.85	3.00
UXC9at	8¢ luminescent (1969)	20.00	3.00	4.00
UXC10	9¢ red & blue (1971)	1.75	.55	1.50

1971 Inscribed U.S. Air Mail

| UXC11 | 15¢ Travel Service | 1.75 | 2.00 | 50.00 |

UXC12

UXC13

1972
Issued with various designs on reverse

| UXC12 | 9¢ Grand Canyon | 1.75 | .85 | 165.00 |
| UXC13 | 15¢ Niagara Falls | 1.75 | .85 | 85.00 |

UXC14

UXC15

1974

| UXC14 | 11¢ red & ultramarine | 1.75 | 1.25 | 22.50 |
| UXC15 | 18¢ Visit USA | 1.75 | 1.25 | 22.50 |

UXC16

1975

| UXC16 | 21¢ Visit USA | 1.75 | 1.00 | 22.50 |

UXC17

UXC18

1978

| UXC17 | 21¢ Curtiss Jenny | 1.75 | 1.25 | 22.50 |

1979

| UXC18 | 21¢ Moscow Olympics | 1.75 | 1.25 | 22.50 |

UXC19

UXC20

1981

| UXC19 | 28¢ Pacific Flight | 1.75 | 1.25 | 22.50 |

1982

| UXC20 | 28¢ Gliders | 1.75 | 1.25 | 22.50 |

SCOTT NO.	DESCRIPTION	FIRST DAY COVER	MINT	USED

UXC21

UXC22

1983

| UXC21 | 28¢ Olympics .... | 1.75 | 1.25 | 22.50 |

1985

| UXC22 | 33¢ China Clipper .... | 1.75 | 1.25 | 22.50 |

UXC23

UXC24

1986

| UXC23 | 33¢ Ameripex '86 .... | 1.75 | 1.25 | 22.50 |

1988

| UXC24 | 36¢ DC-3... | 1.75 | 1.00 | 22.50 |

UXC25

1991

| UXC25 | 40¢ Yankee Clipper............................... | 1.75 | 1.00 | 22.50 |

UXC28

UXC26

1995

| UXC26 | 50¢ Soaring Eagle .... | 1.75 | 1.25 | 22.50 |

UXC27

UXC28

1999

| UXC27 | 55¢ Mount Rainier, Washington .... | 1.75 | 1.35 | 22.50 |

2001

| UXC28 | 70¢ Badlands National Park, South Dakota............. | 2.25 | 1.60 | 12.00 |

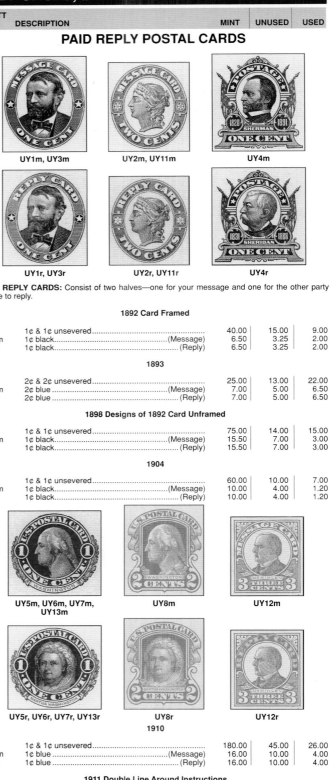

SCOTT NO.	DESCRIPTION	MINT	UNUSED	USED

PAID REPLY POSTAL CARDS

UY1m, UY3m | **UY2m, UY11m** | **UY4m**

UY1r, UY3r | **UY2r, UY11r** | **UY4r**

PAID REPLY CARDS: Consist of two halves—one for your message and one for the other party to use to reply.

1892 Card Framed

UY1	1¢ & 1¢ unsevered......................................	40.00	15.00	9.00
UY1m	1¢ black....................................(Message)	6.50	3.25	2.00
UY1r	1¢ black..(Reply)	6.50	3.25	2.00

1893

UY2	2¢ & 2¢ unsevered......................................	25.00	13.00	22.00
UY2m	2¢ blue.....................................(Message)	7.00	5.00	6.50
UY2r	2¢ blue...(Reply)	7.00	5.00	6.50

1898 Designs of 1892 Card Unframed

UY3	1¢ & 1¢ unsevered......................................	75.00	14.00	15.00
UY3m	1¢ black....................................(Message)	15.50	7.00	3.00
UY3r	1¢ black..(Reply)	15.50	7.00	3.00

1904

UY4	1¢ & 1¢ unsevered......................................	60.00	10.00	7.00
UY4m	1¢ black....................................(Message)	10.00	4.00	1.20
UY4r	1¢ black..(Reply)	10.00	4.00	1.20

UY5m, UY6m, UY7m, UY13m | **UY8m** | **UY12m**

UY5r, UY6r, UY7r, UY13r | **UY8r** | **UY12r**

1910

UY5	1¢ & 1¢ unsevered..	180.00	45.00	26.00
UY5m	1¢ blue ....(Message)	16.00	10.00	4.00
UY5r	1¢ blue ....(Reply)	16.00	10.00	4.00

1911 Double Line Around Instructions

UY6	1¢ & 1¢ unsevered..	180.00	70.00	25.00
UY6m	1¢ green..................................(Message)	25.00	14.00	7.00
UY6r	1¢ green......................................(Reply)	25.00	14.00	7.00

1915 Single Frame Line Around Instruction

UY7	1¢ & 1¢ unsevered..	1.50	.65	.60
UY7m	1¢ green..................................(Message)	.35	.20	.25
UY7r	1¢ green......................................(Reply)	.35	.20	.25

1918

UY8	2¢ & 2¢ unsevered..	95.00	35.00	45.00
UY8m	2¢ red......................................(Message)	32.00	12.00	9.00
UY8r	2¢ red..(Reply)	32.00	12.00	9.00

SCOTT NO.	DESCRIPTION	MINT	UNUSED	USED
	1920 UY8 Surcharged			
UY9	1¢/2¢ & 1¢/2¢ unsevered................................	25.00	11.00	12.00
UY9m	1¢ on 2¢ red .... (Message)	6.00	3.00	4.00
UY9r	1¢ on 2¢ red .... (Reply)	6.00	3.00	4.00
	1924 Designs of 1893			
UY11	2¢ & 2¢ unsevered................................	3.00	1.75	37.00
UY11m	2¢ red................................(Message)	.75	.65	15.00
UY11r	2¢ red................................(Reply)	.75	.65	15.00
	1926			
UY12	3¢ & 3¢ unsevered................................	16.50	7.00	30.00
UY12m	3¢ red................................(Message)	3.25	1.75	7.00
UY12r	3¢ red................................(Reply)	3.25	1.75	7.00

SCOTT NO.	DESCRIPTION	FIRST DAY COVER	MINT	USED
	1951 Design of 1910 Single Line Frame			
UY13	2¢ & 2¢ unsevered................................	2.10	1.40	2.25
UY13m	2¢ carmine ....(Message)	....	.70	1.00
UY13r	2¢ carmine ....(Reply)	....	.70	1.00
	1952 UY7 Surcharged by cancelling machine, light green			
UY14	2¢/1¢ & 2¢/1¢ unsevered................................	....	2.00	2.25
UY14m	2¢ on 1¢ green ....(Message)	....	.50	1.00
UY14r	2¢ on 1¢ green ....(Reply)	....	.50	1.00
	1952 UY7 Surcharge Typographed, dark green			
UY15	2¢/1¢ & 2¢/1¢ unsevered................................	....	140.00	50.00
UY15m	2¢ on 1¢ green ....(Message)	....	20.00	12.00
UY15r	2¢ on 1¢ green ....(Reply)	....	20.00	12.00
	1956 Design of UX45			
UY16	4¢ & 4¢ unsevered................................	1.75	1.25	80.00
UY16m	4¢ carmine ....(Message)	....	.50	40.00
UY16r	4¢ carmine ....(Reply)	....	.50	40.00
	1958 Design of UX46			
UY17	3¢ & 3¢ purple, unsevered................................	1.75	4.00	2.50
	1962 Design of UX48			
UY18	4¢ & 4¢ red violet, unsevered	1.75	4.00	2.75
	1963 Design of UX49			
UY19	7¢ & 7¢ unsevered................................	1.75	3.00	65.00
UY19m	7¢ blue & red................................ (Message)	....	1.00	40.00
UY19r	7¢ blue & red................................ (Reply)	....	1.00	40.00
	1967 Design of UX54			
UY20	8¢ & 8¢ unsevered................................	1.75	3.00	60.00
UY20m	8¢ blue & red................................ (Message)	....	1.00	40.00
UY20r	8¢ blue & red................................ (Reply)	....	1.00	40.00
	1968 Design of UX55			
UY21	5¢ & 5¢ emerald................................	1.75	1.75	2.00
	1971 Design of UX58			
UY22	6¢ & 6¢ brown................................	1.75	1.00	2.00
	1972 Design of UX64			
UY23	6¢ & 6¢ blue................................	1.75	1.25	2.00
	1973 Design of UX66			
UY24	8¢ & 8¢ orange	1.75	1.00	2.00
	1975			
UY25	7¢ & 7¢ design of UX68................................	1.75	1.00	9.00
UY26	9¢ & 9¢ design of UX69................................	1.75	1.00	2.00
	1976			
UY27	9¢ & 9¢ design of UX70................................	1.75	1.25	2.00
	1977			
UY28	9¢ & 9¢ design of UX72................................	1.75	1.25	2.00
	1978			
UY29	(10¢ & 10¢) design of UX74................................	3.00	11.00	10.00
UY30	10¢ & 10¢ design of UX75................................	1.75	1.25	.40

SCOTT NO.	DESCRIPTION	FIRST DAY COVER	MINT	USED
	1981			
UY31	(12¢ & 12¢) "B" Eagle, design of UX88..................	1.75	1.25	2.05
UY32	12¢ & 12¢ light blue, design of UX89.....................	1.75	5.50	2.05
UY33	(13¢ & 13¢) buff, design of UX92.........................	1.75	1.85	2.05
UY34	13¢ & 13¢ buff, design of UX93...........................	1.75	1.00	.25
	1985			
UY35	(14¢ & 14¢) Carroll, design of UX105....................	1.75	2.75	2.05
UY36	14¢ & 14¢ Carroll, design of UX106.....................	1.75	1.25	2.05
UY37	14¢ & 14¢ Wythe, design of UX108......................	1.75	1.00	2.05
	1987			
UY38	14¢ & 14¢ Flag, design of UX117	1.75	1.00	2.25
	1988			
UY39	15¢ & 15¢ America the Beautiful, design of UX120 .	1.75	1.00	1.60
	1991			
UY40	19¢ & 19¢ Flag, design of UX153........................	1.75	1.00	1.50
	1995			
UY41	20¢ & 20¢ Red Barn, design of UX198..................	1.75	1.00	1.25
	1999			
UY42	20¢ & 20¢ Block Island Lighthouse, design of UX306	1.75	1.00	1.25
	2001-08			
UY43	21¢ & 21¢ White Barn, design of UX375	1.75	1.10	1.50
UY44	23¢ & 23¢ Carlsbad Caverns, design of UX381	1.75	1.10	1.50
UY45	24¢ & 24¢ Zebulon Pike Expedition, design of UX449	1.75	1.35	1.50
UY46	26¢ & 26¢ Pineapple, design of UX488..................	1.75	1.45	1.50
UY47	27¢ Corinthian Column double-reply postal card.....	3.75	1.50	1.50

OFFICIAL POSTAL CARDS

UZ1

SCOTT NO.	DESCRIPTION	FIRST DAY COVER	MINT	USED
	1913			
UZ1	1¢ black (Printed Address)................................	......	700.00	475.00

UZ2   UZ3

SCOTT NO.	DESCRIPTION	FIRST DAY COVER	MINT	USED
	1983			
UZ2	13¢ Great Seal................................	1.75	.85	100.00
	1985			
UZ3	14¢ Great Seal................................	1.75	.85	90.00

UZ4   UZ5   UZ6

SCOTT NO.	DESCRIPTION	FIRST DAY COVER	MINT	USED
	1988			
UZ4	15¢ Great Seal................................	1.75	.85	100.00
	1991			
UZ5	19¢ Great Seal................................	1.75	.85	100.00
	1995			
UZ6	20¢ Great Seal................................	1.75	1.00	100.00

SCOTT NO.	DESCRIPTION	IMPERFORATE (a) F	AVG	PART PERF. (b) F	AVG	PERFORATED (c) F	AVG

1862-71 First Issue

When ordering from this issue be sure to indicate whether the "a", "b" or "c" variety is wanted. Example: R27c. Prices are for used singles.

R1-R4   R5-R15   R16-R42

SCOTT NO.	DESCRIPTION	IMP F	IMP AVG	PP F	PP AVG	PERF F	PERF AVG
R1	1¢ Express	75.00	58.00	42.00	30.00	1.50	1.15
R2	1¢ Playing Cards	1850.00	1400.00	1600.00	1200.00	170.00	170.00
R3	1¢ Proprietary	1100.00	900.00	275.00	200.00	.60	.40
R4	1¢ Telegraph	625.00	475.00	....	....	18.00	14.00
R5	2¢ Bank Check, blue	1.50	1.15	3.25	2.00	.60	.40
R6	2¢ Bank Check, orange	....	....	60.00	41.25	.30	.20
R7	2¢ Certificate, blue	15.00	11.00	....	....	31.00	22.00
R8	2¢ Certificate, orange	....	....	....	....	43.00	25.00
R9	2¢ Express, blue	15.00	11.00	31.00	25.00	.50	.35
R10	2¢ Express, orange	....	....	800.00	495.00	13.00	10.00
R11	2¢ Playing Cards, blue	....	....	260.00	175.00	5.00	3.00
R12	2¢ Playing Cards, orange	....	....	....	....	50.00	38.00
R13	2¢ Proprietary, blue	725.00	550.00	260.00	185.00	.50	.40
R14	2¢ Proprietary, orange	....	....	....	....	150.00	95.00
R15	2¢ U.S. Internal Revenue	....	....	....	....	.40	.35
R16	3¢ Foreign Exchange	....	....	525.00	415.00	5.00	3.25
R17	3¢ Playing Cards	....	....	....	....	165.00	115.00
R18	3¢ Proprietary	....	....	525.00	330.00	8.00	6.50
R19	3¢ Telegraph	85.00	63.00	28.00	19.50	3.00	2.10
R20	4¢ Inland Exchange	....	....	....	....	2.25	1.45
R21	4¢ Playing Cards	....	....	....	....	625.00	485.00
R22	4¢ Proprietary	....	....	450.00	350.00	8.00	6.75
R23	5¢ Agreement	....	....	....	....	.50	.40
R24	5¢ Certificate	2.50	1.75	14.00	9.00	.50	.40
R25	5¢ Express	5.50	3.75	8.00	5.50	.50	.40
R26	5¢ Foreign Exchange	....	....	....	....	.50	.40
R27	5¢ Inland Exchange	8.50	6.50	6.50	4.50	.60	.40
R28	5¢ Playing Cards	....	....	....	....	36.00	26.00
R29	5¢ Proprietary	....	....	....	....	28.00	18.00
R30	6¢ Inland Exchange	....	....	....	....	2.00	1.35
R32	10¢ Bill of Lading	55.00	38.00	450.00	325.00	1.75	1.25
R33	10¢ Certificate	260.00	200.00	725.00	600.00	.35	.25
R34	10¢ Contract, blue	....	....	475.00	375.00	.60	.40
R35	10¢ Foreign Exchange	....	....	....	....	13.00	9.00
R36	10¢ Inland Exchange	375.00	250.00	5.00	3.25	.40	.25
R37	10¢ Power of Attorney	850.00	525.00	28.00	19.00	1.00	.65
R38	10¢ Proprietary	....	....	....	....	18.00	12.00
R39	15¢ Foreign Exchange	....	....	....	....	17.00	12.00
R40	15¢ Inland Exchange	40.00	27.00	13.00	9.00	2.00	1.50
R41	20¢ Foreign Exchange	80.00	55.00	....	....	65.00	48.00
R42	20¢ Inland Exchange	16.00	10.00	21.00	15.00	.50	.35

R43-R53   R54-R65   R66-R76

SCOTT NO.	DESCRIPTION	IMP F	IMP AVG	PP F	PP AVG	PERF F	PERF AVG
R43	25¢ Bond	275.00	185.00	7.00	5.00	3.75	2.85
R44	25¢ Certificate	11.00	8.00	7.00	5.00	.60	.40
R45	25¢ Entry of Goods	21.00	12.50	120.00	90.00	1.40	1.10
R46	25¢ Insurance	12.00	9.00	15.00	12.00	.35	.25
R47	25¢ Life Insurance	47.00	35.00	480.00	340.00	10.00	7.00
R48	25¢ Power of Attorney	8.00	5.50	35.00	25.00	1.25	.75
R49	25¢ Protest	35.00	25.00	725.00	525.00	8.00	6.00
R50	25¢ Warehouse Receipt	50.00	35.00	575.00	470.00	45.00	35.00
R51	30¢ Foreign Exchange	125.00	85.00	2100.00	1700.00	55.00	39.00
R52	30¢ Inland Exchange	65.00	45.00	75.00	50.00	9.00	7.75
R53	40¢ Inland Exchange	1300.00	975.00	9.00	6.50	8.00	4.75
R54	50¢ Conveyance, blue	18.00	12.00	3.50	2.75	.40	.30
R55	50¢ Entry of Goods	....	....	15.00	10.00	.50	.35
R56	50¢ Foreign Exchange	60.00	40.00	110.00	80.00	7.00	5.00
R57	50¢ Lease	30.00	21.00	150.00	110.00	10.00	7.00
R58	50¢ Life Insurance	45.00	30.00	70.00	49.00	2.00	1.40
R59	50¢ Mortgage	22.00	16.00	5.00	4.00	.70	.50
R60	50¢ Original Process	6.00	4.00	....	....	1.10	.90
R61	50¢ Passage Ticket	110.00	85.00	275.00	185.00	2.25	1.55
R62	50¢ Probate of Will	60.00	42.00	130.00	90.00	20.00	13.00
R63	50¢ Surety Bond, blue	275.00	185.00	3.00	2.10	.40	.25
R64	60¢ Inland Exchange	110.00	75.00	65.00	45.00	9.00	7.25
R65	70¢ Foreign Exchange	650.00	450.00	180.00	125.00	13.00	9.00

SCOTT NO.	DESCRIPTION	IMP F	IMP AVG	PP F	PP AVG	PERF F	PERF AVG
R66	$1 Conveyance	26.00	20.00	725.00	550.00	27.50	18.50
R67	$1 Entry of Goods	44.00	32.00	....	....	275	2.10
R68	$1 Foreign Exchange	90.00	60.00	....	....	.75	.50
R69	$1 Inland Exchange	16.00	10.00	525.00	360.00	.75	.60
R70	$1 Lease	43.00	32.00	....	....	4.00	3.00
R71	$1 Life Insurance	225.00	165.00	....	....	10.00	6.00
R72	$1 Manifest	49.50	33.00	....	....	38.00	26.50
R73	$1 Mortgage	28.00	19.00	....	....	225.00	155.00
R74	$1 Passage Ticket	310.00	210.00	....	....	300.00	210.00
R75	$1 Power of Attorney	95.00	65.00	....	....	3.00	2.00
R76	$1 Probate of Will	95.00	65.00	....	....	60.00	42.50

R77-R80   R81-R87

SCOTT NO.	DESCRIPTION	IMP F	IMP AVG	PP F	PP AVG	PERF F	PERF AVG
R77	$1.30 Foreign Exchange	....	....	....	....	77.00	59.00
R78	$1.50 Inland Exchange	30.00	21.00	....	....	6.50	5.00
R79	$1.60 Foreign Exchange	1350.00	950.00	....	....	125.00	85.00
R80	$1.90 Foreign Exchange	....	....	....	....	115.00	86.00
R81	$2 Conveyance	195.00	135.00	2100.00	1500.00	4.00	3.00
R82	$2 Mortgage	135.00	95.00	....	....	7.00	5.00
R83	$2 Probate of Will	....	....	....	....	85.00	64.00
R84	$2.50 Inland Exchange	....	....	....	....	22.00	18.00
R85	$3 Charter Party	185.00	125.00	....	....	11.00	9.00
R86	$2 Manifest	165.00	105.00	....	....	52.00	38.00
R87	$3.50 Inland Exchange	....	....	....	....	70.00	53.00

R88-R96   R97-R101

SCOTT NO.	DESCRIPTION	IMP F	IMP AVG	PP F	PP AVG	PERF F	PERF AVG
R88	$5 Charter Party	325.00	225.00	....	....	10.00	8.00
R89	$5 Conveyance	50.00	35.00	....	....	11.00	8.00
R90	$5 Manifest	185.00	125.00	....	....	95.00	65.00
R91	$5 Mortgage	180.00	135.00	....	....	25.00	17.50
R92	$5 Probate of Will	725.00	550.00	....	....	25.00	17.50
R93	$10 Charter Party	800.00	550.00	....	....	35.00	25.00
R94	$10 Conveyance	135.00	95.00	....	....	75.00	50.00
R95	$10 Mortgage	650.00	450.00	....	....	35.00	25.00
R96	$10 Probate of Will	2100.00	1600.00	....	....	42.00	32.00
R97	$15 Mortgage, blue	2800.00	2100.00	....	....	240.00	180.00
R98	$20 Conveyance	150.00	100.00	....	....	115.00	85.00
R99	$20 Probate of Will	2100.00	1500.00	....	....	2100.00	1500.00
R100	$25 Mortgage	1500.00	1050.00	....	....	175.00	115.00
R101	$50 U.S. Internal Revenue	265.00	175.00	....	....	160.00	120.00

R102

SCOTT NO.	DESCRIPTION	IMP F	IMP AVG	PP F	PP AVG	PERF F	PERF AVG
R102	$200 U.S. Internal Revenue	2350.00	1850.00	....	....	900.00	625.00

SCOTT NO.	DESCRIPTION	USED F	AVG

R103, R104, R134, R135, R151

R105-R111, R136-R139

R112-R114

R115-R117, R142-R143

1871 SECOND ISSUE

NOTE: The individual denominations vary in design from the illustrations shown which are more typical of their relative size.

Scott	Description	F	AVG
R103	1¢ blue and black	62.00	52.00
R104	2¢ blue and black	3.00	2.25
R105	3¢ blue and black	36.00	27.00
R106	4¢ blue and black	1100.00	80.00
R107	5¢ blue and black	2.255	1.60
R108	6¢ blue and black	175.00	130.00
R109	10¢ blue and black	1.60	1.20
R110	15¢ blue and black	58.00	46.00
R111	20¢ blue and black	8.00	6.00
R112	25¢ blue and black	1.50	.85
R113	30¢ blue and black	110.00	75.00
R114	40¢ blue and black	90.00	65.00
R115	50¢ blue and black	1.16	.85
R116	60¢ blue and black	150.00	105.00
R117	70¢ blue and black	75.00	58.00

R118-R122, R144

R123-R126, R145-R147

Scott	Description	F	AVG
R118	$1 blue and black	8.50	7.00
R119	$1.30 blue and black	575.00	425.00
R120	$1.50 blue and black	20.00	14.00
R121	$1.60 blue and black	585.00	425.00
R122	$1.90 blue and black	410.00	300.00
R123	$2.00 blue and black	21.00	15.00
R124	$2.50 blue and black	35.00	25.00
R125	$3.00 blue and black	45.00	30.00
R126	$3.50 blue and black	325.00	225.00

R127, R128, R148, R149

R129-R131, R150

Scott	Description	F	AVG
R127	$5 blue and black	27.50	19.00
R128	$10 blue and black	225.00	155.00
R129	$20 blue and black	675.00	525.00
R130	$25 blue and black	675.00	525.00
R131	$50 blue and black	675.00	525.00

1871-72 THIRD ISSUE

Scott	Description	F	AVG
R134	1¢ claret and black	45.00	30.00
R135	2¢ orange and black	.40	.25
R135b	2¢ orange and black (center inverted)	425.00	300.00
R136	4¢ brown and black	75.00	57.00
R137	5¢ orange and black	.40	.25
R138	6¢ orange and black	85.00	64.00
R139	15¢ brown and black	22.00	17.00
R140	30¢ orange and black	32.00	26.00
R141	40¢ brown and black	70.00	55.00
R142	60¢ orange and black	95.00	65.00
R143	70¢ green and black	77.00	56.00
R144	$1 green and black	2.25	1.70
R145	$2 vermillion and black	34.00	25.00
R146	$2.50 claret and black	62.00	47.00
R147	$3 green and black	62.00	47.00
R148	$5 vermillion and black	37.00	26.00
R149	$10 green and black	210.00	160.00
R150	$20 orange and black	650.00	435.00

1874 on greenish paper

Scott	Description	F	AVG
R151	2¢ orange and black	.30	.25
R151a	2¢ orange and black (center inverted)	425.00	300.00

SCOTT NO.	DESCRIPTION	UNUSED F	AVG	USED F	AVG

R152
Liberty

R153 surcharge   **R154, R155 surcharge**

1875-78

Scott	Description	Unused F	AVG	Used F	AVG
R152a	2¢ blue on blue silk paper			.50	.40
R152b	2¢ watermarked ("USIR") paper			.40	.30
R152c	2¢ watermarked, rouletted			35.00	24.00

1898 Postage Stamps 279 & 267 Surcharged

Scott	Description	Unused F	AVG	Used F	AVG
R153	1¢ green, small I.R.	5.00	3.50	3.00	2.10
R154	1¢ green, large I.R.	.40	.30	.30	.25
R155	2¢ carmine, large I.R.	.40	.30	.30	.25

DOCUMENTARY STAMPS
Newspaper Stamp PR121 Surcharged

INT. REV.
$5.
DOCUMENTARY.

Scott	Description	Unused F	AVG	Used F	AVG
R159	$5 dark blue, red surcharge reading down	500.00	350.00	210.00	175.00
R160	$5 dark blue, red surcharge reading up	150.00	110.00	115.00	95.00

R161-R172

R173-R178, R182, R183

1898 Battleships Inscribed "Documentary"

Scott	Description	Unused F	AVG	Used F	AVG
R161	1/2¢ orange	4.00	3.00	20.00	15.00
R162	1/2¢ dark gray	.30	.25	.35	.30
R163	1¢ pale blue	.30	.25	.35	.30
R164	2¢ carmine	.30	.25	.35	.30
R165	3¢ dark blue	3.25	2.10	.35	.30
R166	4¢ pale rose	2.00	1.40	.35	.30
R167	5¢ lilac	.65	.45	.35	.30
R168	10¢ dark brown	2.00	1.40	.35	.30
R169	25¢ purple brown	3.50	2.40	.35	.30
R170	40¢ blue lilac .... (cut cancel .40)	125.00	80.00	1.20	.75
R171	50¢ slate violet	36.00	18.00	.30	.25
R172	80¢ bistre .... (cut cancel .25)	110.00	80.00	.40	.30
R173	$1 dark green	18.00	14.00	.30	.25
R174	$3 dark brown .... (cut cancel .25)	40.00	28.00	1.00	.70
R175	$5 orange red .... (cut cancel .25)	62.00	48.00	2.00	1.40
R176	$10 black .... (cut cancel .70)	130.00	90.00	4.00	2.75
R177	$30 red .... (cut cancel 50.00)	460.00	350.00	160.00	110.00
R178	$50 gray brown .... (cut cancel 2.50)	260.00	210.00	6.00	3.95

SCOTT NO.	DESCRIPTION		UNUSED F	AVG	USED F	AVG

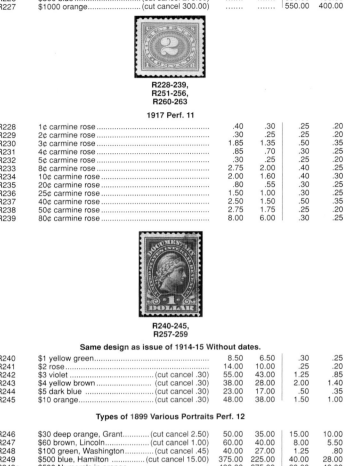

R179, R225, R246, R248   **R180, R226, R249**   **R181, R224, R227, R247, R250**

1899 Various Portraits Inscribed "Series of 1898"

R179	$100 yellow brown & black ..... (cut cancel 20.00)	260.00	200.00	39.00	28.50
R180	$500 carmine lake & black.... (cut cancel 325.00)	1400.00	1100.00	850.00	550.00
R181	$1000 green & black .... (cut cancel 150.00)	1000.00	675.00	385.00	300.00

1900

R182	$1 carmine .... (cut cancel .40)	38.00	29.00	.75	.50
R183	$3 lake .... (cut cancel 7.50)	235.00	175.00	55.00	42.00

R184-R189   **R190-R194**

Designs of R173-78 surcharged

R184	$1 gray .... (cut cancel .25)	28.00	21.00	.40	.25
R185	$2 gray .... (cut cancel .25)	28.00	21.00	.40	.25
R186	$3 gray .... (cut cancel 5.00)	115.00	85.00	12.00	8.00
R187	$5 gray .... (cut cancel 1.50)	75.00	55.00	10.00	7.50
R188	$10 gray .... (cut cancel 4.00)	160.00	115.00	22.00	15.00
R189	$50 gray .... (cut cancel 100.00)	1250.00	950.00	550.00	375.00

1902

R190	$1 green................................... (cut cancel .35)	42.00	33.00	4.00	3.00
R191	$2 green................................... (cut cancel .35)	42.00	33.00	2.00	1.25
R191a	$2 surcharged as R185	125.00	85.00	85.00	60.00
R192	$5 green................................... (cut cancel 5.00)	200.00	140.00	38.00	29.00
R192a	$5 surcharge omitted	250.00	170.00	....	....
R193	$10 green............................... (cut cancel 50.00)	450.00	300.00	145.00	95.00
R194	$50 green.............................. (cut cancel 275.00)	2160.00	1700.00	1100.00	795.00

R195-R216   **R217-R223**

1914 Inscribed "Series of 1914"
Single Line Watermark "USPS"

R195	1/2¢ rose...	14.00	10.00	5.00	3.50
R196	1¢ rose...	2.50	1.75	.40	.25
R197	2¢ rose...	4.00	3.00	.40	.25
R198	3¢ rose...	77.00	55.00	35.00	25.00
R199	4¢ rose...	23.00	17.00	2.25	1.50
R200	5¢ rose...	10.00	7.00	.50	.35
R201	10¢ rose...	8.00	6.00	.35	.25
R202	25¢ rose...	48.00	34.00	.70	.45
R203	40¢ rose...	32.00	24.00	3.00	2.00
R204	50¢ rose...	13.00	10.00	.35	.25
R205	80¢ rose...	210.00	160.00	15.50	12.00

1914 Double Line Watermark "USIR"

R206	1/2¢ rose...	2.00	1.40	.65	.45
R207	1¢ rose...	.35	.25	.30	.20
R208	2¢ rose...	.40	.25	.30	.25
R209	3¢ rose...	2.00	1.40	.35	.25
R210	4¢ rose...	4.00	2.50	.60	.40
R211	5¢ rose...	2.00	1.40	.40	.25
R212	10¢ rose...	.90	.60	.30	.25
R213	25¢ rose...	8.00	6.00	1.75	1.20
R214	40¢ rose.................................... (cut cancel .60)	120.00	85.00	15.00	10.00
R215	50¢ rose...	26.00	18.00	.35	.25
R216	80¢ rose................................... (cut cancel 1.25)	175.00	115.00	28.00	21.00
R217	$1 green.................................... (cut cancel .30)	62.00	48.00	.55	.40
R218	$2 carmine............................... (cut cancel .25)	82.00	58.00	.85	.60
R219	$3 purple.................................. (cut cancel .60)	110.00	80.00	4.00	2.75
R220	$5 blue..................................... (cut cancel .60)	95.00	70.00	4.00	2.75
R221	$10 orange................................ (cut cancel 1.00)	210.00	155.00	6.00	4.00
R222	$30 vermillion........................... (cut cancel 5.50)	625.00	500.00	20.00	14.00
R223	$50 violet............................... (cut cancel 375.00)	1775.00	1275.00	1100.00	800.00

1914-15 Various Portraits Inscribed "Series of 1914" or "Series of 1915"

R224	$60 brown .... (cut cancel 70.00)	200.00	140.00	150.00	100.00
R225	$100 green .... (cut cancel 17.00)	68.00	50.00	45.00	30.00
R226	$500 blue.............................. (cut cancel 275.00)	....	....	650.00	450.00
R227	$1000 orange........................ (cut cancel 300.00)	....	....	550.00	400.00

R228-239, R251-256, R260-263

1917 Perf. 11

R228	1¢ carmine rose	.40	.30	.25	.20
R229	2¢ carmine rose	.30	.25	.25	.20
R230	3¢ carmine rose	1.85	1.35	.50	.35
R231	4¢ carmine rose	.85	.70	.30	.25
R232	5¢ carmine rose	.30	.25	.25	.20
R233	8¢ carmine rose	2.75	2.00	.40	.25
R234	10¢ carmine rose	2.00	1.60	.40	.30
R235	20¢ carmine rose	.80	.55	.30	.25
R236	25¢ carmine rose	1.50	1.00	.30	.25
R237	40¢ carmine rose	2.50	1.50	.50	.35
R238	50¢ carmine rose	2.75	1.75	.25	.20
R239	80¢ carmine rose	8.00	6.00	.30	.25

R240-245, R257-259

Same design as issue of 1914-15 Without dates.

R240	$1 yellow green..	8.50	6.50	.30	.25
R241	$2 rose..	14.00	10.00	.25	.20
R242	$3 violet .... (cut cancel .30)	55.00	43.00	1.25	.85
R243	$4 yellow brown .... (cut cancel .30)	38.00	28.00	2.00	1.40
R244	$5 dark blue .... (cut cancel .30)	23.00	17.00	.50	.35
R245	$10 orange................................ (cut cancel .30)	48.00	38.00	1.50	1.00

Types of 1899 Various Portraits Perf. 12

R246	$30 deep orange, Grant............ (cut cancel 2.50)	50.00	35.00	15.00	10.00
R247	$60 brown, Lincoln.................... (cut cancel 1.00)	60.00	40.00	8.00	5.50
R248	$100 green, Washington............. (cut cancel .45)	40.00	27.00	1.25	.80
R249	$500 blue, Hamilton .... (cut cancel 15.00)	375.00	225.00	40.00	28.00
R249a	$500 Numerals in orange	400.00	275.00	60.00	40.00
R250	$1000 orange, Madison (Perf. In. 3.00) .... (cut cancel 3.50)	160.00	100.00	13.00	8.00

1928-29 Perf. 10

R251	1¢ carmine rose	2.25	1.50	1.80	1.20
R252	2¢ carmine rose	.75	.55	.40	.30
R253	4¢ carmine rose	8.00	5.00	5.00	3.50
R254	5¢ carmine rose	1.80	1.20	.75	.50
R255	10¢ carmine rose	2.75	1.85	1.50	1.00
R256	20¢ carmine rose	7.00	5.00	6.00	4.00
R257	$1 green............................... (cut cancel 2.00)	175.00	120.00	40.00	27.00
R258	$2 rose..	75.00	50.00	3.00	2.00
R259	$10 orange............................... (cut cancel 7.00)	250.00	175.00	50.00	35.00

1929-30 Perf. 11 x 10

R260	2¢ carmine rose	4.00	2.75	3.00	2.00
R261	5¢ carmine rose	3.00	2.00	2.25	1.60
R262	10¢ carmine rose	10.50	7.00	8.00	5.00
R263	20¢ carmine rose	17.00	11.00	9.00	6.00

SCOTT NO.	DESCRIPTION	PLATE BLOCK F/NH	UNUSED F/NH	USED F

R733, R734

1962 CENTENNIAL INTERNAL REVENUE. Inscribed "Established 1862"

R733	10¢ violet blue & green	18.00	1.25	.50

1964 Without Inscription Date

R734	10¢ violet blue & green	32.50	3.50	.75

SCOTT NO.	DESCRIPTION	VIOLET PAPER (a) F	AVG	GREEN PAPER (b) F	AVG

PROPRIETARY STAMPS

RB1-2   **RB3-7**

1871-74 Perforated 12

SCOTT NO.	DESCRIPTION	VIOLET PAPER (a) F	AVG	GREEN PAPER (b) F	AVG
RB1	1¢ green & black	7.00	5.00	12.00	8.00
RB2	2¢ green & black	8.00	6.00	28.00	20.00
RB3	3¢ green & black	25.00	17.00	65.00	40.00
RB4	4¢ green & black	15.00	10.00	24.00	16.00
RB5	5¢ green & black	160.00	110.00	175.00	120.00
RB6	6¢ green & black	60.00	40.00	125.00	85.00
RB7	10¢ green & black	240.00	165.00	65.00	45.00
RB8	50¢ green & black (large)	750.00	500.00	1100.00	750.00

SCOTT NO.	DESCRIPTION	SILK PAPER (a) F	AVG	WMKD PERF. (b) F	AVG	ROULETTE (c) F	AVG

RB11-12   **RB13-19**

SCOTT NO.	DESCRIPTION	SILK PAPER (a) F	AVG	WMKD PERF. (b) F	AVG	ROULETTE (c) F	AVG
RB11	1¢ green	2.50	1.90	.50	.35	125.00	100.00
RB12	2¢ brown	2.75	1.85	1.50	1.00	135.00	95.00
RB13	3¢ orange	14.00	10.00	4.50	3.50	130.00	95.00
RB14	4¢ red brown	11.00	8.00	10.00	6.00	......	......
RB15	4¢ red	......	......	7.00	4.00	260.00	200.00
RB16	5¢ black	180.00	140.00	130.00	90.00	......	1800.00
RB17	6¢ violet blue	38.00	29.00	26.00	19.00	400.00	275.00
RB18	6¢ violet	......	......	37.00	28.00	500.00	350.00
RB19	10¢ blue	......	......	350.00	250.00	......	......

SCOTT NO.	DESCRIPTION	UNUSED F	AVG	USED F	AVG

RB20-31   **RB32-64**   **RB65-73**

1898 Battleship Inscribed "Proprietary"

SCOTT NO.	DESCRIPTION	UNUSED F	AVG	USED F	AVG
RB20	1/8¢ yellow green	.25	.20	.35	.25
RB21	1/4¢ brown	.25	.20	.25	.20
RB22	3/8¢ deep orange	.30	.25	.50	.40
RB23	5/8¢ deep ultramarine	.30	.25	.30	.25
RB24	1¢ dark green	2.25	1.50	.30	.25
RB25	1-1/4¢ violet	.30	.25	.30	.25
RB26	1-7/8¢ dull blue	16.00	12.00	2.25	1.80
RB27	2¢ violet brown	1.50	1.00	.40	.30
RB28	2-1/2¢ lake	4.50	3.15	.30	.25
RB29	3-3/4¢ olive gray	45.00	30.00	16.00	12.00
RB30	4¢ purple	17.00	12.00	1.60	1.10
RB31	5¢ brown orange	17.00	12.00	1.60	1.10

1914 Watermarked "USPS"

SCOTT NO.	DESCRIPTION	UNUSED F	AVG	USED F	AVG
RB32	1/8¢ black	.30	.25	.30	.25
RB33	1/4¢ black	3.30	2.55	1.60	1.00
RB34	3/8¢ black	.40	.30	.30	.25
RB35	5/8¢ black	6.50	5.00	3.00	2.75
RB36	1-1/4¢ black	5.00	3.50	2.00	1.25
RB37	1-7/8¢ black	60.00	48.00	21.00	15.00
RB38	2-1/2¢ black	14.00	10.00	4.00	2.75
RB39	3-1/8¢ black	130.00	90.00	65.00	45.00
RB40	3-3/4¢ black	50.00	35.00	26.00	19.00
RB41	4¢ black	77.00	55.00	42.00	32.00
RB43	5¢ black	155.00	115.00	105.00	85.00

1914 Watermarked "USIR"

SCOTT NO.	DESCRIPTION	UNUSED F	AVG	USED F	AVG
RB44	1/8¢ black	.40	.30	.30	.25
RB45	1/4¢ black	.30	.25	.30	.25
RB46	3/8¢ black	.80	.60	.50	.40
RB47	1/2¢ black	4.00	2.75	3.50	2.50
RB48	5/8¢ black	.30	.25	.30	.25
RB49	1¢ black	6.00	9.50	6.00	4.50
RB50	1-1/4¢ black	.75	.60	.45	.35
RB51	1-1/2¢ black	4.50	3.50	3.00	2.00
RB52	1-7/8¢ black	1.40	1.00	1.00	.80
RB53	2¢ black	7.00	5.50	6.00	4.00

SCOTT NO.	DESCRIPTION	UNUSED F	AVG	USED F	AVG
RB54	2-1/2¢ black	1.80	1.30	2.00	1.40
RB55	3¢ black	5.50	4.00	4.00	3.00
RB56	3-1/8¢ black	7.00	5.00	5.00	4.00
RB57	3-3/4¢ black	15.00	11.00	11.00	8.00
RB58	4¢ black	.60	.50	.30	.25
RB59	4-3/8¢ black	19.00	13.00	11.00	8.00
RB60	5¢ black	4.50	3.50	4.00	3.00
RB61	6¢ black	72.00	60.00	48.00	35.00
RB62	8¢ black	22.00	16.00	15.00	11.00
RB63	10¢ black	17.00	13.00	10.00	7.00
RB64	20¢ black	31.00	23.00	22.00	16.00

1919 Offset Printing

SCOTT NO.	DESCRIPTION	UNUSED F	AVG	USED F	AVG
RB65	1¢ dark blue	.25	.20	.25	.20
RB66	2¢ dark blue	.40	.30	.30	.25
RB67	3¢ dark blue	1.60	1.20	.85	.65
RB68	4¢ dark blue	2.50	2.00	.80	.60
RB69	5¢ dark blue	3.25	2.00	1.40	1.00
RB70	8¢ dark blue	22.00	16.00	14.00	11.00
RB71	10¢ dark blue	10.00	8.00	4.00	2.75
RB72	20¢ dark blue	15.00	12.00	6.00	4.00
RB73	40¢ dark blue	58.00	45.00	15.00	11.00

FUTURE   **FUTURE**

FUTURE DELIVERY STAMPS

DELIVERY   **DELIVERY**

Documentary Stamps of 1917 Overprinted

Type I   Type II

1918-34 Perforated 11, Type I Overprint Lines 8mm. Apart

SCOTT NO.	DESCRIPTION	UNUSED F	AVG	USED F	AVG
RC1	2¢ carmine rose	8.00	5.00	.30	.25
RC2	3¢ carmine rose (cut cancel 13.50)	42.00	32.00	35.00	29.00
RC3	4¢ carmine rose	13.00	9.00	.30	.25
RC3A	5¢ carmine rose	95.00	60.00	4.00	2.75
RC4	10¢ carmine rose	22.00	15.00	.30	.25
RC5	20¢ carmine rose	35.00	25.00	.30	.25
RC6	25¢ carmine rose (cut cancel .25)	65.00	45.00	.75	.55
RC7	40¢ carmine rose (cut cancel .25)	75.00	50.00	.75	.55
RC8	50¢ carmine rose	16.00	11.00	.30	.25
RC9	80¢ carmine rose (cut cancel 1.00)	135.00	95.00	10.00	7.00
RC10	$1 green (cut cancel .25)	60.00	45.00	.30	.25
RC11	$2 rose (cut cancel .25)	65.00	45.00	.30	.25
RC12	$3 violet (cut cancel .30)	185.00	145.00	4.00	3.25
RC13	$5 dark blue (cut cancel .25)	110.00	90.00	.75	.50
RC14	$10 orange (cut cancel .35)	135.00	95.00	1.50	1.00
RC15	$20 olive bistre (cut cancel .75)	250.00	170.00	8.00	6.00

Perforated 12

SCOTT NO.	DESCRIPTION	UNUSED F	AVG	USED F	AVG
RC16	$30 vermillon (cut cancel 2.00)	110.00	85.00	7.00	5.00
RC17	$50 olive green (cut cancel 2.00)	90.00	75.00	6.00	5.00
RC18	$60 brown (cut cancel 1.25)	120.00	90.00	9.00	7.00
RC19	$100 yellow green (cut cancel 8.00)	200.00	180.00	40.00	30.00
RC20	$500 blue (cut cancel6.00)	160.00	130.00	16.00	12.00
RC21	$1000 orange (cut cancel 1.75)	185.00	150.00	8.00	6.00
RC22	1¢ carmine rose (lines 2mm apart)	1.20	.75	.30	.25
RC23	80¢ carmine rose (lines 2mm apart) (cut cancel .40)	150.00	120.00	3.50	2.00

1925-34 Perforated 11 Type II Overprint

SCOTT NO.	DESCRIPTION	UNUSED F	AVG	USED F	AVG
RC25	$1 green (cut cancel .10)	55.00	40.00	1.00	1.00
RC26	$10 orange (cut cancel 5.75)	150.00	100.00	15.00	24.00

STOCK   **STOCK**

STOCK TRANSFER STAMPS

TRANSFER   **TRANSFER**

Documentary Stamps Overprinted

Type I   Type II

1918-22 Perforated 11 Type I Overprint

SCOTT NO.	DESCRIPTION	UNUSED F	AVG	USED F	AVG
RD1	1¢ carmine rose	1.00	.70	.30	.25
RD2	2¢ carmine rose	.30	.25	.30	.25
RD3	4¢ carmine rose	.30	.25	.30	.25
RD4	5¢ carmine rose	.35	.30	.30	.25
RD5	10¢ carmine rose	.35	.30	.30	.25
RD6	20¢ carmine rose	.65	.45	.30	.25
RD7	25¢ carmine rose (cut cancel .25)	2.25	1.75	.30	.25
RD8	40¢ carmine rose	2.25	1.15	.30	.25
RD9	50¢ carmine rose	.80	.50	.30	.25
RD10	80¢ carmine rose (cut cancel .25)	9.00	7.00	.50	.35
RD11	$1 green (red ovverprint) (cut cancel 4.00)	150.00	120.00	28.00	23.00
RD12	$1 green (black overprint)	3.00	2.00	.40	.25
RD13	$2 rose	3.00	2.00	.30	.25
RD14	$3 violet (cut cancel .25)	26.00	19.00	7.00	5.00
RD15	$4 yellow brown (cut cancel .25)	12.00	8.00	.30	.25
RD16	$5 dark blue (cut cancel .25)	8.00	5.00	.30	.25
RD17	$10 orange (cut cancel .25)	25.00	20.00	.50	.45
RD18	$20 olive bistre (cut cancel 3.50)	120.00	95.00	20.00	14.00

Perforated 12

SCOTT NO.	DESCRIPTION	UNUSED F	AVG	USED F	AVG
RD19	$30 vermillion (cut cancel 1.20)	39.00	33.00	6.00	4.00
RD20	$50 olive green (cut cancel 26.00)	130.00	110.00	65.00	55.00
RD21	$60 brown (cut cancel 10.00)	230.00	200.00	28.00	22.00
RD22	$100 green (cut cancel 3.50)	45.00	35.00	7.00	5.00
RD23	$500 blue (cut cancel 80.00)	......	......	160.00	120.00
RD24	$1000 orange (cut cancel 33.00)	......	......	100.00	85.00

SCOTT NO.	DESCRIPTION	UNUSED F	UNUSED AVG	USED F	USED AVG
	1928 Perforated 10 Type I Overprint				
RD25	2¢ carmine rose	5.00	4.00	.40	.35
RD26	4¢ carmine rose	5.00	4.00	.40	.35
RD27	10¢ carmine rose	5.00	4.00	.40	.35
RD28	20¢ carmine rose	6.00	5.00	.40	.35
RD29	50¢ carmine rose	10.00	8.00	.60	.45
RD30	$1 green	40.00	28.00	.40	.30
RD31	$2 carmine rose	40.00	28.00	.35	.30
RD32	$10 orange ....(cut cancel .25)	40.00	28.00	.50	.35
RD33	2¢ carmine rose	8.00	5.00	1.00	.70
RD34	10¢ carmine rose	3.00	2.00	.40	.35
RD35	20¢ carmine rose	6.00	4.00	.30	.25
RD36	50¢ carmine rose	5.00	4.00	.30	.25
RD37	$1 green ....(cut cancel .30)	60.00	40.00	13.00	9.00
RD38	$2 rose ....(cut cancel .30)	70.00	60.00	13.00	9.00
	1920-28 Perforated 10 Type II overprint				
RD39	2¢ carmine rose	11.00	9.00	1.00	.70
RD40	10¢ carmine rose	4.00	2.00	.60	.40
RD41	20¢ carmine rose	6.00	4.00	.30	.25

SILVER TAX STAMPS

Documentary Stamps of 1917 Overprinted

1934-36

SCOTT NO.	DESCRIPTION	UNUSED F	UNUSED AVG	USED F	USED AVG
RG1	1¢ carmine rose	1.50	1.00	1.00	.70
RG2	2¢ carmine rose	1.75	1.25	.75	.50
RG3	3¢ carmine rose	1.95	1.35	.90	.60
RG4	4¢ carmine rose	2.00	1.40	1.75	1.25
RG5	5¢ carmine rose	3.50	2.50	1.50	1.00
RG6	8¢ carmine rose	4.50	3.00	3.50	2.50
RG7	10¢ carmine rose	5.00	3.50	4.00	2.50
RG8	20¢ carmine rose	7.00	5.00	4.00	2.50
RG9	25¢ carmine rose	6.00	4.00	5.00	3.50
RG10	40¢ carmine rose	7.00	5.00	6.50	4.50
RG11	50¢ carmine rose	10.00	7.00	8.00	5.00

SCOTT NO.	DESCRIPTION	UNUSED F	UNUSED AVG	USED F	USED AVG
RG12	80¢ carmine rose	18.00	12.00	11.00	7.00
RG13	$1 green	35.00	25.00	18.00	13.00
RG14	$2 rose	43.00	35.00	27.00	18.00
RG15	$3 violet	75.00	50.00	40.00	28.00
RG16	$4 yellow brown	65.00	50.00	25.00	17.00
RG17	$5 dark blue	82.00	60.00	30.00	20.00
RG18	$10 orange	105.00	90.00	25.00	17.00
RG19	$30 vermillion ....(cut cancel 20.00)	200.00	140.00	60.00	40.00
RG20	$60 brown ....(cut cancel 30.00)	225.00	150.00	85.00	60.00
RG21	$100 green	275.00	185.00	35.00	22.50
RG22	$500 blue ....(cut cancel 110.00)	600.00	400.00	235.00	160.00
RG23	$1000 orange ....(cut cancel 70.00)	......	......	120.00	77.50
RG26	$100 green, 11mm spacing	550.00	400.00	85.00	55.00
RG27	$1000 orange, 11mm spacing	......	......	1550.00	1300.00

TOBACCO SALE TAX STAMPS

Documentary Stamps of 1917 Overprinted

1934

SCOTT NO.	DESCRIPTION	UNUSED F	UNUSED AVG	USED F	USED AVG
RJ1	1¢ carmine rose	.40	.35	.25	.20
RJ2	2¢ carmine rose	.45	.30	.25	.20
RJ3	5¢ carmine rose	1.40	.90	.45	.30
RJ4	10¢ carmine rose	1.75	1.15	.45	.30
RJ5	25¢ carmine rose	4.75	3.00	1.85	1.20
RJ6	50¢ carmine rose	4.75	3.00	1.85	1.20
RJ7	$1 green	12.00	8.00	1.85	1.20
RJ8	$2 rose	20.00	14.00	2.15	1.40
RJ9	$5 dark blue	25.00	17.00	4.75	3.00
RJ10	$10 orange	40.00	27.00	12.00	7.75
RJ11	$20 olive bistre	100.00	70.00	15.00	9.75

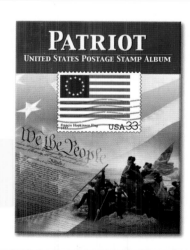

HUNTING PERMIT

SCOTT NO.	DESCRIPTION	VF	UNUSED F	AVG	VF	USED F	AVG

RW1

RW2

RW3

RW4

RW5

1934-1938 Inscribed: DEPARTMENT OF AGRICULTURE (NH + 75%)

SCOTT NO.	DESCRIPTION	VF	UNUSED F	AVG	VF	USED F	AVG
RW1	1934 $1 Mallards	1150.00	725.00	500.00	160.00	110.00	90.00
RW2	1935 $1 Canvasbacks	1050.00	675.00	525.00	200.00	150.00	110.00
RW3	1936 $1 Canada Geese	575.00	400.00	350.00	95.00	65.00	45.00
RW4	1937 $1 Scaup Ducks	485.00	340.00	235.00	65.00	45.00	29.50
RW5	1938 $1 Pintail Drake .	795.00	440.00	335.00	75.00	50.00	32.50

RW6

RW7

RW8

RW9

RW10

Note: NH premiums RW6-9 (75%) RW10-16 (50%) RW17-25 (40%)
1939-1958 Inscribed: DEPARTMENT OF INTERIOR

SCOTT NO.	DESCRIPTION	VF	UNUSED F	AVG	VF	USED F	AVG
RW6	1939 $1 Green-Winged Teal	350.00	265.00	150.00	55.00	40.00	25.00
RW7	1940 $1 Black Mallards .	350.00	265.00	150.00	55.00	40.00	25.00
RW8	1941 $1 Ruddy Ducks ...	350.00	265.00	150.00	55.00	40.00	25.00
RW9	1942 $1 Baldpates	395.00	265.00	150.00	55.00	40.00	25.00
RW10	1943 $1 Wood Ducks	160.00	100.00	75.00	50.00	40.00	25.00

RW11

RW12

RW13

RW14

RW15

SCOTT NO.	DESCRIPTION	VF	UNUSED F	AVG	VF	USED F	AVG
RW11	1944 $1 White Fronted Geese	200.00	115.00	80.00	33.50	24.00	16.00
RW12	1945 $1 Shoveller Ducks	140.00	85.00	70.00	27.00	18.00	14.00
RW13	1946 $1 Redhead Ducks	37.00	45.00	40.00	21.00	15.00	10.50
RW14	1947 $1 Snow Geese....	77.00	45.00	40.00	21.00	15.00	10.50
RW15	1948 $1 Buffleheads	85.00	60.00	50.00	21.00	15.00	10.50

RW16

RW17

RW18

RW19

RW20

SCOTT NO.	DESCRIPTION	VF	UNUSED F	AVG	VF	USED F	AVG
RW16	1949 $2 Goldeneye Ducks	95.00	65.00	55.00	15.50	11.00	7.50
RW17	1950 $2 Trumpeter Swans	130.00	90.00	70.00	14.00	11.00	7.50
RW18	1951 $2 Gadwall Ducks	130.00	90.00	70.00	14.00	11.00	7.50
RW19	1952 $2 Harlequin Ducks	130.00	90.00	70.00	14.00	11.00	7.50
RW20	1953 $2 Blue-Winged Teal	135.00	90.00	75.00	14.00	11.00	7.50

Notes on Hunting Permit Stamps
1. Unused stamps without gum (uncancelled) are priced at one-half gummed price.
2. The date printed on the stamp is one year later than the date of issue listed above.
3. #RW1-RW25 and RW31 are plate blocks of 6.

SCOTT NO.	DESCRIPTION	UNUSED VF	F	AVG	USED VF	F	AVG

RW21

RW22

RW23

RW24

RW25

RW21	1954 $2 Ringed-Necked Ducks	130.00	90.00	75.00	11.50	8.25	5.75
RW22	1955 $2 Blue Geese	130.00	90.00	75.00	11.50	8.25	5.75
RW23	1956 $2 American Merganser	130.00	90.00	75.00	11.50	8.25	5.75
RW24	1957 $2 Ameriacn Eider	130.00	90.00	75.00	11.50	8.25	5.75
RW25	1958 $2 Canada Geese	130.00	90.00	75.00	11.50	8.25	5.75

PLATE BLOCKS RW1-RW25

SCOTT NO.	UNUSED NH F	AVG	UNUSED OG F	AVG	SCOTT NO.	UNUSED NH F	AVG	UNUSED OG F	AVG
	PLATE BLOCKS OF 6					PLATE BLOCKS OF 6			
RW1	16000.00	12000.00	13500.00	9500.00	RW14	475.00	375.00	350.00	325.00
RW2	12000.00	9000.00	9500.00	7500.00	RW15	500.00	425.00	425.00	375.00
RW3	5200.00	4300.00	4500.00	3200.00	RW16	575.00	450.00	450.00	400.00
RW4	4600.00	3500.00	4200.00	3300.00	RW17	795.00	650.00	650.00	550.00
RW5	5100.00	4200.00	4400.00	3300.00	RW18	795.00	650.00	650.00	550.00
RW6	4700.00	3800.00	3600.00	2900.00	RW19	795.00	650.00	650.00	550.00
RW7	4700.00	3800.00	3700.00	3100.00	RW20	825.00	675.00	675.00	575.00
RW8	4800.00	3800.00	3700.00	3100.00	RW21	795.00	675.00	675.00	600.00
RW9	4300.00	3600.00	3500.00	2900.00	RW22	795.00	675.00	675.00	600.00
RW10	1000.00	850.00	925.00	775.00	RW23	840.00	725.00	725.00	640.00
RW11	1200.00	875.00	925.00	775.00	RW24	795.00	675.00	650.00	575.00
RW12	850.00	650.00	675.00	550.00	RW25	795.00	675.00	650.00	575.00
RW13	500.00	400.00	350.00	325.00					

RW26

RW27

RW28

RW29

RW30

1959-1971 (NH + 40%)

RW26	1959 $3 Dog & Mallard	165.00	140.00	12.00	9.00
RW27	1960 $3 Redhead Ducks	160.00	120.00	11.50	8.25
RW28	1961 $3 Mallard Hen & Ducklings	160.00	120.00	11.50	8.25
RW29	1962 $3 Pintail Drakes	160.00	120.00	12.00	9.00
RW30	1963 $3 Brant Ducks Landing	160.00	120.00	12.00	9.00

RW31

RW32

RW33

RW34

RW31	1964 $3 Hawaiian Nene Goose	145.00	120.00	12.00	9.00
RW32	1965 $3 Canvasback Drakes	145.00	120.00	12.00	9.00
RW33	1966 $3 Whistling Swans	145.00	120.00	12.00	9.00
RW34	1967 $3 Old Squaw Ducks	165.00	120.00	12.00	9.00

RW35

RW36

RW37

RW38

RW35	1968 $3 Hooded Mergansers	100.00	75.00	12.00	9.00
RW36	1969 $3 White-Winged Scoters	100.00	75.00	9.50	6.75
RW37	1970 $3 Ross's Geese	100.00	75.00	9.50	6.75
RW38	1971 $3 Three Cinnamon Teal	70.00	50.00	9.50	6.75

Notes on Hunting Permit Stamps
1. Unused stamps without gum (uncancelled) are priced at one-half gummed price.
2. The date printed on the stamp is one year later than the date of issue listed above.
3. #RW1-RW25 and RW31 are plate blocks of 6.

SCOTT NO.	DESCRIPTION	UNUSED NH VF	F	USED VF	F

RW39

RW40

RW41

RW42

RW43

1972-1978

RW39	1972 $5 Emperor Geese	40.00	30.00	9.00	7.50
RW40	1973 $5 Steller's Eider	35.00	25.00	9.00	7.50
RW41	1974 $5 Wood Ducks	35.00	25.00	8.00	6.50
RW42	1975 $5 Canvasbacks	35.00	25.00	8.00	6.50
RW43	1976 $5 Canada Geese	35.00	25.00	8.00	6.50

RW44

RW45

RW44	1977 $5 Pair of Ross's Geese	30.00	20.00	8.00	6.50
RW45	1978 $5 Hooded Merganser Drake	30.00	20.00	8.00	6.50

RW46

RW47

RW48

RW49

1979-1986

RW46	1979 $7.50 Green-Winged Teal	30.00	20.00	8.00	7.00
RW47	1980 $7.50 Mallards	30.00	20.00	8.00	7.00
RW48	1981 $7.50 Ruddy Ducks	30.00	20.00	8.00	7.00
RW49	1982 $7.50 Canvasbacks	30.00	20.00	8.00	7.00

RW50

RW51

RW52

RW53

RW50	1983 $7.50 Pintails	30.00	20.00	8.00	7.00
RW51	1984 $7.50 Widgeon	30.00	20.00	8.00	7.00
RW52	1985 $7.50 Cinnamon Teal	30.00	20.00	8.00	7.00
RW53	1986 $7.50 Fulvous Whistling	30.00	20.00	8.00	7.00

RW54

RW55

RW56

RW57

1987-1993

RW54	1987 $10.00 Redhead Ducks	35.00	25.00	11.00	9.00
RW55	1988 $10.00 Snow Goose	35.00	25.00	12.00	10.00
RW56	1989 $12.50 Lesser Scaup	35.00	25.00	12.00	10.00
RW57	1990 $12.50 Black Bellied Whistling Duck	35.00	25.00	12.00	10.00

RW58

RW59

RW60

RW58	1991 $15.00 King Eiders	55.00	40.00	18.00	15.00
RW59	1992 $15.00 Spectacled Eider	50.00	35.00	16.50	12.50
RW60	1993 $15.00 Canvasbacks	50.00	35.00	16.50	12.50

SCOTT NO.	DESCRIPTION	UNUSED NH VF	F	USED VF	F

RW61

RW62

RW63

RW64

RW65

RW66

1992-1998

Scott	Description	UNUSED NH VF	F	USED VF	F
RW61	1994 $15.00 Red-breasted Merganser	50.00	35.00	16.50	12.50
RW62	1995 $15.00 Mallards	50.00	35.00	16.50	12.50
RW63	1996 $15.00 Surf Scoters	50.00	35.00	16.50	12.50
RW64	1997 $15.00 Canada Goose	50.00	35.00	16.50	12.50
RW65	1998 $15.00 Barrow's Goldeneye	60.00	48.00	16.50	12.50
RW65a	1998 $15.00 Barrow's Goldeneye, self-adhesive, pane of 1	42.00	....	18.00	....
RW66	1999 $15.00 Greater Scaup	42.00	35.00	16.50	....
RW66a	1999 $15.00 Greater Scaup, self-adhesive, pane of 1	35.00	....	18.00	....

RW67

RW68

2000-2001

Scott	Description	UNUSED NH VF	F	USED VF	F
RW67	2000 $15.00 Mottled Duck	40.00	30.00	16.50	....
RW67a	2000 $15.00 Mottled Duck, self-adhesive, pane of 1	35.00	....	18.00	....
RW68	2001 $15.00 Northern Pintail	35.00	30.00	16.50	....
RW68a	2001 $15.00 Northern Pintail, self-adhesive, pane of 1	35.00	....	18.00	....

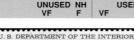

RW69

RW70

2002

Scott	Description	UNUSED NH VF	F	USED VF	F
RW69	2002 $15.00 Black Scoters	35.00	30.00	16.50	....
RW69a	2002 $15.00 Black Scoters, self-adhesive, pane of 1	35.00	....	18.00	....

SCOTT NO.	DESCRIPTION	UNUSED NH VF	F	USED VF	F

RW71

RW72

2003-2005

Scott	Description	UNUSED NH VF	F	USED VF	F
RW70	2003 $15.00 Snow Geese	40.00	30.00	16.50	....
RW70a	2003 $15.00 Snow Geese, self-adhesive, pane of 1	35.00	....	18.00	....
RW71	2004 $15.00 Redheads	35.00	30.00	16.50	....
RW71a	2004 $15.00 Redheads, self-adhesive, pane of 1	35.00	....	18.00	....
RW72	2005 $15.00 Hooded Mergansers	35.00	30.00	17.75	....
RW72a	2005 $15.00 Hooded Mergansers, self-adhesive, pane of 1	35.00	....	20.00	....

RW73

RW74

2006-2007

Scott	Description	UNUSED NH VF	F	USED VF	F
RW73	2006 $15.00 Ross's Goose	35.00	30.00	18.00	....
RW73a	2006 $15.00 Ross's Goose, self-adhesive, pane of 1	35.00	....	20.00	....
RW74	2007 $15.00 Ringed-Necked Ducks	35.00	30.00	19.00	....
RW74a	2007 $15.00 Ringed-Necked Ducks, self-adhesive, pane of 1	35.00	....	22.00	....
RW75	$15 Pintail Ducks	35.00	30.00	19.00	....
RW75a	$15 Pintail Ducks, self-adhesive	35.00	30.00	22.00	....

PLATE BLOCKS RW26-RW74

SCOTT NO.		UNUSED NH F	UNUSED OG F
RW26	1959 $3.00 Dog & Mallard	600.00	450.00
RW27	1960 $3.00 Redhead Ducks	475.00	360.00
RW28	1961 $3.00 Mallard Hen &Ducklings	550.00	360.00
RW29	1962 $3.00 Pintail Drakes	625.00	450.00
RW30	1963 $3.00 Brant Ducks Landing	525.00	400.00
RW31(6)	1964 $3.00 Hawaiian Nene Goose	2300.00	1950.00
RW32	1965 $3.00 Canvasback Drakes	575.00	400.00
RW33	1966 $3.00 Whistling Swans	575.00	400.00
RW34	1967 $3.00 Old Squaw Ducks	625.00	450.00
RW35	1968 $3.00 Hooded Mergansers	350.00	275.00
RW36	1969 $3.00 White-Winged Scoters	325.00	250.00
RW37	1970 $3.00 Ross's Geese	325.00	250.00
RW38	1971 $3.00 Three Cinnamon Teal	225.00	160.00
RW39	1972 $5.00 Emperor Geese	140.00	....
RW40	1973 $5.00 Steller's Eider	125.00	....
RW41	1974 $5.00 Wood Ducks	100.00	....
RW42	1975 $5.00 Canvasbacks	100.00	....
RW43	1976 $5.00 Canada Geese	85.00	....
RW44	1977 $5.00 Pair of Ross's Geese	85.00	....
RW45	1978 $5.00 Hooded Merganser Drake	85.00	....
RW46	1979 $7.50 Green-Winged Teal	85.00	....
RW47	1980 $7.50 Mallards	85.00	....
RW48	1981 $7.50 Ruddy Ducks	85.00	....
RW49	1982 $7.50 Canvasbacks	85.00	....
RW50	1983 $7.50 Pintails	85.00	....
RW51	1984 $7.50 Widgeon	85.00	....
RW52	1985 $7.50 Cinnamon Teal	85.00	....
RW53	1986 $7.50 Fulvous Whistling	85.00	....
RW54	1987 $10.00 Redhead Ducks	110.00	....
RW55	1988 $10.00 Snow Goose	110.00	....
RW56	1989 $12.50 Lesser Scaup	120.00	....
RW57	1990 $12.50 Black Bellied Whistling Duck	120.00	....
RW58	1991 $15.00 King Eiders	150.00	....
RW59	1992 $15.00 Spectacled Eider	150.00	....
RW60	1993 $15.00 Canvasbacks	150.00	....
RW61	1994 $15.00 Red-breasted Merganser	150.00	....
RW62	1995 $15.00 Mallards	150.00	....
RW63	1996 $15.00 Surf Scoters	150.00	....
RW64	1997 $15.00 Canada Goose	150.00	....
RW65	1998 $15.00 Barrow's Goldeneye	150.00	....
RW66	1999 $15.00 Greater Scaup	150.00	....
RW67	2000 $15.00 Mottled Duck	150.00	....
RW68	2001 $15.00 Northern Pintail	150.00	....
RW69	2002 $15.00 Black Scoters	150.00	....
RW70	2003 $15.00 Snow Geese	150.00	....
RW71	2004 $15.00 Redheads	150.00	....
RW72	2005 $15.00 Hooded Mergansers	150.00	....
RW73	2006 $15.00 Ross's Goose	150.00	....
RW74	2007 $15.00 Ringed-Necked Ducks	150.00	....

Note: #RW1-RW25 and RW31 are plate blocks of six. All others are plate blocks of four.

STATE HUNTING PERMIT

NO.	DESCRIPTION	F-VF NH

AL7
ALABAMA

AL1	'79 $5 Wood Ducks	10.25
AL2	'80 $5 Mallards	10.25
AL3	'81 $5 Canada Geese	10.25
AL4	'82 $5 Green-Winged Teal	10.25
AL5	'83 $5 Widgeons	11.00
AL6	'84 $5 Buffleheads	20.00
AL7	'85 $5 Wood Ducks	14.00
AL8	'86 $5 Canada Geese	14.00
AL9	'87 $5 Pintails	15.00
AL10	'88 $5 Canvasbacks	11.00
AL11	'89 $5 Hooded Mergansers	10.25
AL12	'90 $5 Wood Ducks	10.25
AL13	'91 $5 Redheads	10.25
AL14	'92 $5 Cinnamon Teal	10.25
AL15	'93 $5 Green-Winged Teal	10.25
AL16	'94 $5 Canvasbacks	10.25
AL17	'95 $5 Canada Geese	10.25
AL18	'96 $5 Wood Ducks	10.25
AL19	'97 $5 Snow Geese	10.25
AL20	'98 $5 Barrows Goldeneye	10.25
AL21	'99 $5 Redheads	10.25
AL22	'00 $5 Buffleheads	10.25
AL23	'01 $5 Ruddy Duck	10.25
AL24	'02 $5 Pintail	10.25
AL25	'03 $5 Wood Duck	10.25
AL26	'04 $5 Ring-Necked Duck	10.25
AL27	'05 $5 Canada Geese	10.25
AL28	'06 $5 Canvasback	10.25

AK1
ALASKA

AK1	'85 $5 Emperor Geese	14.00
AK2	'86 $5 Steller's Eiders	11.00
AK3	'87 $5 Spectacled Eiders	15.00
AK4	'88 $5 Trumpeter Swans	10.00
AK5	'89 $5 Barrow's Goldeneyes	9.25
AK6	'90 $5 Old Squaws	9.25
AK7	'91 $5 Snow Geese	9.25
AK8	'92 $5 Canvasbacks	9.25
AK9	'93 $5 Tule White Front Geese	9.25
AK10	'94 $5 Harlequin Ducks	20.00
AK11	'95 $5 Pacific Brant	20.00
AK12	'96 $5 Aleutian Canada Geese	25.00
AK13	'97 $5 King Eiders	20.00
AK14	'98 $5 Barrows Goldeneye	15.00
AK15	'99 $5 Pintail	15.00
AK16	'00 $5 Common Eiders	15.00
AK17	'01 $5 Buffleheads	15.00
AK18	'02 $5 Black Scoter	9.25
AK19	'03 $5 Canada Geese	9.25
AK20	'04 $5 Lesser Scaup	9.25
AK21	'05 $5 Hooded Merganser	9.25
AK22	'06 $5 Pintails, Mallard, green-winged teal	9.25

AZ1
ARIZONA

AZ1	'87 $5.50 Pintails	12.00
AZ2	'88 $5.50 Green-Winged Teal	11.25
AZ3	'89 $5.50 Cinnamon Teal	11.25
AZ4	'90 $5.50 Canada Geese	11.25
AZ5	'91 $5.50 Blue-Winged Teal	11.25
AZ6	'92 $5.50 Buffleheads	11.25
AZ7	'93 $5.50 Mexican Ducks	11.25
AZ8	'94 $5.50 Mallards	11.25
AZ9	'95 $5.50 Widgeon	11.25
AZ10	'96 $5.50 Canvasback	11.25
AZ11	'97 $5.50 Wood Duck	11.25
AZ12	'98 $5.50 Gadwall	11.25
AZ13	'99 $5.50 Snow Geese	11.25
AZ14	'00 $7.50 Ruddy Ducks	13.50
AZ15	'01 $7.50 Redheads	13.50
AZ16	'02 $7.50 Ring-necked ducks	13.50
AZ17	'03 $7.50 Northern Shoveler	13.50

AZ18	'04 $7.50 Lesser Scaup	13.50
AZ19	'05 $7.50 Pintails	13.50
AZ20	'06 $7.50 Canada Geese	13.50

AR5
ARKANSAS

AR1	'81 $5.50 Mallards	60.00
AR2	'82 $5.50 Wood Ducks	50.00
AR3	'83 $5.50 Green-Winged Teal	70.00
AR4	'84 $5.50 Pintails	26.00
AR5	'85 $5.50 Mallards	14.50
AR6	'86 $5.50 Black Swamp Mallards	12.50
AR7	'87 $7 Wood Ducks	12.50
AR8	'88 $7 Pintails	11.50
AR9	'89 $7 Mallards	11.50
AR10	'90 $7 Black Ducks & Mallards	11.50
AR11	'91 $7 Sulphur River Widgeons	11.50
AR12	'92 $7 Shirey Bay Shovelers	11.50
AR13	'93 $7 Grand Prairie Mallards	11.00
AR14	'94 $7 Canada Goose	11.00
AR15	'95 $7 White River Mallards	11.00
AR16	'96 $7 Black Lab	20.00
AR17	'97 $7 Chocolate Lab	11.00
AR18	'98 $7 Labrador retriever, mallards	11.00
AR19	'99 $7.00 Wood Duck	11.00
AR20	'00 $7 Mallards and Golden Retriever	11.00
AR21	'01 $7 Canvasback	11.00
AR22	'02 $7 Mallards	11.00
AR23	'03 $7 Mallards & Chesapeake Bay Retriever	11.00
AR24	'04 $7 Mallards	11.00
AR25	'04 $20 Mallards	30.00
AR26	'04 $7 Mallards and Labrador Retriever	11.00
AR27	'04 $20 Mallards and Labrador Retriever	30.00
AR28	'06 $7 Mallards	11.00
AR29	'06 $20 Mallards	30.00

CA16
CALIFORNIA

CA1	'71 $1 Pintails	850.00
CA2	'72 $1 Canvasbacks	3,250.00
CA3	'73 $1 Mallards	15.00
CA4	'74 $1 White-Fronted Geese	4.50
CA5	'75 $1 Green-Winged Teal	42.50
CA6	'76 $1 Widgeons	19.00
CA7	'77 $1 Cinnamon Teal	50.00
CA8	'78 $5 Cinnamon Teal	9.00
CA9	'78 $5 Hooded Mergansers	150.00
CA10	'79 $5 Wood Ducks	9.50
CA11	'80 $5 Pintails	9.50
CA12	'81 $5 Canvasbacks	9.75
CA13	'82 $5 Widgeons	9.75
CA14	'83 $5 Green-Winged Teal	9.75
CA15	'84 $7.50 Mallard Decoy	12.50
CA16	'85 $7.50 Ring-Necked Ducks	12.50
CA17	'86 $7.50 Canada Goose	12.50
CA18	'87 $7.50 Redheads	12.50
CA19	'88 $7.50 Mallards	12.50
CA20	'89 $7.50 Cinnamon Teal	12.50
CA21	'90 $7.50 Canada Goose	12.50
CA22	'91 $7.50 Gadwalls	12.50
CA23	'92 $7.90 White-Fronted Goose	12.50
CA24	'93 $10.50 Pintails	15.00
CA25	'94 $10.50 Wood Duck	15.00
CA26	'95 $10.50 Snow Geese	15.00
CA27	'96 $10.50 Mallard	15.00
CA28	'97 $10.50 Pintails	15.00
CA29	'98 $10.50 Green-Winged Teal (pair)	35.00
CA30	'99 $10.50 Wood Duck (pair)	35.00
CA31	'00 $10.50 Canada geese, mallard, widgeon	16.00
CA32	'01 $10.50 Redheads	16.00
CA33	'02 $10.50 Pintails	16.00
CA34	'03 $10.50 Mallards	16.00
CA35	'04 $13.90 Cinnamon Teal	19.50
CA36	'05 $14.20 Pintails	20.00
CA37	'06 $14.95 White-Fronted Goose	22.00

CO1

NO.	DESCRIPTION	F-VF NH
	COLORADO	
CO1	'90 $5 Canada Geese	17.00
CO2	'91 $5 Mallards	17.00
CO3	'92 $5 Pintails	12.00
CO4	'93 $5 Green-Winged Teal	12.00
CO5	'94 $5 Wood Ducks	12.00
CO6	'95 $5 Buffleheads	12.00
CO7	'96 $5 Cinnamon Teal	12.00
CO8	'97 $5 Widgeon	12.00
CO9	'98 $5 Redhead	12.00
CO10	'99 $5 Blue-winged Teal	12.00
CO11	'00 $5 Gadwalls	12.00
CO12	'01 $5 Ruddy Duck	12.00
CO13	'02 $5 Common Goldeneyes	12.00
CO14	'03 $5 Canvasbacks	12.00
CO15	'04 $5 Snow Geese	12.00
CO16	'05 $5 Shovelers	9.25
CO17	'06 $5 Ring-Necked Ducks	10.00

CONNECTICUT

CT1	'93 $5 Black Ducks	15.00
CT2	'94 $5 Canvasbacks	15.00
CT3	'95 $5 Mallards	15.00
CT4	'96 $5 Old Squaw	15.00
CT5	'97 $5 Green Winged Teal	15.00
CT6	'98 $5 Mallards	15.00
CT7	'99 $5 Canada Geese	23.00
CT8	'00 $5 Wood Duck	15.00
CT9	'01 Bufflehead	15.00
CT10	'02 Greater Scaups	15.00
CT11	'03 $5 Black Duck	15.00
CT12	'04 $5 Wood Duck	15.00
CT13	'05 $10 Mallards	20.00
CT14	'06 $10 Buffleheads	20.00

DE1
DELAWARE

DE1	'80 $5 Black Ducks	95.00
DE2	'81 $5 Snow Geese	85.00
DE3	'82 $5 Canada Geese	80.00
DE4	'83 $5 Canvasbacks	55.00
DE5	'84 $5 Mallards	25.00
DE6	'85 $5 Pintail	14.00
DE7	'86 $5 Widgeons	12.00
DE8	'87 $5 Redheads	12.00
DE9	'88 $5 Wood Ducks	10.50
DE10	'89 $5 Buffleheads	9.75
DE11	'90 $5 Green-Winged Teal	9.75
DE12	'91 $5 Hooded Merganser	9.75
DE13	'92 $5 Blue-Winged Teal	9.75
DE14	'93 $5 Goldeneye	9.75
DE15	'94 $5 Blue Goose	9.75
DE16	'95 $5 Scaup	9.75
DE17	'96 $6 Gadwall	9.75
DE18	'97 $6 White Winged Scoter	9.75
DE19	'98 $6 Blue Winged Teal	9.75
DE20	'99 $6 Tundra Swan	9.75
DE21	'00 $6 American brant	9.75
DE22	'01 $6 Old Squaw	9.75
DE23	'02 $6 Ruddy Ducks	9.75
DE24	'03 $9 Ring-Necked Duck	14.00
DE25	'04 $9 Black Scoter	14.00
DE26	'05 $9 Common Merganser and Lighthouse	14.00
DE27	'06 $9 Red-Breasted Mergansers	14.00

FL8
FLORIDA

FL1	'79 $3.25 Green-Winged Teal	175.00
FL2	'80 $3.25 Pintails	25.00
FL3	'81 $3.25 Widgeon	25.00
FL4	'82 $3.25 Ring-Necked Ducks	35.00
FL5	'83 $3.25 Buffleheads	60.00
FL6	'84 $3.25 Hooded Merganser	20.00
FL7	'85 $3.25 Wood Ducks	18.00
FL8	'86 $3 Canvasbacks	11.25
FL9	'87 $3.50 Mallards	9.75
FL10	'88 $3.50 Redheads	9.75
FL11	'89 $3.50 Blue-Winged Teal	7.25
FL12	'90 $3.50 Wood Ducks	7.25
FL13	'91 $3.50 Northern Pintails	7.25
FL14	'92 $3.50 Ruddy Duck	7.25
FL15	'93 $3.50 American Widgeon	7.00
FL16	'94 $3.50 Mottled Duck	7.00

NO.	DESCRIPTION	F-VF NH
FL17	'95 $3.50 Fulvous Whistling Duck	10.00
FL18	'96 $3.50 Goldeneyes	15.00
FL19	'97 $3.50 Hooded Mergansers	10.00
FL20	'98 $3.50 Shoveler	20.00
FL21	'99 $3 Pintail	12.00
FL22	'00 $3.50 Rin-necked duck	12.00
FL23	'01 $3.50 Canvasback	7.00
FL24	'02 $3.50 Mottled Duck	7.00
FL25	'03 $3.50 Canvasback	

GA1

GEORGIA

GA1	'85 $5.50 Wood Ducks	15.00
GA2	'86 $5.50 Mallards	10.00
GA3	'87 $5.50 Canada Geese	9.00
GA4	'88 $5.50 Ring-Necked Ducks	9.00
GA5	'89 $5.50 Duckling & Golden Retriever Puppy	20.00
GA6	'90 $5.50 Wood Ducks	9.00
GA7	'91 $5.50 Green-Winged Teal	9.00
GA8	'92 $5.50 Buffleheads	9.00
GA9	'93 $5.50 Mallards	9.00
GA10	'94 $5.50 Ring-Necked Ducks	9.00
GA11	'95 $5.50 Widgeons, Labrador Retriever	35.00
GA12	'96 $5.50 Black Ducks	35.00
GA13	'97 $5.50 Lesser Scaup	35.00
GA14	'98 $5.50 Black Lab with Ringnecks	35.00
GA15	'99 $5.50 Pintails	35.00

HAWAII

HI1	'96 $5 Nene Geese	9.25
HI2	'97 $5 Hawaiian Duck	9.25
HI3	'98 $5 Wild Turkey	9.25
HI4	'99 $5 Ring-necked Pheasant	15.00
HI5	'00 $5 Erckesls Francolin	15.00
HI6	'01 $5 Japanese Green Pheasant	15.00
HI7	'02 $10 Chukar Partridge	18.00
HI8	'03 $10 Nene Geese	18.00
HI9	'04 $10 Nene Geese	18.00
HI10	'05 $10 California Quail	18.00
HI11	'06 $10 Black Francolin	18.00

ID1

IDAHO

ID1	'87 $5.50 Cinnamon Teal	20.00
ID2	'88 $5.50 Green-Winged Teal	13.50
ID3	'89 $5 Blue-Winged Teal	11.50
ID4	'90 $6 Trumpeter Swans	20.00
ID6	'91 $6 Widgeons	10.00
ID7	'92 $6 Canada Geese	10.00
ID8	'93 $6 Common Goldeneye	10.00
ID9	'94 $6 Harlequin Ducks	10.00
ID10	'95 $6 Wood Ducks	20.00
ID11	'96 $6 Mallard	20.00
ID12	'97 $6.50 Shovelers	20.00
ID13	'98 $6.50 Canada Geese	10.00

IL11

ILLINOIS

IL1	'75 $5 Mallard	700.00
IL2	'76 $5 Wood Ducks	300.00
IL3	'77 $5 Canada Goose	200.00
IL4	'78 $5 Canvasbacks	150.00
IL5	'79 $5 Pintail	110.00
IL6	'80 $5 Green-Winged Teal	110.00
IL7	'81 $5 Widgeons	110.00
IL8	'82 $5 Black Ducks	80.00
IL9	'83 $5 Lesser Scaup	70.00
IL10	'84 $5 Blue-Winged Teal	70.00
IL11	'85 $5 Redheads	21.00
IL12	'86 $5 Gadwalls	15.50
IL13	'87 $5 Buffleheads	12.50
IL14	'88 $5 Common Goldeneyes	12.50
IL15	'89 $5 Ring-Necked Ducks	10.50
IL16	'90 $10 Lesser Snow Geese	16.00
IL17	'91 $10 Labrador Retriever & Canada Goose	15.50

IL18	'92 $10 Retriever & Mallards	30.00
IL19	'93 $10 Pintail Decoys & Puppy	30.00
IL20	'94 $10 Canvasbacks & Retrievers	30.00
IL21	'95 $10 Retriever, Green-Winged Teal, Decoys	30.00
IL22	'96 $10 Wood Ducks	15.00
IL23	'97 $10 Canvasbacks	15.00
IL24	'98 $10 Canada Geese	15.00
IL25	'99 $10 Canada Geese, black labrador retriever	15.00
IL26	'00 $10 Mallards, golden retriever	25.00
IL27	'01 $10 Canvasback, yellow labrador	25.00
IL28	'02 $10 Canvasbacks, Chesapeake Retriever	25.00
IL29	'03 $10 Chocolate Lab, Green-winged Teal	15.00
IL30	'04 $10 Wood Ducks	15.00
IL31	'05 $10 Green-winged Teal	15.00
IL32	'06 $10 Northern Pintails	15.00

IN10

INDIANA

IN1	'76 $5 Green-Winged Teal	9.50
IN2	'77 $5 Pintail	9.50
IN3	'78 $5 Canada Geese	9.50
IN4	'79 $5 Canvasbacks	9.50
IN5	'80 $5 Mallard Ducklings	9.50
IN6	'81 $5 Hooded Mergansers	9.50
IN7	'82 $5 Blue-Winged Teal	9.50
IN8	'83 $5 Snow Geese	9.50
IN9	'84 $5 Redheads	9.50
IN10	'85 $5 Pintail	9.50
IN11	'86 $5 Wood Duck	9.50
IN12	'87 $5 Canvasbacks	9.50
IN13	'88 $6.75 Redheads	11.25
IN14	'89 $6.75 Canada Goose	11.25
IN15	'90 $6.75 Blue-Winged Teal	11.25
IN16	'91 $6.75 Mallards	11.25
IN17	'92 $6.75 Green-Winged Teal	11.25
IN18	'93 $6.75 Wood Ducks	11.25
IN19	'94 $6.75 Pintail	11.25
IN20	'95 $6.75 Goldeneyes	11.25
IN21	'96 $6.75 Black Ducks	11.25
IN22	'97 $6.75 Canada Geese	11.25
IN23	'98 $6.75 Widgeon	11.25
IN24	'99 $6.75 Bluebills	11.25
IN25	'00 $6.75 Ring-necked Duck	11.25
IN26	'01 $6.75 Green-winged Teal	11.25
IN27	'02 $6.75 Green-winged Teal	11.25
IN28	'03 $6.75 Shoveler	11.25
IN29	'04 $6.75 Hooded Mergansers	11.25
IN30	'05 $6.75 Buffleheads	11.25
IN31	'06 $6.75 Gadwalls	11.25

IA14

IOWA

IA1	'72 $1 Mallards	200.00
IA2	'73 $1 Pintails	47.50
IA3	'74 $1 Gadwalls	100.00
IA4	'75 $1 Canada Geese	130.00
IA5	'76 $1 Canvasbacks	26.00
IA6	'77 $1 Lesser Scaup	26.00
IA7	'78 $1 Wood Ducks	55.00
IA8	'79 $5 Buffleheads	400.00
IA9	'80 $5 Redheads	40.00
IA10	'81 $5 Green-Winged Teal	35.00
IA11	'82 $5 Snow Geese	19.00
IA12	'83 $5 Widgeons	20.00
IA13	'84 $5 Wood Ducks	42.00
IA14	'85 $5 Mallard & Mallard Decoy	25.00
IA15	'86 $5 Blue-Winged Teal	16.50
IA16	'87 $5 Canada Goose	14.50
IA17	'88 $5 Pintails	12.50
IA18	'89 $5 Blue-Winged Teal	12.50
IA19	'90 $5 Canvasbacks	8.50
IA20	'91 $5 Mallards	8.50
IA21	'92 $5 Labrador Retriever & Ducks	10.00
IA22	'93 $5 Mallards	9.25
IA23	'94 $5 Green-Winged Teal	9.25
IA24	'95 $5 Canada Geese	9.25
IA25	'96 $5 Canvasbacks	9.25
IA 26	'97 $5 Canada Geese	9.25
IA27	'98 $5 Pintails	9.25
IA28	'99 $5 Trumpeter Swan	9.25
IA29	'00 $5.50 Hooded Merganser	9.25
IA30	'01 $6 Snow Geese	10.25
IA31	'02 $8.50 Northern Shoveler	13.00
IA32	'03 $8.50 Ruddy Duck	13.00
IA33	'04 $8.50 Wood Ducks	13.00
IA34	'05 $8.50 Green-winged Teals	13.00
IA35	'06 Ring-Necked Duck	15.00

KS1

KANSAS

KS1	'87 $3 Green-Winged Teal	9.00
KS2	'88 $3 Canada Geese	7.00
KS3	'89 $3 Mallards	6.50
KS4	'90 $3 Wood Ducks	6.50
KS5	'91 $3 Pintail	6.50
KS6	'92 $3 Canvasbacks	6.50
KS7	'93 $3 Mallards	6.50
KS8	'94 $3 Blue-Winged Teal	6.50
KS9	'95 $3 Barrow's Goldeneye	6.50
KS10	'96 $3 Widgeon	6.50
KS11	'97 $3 Mallard	6.50
KS12	'98 $3 Mallard	6.50
KS13	'99 $3 Mallard (red)	6.50
KS14	'00 $3 Mallard (purple)	6.50
KS15	'01 $3 Mallard (orange)	6.50
KS16	'02 $5 Pintail (blue)	9.00
KS17	'03 $5 Green	9.00
KS18	'04 $5 Red	9.00

KENTUCKY

KY1	'85 $5.25 Mallards	15.00
KY2	'86 $5.25 Wood Ducks	10.00
KY3	'87 $5.25 Black Ducks	10.00
KY4	'88 $5.25 Canada Geese	10.00
KY5	'89 $5.25 Retriever & Canvasbacks	10.00
KY6	'90 $5.25 Widgeons	10.00
KY7	'91 $5.25 Pintails	10.00
KY8	'92 $5.25 Green-Winged Teal	12.50
KY9	'93 $5.25 Canvasbacks & Decoy	25.00
KY10	'94 $5.25 Canada Goose	9.75
KY11	'95 $7.50 Retriever, Decoy, Ringnecks	25.00
KY12	'96 $7.50 Blue-Winged Teal	12.00
KY13	'97 $7.50 Shovelers	12.00
KY14	'98 $7.50 Gadwalls	12.00
KY15	'99 $7.50 Common Goldeneyes	12.00
KY16	'00 $7.50 Hooded Merganser	12.00
KY17	'01 $7.50 Mallard	12.00
KY18	'02 $7.50 Pintails	12.00
KY19	'03 $7.50 Snow Goose	12.00
KY20	'04 $7.50 Black Ducks	12.00
KY21	'05 $7.50 Canada Geese	12.00
KY22	'06 $7.50 Mallards	12.00

LA1

LOUISIANA

LA1	'89 $5 Blue-Winged Teal	12.50
LA2	'89 $7.50 Blue-Winged Teal	10.00
LA3	'90 $5 Green-Winged Teal	9.25
LA4	'90 $7.50 Green-Winged Teal	13.50
LA5	'91 $5 Wood Ducks	9.75
LA6	'91 $7.50 Wood Ducks	13.50
LA7	'92 $5 Pintails	8.75
LA8	'92 $7.50 Pintails	12.00
LA9	'93 $5 American Widgeon	8.75
LA10	'93 $7.50 American Widgeon	12.00
LA11	'94 $5 Mottled Duck	8.75
LA12	'94 $7.50 Mottled Duck	12.00
LA13	'95 $5 Speckle Bellied Goose	8.75
LA14	'95 $7.50 Speckle Bellied Goose	12.00
LA15	'96 $5 Gadwall	8.75
LA16	'96 $7.50 Gadwell	12.00
LA17	'97 $5.00 Ring Necked Duck	8.75
LA18	'97 $13.50 Ring Necked Duck	18.00
LA19	'98 $5.50 Mallards	8.75
LA20	'98 $13.50 Mallards	18.00
LA21	'99 $5.50 Snow Goose	8.75
LA22	'99 $13.50 Snow Geese	18.00
LA23	'00 $5.50 Lesser Scaup	8.75
LA24	'00 $13.50 Lesser Scaup	18.00
LA25	'01 $5.50 Northern Shoveler	8.75
LA26	'01 $13.50 Northern Shoveler	18.00
LA27	'02 $5.50 Canvasbacks	8.75
LA28	'02 $25 Canvasbacks	32.50
LA29	'03 $5.50 Redhead	8.75
LA30	'03 $25.00 Redhead	32.50
LA31	'04 $5.50 Hooded Merganser	8.75
LA32	'04 $25 Hooded Merganser	32.50
LA33	'05 $5.50 Pintails and Labrador Retriever	8.75
LA34	'05 $25 Pintails and Labrador Retriever	32.50
LA35	'06 $5.50 Mallards, Labrador Retriever	8.75
LA36	'06 $25 Mallards, Labrador Retriever	32.50

NO.	DESCRIPTION	F-VF NH

ME2

MAINE

ME1	'84 $2.50 Black Ducks	25.00
ME2	'85 $2.50 Common Eiders	55.00
ME3	'86 $2.50 Wood Ducks	10.00
ME4	'87 $2.50 Buffleheads	8.75
ME5	'88 $2.50 Green-Winged Teal	8.75
ME6	'89 $2.50 Common Goldeneyes	6.50
ME7	'90 $2.50 Canada Geese	6.50
ME8	'91 $2.50 Ring-Necked Duck	6.50
ME9	'92 $2.50 Old Squaw	6.50
ME10	'93 $2.50 Hooded Merganser	6.50
ME11	'94 $2.50 Mallards	6.50
ME12	'95 $2.50 White-Winged Scoters	6.50
ME13	'96 $2.50 Blue-Winged Teal	6.50
ME14	'97 $2.50 Greater Scaup	6.50
ME15	'98 $2.50 Surf Scoters	6.50
ME16	'99 $2.50 Black Duck	6.50
ME17	'00 $2.50 Common Eider	6.50
ME18	'01 $2.50 Wood Duck	6.50
ME19	'02 $2.50 Bufflehead	6.50
ME20	'03 $5.50 Green-winged Teal	11.00
ME21	'04 $5.50 Barrows Goldeneyes	11.00
ME22	'05 $8.50 Canada Goose	16.00
ME23	'06 $7.50 Ring-Necked Ducks	14.00

MD1

MARYLAND

MD1	'74 $1.10 Mallards	14.00
MD2	'75 $1.10 Canada Geese	12.50
MD3	'76 $1.10 Canvasbacks	12.50
MD4	'77 $1.10 Greater Scaup	12.50
MD5	'78 $1.10 Redheads	12.50
MD6	'79 $1.10 Wood Ducks	12.50
MD7	'80 $1.10 Pintail Decoy	12.50
MD8	'81 $3 Widgeon	7.50
MD9	'82 $3 Canvasback	10.50
MD10	'83 $3 Wood Duck	14.50
MD11	'84 $6 Black Ducks	12.50
MD12	'85 $6 Canada Geese	11.25
MD13	'86 $6 Hooded Mergansers	11.25
MD14	'87 $6 Redheads	11.25
MD15	'88 $6 Ruddy Ducks	11.25
MD16	'89 $6 Blue-Winged Teal	10.25
MD17	'90 $6 Lesser Scaup	10.25
MD18	'91 $6 Shovelers	10.25
MD19	'92 $6 Bufflehead	10.25
MD20	'93 $6 Canvasbacks	10.25
MD21	'94 $6 Redheads	10.25
MD22	'95 $6 Mallards	10.25
MD23	'96 $6 Canada Geese	10.25
MD24	'97 $6 Canvasbacks	10.25
MD25	'98 $6 Pintails	10.25
MD26	'99 $5 Wood Ducks	10.25
MD27	'00 $6 Oldsquaws	10.25
MD28	'01 $6 American Widgeon	10.25
MD29	'02 $9 Black Scoters	13.00
MD30	'03 $9 Lesser Scaup	13.00
MD31	'04 $9 Pintails	13.00
MD32	'05 $9 Ruddy Duck	13.00
MD33	'06 $9 Canada Geese	13.00

MA12

MASSACHUSETTS

MA1	'74 $1.25 Wood Duck Decoy	16.50
MA2	'75 $1.25 Pintail Decoy	12.75
MA3	'76 $1.25 Canada Goose Decoy	12.75
MA4	'77 $1.25 Goldeneye Decoy	12.75
MA5	'78 $1.25 Black Duck Decoy	12.75
MA6	'79 $1.25 Ruddy Turnstone Duck Decoy	20.00
MA7	'80 $1.25 Old Squaw Decoy	12.75
MA8	'81 $1.25 Red-Breasted Merganser Decoy	18.00

NO.	DESCRIPTION	F-VF NH
MA9	'82 $1.25 Greater Yellowlegs Decoy	18.00
MA10	'83 $1.25 Redhead Decoy	18.00
MA11	'84 $1.25 White-Winged Scoter Decoy	18.00
MA12	'85 $1.25 Ruddy Duck Decoy	18.00
MA13	'86 $1.25 Preening Bluebill Decoy	18.00
MA14	'87 $1.25 American Widgeon Decoy	18.00
MA15	'88 $1.25 Mallard Decoy	18.00
MA16	'89 $1.25 Brant Decoy	9.00
MA17	'90 $1.25 Whistler Hen Decoy	9.00
MA18	'91 $5 Canvasback Decoy	9.00
MA19	'92 $5 Black-Bellied Plover Decoy	9.00
MA20	'93 $5 Red-Breasted Merganser Decoy	9.00
MA21	'94 $5 White-Winged Scoter Decoy	9.00
MA22	'95 $5 Female Hooded Merganser Decoy	9.00
MA23	'96 $5 Eider Decoy	9.00
MA24	'97 $5 Curlew Shorebird	10.25
MA25	'98 $5 Canada Goose	10.25
MA26	'99 $5 Oldsquaw Decoy	10.25
MA27	'00 $5 Merganser Hen decoy	10.25
MA28	'01 $5 Black Duck decoy	10.25
MA29	'02 $5 Bufflehead decoy	10.25
MA30	'03 $5 Green-winged Teal decoy	10.25
MA31	'04 $5 Wood Duck Decoy	10.25
MA32	'05 $5 Oldsquaw Drake Decoy	10.25
MA33	'06 $5 Long-Bellied Curlew Decoy	10.25

MI10

MICHIGAN

MI1	'76 $2.10 Wood Duck	5.00
MI2	'77 $2.10 Canvasbacks	325.00
MI3	'78 $2.10 Mallards	30.00
MI4	'79 $2.10 Canada Geese	70.00
MI5	'80 $3.75 Lesser Scaup	24.50
MI6	'81 $3.75 Buffleheads	29.00
MI7	'82 $3.75 Redheads	29.00
MI8	'83 $3.75 Wood Ducks	29.00
MI9	'84 $3.75 Pintails	29.00
MI10	'85 $3.75 Ring-Necked Ducks	29.00
MI11	'86 $3.75 Common Goldeneyes	21.50
MI12	'87 $3.85 Green-Winged Teal	11.50
MI13	'88 $3.85 Canada Geese	11.50
MI14	'89 $3.85 Widgeons	8.25
MI15	'90 $3.85 Wood Ducks	8.25
MI16	'91 $3.85 Blue-Winged Teal	7.50
MI17	'92 $3.85 Red-Breasted Merganser	7.50
MI18	'93 $3.85 Hooded Merganser	7.50
MI19	'94 $3.85 Black Duck	7.50
MI20	'95 $4.35 Blue Winged Teal	8.25
MI21	'96 $4.35 Canada Geese	8.25
MI22	'97 $5 Canvasbacks	20.00
MI23	'98 $5 Pintail	8.25
MI24	'99 $5 Shoveler	8.25
MI25	'00 $5 Mallards	25.00
MI26	'01 $5 Ruddy Duck	8.25
MI27	'02 $5 Wigeons	8.25
MI28	'03 $5 Redhead	8.25
MI29	'04 $5 Wood Duck	8.25
MI30	'05 $5 Blue-winged Teals	8.25
MI31	'06 $5 Widgeon	10.00

MN2

MINNESOTA

MN1	'77 $3 Mallards	20.00
MN2	'78 $3 Lesser Scaup	15.00
MN3	'79 $3 Pintails	15.00
MN4	'80 $3 Canvasbacks	15.00
MN5	'81 $3 Canada Geese	15.00
MN6	'82 $3 Redheads	15.00
MN7	'83 $3 Blue Geese & Snow Goose	15.00
MN8	'84 $3 Wood Ducks	15.00
MN9	'85 $3 White-Fronted Geese	11.00
MN10	'86 $3 Lesser Scaup	11.00
MN11	'87 $5 Common Goldeneyes	11.50
MN12	'88 $5 Buffleheads	11.50
MN13	'89 $5 Widgeons	11.50
MN14	'90 $5 Hooded Mergansers	30.00
MN15	'91 $5 Ross's Geese	9.25
MN16	'92 $5 Barrow's Goldeneyes	9.25
MN17	'93 $5 Blue-Winged Teal	9.25
MN18	'94 $5 Ringneck Duck	9.25
MN19	'95 $5 Gadwall	9.25
MN20	'96 $5 Greater Scaup	9.25

NO.	DESCRIPTION	F-VF NH
MN21	'97 $5 Shoveler with Decoy	9.25
MN22	'98 $5 Harlequin Ducks	9.25
MN23	'99 $5 Green-winged Teal	9.25
MN24	'00 $5 Red-beasted Merganser	9.25
MN25	'01 $5 Black Duck	9.25
MN26	'02 $5 Ruddy Duck	9.25
MN27	'03 $5 Long Tailed Duck	9.25
MN28	'04 $7.50 Common Merganser	11.75
MN29	'05 $7.50 White-winged Scoters and Lighthouse	11.75
MN30	'06 $7.50 Mallard	11.75

MS10

MISSISSIPPI

MS1	'76 $2 Wood Duck	24.50
MS2	'77 $2 Mallards	9.25
MS3	'78 $2 Green-Winged Teal	9.25
MS4	'79 $2 Canvasbacks	9.25
MS5	'80 $2 Pintails	9.25
MS6	'81 $2 Redheads	9.25
MS7	'82 $2 Canada Geese	15.00
MS8	'83 $2 Lesser Scaup	9.25
MS9	'84 $2 Black Ducks	9.25
MS10	'85 $2 Mallards	20.00
MS11	'86 $2 Widgeons	9.25
MS12	'87 $2 Ring-Necked Ducks	9.25
MS13	'88 $2 Snow Geese	9.25
MS14	'89 $2 Wood Ducks	7.00
MS15	'90 $2 Snow Geese	14.50
MS16	'91 $2 Labrador Retriever & Canvasbacks	6.00
MS17	'92 $2 Green-Winged Teal	5.25
MS18	'93 $2 Mallards	8.25
MS19	'94 $2 Canvasbacks	15.00
MS20	'95 $5 Blue-Winged Teal	15.00
MS21	'96 $5 Hooded Merganser	15.00
MS22	'97 $5Wood Duck	15.00
MS23	'98 $5 Pintails	9.25
MS24	'99 $5 Ring-necked Duck	9.25
MS25	'00 $5 Mallards	9.25
MS26	'01 $10 Gadwall	14.50
MS27	'02 $10 Wood Duck	14.50
MS28	'03 $10 Pintail	14.50
MS29	'04 $10 Wood Ducks	14.50
MS30	'05 $10 Blue-winged Teal	14.50
MS31	'06 $10 Wood Duck	15.00
MS32	'06 $10 Wood Duck, self adhesive, die-cut	22.00

MO9

MISSOURI

MO1	'79 $3.40 Canada Geese	710.00
MO2	'80 $3.40 Wood Ducks	140.00
MO3	'81 $3 Lesser Scaup	72.50
MO4	'82 $3 Buffleheads	62.50
MO5	'83 $3 Blue-Winged Teal	52.50
MO6	'84 $3 Mallards	42.50
MO7	'85 $3 American Widgeons	25.00
MO8	'86 $3 Hooded Mergansers	16.00
MO9	'87 $3 Pintails	12.50
MO10	'88 $3 Canvasback	11.25
MO11	'89 $3 Ring-Necked Ducks	9.25
MO12	'90 $5 Redheads	8.25
MO13	'91 $5 Snow Geese	8.25
MO14	'92 $5 Gadwalls	8.25
MO15	'93 $5 Green-Winged Teal	8.25
MO16	'94 $5 White-Fronted Goose	8.25
MO17	'95 $5 Goldeneyes	12.00
MO18	'96 $5 Black Duck	12.00

MT34

MONTANA

MT34	'86 $5 Canada Geese	17.50
MT35	'87 $5 Redheads	18.00
MT36	'88 $5 Mallards	14.50
MT37	'89 $5 Black Labrador Retriever & Pintail	10.00
MT38	'90 $5 Blue-Winged & CinnamonTeal	9.00

NO.	DESCRIPTION	F-VF NH
MT39	'91 $5 Snow Geese	.8.50
MT40	'92 $5 Wood Ducks	.8.50
MT41	'93 $5 Harlequin Ducks	.9.00
MT42	'94 $5 Widgeons	.9.00
MT43	'95 $5 Tundra Swans	.9.00
MT44	'96 $5 Canvasbacks	.9.00
MT45	'97 $5 Golden Retriever	.11.00
MT46	'98 $5 Gadwalls	.9.00
MT47	'99 $5 Barrow's Goldeneye	.9.00
MT48	'00 $5 Mallard decoy, Chesapeake retriever	.9.00
MT49	'01 $5 Canada Geese, Steamboat	.9.00
MT50	'02 ($5) Sandhill crane	.9.00
MT51	'03 $5 Mallards	.9.00

NE1

NEBRASKA

NO.	DESCRIPTION	F-VF NH
NE1	'91 $6 Canada Geese	.12.00
NE2	'92 $6 Pintails	.12.00
NE3	'93 $6 Canvasbacks	.12.00
NE4	'94 $6 Mallards	.12.00
NE5	'95 $6 Wood Ducks	.12.00
NE6	'06 $5 Wood Ducks	.12.00

NV7

NEVADA

NO.	DESCRIPTION	F-VF NH
NV1	'79 $2 Canvasbacks & Decoy	.55.00
NV2	'80 $2 Cinnamon Teal	.10.00
NV3	'81 $2 Whistling Swans	.10.00
NV4	'82 $2 Shovelers	.10.00
NV5	'83 $2 Gadwalls	.12.50
NV6	'84 $2 Pintails	.12.50
NV7	'85 $2 Canada Geese	.17.50
NV8	'86 $2 Redheads	.16.00
NV9	'87 $2 Buffleheads	.20.00
NV10	'88 $2 Canvasbacks	.12.50
NV11	'89 $2 Ross's Geese	.8.25
NV12	'90 $5 Green-Winged Teal	.9.25
NV13	'91 $5 White-Faced Ibis	.20.00
NV14	'92 $5 American Widgeon	.9.00
NV15	'93 $5 Common Goldeneye	.9.00
NV16	'94 $5 Mallards	.9.00
NV17	'95 $5 Wood Duck	.9.00
NV18	'96 $5 Ring Necked Duck	.9.00
NV19	'97 $5 Ruddy Duck	.9.00
NV20	'98 $5 Hooded Merganser	.9.00
NV21	'99 $5 Canvasback Decoy	.9.00
NV22	'00 $5 Canvasbacks	.9.00
NV23	'01 $5 Lesser Scaup	.9.00
NV24	'02 $5 Cinnamon teal	.9.00
NV25	'03 $5 Green-winged Teal	.9.00
NV26	'04 $10 Redhead	.14.00
NV27	'05 $10 Gadwalls	.14.00
NV28	'06 $10 Tundra Swans	.16.00

NH2

NEW HAMPSHIRE

NO.	DESCRIPTION	F-VF NH
NH1	'83 $4 Wood Ducks	.150.00
NH2	'84 $4 Mallards	.130.00
NH3	'85 $4 Blue-Winged Teal	.110.00
NH4	'86 $4 Hooded Mergansers	.25.00
NH5	'87 $4 Canada Geese	.17.50
NH6	'88 $4 Buffleheads	.10.00
NH7	'89 $4 Black Ducks	.8.50
NH8	'90 $4 Green-Winged Teal	.8.25
NH9	'91 $4 Golden Retriever & Mallards	.15.00
NH10	'92 $4 Ring-Necked Ducks	.8.25
NH11	'93 $4 Hooded Mergansers	.8.25
NH12	'94 $4 Common Goldeneyes	.8.25
NH13	'95 $4 Northern Pintails	.8.25
NH14	'96 $4 Surf Scoters	.8.25
NH15	'97 $4 Old Squaws	.8.25
NH16	'98 $4 Canada Goose	.8.25
NH17	'99 $4 Mallards	.8.25

NO.	DESCRIPTION	F-VF NH
NH18	'00 $4 Black Ducks	.8.25
NH19	'01 $4 Blue-winged Teal	.8.25
NH20	'02 $4 Pintails	.8.25
NH21	'03 $4 Wood Ducks	.8.25
NH22	'04 $4 Wood Ducks	.8.25
NH23	'05 $4 Oldsquaw and Lighthouse	.8.25
NH24	'06 $4 Common Elders	.8.50

NJ1

NEW JERSEY

NO.	DESCRIPTION	F-VF NH
NJ1	'84 $2.50 Canvasbacks	.50.00
NJ2	'84 $5 Canvasbacks	.60.00
NJ3	'85 $2.50 Mallards	.18.00
NJ4	'85 $5 Mallards	.20.00
NJ5	'86 $2.50 Pintails	.12.50
NJ6	'86 $5 Pintails	.16.00
NJ7	'87 $2.50 Canada Geese	.12.50
NJ8	'87 $5 Canada Geese	.12.50
NJ9	'88 $2.50 Green-Winged Teal	.9.00
NJ10	'88 $5 Green-Winged Teal	.10.00
NJ11	'89 $2.50 Snow Geese	.12.00
NJ12	'89 $5 Snow Geese	.10.50
NJ13	'90 $2.50 Wood Ducks	.12.00
NJ14	'90 $5 Wood Ducks	.10.00
NJ17	'91 $2.50 Atlantic Brant	.15.00
NJ18	'91 $5 Atlantic Brant	.10.00
NJ19	'92 $2.50 Bluebills	.12.00
NJ20	'92 $5 Bluebills	.9.00
NJ21	'93 $2.50 Buffleheads	.10.00
NJ22	'93 $5 Buffleheads	.10.00
NJ23	'94 $2.50 Black Ducks	.10.00
NJ24	'94 $5 Black Ducks	.9.00
NJ25	'95 $2.50 Widgeon, Lighthouse	.6.50
NJ26	'95 $5 Widgeon, Lighthouse	.9.00
NJ27	'96 $2.50 Goldeneyes	.8.50
NJ28	'96 $5 Goldeneyes	.16.00
NJ29	'97 $5 Oldsquaws	.9.00
NJ30	'97 $10 Oldsquaws	.16.00
NJ31	'98 $5 Mallards	.9.00
NJ32	'98 $10.00 Mallards	.16.00
NJ33	'99 $5 Redheads	.9.00
NJ34	'99 $10 Redheads	.16.00
NJ35	'00 $5 Canvasbacks	.9.00
NJ36	'00 $10 Canvasbacks	.16.00
NJ37	'01 $5 Tundra Swans	.9.00
NJ38	'01 $10 Tundra Swans	.16.00
NJ39	'02 $5 Wood Ducks	.9.00
NJ40	'02 $10 Wood Ducks	.16.00
NJ41	'03 $5 Pintails & Black Lab	.9.00
NJ42	'03 $10 Pintails & Black Lab	.16.00
NJ43	'04 $5 Merganser/Puppy	.9.00
NJ44	'04 $10 Merganser/Puppy	.16.00
NJ45	'05 $5 Canvasback Decoys and Retriever	.9.00
NJ47	'06 $5 Wood Duck Decoy, Golden Retriever	.9.00
NJ48	'06 $10 Wood Duck Decoy, Golden Retriever	.16.00

NM1

NEW MEXICO

NO.	DESCRIPTION	F-VF NH
NM1	'91 $7.50 Pintails	.20.00
NM2	'92 $7.50 American Widgeon	.20.00
NM3	'93 $7.50 Mallard	.20.00
NM4	'94 $7.50 Green-Winged Teal	.20.00

NY3

NEW YORK

NO.	DESCRIPTION	F-VF NH
NY1	'85 $5.50 Canada Geese	.16.00
NY2	'86 $5.50 Mallards	.12.00
NY3	'87 $5.50 Wood Ducks	.10.00
NY4	'88 $5.50 Pintails	.9.50
NY5	'89 $5.50 Greater Scaup	.9.50
NY6	'90 $5.50 Canvasbacks	.9.00
NY7	'91 $5.50 Redheads	.9.00
NY8	'92 $5.50 Wood Ducks	.9.00
NY9	'93 $5.50 Blue-Winged Teal	.9.00
NY10	'94 $5.50 Canada Geese	.9.00

NO.	DESCRIPTION	F-VF NH
NY11	'95 $5.50 Common Goldeneye	.9.00
NY12	'96 $5.50 Common Loon	.9.00
NY13	'97 $5.50 Hooded Merganser	.9.00
NY14	'98 $5.50 Osprey	.9.00
NY15	'99 $5.50 Buffleheads	.12.00
NY16	'00 $5.50 Wood Ducks	.9.00
NY17	'01 $5.50 Pintails	.9.00
NY18	'02 $5.50 Canvasbacks	.9.00

NC1

NORTH CAROLINA

NO.	DESCRIPTION	F-VF NH
NC1	'83 $5.50 Mallards	.85.00
NC2	'84 $5.50 Wood Ducks	.55.00
NC3	'85 $5.50 Canvasbacks	.35.00
NC4	'86 $5.50 Canada Geese	.30.00
NC5	'87 $5.50 Pintails	.16.00
NC6	'88 $5 Green-Winged Teal	.10.50
NC7	'89 $5 Snow Geese	.20.00
NC8	'90 $5 Redheads	.20.00
NC9	'91 $5 Blue-Winged Teal	.20.00
NC10	'92 $5 American Widgeon	.20.00
NC11	'93 $5 Tundra Swans	.20.00
NC12	'94 $5 Buffleheads	.20.00
NC13	'95 $5 Brant, Lighthouse	.20.00
NC14	'96 $5 Pintails	.20.00
NC15	'97 $5 Wood Ducks	.20.00
NC16	'97 $5 Wood Ducks, self-adhesive	.15.00
NC17	'98 $5 Canada Geese	.15.00
NC18	'98 $5 Canada Geese, self-adhesive	.15.00
NC19	'99 $5 Green-winged Teal	.15.00
NC20	'99 $5 Green-winged Teal, self-adhesive	.15.00
NC21	'00 $10 Green-winged Teal	.15.00
NC22	'00 $10 Green-winged Teal, self-adhesive	.15.00
NC23	'01 $10 Black Duck, lighthouse	.15.00
NC24	'01 $10 Black Duck, lighthouse, self-adhesive	.15.00
NC25	'02 $10 Pintails, Hunters, Dog	.16.00
NC26	'02 $10 Pintails, Hunters, Dog, self-adhesive	.16.00
NC27	'03 $10 Ringneck & Brittney Spaniel	.15.00
NC28	'03 $10 Ringneck & Brittney Spaniel, self-adhesive	.17.00
NC29	'04 $10 Mallard	.15.00
NC30	'04 $10 Mallard, self-adhesive	.17.00
NC31	'04 $10 Green-winged Teals	.17.00
NC32	'04 $10 Green-winged Teals, self-adhesive	.17.00
NC33	'06 $10 Lesser Scaups, perf.	.17.00
NC34	'06 $10 Lesser Scaups, self-adhesive, die-cut	.17.00

NORTH DAKOTA

NO.	DESCRIPTION	F-VF NH
ND32	'82 $9 Canada Geese	.150.00
ND35	'83 $9 Mallards	.80.00
ND38	'84 $9 Canvasbacks	.37.50
ND41	'85 $9 Bluebills	.25.00
ND44	'86 $9 Pintails	.20.00
ND47	'87 $9 Snow Geese	.22.00
ND50	'88 $9 White-Winged Scoters	.15.00
ND53	'89 $6 Redheads	.12.50
ND56	'90 $6 Labrador Retriever & Mallard	.12.50
ND59	'91 $6 Green-Winged Teal	.12.00
ND62	'92 $6 Blue-Winged Teal	.9.50
ND65	'93 $6 Wood Ducks	.9.50
ND67	'94 $6 Canada Geese	.9.50
ND69	'95 $6 Widgeon	.9.50
ND71	'96 $6 Mallards	.9.50
ND73	'97 $6 White Fronted Geese	.9.50
ND75	'98 $6 Blue Winged Teal	.9.50
ND77	'99 $6 Gadwalls	.9.50
ND79	'00 $6 Pintails	.9.50
ND81	'01 $6 Canada Geese	.9.50
ND83	'02 $6 Text, black on green	.9.50
ND84	'03 $6 Text, black on green	.9.50
ND85	'04 $6 Text, black on green	.9.50
ND86	'05 $6 Text, black on green	.9.50
ND87	'06 $6 black, green	.9.50

OH4

OHIO

NO.	DESCRIPTION	F-VF NH
OH1	'82 $5.75 Wood Ducks	.85.00
OH2	'83 $5.75 Mallards	.85.00
OH3	'84 $5.75 Green-Winged Teal	.75.00
OH4	'85 $5.75 Redheads	.50.00
OH5	'86 $5.75 Canvasback	.32.50
OH6	'87 $6 Blue-Winged Teal	.15.00
OH7	'88 $6 Common Goldeneyes	.12.50
OH8	'89 $6 Canada Geese	.12.50
OH9	'90 $9 Black Ducks	.15.00
OH10	'91 $9 Lesser Scaup	.15.00
OH11	'92 $9 Wood Ducks	.14.00
OH12	'93 $9 Buffleheads	.14.00
OH13	'94 $11 Mallards	.16.50

NO.	DESCRIPTION	F-VF NH
OH14	'95 $11 Pintails	.16.50
OH15	'96 $11 Hooded Mergansers	.16.50
OH16	'97 $11 Widgeons	.16.50
OH17	'98 $11 Gadwall	.16.50
OH18	'99 $11 Mallard	.16.50
OH19	'00 $11 Buffleards	.16.50
OH20	'01 $11 Canvasback	.16.50
OH21	'02 $11 Ring Neck	.16.50
OH22	'03 $11 Hooded Merganser	.16.50
OH23	'04 $15 Tundra Swans	.21.50
OH24	'05 $15 Wood Duck	.21.50
OH25	'06 $15 Pintail	.21.50

OK4

OKLAHOMA

NO.	DESCRIPTION	F-VF NH
OK1	'80 $4 Pintails	.70.00
OK2	'81 $4 Canada Goose	.27.50
OK3	'82 $4 Green-Winged Teal	.12.00
OK4	'83 $4 Wood Ducks	.12.00
OK5	'84 $4 Ring-Necked Ducks	.9.50
OK6	'85 $4 Mallards	.8.00
OK7	'86 $4 Snow Geese	.8.00
OK8	'87 $4 Canvasbacks	.8.00
OK9	'88 $4 Widgeons	.8.00
OK10	'89 $4 Redheads	.8.00
OK11	'90 $4 Hooded Merganser	.8.00
OK12	'91 $4 Gadwalls	.7.50
OK13	'92 $4 Lesser Scaup	.7.50
OK14	'93 $4 White-Fronted Geese	.7.50
OK15	'94 $4 Blue-Winged Teal	.7.50
OK16	'95 $4 Ruddy Ducks	.7.50
OK17	'96 $4 Buffleheads	.7.50
OK18	'97 $4 Goldeneyes	.7.50
OK19	'98 $4 Shoveler	.7.50
OK20	'99 $4 Canvasbacks	.7.50
OK21	'00 $4 Pintails	.7.50
OK22	'01 $4 Canada Goose	.7.50
OK23	'02 $4 Green-winged Teal	.7.50
OK24	'03 $10 Wood Duck	.14.00
OK25	'04 $10 Mallard	.14.00
OK26	'05 $10 Snow Geese	.14.00
OK27	'06 $10 Widgeons	.14.00

OR1

OREGON

NO.	DESCRIPTION	F-VF NH
OR1	'84 $5 Canada Geese	.35.00
OR2	'85 $5 Lesser Snow Goose	.45.00
OR3	'86 $5 Pacific Brant	.17.50
OR4	'87 $5 White-Fronted Geese	.12.00
OR5	'88 $5 Great Basin Canada Geese	.10.00
OR7	'89 $5 Black Labrador Retriever & Pintails	.10.00
OR8	'90 $5 Mallards & Golden Retriever	.12.50
OR9	'91 $5 Buffleheads & Chesapeake Bay Retriever	.11.00
OR10	'92 $5 Green-Winged Teal	.11.00
OR11	'93 $5 Mallards	.11.00
OR12	'94 $5 Pintails	.11.00
OR14	'95 $5 Wood Ducks	.11.00
OR16	'96 $5 Mallard/Widgeon/Pintail	.11.00
OR18	'97 $5 Canvasbacks	.11.00
OR20	'98 $5 Pintail	.11.00
OR22	'99 $5 Canada Geese	.11.00
OR24	'00 $7.50 Canada Geese, Mallard, Widgeon	.13.50
OR25	'01 $7.50 Canvasbacks	.13.50
OR26	'02 $7.50 American Wigeon	.13.50
OR27	'03 $7.50 Wood Duck	.13.50
OR28	'04 $7.50 Ross' Goose	.13.50
OR29	'05 $7.50 Hooded Merganser	.13.50
OR30	'06 $7.50 Pintail, Mallard	.13.50

PA1

PENNSYLVANIA

NO.	DESCRIPTION	F-VF NH
PA1	'83 $5.50 Wood Ducks	.25.00
PA2	'84 $5.50 Canada Geese	.22.50
PA3	'85 $5.50 Mallards	.12.00
PA4	'86 $5.50 Blue-Winged Teal	.10.00
PA5	'87 $5.50 Pintails	.10.00
PA6	'88 $5.50 Wood Ducks	.10.00

NO.	DESCRIPTION	F-VF NH
PA7	'89 $5.50 Hooded Mergansers	.9.50
PA8	'90 $5.50 Canvasbacks	.9.50
PA9	'91 $5.50 Widgeons	.9.50
PA10	'92 $5.50 Canada Geese	.9.50
PA11	'93 $5.50 Northern Shovelers	.9.00
PA12	'94 $5.50 Pintails	.9.00
PA13	'95 $5.50 Buffleheads	.9.00
PA14	'96 $5.50 Black Ducks	.9.00
PA15	'97 $5.50 Hooded Merganser	.9.00
PA16	'98 $5.50 Wood Duck	.9.00
PA17	'99 $5.50 Ring-necked Ducks	.9.00
PA18	'00 $5.50 Green-Winged Teal	.9.00
PA19	'01 $5.50 Pintails	.9.00
PA20	'02 $5.50 Snow Geese	.9.00
PA21	'03 $5.50 Canvasbacks	.9.00
PA22	'04 $5.50 Hooded Mergansers	.9.00
PA23	'05 $5.50 Red-breasted Mergansers	.9.00
PA24	'06 $5.50 Pintails	.9.00

RI1

RHODE ISLAND

NO.	DESCRIPTION	F-VF NH
RI1	'89 $7.50 Canvasbacks	.12.50
RI2	'90 $7.50 Canada Geese	.12.00
RI3	'91 $7.50 Wood Ducks & Labrador Retriever	.14.00
RI4	'92 $7.50 Blue-Winged Teal	.12.50
RI5	'93 $7.50 Pintails	.11.50
RI6	'94 $7.50 Wood Ducks	.11.50
RI7	'95 $7.50 Hooded Mergansers	.11.50
RI8	'96 $7.50 Harlequin	.11.50
RI9	'97 $7.50 Black Ducks	.11.50
RI10	'98 $7.50 Black Ducks	.11.50
RI11	'99 $7.50 Common Eiders	.11.50
RI12	'00 $7.50 Canvasbacks	.11.50
RI13	'01 $7.50 Canvasbacks, Mallard, Lighthouse	.11.50
RI14	'02 $7.50 White-winged Scoter	.11.50
RI15	'03 $7.50 Oldsquaw	.11.50
RI16	'04 $7.50 Canvasbacks	.11.50
RI17	'05 $7.50 Black Ducks and Lighthouse	.11.50
RI18	'06 $7.50 Canvasbacks, Lighthouse	.11.50

SC5

SOUTH CAROLINA

NO.	DESCRIPTION	F-VF NH
SC1	'81 $5.50 Wood Ducks	.75.00
SC2	'82 $5.50 Mallards	.110.00
SC3	'83 $5.50 Pintails	.110.00
SC4	'84 $5.50 Canada Geese	.70.00
SC5	'85 $5.50 Green-Winged Teal	.65.00
SC6	'86 $5.50 Canvasbacks	.30.00
SC7	'87 $5.50 Black Ducks	.20.00
SC8	'88 $5.50 Widgeon & Spaniel	.25.00
SC9	'89 $5.50 Blue-Winged Teal	.15.00
SC10	'90 $5.50 Wood Ducks	.10.00
SC11	'91 $5.50 Labrador Retriever, Pintails & Decoy	.15.00
SC12	'92 $5.50 Buffleheads	.15.00
SC13	'93 $5.50 Lesser Scaup	.15.00
SC14	'94 $5.50 Canvasbacks	.15.00
SC15	'95 $5.50 Shovelers, Lighthouse	.15.00
SC16	'96 $5.50 Redheads, Lighthouse	.15.00
SC17	'97 $5.50 Old Squaws	.15.00
SC18	'98 $5.50 Ruddy Ducks	.15.00
SC19	'99 $5.50 Barrow's goldeneye	.15.00
SC20	'00 $5.50 Wood Ducks, boykin spaniel	.15.00
SC21	'01 $5.50 Mallard, yellow labrador,decoy	.15.00
SC22	'02 $5.50 Widgeon, Chocolate Labrador	.9.00
SC23	'03 $5.50 Green-winged Teal	.9.00
SC24	'04 $5.50 Black Labrador	.9.00
SC25	'05 $5.50 Canvasbacks	.9.00
SC26	'06 $5.50 Black Ducks	.9.00

SD6

SOUTH DAKOTA

NO.	DESCRIPTION	F-VF NH
SD3	'76 $1 Mallards	.45.00
SD4	'77 $1 Pintails	.85.00

NO.	DESCRIPTION	F-VF NH
SD5	'78 $1 Canvasbacks	.30.00
SD6	'86 $2 Canada Geese	.20.00
SD7	'87 $2 Blue Geese	.10.00
SD8	'88 $2 White-Fronted Geese	.6.00
SD9	'89 $2 Mallards	.6.00
SD10	'90 $2 Blue-Winged Teal	.5.50
SD11	'91 $2 Pintails	.5.50
SD12	'92 $2 Canvasbacks	.5.50
SD13	'93 $2 Lesser Scaup	.5.50
SD14	'94 $2 Redheads	.5.50
SD15	'95 $2 Wood Ducks	.5.50
SD16	'96 $2 Canada Goose	.5.50
SD17	'97 $2 Widgeons	.5.50
SD18	'98 $2 Green Winged Teal	.5.50
SD19	'99 $2 Tundra Swam	.5.50
SD20	'00 $3 Buffleheads	.8.00
SD21	'01 $3 Mallards	.8.00
SD22	'02 $3 Canvasbacks	.8.00
SD23	'03 $3 Pintail	.8.00
SD24	'04 $3 Text, purple	.8.00
SD25	'05 $5 Text, magenta	.10.00
SD26	'06 $5 Brown, Orange	.10.00

TN9

TENNESSEE

NO.	DESCRIPTION	F-VF NH
TN1	'79 $2.30 Mallards	.175.00
TN2	'79 $5 Mallards, Non-Resident	.1,200.00
TN3	'80 $2.30 Canvasbacks	.65.00
TN4	'80 $5 Canvasbacks, Non-Resident	.525.00
TN5	'81 $2.30 Wood Ducks	.50.00
TN6	'82 $6.50 Canada Geese	.65.00
TN7	'83 $6.50 Pintails	.60.00
TN8	'84 $6.50 Black Ducks	.70.00
TN9	'85 $6.50 Blue-Winged Teal	.25.00
TN10	'86 $6.50 Mallard	.15.00
TN11	'87 $6.50 Canada Geese	.15.00
TN12	'88 $6.50 Canvasbacks	.20.00
TN13	'89 $6.50 Green-Winged Teal	.20.00
TN14	'90 $13 Redheads	.20.00
TN15	'91 $13 Mergansers	.19.00
TN16	'92 $14 Wood Ducks	.19.00
TN17	'93 $14 Pintails & Decoy	.19.00
TN18	'94 $16 Mallard	.40.00
TN19	'95 $16 Ring-Necked Duck	.22.50
TN20	'96 $18 Black Ducks	.25.00
TN21	'99 $10 Mallard	.18.00
TN22	'00 $10 Bufflehead	.18.00
TN23	'01 $10 Wood Ducks	.18.00
TN24	'02 $10 Green-winged Teal	.18.00
TN25	'03 $10 Canada Geese	.18.00
TN26	'04 $10 Wood Ducks	.18.00
TN27	'05 $10 Mallards	.18.00
TN28	'06 $10 Canada Goose	.18.00

TX5

TEXAS

NO.	DESCRIPTION	F-VF NH
TX1	'81 $5 Mallards	.55.00
TX2	'82 $5 Pintails	.40.00
TX3	'83 $5 Widgeons	.190.00
TX4	'84 $5 Wood Ducks	.35.00
TX5	'85 $5 Snow Geese	.15.00
TX6	'86 $5 Green-Winged Teal	.12.00
TX7	'87 $5 White-Fronted Geese	.12.00
TX8	'88 $5 Pintails	.12.00
TX9	'89 $5 Mallards	.12.00
TX10	'90 $5 American Widgeons	.12.00
TX11	'91 $7 Wood Duck	.12.00
TX12	'92 $7 Canada Geese	.12.00
TX13	'93 $7 Blue-Winged Teal	.12.00
TX14	'94 $7 Shovelers	.12.00
TX15	'95 $7 Buffleheads	.12.00
TX16	'96 $3 Gadwalls	.85.00
TX17	'97 $3 Cinnamon Teal	.85.00
TX18	'98 $3 Pintail, Labrador Retriever	.85.00
TX19	'99 $3 Canvasbacks	.35.00
TX20	'00 $3 Hooded Merganser	.35.00
TX21	'01 $3 Snow Goose	.20.00
TX22	'02 $3 Redheads	.20.00
TX23	'03 $3 Mottled Duck	.20.00
TX24	'04 $3 American Goldeneye	.20.00
TX25	'05 $7 Mallards	.16.00
TX26	'06 $7 Green-Winged Teals	.16.00

NO.	DESCRIPTION	F-VF NH

UT1

UTAH

NO.	DESCRIPTION	F-VF NH
UT1	'86 $3.30 Whistling Swans	12.00
UT2	'87 $3.30 Pintails	12.00
UT3	'88 $3.30 Mallards	8.50
UT4	'89 $3.30 Canada Geese	7.50
UT5	'90 $3.30 Canvasbacks	7.50
UT6	'91 $3.30 Tundra Swans	7.50
UT7	'92 $3.30 Pintails	7.50
UT8	'93 $3.30 Canvasbacks	7.50
UT9	'94 $3.30 Chesapeake Retriever & Ducks	100.00
UT10	'95 $3.30 Green-Winged Teal	10.00
UT11	'96 $7.50 White-Fronted Goose	14.50
UT12	'97 $7.50 Redheads, pair	50.00

VT1

VERMONT

NO.	DESCRIPTION	F-VF NH
VT1	'86 $5 Wood Ducks	14.00
VT2	'87 $5 Common Goldeneyes	10.00
VT3	'88 $5 Black Ducks	10.00
VT4	'89 $5 Canada Geese	9.50
VT5	'90 $5 Green-Winged Teal	9.50
VT6	'91 $5 Hooded Mergansers	9.50
VT7	'92 $5 Snow Geese	9.50
VT8	'93 $5 Mallards	9.50
VT9	'94 $5 Ring-Necked Duck	8.50
VT10	'95 $5 Bufflehead	8.50
VT11	'96 $5 Bluebills	8.50
VT12	'97 $5 Pintail	8.50
VT13	'98 $5 Blue-Winged Teal	8.50
VT14	'99 $5 Canvasbacks	8.50
VT15	'00 $5 Widgeons	8.50
VT16	'01 $5 Old Squaw	8.50
VT17	'02 $5 Greater Scaups	8.50
VT18	'03 $5 Mallard	8.50
VT19	'04 $5 Pintails	8.50
VT20	'05 $5 Canvasbacks	8.50
VT21	'06 $5 Canada Goose	8.50

VA1

VIRGINIA

NO.	DESCRIPTION	F-VF NH
VA1	'88 $5 Mallards	15.00
VA2	'89 $5 Canada Geese	18.00
VA3	'90 $5 Wood Ducks	9.50
VA4	'91 $5 Canvasbacks	9.50
VA5	'92 $5 Buffleheads	9.50
VA6	'93 $5 Black Ducks	9.00
VA7	'94 $5 Lesser Scaup	9.00
VA8	'95 $5 Snow Geese	9.00
VA9	'96 $5 Hooded Mergansers	9.00
VA10	'97 $5 Pintail, Labrador Retriever	9.00
VA11	'98 $5 Mallards	9.00
VA12	'99 $5 Green-winged Teal	9.00
VA13	'00 $5 Mallards	9.00
VA14	'01 $5 Blue-winged Teal	9.00
VA15	'02 $5 Canvasbacks	9.00
VA16	'03 $5 Mallard	9.00
VA17	'04 $5 Goldeneyes	9.00
VA18	'05 $9.75 Wood Ducks, perforated	19.50
VA19	'05 $9.75 Wood Ducks, rouletted	19.50
VA20	'05 $9.75 Wood Ducks, self-adhesive, die cut	19.50
VA21	'06 $9.75 Black Ducks, perforated	19.50
VA22	'06 $9.75 Wood Ducks, self-adhesive, die cut	19.50

WA1

WASHINGTON

NO.	DESCRIPTION	F-VF NH
WA1	'86 $5 Mallards	12.50
WA2	'87 $5 Canvasbacks	16.00
WA3	'88 $5 Harlequin	9.50
WA4	'89 $5 American Widgeons	9.50
WA5	'90 $5 Pintails & Sour Duck	9.50
WA6	'91 $5 Wood Duck	9.50
WA7	'92 $6 Labrador Puppy & Canada Geese	9.50
WA8	'93 $6 Snow Geese	9.50
WA9	'94 $6 Black Brant	9.50
WA10	'95 $6 Mallards	9.50
WA11	'96 $6 Redheads	9.50
WA12	'97 $6 Canada Geese	9.50
WA13	'98 $6 Goldeneye	9.50
WA14	'99 $6 Bufflehead	9.50
WA15	'00 $6 Canada Geese, Mallard, Widgeon	14.00
WA16	'01 $6 Mallards	14.00
WA17	'02 $10 Green-winged Teal	14.00
WA18	'03 $10 Pintail	14.00
WA19	'04 $10 Canada Goose	14.00
WA20	'05 $10 Barrow's Goldeneyes	14.00
WA21	'06 $10 Widgeons, Mallard	14.00
WA22		

WV1

WEST VIRGINIA

NO.	DESCRIPTION	F-VF NH
WV1	'87 $5 Canada Geese	15.00
WV2	'87 $5 Canada Geese, Non-Resident	15.00
WV3	'88 $5 Wood Ducks	12.00
WV4	'88 $5 Wood Ducks, Non-Resident	20.00
WV5	'89 $5 Decoys	13.00
WV6	'89 $5 Decoys, Non-Resident	13.00
WV7	'90 $5 Labrador Retriever & Decoy	12.50
WV8	'90 $5 Labrador Retriever & Decoy, Non-Resident	12.50
WV9	'91 $5 Mallards	10.00
WV10	'91 $5 Mallards, Non-Resident	10.00
WV11	'92 $5 Canada Geese	10.00
WV12	'92 $5 Canada Geese, Non-Resident	10.00
WV13	'93 $5 Pintails	10.00
WV14	'93 $5 Pintails, Non-Resident	10.00
WV15	'94 $5 Green-Winged Teal	10.00
WV16	'94 $5 Green-Winged Teal, Non-Resident	10.00
WV17	'95 $5 Mallards	10.00
WV18	'95 $5 Mallards, Non-Resident	10.00
WV19	'96 $5 American Widgeons	10.00
WV20	'96 $5 Widgeon, Non-Resident	10.00

WI3

WISCONSIN

NO.	DESCRIPTION	F-VF NH
WI1	'78 $3.25 Wood Ducks	125.00
WI2	'79 $3.25 Buffleheads	45.00
WI3	'80 $3.25 Widgeons	15.00
WI4	'81 $3.25 Lesser Scaup	11.00
WI5	'82 $3.25 Pintails	8.00
WI6	'83 $3.25 Blue-Winged Teal	9.00
WI7	'84 $3.25 Hooded Merganser	9.00
WI8	'85 $3.25 Lesser Scaup	20.00
WI9	'86 $3.25 Canvasbacks	20.00
WI10	'87 $3.25 Canada Geese	7.00
WI11	'88 $3.25 Hooded Merganser	7.00
WI12	'89 $3.25 Common Goldeneye	7.00
WI13	'90 $3.25 Redheads	7.00
WI14	'91 $5.25 Green-Winged Teal	9.00
WI15	'92 $5.25 Tundra Swans	9.00
WI16	'93 $5.25 Wood Ducks	9.00
WI17	'94 $5.25 Pintails	9.00
WI18	'95 $5.25 Mallards	9.00

NO.	DESCRIPTION	F-VF NH
WI19	'96 $5.25 Green-Winged Teal	9.00
WI20	'97 $7 Canada Geese	9.00
WI21	'98 $7 Snow Geese	9.00
WI22	'99 $7 Greater Scaups	11.00
WI23	'00 $7 Canvasbacks	11.00
WI24	'01 $7 Common Goldeneye	15.00
WI25	'02 $7 Shovelers	11.00
WI26	'03 $7 Canvasbacks	11.00
WI27	'04 $7 Pintail	11.00
WI28	'05 $7 Wood Ducks	11.00
WI29	'06 $7 Green-Winged Teals	11.00

WY10

WYOMING

NO.	DESCRIPTION	F-VF NH
WY1	'84 $5 Meadowlark	60.00
WY2	'85 $5 Canada Geese	60.00
WY3	'86 $5 Antelope	90.00
WY4	'87 $5 Grouse	100.00
WY5	'88 $5 Fish	100.00
WY6	'89 $5 Deer	200.00
WY7	'90 $5 Bear	45.00
WY8	'91 $5 Rams	45.00
WY9	'92 $5 Bald Eagle	40.00
WY10	'93 $5 Elk	20.00
WY11	'94 $5 Bobcat	20.00
WY12	'95 $5 Moose	20.00
WY13	'96 $5 Turkey	20.00
WY14	'97 $5 Rocky Mountain Goats	30.00
WY15	'98 $5 Thunder Swans	30.00
WY16	'99 $5 Brown Trout	30.00
WY17	'00 $5 Buffalo	30.00
WY18	'01 $10 Whitetailed Deer	20.00
WY19	'02 $10 River Otters	20.00
WY20	'03 $10 Mountain Bluebird	20.00
WY21	'04 $10 Cougar	20.00
WY22	'05 $10 Burrowing Owls	20.00
WY23	'06 $10.50 Cut-Throat Trout	20.00

CANAL ZONE

SCOTT NO.	DESCRIPTION	UNUSED NH F	AVG	UNUSED OG F	AVG	USED F	AVG

CANAL ZONE

PANAMA

1904
U.S. Stamp 300, 319, 304, 306-07 overprinted

4	1¢ blue green	100.00	70.00	50.00	30.00	25.00	15.00
5	2¢ carmine.................	90.00	60.00	40.00	25.00	25.00	15.00
6	5¢ blue.....................	300.00	200.00	150.00	100.00	65.00	40.00
7	8¢ violet black...........	550.00	350.00	270.00	175.00	95.00	60.00
8	10¢ pale red brown.....	550.00	350.00	270.00	175.00	100.00	60.00

CANAL

ZONE

1924-25
U.S. Stamps 551-54, 557, 562, 564-66, 569-71 overprinted

Type 1 Flat Tops on Letters "A". Perf. 11

70	1/2¢ olive brown	2.50	1.70	1.40	1.00	.75	.55
71	1¢ deep green	2.25	1.35	1.50	.95	1.10	.70
71e	same, bklt pane of 6 ...	300.00	200.00	170.00	100.00	....	....
72	1-1/2¢ yellow brown ...	3.00	2.25	2.10	1.50	1.60	1.10
73	2¢ carmine.................	20.00	15.00	10.00	7.00	1.75	1.25
73a	same, bklt pane of 6 ...	400.00	300.00	250.00	170.00	....	....
74	5¢ dark blue..............	50.00	35.00	25.00	20.00	9.00	5.50
75	10¢ orange	100.00	75.00	50.00	40.00	24.00	17.00
76	12¢ brown violet	100.00	75.00	50.00	40.00	27.00	19.50
77	14¢ dark blue.............	75.00	55.00	40.00	30.00	20.00	14.00
78	15¢ gray	120.00	75.00	50.00	40.00	33.00	22.00
79	30¢ olive brown	100.00	60.00	45.00	30.00	25.00	16.50
80	50¢ lilac	200.00	120.00	100.00	70.00	42.00	25.00
81	$1 violet brown	500.00	380.00	300.00	200.00	100.00	70.00

CANAL

ZONE

1925-28
U.S. Stamps 554-55, 557, 564-66, 623, 567, 569-71, overprinted

Type II Pointed Tops on Letters "A"

84	2¢ carmine.................	80.00	50.00	40.00	30.00	10.00	6.00
84d	same, bklt pane of 6 ...	400.00	300.00	250.00	170.00	....	....
85	3¢ violet	10.00	7.00	5.00	3.00	2.75	1.75
86	5¢ dark blue...............	10.00	7.00	5.00	3.00	2.75	1.75
87	10¢ orange	90.00	60.00	40.00	30.00	10.00	6.00
88	12¢ brown violet	60.00	40.00	30.00	20.00	14.00	9.00
89	14¢ dark blue.............	60.00	40.00	30.00	20.00	18.00	11.00
90	15¢ gray	20.00	12.00	10.00	7.00	4.00	2.50
91	17¢ black	10.00	7.00	5.00	3.00	3.00	1.95
92	20¢ carmine rose........	20.00	12.00	10.00	7.00	4.00	2.65
93	30¢ olive brown	15.00	10.00	7.00	5.00	4.00	2.50
94	50¢ lilac	600.00	400.00	300.00	210.00	140.00	82.50
95	$1 violet brown	300.00	200.00	180.00	110.00	50.00	31.50

1926
Type II overprint on U.S. Stamp 627

96	2¢ carmine rose..........	10.00	7.00	6.00	4.00	3.75	2.50

1927
Type II overprint on U.S. Stamp 583-84, 591
Rotary Press Printing, Perf. 10

97	2¢ carmine.................	110.00	100.00	75.00	40.00	10.50	6.00
98	3¢ violet	25.00	18.00	10.00	6.00	5.00	3.00
99	10¢ orange	50.00	35.00	30.00	15.00	6.75	4.00

SCOTT NO.	DESCRIPTION	PLATE BLOCK F/NH	F	AVG	UNUSED F/NH	F	AVG	USED F	AVG
100	1¢ green	25.00	20.00	16.00	2.65	1.95	1.35	1.30	.80
101	2¢ carmine...........	30.00	24.50	19.00	2.75	2.00	1.20	.90	.55
101a	same, bklt pane of 6	....	....	....	200.00	150.00	125.00	....	....
102	3¢ violet (1931)....	110.00	85.00	68.00	6.50	4.50	2.25	3.50	2.25
103	5¢ dark blue.........	185.00	155.00	125.00	30.00	22.00	15.00	11.00	7.25
104	10¢ orange (1930)	225.00	180.00	145.00	25.00	17.00	12.00	12.00	8.00

VERY FINE QUALITY: To determine the Very Fine price, add the difference between the Fine and Average prices to the Fine quality price. For example: if the Fine price is $10.00 and the Average price is $6.00, the Very Fine price would be $14.00. From 1935 to date, add 20% to the Fine price to arrive at the Very Fine price.

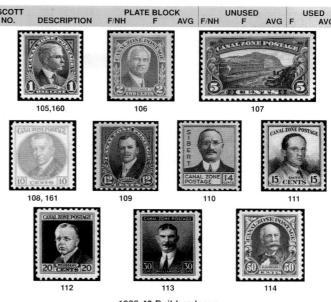

105,160   106   107

108, 161   109   110   111

112   113   114

1928-40 Builders Issue

SCOTT NO.	DESCRIPTION	PLATE BLOCK F/NH	F	AVG	UNUSED F/NH	F	AVG	USED F	AVG
105-14	1¢-50¢ complete, 10 varieties........	....	....	....	10.40	8.05	4.95	5.70	3.45
105	1¢ Gorgas............	3.00	2.00	1.40	.30	.25	.20	.25	.20
106	2¢ Goethals.........	3.00(6)	2.25	1.30	.30	.25	.20	.25	.20
106a	same, bklt pane of 6	....	....	....	18.00	13.00	8.50	....	....
107	5¢ Gaillard Cut (1929)	15.00(6)	10.00	6.50	1.50	1.20	.85	.50	.40
108	10¢ Hodges (1932)	6.00(6)	4.00	3.50	.40	.30	.20	.25	.20
109	12¢ Gaillard (1929)	14.50(6)	11.00	6.50	1.00	.80	.60	.85	.50
110	14¢ Sibert (1937).	17.00(6)	12.50	9.00	1.10	.90	.70	1.10	.70
111	15¢ Smith (1932).	10.00(6)	6.50	4.00	.65	.50	.30	.50	.30
112	20¢ Rousseau (1932)	11.00(6)	7.50	4.50	.95	.75	.45	.30	.20
113	30¢ Williamson (1940)	13.50(6)	10.00	6.00	1.00	.80	.60	.95	.55
114	50¢ Blackburn (1929)	22.00(6)	16.00	9.50	2.00	1.60	1.10	.85	.50

1933
Type II overprint on U.S. Stamps 720 & 695
Rotary Press Printing, Perf. 11 x 10-1/2

115	3¢ Washington.....	37.50	27.00	16.00	4.00	2.75	1.95	.35	.25
116	14¢ Indian...........	72.50	50.00	36.00	8.00	6.00	4.00	3.35	2.00

117, 153

1934

117	3¢ Goethals.........	1.50(6)	1.10	.90	.30	.25	.20	.25	.20
117a	same, bklt pane of 6	....	....	....	100.00	60.00	50.00	....	....

SCOTT NO.	DESCRIPTION	PLATE BLOCK F/NH	F/OG	UNUSED F/NH	F/OG	USED F
		1939 U.S. Stamps 803, 805 overprint				
118	1/2¢ red orange............	2.75	2.25	.30	.25	.20
119	1-1/2¢ bistre brown	2.75	2.25	.30	.25	.20

**FOR CONVENIENCE IN ORDERING,
COMPLETE SETS ARE LISTED BEFORE
SINGLE STAMP LISTINGS.**

SCOTT NO.	DESCRIPTION	PLATE BLOCK F/NH	F/OG	UNUSED F/NH	F/OG	USED F

120
Balboa—Before

121
Balboa—After

122 Gaillard Cut—Before	**123** After
124 Bas Obispo—Before	**125** After
126 Gatun Locks—Before	**127** After
128 Canal Channel—Before	**129** After
130 Gamboa—Before	**131** After
132 Pedro Miguel Locks—Before	**133** After
134 Gatun Spillway—Before	**135** After

1939 25th ANNIVERSARY ISSUE

SCOTT NO.	DESCRIPTION	PLATE BLOCK F/NH	F/OG	UNUSED F/NH	F/OG	USED F
120-35	1¢-50¢ complete, 16 varieties	....	....	155.00	135.00	89.50
120	1¢ yellow green	20.00(6)	16.00	1.25	.85	.40
121	2¢ rose carmine	20.00(6)	16.00	1.25	.85	.50
122	3¢ purple	20.00(6)	16.00	1.25	.85	.25
123	5¢ dark blue	32.00(6)	28.00	2.75	2.00	1.30
124	6¢ red orange	80.00(6)	67.00	5.50	3.75	3.50
125	7¢ black	80.00(6)	67.00	6.00	4.00	3.50
126	8¢ green	88.00(6)	74.00	700	5.00	5.50
127	10¢ ultramarine	88.00(6)	74.00	7.00	5.00	6.00
128	11¢ blue hreen	180.00(6)	160.00	12.00	9.00	8.00
129	12¢ brown carmine	160.00(6)	135.00	12.00	9.00	8.00
130	14¢ dark violet	180.00(6)	160.00	12.00	9.00	8.00
131	15¢ olive green	210.00(6)	165.00	16.00	12.00	7.00
132	18¢ rose pink	200.00(6)	160.00	17.00	13.00	8.00
133	20¢ brown	240.00(6)	200.00	18.00	14.00	8.00
134	25¢ orange	425.00(6)	350.00	27.00	22.00	18.00
135	50¢ violet brown	475.00(6)	360.00	32.00	25.00	7.00

136

137

138

139

140

1945-49

SCOTT NO.	DESCRIPTION	PLATE BLOCK F/NH	F/OG	UNUSED F/NH	F/OG	USED F
136-40	1/2¢-25¢ complete 5 varieties	....	....	2.35	1.95	1.75
136	1/2¢ Major General Davis (1948)	3.00(6)	2.50	.40	.30	.25
137	1-1/2¢ Gov. Magoon (1948)	3.00(6)	2.50	.40	.30	.25
138	2¢ T. Roosevelt (1948).	.70(6)	.50	.25	.20	.25
139	5¢ Stevens	3.00(6)	2.00	.45	.40	.25
140	25¢ J.F. Wallace (1948)	9.00(6) 7.00	1.00	.85	.85	

141

1948 CANAL ZONE BIOLOGICAL AREA

141	10¢ Map & Coat-mundi	10.00(6)	8.00	1.85	1.15	1.00

142

143

144

145

1949 CALIFORNIA GOLD RUSH

SCOTT NO.	DESCRIPTION	PLATE BLOCK F/NH	F/OG	UNUSED F/NH	F/OG	USED F
142-45	3¢-18¢ complete 4 varieties	....	....	5.00	3.95	3.65
142	3¢ "Forty Niners"	7.00(6)	5.00	.70	.55	.35
143	6¢ Journey—Las Cruces	8.25(6)	6.00	.75	.60	.40
144	12¢ Las Cruces—Panama Trail	23.00(6)	17.00	1.35	1.00	1.10
145	18¢ Departure—San Francisco	25.00(6)	21.00	2.50	2.00	2.00

146

147

148

149

150

1951-58

146	10¢ West Indian Labor.	25.00(6)	20.00	3.25	2.50	1.70
147	3¢ Panama R.R.(1955)	7.00(6)	5.50	.80	.60	.65
148	3¢ Gorgas Hospital (1957)	5.00	3.50	.60	.50	.45
149	4¢ S.S. Ancon (1958)	3.50	2.60	.55	.45	.40
150	4¢ T. Roosevelt (1958).	4.00	3.00	.60	.50	.45

151

152, 154

1960-62

151	4¢ Boy Scout Badge	5.00	3.75	.60	.50	.45
152	4¢ Adminstration Building	1.10	.80	.30	.25	.20

LINE PAIR

153	3¢ G.W. Goethals, coil .	1.00	.85	.25	.20	.20
154	4¢ Adminstration Building, coil	1.25	1.05	.25	.20	.20
155	5¢ J.F. Stevens, coil (1962)	1.50	1.20	.35	.30	.25

156

157

PLATE BLOCK

156	4¢ Girl Scout Badge (1962)	3.00	2.20	.45	.40	.35
157	4¢ Thatcher Ferry Bridge (1962)	5.00	4.00	.40	.35	.30
157a	same, silver omitted (bridge)	....	....	8500.00	....	....

158

159